D0008260

Introduction to

OPERATIONS RESEARCH

HOLDEN-DAY SERIES IN
INDUSTRIAL ENGINEERING AND MANAGEMENT SCIENCE

Introduction to OPERATIONS RESEARCH

Frederick S. Hillier

STANFORD UNIVERSITY

Gerald J. Lieberman

STANFORD UNIVERSITY

HOLDEN-DAY, INC.

San Francisco, Cambridge, London, Amsterdam

First printing August 1967
Second printing February 1968
Third printing September 1968
Fourth printing July 1969
Fifth printing December 1969
Sixth printing July 1970
Seventh printing June 1971
Eighth printing March 1972

Library of Congress Catalog Card Number: 67-27772
Printed in the United States of America

TO OUR PARENTS

Preface

The field of operations research has experienced a remarkable growth and development during its short existence. The inevitable result has been a sparsity of truly up-to-date text material for college survey courses in this area. However, it appears that the field is now stabilizing sufficiently to permit a comprehensive survey of its basic methodology and techniques. This book is intended to be such a survey.

The book has been designed especially to serve as a textbook for an introductory course or sequence of courses on operations research. Thus, Part I provides a general introduction to the field, including a discussion of the planning that goes into an operations research study. Part II and the appendices deal with those aspects of probability theory, statistics, and mathematics which are most relevant to operations research. This material can be used either as a primer or a review by students. The remainder of the book concentrates on the basic models and analytical techniques of operations research. It is organized to provide as much flexibility as possible. Thus, the presentation of mathematical programming is divided into two parts, with Part III giving a complete elementary introduction, and the more advanced material reserved for Part V. Furthermore, the chapters in these parts are essentially independent, with the one exception that they all use the basic material presented in Chapter 5. As a result, there is almost complete freedom for the selection of topics and the depth of coverage. Similarly, there is considerable flexibility of coverage in Part IV, which deals with probabilistic models of operations research.

Because of this flexibility, the book can readily be used for a course of study as short as a quarter or as long as a year, with an opportunity for a wide variability of emphasis in the selection of topics. In fact, it could even be used for a course on just mathematical programming or on just probabilistic models in operations research.

The material in the book is presented primarily from a mathematical viewpoint, although at a relatively elementary level. The intention is to acquaint the student with the more important models and techniques of operations research. Therefore, the emphasis is on motivation and simplicity of explanation rather than rigorous proofs and technical details. The mathematical level is well suited for students who have had a basic course in calculus. (Although calculus is used in only a few portions of the book, this is the general level of mathematical maturity that is assumed, with perhaps somewhat less required in Part III and more preferred in Part V.) If Part IV is to be covered, it is necessary either for the students to have had an introductory course in probability theory and statistics (especially the former), or to first cover the material in Part II.

We are deeply indebted to many people for their part in making this book possible. In particular, we acknowledge the help of a number of people who read a portion of the manuscript and made many valuable suggestions. These especially include Richard Cottle, Cyrus Derman, Melvin Dresher, Raymond Fulkerson, Arthur Geoffrion, Donald Guthrie, Donald Iglehart, William Maxwell, Sheldon Ross, Bertram Schoner, Matthew Sobel, Arthur Veinott, Jr., Alan Wheeler, and Philip Wolfe. They also include many of the more than 1000 students who used preliminary editions of the book. We also express our appreciation to Mrs. Karen Oxendine, Mrs. Helen Butler, and their staffs for preparing the preliminary editions, to Mrs. Judy McPhie for preparing part of the final manuscript, and, above all, to Mrs. Faye Weir for her dedication in preparing most of the final manuscript in a timely fashion. Last, but not least, we thank our wives, Ann and Helen, for their editorial assistance, and we thank both them and our children, David, John, and Mark Hillier and Janet, Joanne, Michael, and Diana Lieberman, for their encouragement and understanding in allowing us to spend many long days and evenings with our mistress, the book.

FREDERICK S. HILLIER
GERALD J. LIEBERMAN

Stanford, California
January, 1967

Contents

Part I

METHODOLOGY

CHAPTER 1

Introduction

1.1 THE ORIGINS OF OPERATIONS RESEARCH

Since the advent of the industrial revolution, the world has seen a remarkable growth in the size and complexity of organizations. The artisans' small shops of an earlier era have evolved into the billion dollar corporations of today. An integral part of this revolutionary change has been a tremendous increase in the division of labor and segmentation of management responsibilities in these organizations. The results have been spectacular. However, along with its blessings, this increasing specialization also has created new problems. One of these is a tendency for the many components of an organization to grow into relatively autonomous empires with their own goals and value systems, thereby losing sight of how their activities and objectives mesh with those of the over-all organization. What is best for one component frequently is detrimental to another, so they may end up working at cross purposes. A related problem is that, as the complexity and specialization in an organization increases, it becomes more and more difficult to allocate its available resources to its various activities in a way that is most effective for the organization as a whole. These were the kinds of problems, and the need to find a better way to resolve them, that provided the environment for the emergence of operations research.

The roots of operations research can be traced back many decades when early attempts were made to use a scientific approach in the management of organizations. However, the beginning of the activity called operations research has generally been attributed to the military services early in World War II. Because of the war effort, there was an urgent need to allocate scarce resources to the various military operations, and to the activities within each operation, in an effective manner. Therefore, the British and then the American military management called upon scientists in great numbers to apply a scientific approach to dealing with this problem, as well as other strategic and tactical problems. In effect, they were asked to do research on (military) operations. These teams of scientists were the first operations research teams. Their efforts allegedly were instrumental in winning the "Air Battle of Britain," the "Island Campaign in the Pacific," the "Battle of the North Atlantic," etc.

Spurred on by the apparent success of operations research in the military, industry gradually became interested in this new field. As the industrial boom following the war was running its course, the problems caused by the increasing complexity and specialization in organizations were again coming to the forefront. It was becoming apparent to a growing number of people, including business consultants who had served on or with the operations research teams during the war, that these were basically the same problems in a different context that had been faced by the military. In this way, operations research began to creep into industry, business, and civil government. By 1951, it had already taken hold in Great Britain, and was in the process of doing so in the United States. Since then, the field has developed very rapidly, as will be described further in Section 1.3.

At least two other factors can be identified that played a key role in the rapid growth of operations research during this period. One of these was the substantial progress that was made early in improving the techniques available to operations research. After the war, many of the scientists who had participated on operations research teams or had heard about this work were motivated to pursue research relevant to the field, and important advancements in the state of the art resulted. A prime example is the simplex method for solving linear programming problems, which was developed by George Dantzig in 1947. Many of the standard tools of operations research, e.g., linear programming, dynamic programming, queueing theory, and inventory theory, were relatively well developed before the end of the 1950's. In addition to this rapid advancement in the theory of operations research, a second factor that gave great impetus to the growth of the field was the onslaught of the computer revolution. In order to deal most effectively with the complex problems typically considered by operations research, a large amount of computation usually is required. Doing this by hand often would be out of the question. Therefore, the development of the electronic digital computers, with their ability to perform arithmetic calculations thousands or even millions of times faster than a human, was a tremendous boon to operations research.

1.2 THE NATURE OF OPERATIONS RESEARCH

What is operations research? One way of trying to answer this question is to give a definition. For example, operations research may be described as a scientific approach to decision making that involves the operations of organizational systems. However, this description, like earlier attempts at a definition, is so general that it is equally applicable to many other fields as well. Therefore, perhaps the best way of grasping the unique nature of operations research is to examine its outstanding characteristics.

As its name implies, operations research involves "research on operations." This says something about both the approach and the area of application of the field. Thus, operations research is applied to problems that concern how to conduct and coordinate the operations or activities within an organization. The nature of the organization is essentially immaterial and, in fact, operations research has been applied extensively in business, industry, the military, civil government and agencies, hospitals, etc. Thus, the breadth of application is unusually wide. The approach of operations research is that of the scientific method. In particular, the process begins by carefully observing and formulating the problem, and then constructing a scientific (typically mathematical) model that attempts to abstract the essence of the real problem. It is then hypothesized that this model is a sufficiently precise representation of the essential features of the situation, so that the conclusions (solutions) obtained from the model are also valid for the real problem. This hypothesis is then modified and verified by suitable experimentation. (This entire process is described and interpreted in detail in Chapter 2.) Thus, in a certain sense, operations research involves creative scientific research into the fundamental properties of operations. However, there is more to it than this. Specifically, operations research also is concerned with the practical management of the organization. Therefore, to be successful it must also provide positive, understandable conclusions to the decision-maker(s) when they are needed. In short, operations research involves research on operations, but without the benefit of an ivory tower.

Still another characteristic of operations research is its broad viewpoint. As implied in the preceding section, operations research adopts an organizational point of view. Thus, it attempts to resolve the conflicts of interest among the components of the organization in a way that is best for the organization as a whole. As discussed in Sec. 2.2, this does not imply that the study of each problem must give explicit consideration to all aspects of the organization, but rather that the objectives being sought must be consistent with those of the over-all organization. An additional characteristic that has been mentioned here in passing is that operations research attempts to find the best or optimal solution to the problem under consideration. Thus, rather than being content with merely improving the status quo, the goal is to identify the best possible course of action. Although it must be interpreted carefully (see Sec. 2.4), this "search for optimality" is a very important theme in operations research.

All of these characteristics lead quite naturally to still another one. It is evident that no single individual should be expected to be an expert on all of the many aspects of operations research work or of the problems typically considered. This would require a group of individuals having diverse backgrounds and skills. Therefore, when undertaking a full-fledged operations research study of a new problem, it is usually necessary to use a team approach. Such an operations research team typically would need to include individuals who collectively are highly trained in mathematics, statistics and probability theory, economics, business administration, electronic computing, engineering and the physical sciences, the behavioral sciences, and the special techniques of operations research. The team also would need to have the experience and variety of skills required to give appropriate consideration to the many ramifications of the problem throughout the organization and to execute effectively all of the diverse phases of the operations research study.

In summary then, operations research, like many other fields, is concerned with decision-making for situations which originate from real life. These applications, occurring in government, business, engineering, economics, and the natural and social sciences, are largely characterized by the need to allocate limited resources. In these situations, considerable insight can be obtained from scientific analysis such as that provided by operations research. The contribution from the operations research approach stems primarily from the following:

(1) The structuring of the real life situation into a mathematical model, abstracting the essential elements so that a solution relevant to the decision-maker's objectives can be sought. This involves looking at the problem in the context of the entire system.
(2) Exploring the structure of such solutions and developing systematic procedures for obtaining them.
(3) Developing a solution that yields an optimal value of the system measure of desirability (or possibly comparing alternative courses of action by evaluating their measure of desirability).

1.3 THE IMPACT OF OPERATIONS RESEARCH

Operations research has had an increasingly great impact on the management of organizations in recent years. Both the number and the variety of its applications continue to grow rapidly, and no slowdown is in sight. In fact, with the exception of the advent of the electronic computer, the extent of this impact seems to be unrivaled by that of any other recent development.

After their success with operations research during World War II, the British and American military services continued to have active operations research groups, often at different levels of command. As a result, there now exists a large number of people called "military operations researchers" who are applying an operations research approach to problems of national defense. For example, they engage in tactical planning for requirements and use of weapon systems, as well as considering the larger problems of the allocation and integration of effort. Some of their techniques involve quite sophisticated ideas in political science, mathematics, economics, probability theory, and statistics.

In addition to the military, operations research is also being used widely in other types of organizations, including business and industry. Almost all of the dozen or so largest corporations in the world, and a sizable proportion of the small industrial organizations, have well-established operations research groups. Many industries, including the aircraft and missile, automobile, communication, computer, electric power, electronics, food, metallurgy, mining, paper, petroleum, and transportation, have made widespread use of operations research. Financial institutions, governmental agencies, and hospitals also are rapidly increasing their use of operations research.

To be more specific, consider some of the problems which have been solved by particular techniques of operations research. Linear programming has been used successfully in the solution of problems concerned with assignment of personnel, blending of materials, distribution and transportation, and investment portfolios. Dynamic programming has been successfully applied to such areas as planning advertising expenditures, distributing sales effort, and production scheduling. Queueing theory has had application in solving problems concerned with traffic congestion, servicing machines subject to breakdown, determining the level of a service force, air traffic scheduling, design of dams, production scheduling, and hospital operation. Other techniques of operations research, such as inventory theory, game theory, and simulation, also have been successfully applied in a variety of contexts.

In 1965 Schumacher and Smith[1] reported on a survey of operations research activities which provided a snapshot of activities at that time. Mail questionnaires were sent to 168 companies. These were selected by cross-indexing *Fortune* Magazine's "top 500" industrial corporations with firms listed in the 1964 *College Placement Annual* as seeking engineers and/or mathematicians. Companies ranged in size from less than 2,000 to more than 500,000 employees (median 15,000). (Thus, this method of selection clearly was biased in favor of the company being engaged in operations research activities.) Sixty-five questionnaires were returned of which 49 (or approximately 75%) reported ongoing operations research activities.

[1] C. C. Schumacher and B. E. Smith, "A Sample Survey of Industrial Operations Research Activities II," *Operations Research*, **13**, 1023–1027 (1965).

Of these 49 responses, 62% indicated that their operations research staff was organized as a separate activity. The activities reported on the 49 questionnaires were then tabulated to determine how widely operations research had been applied to various kinds of problems. The results are shown in Table 1.1.

Because of the great impact of operations research, professional societies devoted to this field and related activities have been founded in a

TABLE 1.1. Areas of Application of Operations Research (Schumacher–Smith Survey)

Area of application	*Percent of Companies Reporting Activities*
Forecasting	73
Production scheduling	90
Inventory control	90
Quality control	51
Transportation	54
Advertising and sales research	27
Maintenance and repairs	32
Accounting procedures	17
Plant location	32
Equipment replacement	27
Packaging	7
Capital budgeting	39

number of countries throughout the world. In the United States, the Operations Research Society of America (ORSA) was established in 1952 and had close to 6,000 members by 1967, whereas The Institute of Management Sciences (TIMS) was founded a year later and had over 4,000 members by 1967. Each of these societies publishes a journal (*Operations Research* and *Management Science*, respectively) that now contains over 1,000 pages per year reporting new research and applications in the field. In addition, there are many other similar journals published in such countries as the United States, England, France, India, Japan, Canada, and West Germany.

Operations research also has had considerable impact in the colleges and universities. Most of the major American universities today offer courses in this field, and many offer advanced degrees that are either in or with specialization in operations research. As a result, there now are thousands of students taking at least one course in operations research each year. Much of the basic research in the field is also being done in the universities.

1.4 TRAINING FOR A CAREER IN OPERATIONS RESEARCH

Because of the great growth of operations research, career opportunities in this field appear to be outstanding. The demand for trained people continues to far exceed the supply, and both attractive starting positions and rapid advancement are readily available. Because of the nature of their work, operations research groups tend to have a prominent staff position with access to higher level management in the organization. The problems they work on tend to be important, challenging, and interesting. Therefore, any individual with a mathematics and science orientation who is also interested in the practical management of organizations is likely to find a career in operations research very rewarding.

Three complementary types of academic training are particularly relevant for a career in operations research. The first would be a basic training in the fundamentals upon which operations research is based. This includes the basic methodology of mathematics and science, as well as such topics as linear algebra and matrix theory, probability theory, statistical inference, stochastic processes, computer science, microeconomics, accounting and business administration, organization theory, and the behavioral sciences.

A second important type of training would be in operations research per se, including special techniques of the field such as linear and nonlinear programming, dynamic programming, inventory theory, network flow theory, queueing models, game theory, and simulation. It should also include an introduction to the methodology of operations research, where the various techniques and their role in an operations research study involving specific problem areas would be placed in perspective. Often courses covering certain of these topics are offered in more than one department within a university, including Departments of Business, Industrial Engineering, Mathematics, Statistics, Computer Science, Economics, and Electrical Engineering. This is a natural reflection of the broad scope of application of the field. Since it does tread across traditional disciplinary lines, separate programs or departments in operations research also are being established in some universities.

Finally, it is also well to have specialized training in some field other than operations research. For example, this might be in mathematics, statistics, industrial engineering, business, or economics. This additional training provides one with an area of special competence for applying operations research, and it should make that person a more valuable member of an operations research team.

The early operations researchers were people whose primary training and work had been in some traditional field, such as physics, chemistry, mathematics, engineering, or economics. They tended to have little or no formal education in operations research per se. However, as the body of special knowledge has expanded, it has become increasingly more difficult to enter the field without considerable prior education in this area. As a result, although it is still common for new operations researchers to have their college degree(s) in a traditional field, they generally have specialized, too, in operations research as part of their academic program. The traditional fields that have most commonly served as a vehicle into operations research are indicated in Table 1.2, which is based on the 1965 survey by Schumacher and Smith described in the preceding section. However, present trends suggest that many operations researchers in the future will have both an undergraduate degree in a traditional field and a graduate degree in operations research itself.

TABLE 1.2. Educational Background of Operations Research Personnel (Schumacher-Smith Survey)

	Percentage of total at degree level			
Major field of study	*Bachelors*	*Masters*	*Doctorate*	*All degree levels*
Mathematics and statistics	26	33	37	30
Engineering	45	28	14	35
Business	5	14	2	8
Economics	5	9	12	7
Chemistry	6	3	22	6
Other	13	13	13	14
Percentage of total	48.3	41.2	10.5	

1.5 AN OVERVIEW OF THE BOOK

As an introduction to operations research, this book presents a general coverage of its methodology, fundamentals, and techniques. Thus, Part I (this chapter and the next) briefly introduces the basic methodology of the field, including its general orientation and the way in which it adapts the scientific method to the study of operational problems. Part II and the Appendices then review certain of the fundamentals upon which operations research is based. Each of the fundamental fields of knowledge named in the preceding section is presented in many other books, so it is both impossible and unnecessary to cover all of them in a meaningful way in this volume. Therefore, only those fundamentals that are particularly important for an understanding of subsequent portions of the book (namely, probability theory, statistical inference and decision theory, and certain topics in mathematics) will be summarized here for convenient reference by the reader. Finally, the remainder of the book is devoted to the more important models and analytical techniques of operations research. This material is divided into three parts on the basis of its content and degree of difficulty. Thus, Part III presents an introduction to mathematical programming, which is a very prominent area of operations research largely concerned with how to allocate limited resources among the various activities of an organization. Part IV considers a number of probabilistic models, which take into account the uncertainty associated with future events in order to analyze certain important types of problems. Part V then discusses some relatively advanced topics in mathematical programming that are important for anyone specializing in operations research. Thus, Parts I, II, III, and IV provide a basic introductory survey of operations research, and Part V presents additional material for those who want to go further.

CHAPTER 2

Planning an Operations Research Study

2.1 INTRODUCTION

The bulk of this book is devoted to the mathematical methods of operations research. This is quite appropriate since these quantitative techniques comprise the main part of what is known about operations research. However, it does not imply that practical operations research studies are primarily mathematical exercises. As a matter of fact, the mathematical analysis often represents only a relatively small part of the total effort required. The purpose of this chapter is to place things into better perspective by describing all of the major phases of a typical operations research study.

One way of summarizing the usual phases of an operations research study is the following[2]:

(1) Formulating the problem.
(2) Constructing a mathematical model to represent the system under study.
(3) Deriving a solution from the model.
(4) Testing the model and the solution derived from it.
(5) Establishing controls over the solution.
(6) Putting the solution to work: implementation.

Each of these phases will be discussed in turn in the following sections.

2.2 FORMULATING THE PROBLEM

In contrast to textbook examples, most practical problems are initially communicated to an operations research team in a vague, imprecise way.

[2] Russell L. Ackoff, "The Development of Operations Research as a Science," *Operations Research*, **4,** 265f (1956).

Therefore, the first order of business is to study the relevant system and develop a well defined statement of the problem to be considered. This includes determining such things as the appropriate objectives, the constraints on what can be done, interrelationships between the area to be studied and other areas of the organization, the possible alternative courses of action, time limits for making a decision, etc. This process of problem formulation is a crucial one since it greatly affects how relevant the conclusions of the study will be. It is difficult to extract a "right" answer from the "wrong" problem! Therefore, this phase should be executed with considerable care, and the initial formulation should be continually re-examined in the light of new insights obtained during the later phases.

Determining the appropriate objectives is a very important aspect of problem formulation. To do this, it is necessary to first identify the person (or persons) who will be making the decisions concerning the system under study, and then to probe into all of his pertinent objectives relative to the problem. After eliciting the decision-maker's objectives, they should be analyzed and edited in order to identify the ultimate objectives that encompass the others, to determine the relative importance of these ultimate objectives, and to state them precisely in a way that does not eliminate worthwhile goals and alternatives.

By its nature, operations research is concerned with the welfare of the entire organization rather than that of only certain of its components. Thus, an operations research study seeks solutions that are optimal for the over-all organization rather than suboptimal solutions that are best for only one component. Therefore, the objectives that are formulated should ideally be those of the entire organization. However, this is not always convenient to do. Many problems primarily concern only a portion of the organization. And so the analysis would become unwieldy if the stated objectives were too general and if explicit consideration were given to all side effects on the rest of the organization. Granted that operations research takes the viewpoint of the over-all organization, this does not imply that each problem should be broadened into a study of the entire organization. Instead, the objectives used in the study should be as specific as they can be while still encompassing the main goals of the decision-maker and maintaining a reasonable degree of consistency with the higher level objectives of the organization. Side effects on other segments of the organization must then be considered only to the extent that there are questions of consistency with these higher level objectives.

One possible approach to circumventing the problem of suboptimization discussed above is to use long-run profit maximization as the sole objective. At first glance, this approach appears to have considerable merit. In particular, the objective of long-run profit maximization is specific enough to be used conveniently, and yet it seems to be broad enough to encompass the basic goal of most organizations. In fact, some people tend to feel that all other legitimate objectives can be translated into this one. However, this is such an oversimplification that considerable caution is required! A number of studies have found that, instead of profit maximization, the goal of satisfactory profits combined with other objectives is characteristic of American corporations. In particular, typical objectives might be to maintain stable profits, increase (or maintain) one's share of the market, product diversification, maintain stable prices, improve worker morale, maintain family control of the business, and increase company prestige. These objectives might be compatible with long-run profit maximization, but the relationship is sufficiently obscure that it may not be convenient to incorporate them into this one objective. Furthermore, there are additional considerations involving social responsibilities that are distinct from the profit motive. The five parties affected by a business firm are: (1) the owners (stockholders), who desire profits (dividends, stock appreciation, etc.), (2) the employees, who desire steady employment at reasonable wages, (3) the customers, who desire a reliable product at a reasonable price, (4) the vendors, who desire integrity and a reasonable selling price for their goods, and (5) the government and, hence, the nation, which desires payment of fair taxes and consideration of the national interest. All five parties make essential contributions to the firm, and the firm should not be viewed as the exclusive servant of any one party for the exploitation of the others. Therefore, while granting that management's prime responsibility is to make profits, its broader social responsibilities also must be recognized.

2.3 CONSTRUCTING A MATHEMATICAL MODEL

After formulating the decision-maker's problem, the next phase is to reformulate this problem into a form that is convenient for analysis. The conventional operations research approach for doing this is to construct a mathematical model that represents the essence of the problem. Before discussing how to construct it, let us first explore the nature of models in general and mathematical models in particular.

Models, or idealized representations, are an integral part of everyday life. Common examples include model airplanes, portraits, globes, etc. Similarly, models play an important role in science or business, as illustrated by models of the atom, models of the genetic structure, mathematical equations describing physical laws of motion or chemical reactions, graphs, organization charts, and industrial accounting systems. Such models are invaluable for abstracting the essence of the subject of inquiry, showing interrelationships, and facilitating analysis.

Mathematical models are also idealized representations, but they are expressed in terms of mathematical symbols and expressions. Such laws of physics as $F = ma$ and $E = mc^2$ are familiar examples. Similarly, the mathematical model of a business problem is the system of equations and related mathematical expressions that describe the essence of the problem. Thus, if there are n related quantifiable decisions to be made, they are represented as *decision variables* (say $x_1, x_2, \cdots, x_n$) whose respective values are to be determined. The composite measure of effectiveness (e.g., profit) is then expressed as a mathematical function of these decision variables (e.g., $P = 3x_1 + 2x_2 + \cdots + 5x_n$). This function is called the "*objective function.*" Any restrictions on the values that can be assigned to these decision variables are also expressed mathematically, typically by means of inequalities or equations (e.g., $x_1 + 3x_1x_2 + 2x_2 \leq 10$). Such mathematical expressions for the restrictions often are called "*constraints.*" The mathematical model might then say that the problem is to choose the values of the decision variables so as to maximize the objective function, subject to the specified constraints. Such a model, and minor variations of it, typify the models used in operations research.

Mathematical models have many advantages over a verbal description of the problem. One obvious advantage is that a mathematical model describes a problem much more concisely. This tends to make the over-all structure of the problem more comprehensible, and it helps to reveal important cause-and-effect relationships. In this way, it indicates more clearly what additional data are relevant to the analysis. It also facilitates dealing with the problem in its entirety and considering all of its interrelationships simultaneously. Finally, a mathematical model forms a bridge to the use of high-powered mathematical techniques and electronic computers to analyze the problem.

On the other hand, there are pitfalls to be avoided when using mathematical models. Such a model is necessarily an abstract idealization of the problem, and approximations and simplifying assumptions generally are required if the model is to be tractable. Therefore, care must be taken to insure that the model remains a valid representation of the problem. The proper criterion for judging the validity of a model is whether or not it predicts the relative effects of the alternative courses of action with sufficient accuracy to permit a sound decision. Therefore, it is not necessary to include unimportant details or factors that have approximately the same effect for all of the alternative courses of action considered. It is not even necessary that the absolute magnitude of the measure of effectiveness be approximately correct for the various alternatives, provided that their relative values (i.e., the differences between their values) are sufficiently precise. Thus, all that is required is that there be a high *correlation* between the prediction by the model and what would actually happen in the real world. In order to ascertain whether this requirement is satisfied or not, it is important to do considerable testing and consequent modifying of the model, which will be the subject of Sec. 2.5.

A crucial step in formulating the mathematical model is constructing the objective function. This requires developing a quantitative measure of effectiveness relative to each objective. If more than one objective has been formulated for the study, it is then necessary to transform and combine the respective measures into a composite measure of effectiveness. This composite measure would sometimes be something tangible (e.g., profit) corresponding to a higher goal of the organization, or it would sometimes need to be abstract (e.g., "utility"). In the latter case, the task of developing this measure tends to be a complex one requiring a careful comparison of the objectives and their relative importance. After developing the composite measure of effectiveness, the objective function is then obtained by expressing this measure as a mathematical function of the decision variables.

2.4 DERIVING A SOLUTION

After formulating a mathematical model for the problem under consideration, the next phase in an operations research study is to derive a solution from this model. Since most of this book is devoted to the subject of how to obtain solutions for various important types of mathematical models, little needs to be said about it here. However, it may be worthwhile to discuss briefly the nature of such solutions.

A common theme in operations research is the search for an "optimal" or best solution. Indeed, many procedures have been developed, and are presented in this book, for finding such solutions for certain kinds of problems. However, it needs to be recognized that these solutions are optimal only with respect to the model being used. Since the model necessarily is an idealized rather than exact representation of the real problem, there cannot be any Utopian guarantee that the optimal solution for the model will prove to be the best possible solution that could have been implemented for the real problem. With the many imponderables and uncertainties associated with most real problems, this is only to be expected. However, if the model is well formulated and tested, the resulting solution should tend to be a good approximation to the ideal course of action for the real problem. Therefore, rather than be deluded into demanding the impossible, the test of the practical success of an operations research study should be whether it provides a better guide for action than can be obtained by other means.

The eminent management scientist, Herbert Simon, has introduced the concept that the goal of an operations research study should be to "satisfice" rather than optimize. In other words, the appropriate goal is to find a good answer, one that the decision-maker considers a satisfactory guide for action in a reasonable period of time, rather than to search for an optimal solution. Or to put this in another way that reconciles the two viewpoints, the goal should be to conduct the study in an optimal manner, regardless of whether this involves finding an optimal solution to the model or not. Thus, in addition to considering the composite measure of effectiveness in the model, one should also consider the cost of the study and the disadvantages of delaying its completion, and then attempt to maximize the net benefits resulting from the study. In recognition of this concept, operations research teams occasionally use only "heuristic" procedures (i.e., intuitively designed procedures that do not guarantee an optimal solution) in order to find a good "suboptimal" solution. This is especially the case when the time or cost required to find an optimal solution for an adequate model of the problem would be very large.

The discussion thus far has implied that an operations research study seeks to find only one solution (which may or may not be required to be optimal). In fact, this is often not the case. An optimal solution for the original model may be far from ideal for the real problem. Therefore, it is common to obtain a sequence of solutions which comprise a series of improving approximations to the ideal course of action. Thus, the apparent weaknesses in the initial solution are used to suggest improvements in the model, its input data, and perhaps the solution procedure. (Sensitivity analysis also may be conducted to determine which input parameters are most critical in determining the solution and therefore require more careful estimation.) A new solution is then obtained and the cycle is repeated. This process continues until the improvements in the succeeding solutions become too small to warrant continuation. Even then, a number of alternative solutions (perhaps solutions that are optimal for one of several plausible versions of the model and its input data) may be presented to the decision-maker for the final selection. This would normally be done whenever the final choice among these decisions should be based on considerations that are best left to the judgment of the decision-maker.

Ways in which the model and its solution are evaluated and improved will be discussed in the next section.

2.5 TESTING THE MODEL AND SOLUTION

One of the first lessons of operations research is that it is not generally sufficient to rely solely on one's intuition. This applies not only in obtaining a solution to a problem, but also in evaluating the model that has been formulated to represent this problem. As indicated in Section 2.3, the proper criterion for judging the validity of a model is whether or not it predicts the relative effects of the alternative courses of action with sufficient accuracy to permit a sound decision. No matter how plausible the model may appear to be, it should not be accepted on faith that this condition is satisfied. Given the difficulty of communicating and understanding all of the aspects and subtleties of a complex operational problem, there is a distinct possibility that the operations research team either has not been given all of the true facts of the situation or has not interpreted them properly. For example, an important factor or interrelationship may not have been incorporated into the model, or perhaps certain input parameters have not been estimated accurately.

Before undertaking more elaborate tests, it is well to begin by checking for obvious errors or oversights in the model. Re-examining the formulation of the problem and comparing it with the model may help to reveal any such mistakes. Another useful check is to make sure that all of the mathematical expressions are dimensionally consistent in the units they use. Additional insight into the validity of the model can sometimes be obtained by varying the input parameters and/or the decision variables and checking if the output from the model behaves in a plausible manner. This is often especially revealing when the parameters or variables are assigned extreme values near their maxima or minima. Finally, either the operations research team or the decision-maker may detect shortcomings in the solution yielded by the model that will suggest particular omissions or errors in the model.

A more systematic approach to testing the model is to use a "retrospective" test. When it is applicable, this test involves using historical data to reconstruct the past, and then determining how well the model and the resulting solution would have performed if it had been used. Comparing the effectiveness of this hypothetical performance with what actually happened then indicates whether using this model tends to yield a significant improvement over current practice or not. It may also indicate areas where the model has shortcomings and requires modifications. Furthermore, by using alternative solutions from the model and determining their hypothetical historical performances, considerable evidence can be gathered regarding how well the model predicts the relative effects of alternative courses of actions. On the other hand, a disadvantage of retrospective testing is that it uses the same data that guided the formulation of the model. The crucial question is whether or not the past is truly representative of the future. If it is not, then the model might perform quite differently in the future than it would have in the past.

In order to circumvent this disadvantage of retrospective testing, it is sometimes useful to temporarily continue the status quo. This provides new data that were not available when the model was constructed. These data are then used in the same ways as described above in order to evaluate the model.

If the final solution is used repeatedly, it is important to continue checking the model and solution after the initial implementation to make sure that they remain valid. The establishment of such controls is the subject of the next section.

2.6 ESTABLISHING CONTROL OVER THE SOLUTION

Suppose that, after a series of tests and consequent improvements, an acceptable model and solution are developed. Suppose further that this solution is to be used repeatedly. It is evident that this one remains a valid solution for the real problem only as long as this specific model remains valid. However, conditions are constantly changing in the real world. Therefore, changes might occur that would indeed invalidate this model, e.g., the values of the input parameters may change significantly. If this should happen, it is vital that it be detected as soon as possible so that the model, its solution, and the resulting course of action can be modified accordingly. Thus, whenever a solution and the resulting strategy for future action are applied repeatedly, this solution must be controlled in a way such as that described below.

In addition to maintaining a general surveillance of the situation, it is often worthwhile to establish systematic procedures for controlling the solution. To do this, it is necessary to identify the critical input parameters of the model, i.e., those parameters subject to changes which would significantly affect the solution. This is done by sensitivity analysis, whereby the respective parameters are varied over their possible values in order to determine the degree of variation in the resulting solution. Next, a procedure is established for detecting statistically significant changes in each of these critical parameters. This can sometimes be done by the process control charts used in statistical quality control.[3] Finally, provision is made for adjusting the solution and consequent course of action whenever such a change is detected.

2.7 IMPLEMENTATION

The last phase of an operations research study is to implement the final solution as approved by the decision-maker. This phase is a critical one since it is here, and only here, that the benefits of the study are reaped. Therefore, it is important for the operations research team to participate in launching this phase, both to make sure that the solution is accurately translated into an operating procedure and to rectify any flaws in the solution that are then uncovered.

The success of the implementation phase depends a great deal on the support of both top management and operating management (or their

[3] For example, see Eugene L. Grant, *Statistical Quality Control*, McGraw-Hill, New York, 1964, Part Two.

counterparts in nonbusiness organizations). Therefore, the operations research team should encourage the active participation of management in formulating the problem and evaluating the solution. Obtaining the guidance of management is valuable in its own right for identifying relevant special considerations and thereby avoiding potential pitfalls during these phases. However, by making management a party to the study, this also serves to enlist their active support for its implementation.

The implementation phase involves several steps. First, the operations research team gives operating management a careful explanation of the solution to be adopted and how it relates to operating realities. Next, these two parties share the responsibility for developing the procedures required to put this solution into operation. Operating management then sees that a detailed indoctrination is given to the personnel involved, and the new course of action is initiated. Finally, if the nature of the problem permits it, the initial experience with this course of action is used by the operations research team to detect modifications that should be made in the future.

In concluding this discussion of the major phases of an operations research study, it should be emphasized that there are many exceptions to the "rules" prescribed above. By its very nature, operations research (i.e., research on operations) requires considerable ingenuity and innovation, so it is impossible to write down any standard procedure that should always be followed by operations research teams. Rather, the above description may be viewed as a "model" that roughly represents how successful operations research studies are conducted.

SELECTED REFERENCES

1. Arrow, Kenneth J., "Decision Theory and Operations Research," *Operations Research,* **5,** 765–774 (1957).
2. Churchman, C. West, Ackoff, Russell L., and Arnoff, E. Leonard, *Introduction to Operations Research,* Wiley, New York, 1957, Parts I, II, III, and IX.
3. Miller, David W., and Starr, Martin K., *Executive Decisions and Operations Research,* Prentice-Hall, Englewood Cliffs, N.J., 1960.
4. Shuchman, Abe, *Scientific Decision Making in Business* (Readings in Operations Research for Nonmathematicians), Holt, Rinehart, and Winston, New York, 1963, Parts I and II.
5. Wagner, Harvey M., "Practical Slants on Operations Research," *Harvard Business Review,* **41,** 61–71 (1963).

Part II

FUNDAMENTALS

CHAPTER 3

Probability Theory

3.1 INTRODUCTION

In decision-making problems, one is often faced with making decisions based upon phenomena which have uncertainty associated with them. This uncertainty is caused by inherent variation due to sources of variation that elude control or the inconsistency of natural phenomena. Rather than treat this variability qualitatively, one can incorporate it into the mathematical model, and thus handle it quantitatively. This generally can be accomplished if the natural phenomena exhibit some degree of regularity so that their variation can be described by a probability model. The ensuing sections are concerned with methods for characterizing these probability models.

3.2 SAMPLE SPACE

Suppose the demand for a product over a period of time, say a month, is of interest. From a realistic point of view, demand is not generally constant but exhibits the type of variation alluded to in the previous section. Suppose an experiment is run which will result in observing the demand for the product during the month. Whereas the outcome of the experiment cannot be predicted exactly, each *possible* outcome can be described. The demand during the period can be any one of the values $0, 1, 2, \cdots$, i.e., the entire set of non-negative integers. The set of all possible outcomes of the experiment is called the sample space, and will be denoted by Ω. Each outcome in the sample space is called a point and will be denoted by ω. Actually, in the experiment just described, the possible demands may be bounded from above by N, where N would represent the size of the population that has any use for the product. Hence, the sample space would then consist of the set of the integers 0, 1, 2, $\cdots$, N. Strictly speaking, the sample space is much more complex than just described. In fact, it may be extremely difficult to characterize precisely. Associated with this experiment are such factors as the dates and times that the demands occur, the prevailing weather, the disposition of the personnel meeting the demand, etc. Many more factors could be listed, most of which are irrelevant. Fortunately, as noted in the next section, it is not necessary to describe completely the sample space, but only to record those factors which appear to be necessary for the purposes of the experiment.

Another experiment may be concerned with the time until the first customer arrives at a store. Since the first customer may arrive at any time until the store closes (assuming an eight-hour day), for the purpose of this experiment the sample space can be considered to be all points on the real line between zero and eight hours. Thus, Ω consists of all points ω such that

$$0 \leq \omega \leq 8 .$$[4]

Now consider a third example. Suppose that a modification of the first experiment is made by observing the demands during the first two months. The sample space Ω consists of all points (x_1, x_2) where x_1 represents the demand during the first month, $x_1 = 0, 1, 2, \cdots$, and x_2 represents the demand during the second month, $x_2 = 0, 1, 2, \cdots$. Thus, Ω consists of the set of all possible points ω, where ω represents a pair of non-negative integer values, (x_1, x_2). The point $\omega = (3, 6)$ represents a possible outcome of the experiment where the demand in the first month is 3 units and the demand in the second month is 6 units. In a similar manner, the experiment can be extended to observing the demands during the first n months. In this situation, Ω consists of all possible points $\omega = (x_1, x_2, \cdots, x_n)$, where x_i represents the demand during the ith month.

The experiment that is concerned with the time until the first arrival appears can also be modified. Suppose an experiment is performed which measures the times of the arrival of the first customer on each of two days. The set of all possible outcomes of the experiment, Ω, consists of all points (x_1, x_2), $0 \leq x_1, x_2 \leq 8$, where x_1 represents the time the first customer arrives on the first day, and x_2 represents the time the first customer arrives on the second day. Thus, Ω consists of the set of all possible points ω where ω represents a point in two space lying in the square shown in Fig. 3.1.

This experiment can also be extended to observing the times of the arrival of the first customer on each of n days. The sample space, Ω, consists of all points $\omega = (x_1, x_2, \cdots, x_n)$, such that $0 \leq x_i \leq 8$ $(i = 1, 2, \cdots, n)$, where x_i represents the time the first customer arrives on the ith day.

An event is defined as a set of outcomes of the experiment. Thus, there are many events that can be of interest. For example, in the experiment

[4] It will be assumed that at least one customer arrives each day.

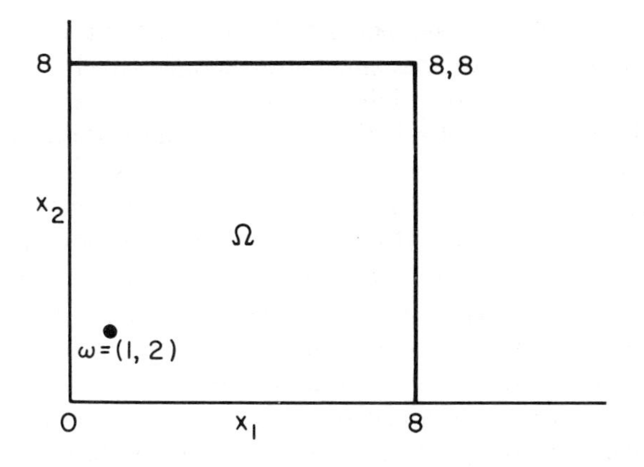

FIGURE 3.1. Sample space of the arrival time experiment.

concerned with observing the demand for a product in a given month, if the event is the set $\{\omega = 0, \omega = 1, \omega = 2, \cdots, \omega = 10\}$, then this set includes those experimental results for which a demand for the product does not exceed 10 units. Similarly, the set $\{\omega = 0\}$ denotes the event of no demand for the product during the month. In the experiment which measures the times of the arrival of the first customer on each of two days, if the event is the set $\{\omega = (x_1, x_2); x_1 < 1, x_2 < 1\}$, then this set includes those experimental results for which the first arrival on each day occurs before the first hour.

3.3 RANDOM VARIABLES

It may frequently occur that in performing an experiment one is not interested directly in the entire sample space or in events defined over the sample space. For example, suppose that the experiment which measures the times of the first arrival on two days was performed to determine at what time to open the store. Prior to performing the experiment, the store owner decides that if the average of the arrival times is greater than an hour, thereafter he will not open his store until 10 a.m. (9 a.m. being the previous opening time). The average of x_1 and x_2 (the two arrival times) is not a point in the sample space, and hence he cannot make his decision by looking directly at the outcome of his experiment. Instead, he makes his decision according to the results of a rule which assigns the average of x_1 and x_2 to *each point* (x_1, x_2) in Ω. This resultant set is then partitioned into two parts: those points which are below 1 and those which are above 1. If the observed result of this rule (average of the two arrival times) lies in the partition with points greater than 1, the store will be opened at 10 a.m. Otherwise, the store will continue to open at 9 a.m. The rule which assigns the average of x_1 and x_2 to each point in the sample space is called a random variable. Thus, a random variable is a numerically valued function defined over the sample space. Note that a function, in a mathematical sense, is just a rule which assigns a number to each value in the domain of definition, the sample space in this context.

Random variables play an extremely important role in probability theory. Experiments are usually very complex, and contain information which may or may not be superfluous. For example, in measuring the arrival time of the first customer, the color of his shoes may be pertinent. Although this is unlikely, the prevailing weather may certainly be relevant. Hence, the choice of the random variable enables the experimenter to describe the factors of importance to him, and permits him to discard the superfluous characteristics which may be extremely difficult to characterize.

There is a multitude of random variables associated with each experiment. In the experiment concerning the arrival of the first customer on each of two days, it has already been pointed out that the average of the arrival times, $\bar{X}$, is a random variable. Notationally, random variables will be characterized by capital letters, and the values the random variable takes on will be denoted by lower case letters. Actually, to be precise, $\bar{X}$ should be written as $\bar{X}(\omega)$, where ω is any point shown in the square in Fig. 3.1, since $\bar{X}$ is a function. Thus, $\bar{X}(1, 2) = (1 + 2)/2 = 1.5$; $\bar{X}(1.6, 1.8) = (1.6 + 1.8)/2 = 1.7$, $\bar{X}(1.5, 1.5) = (1.5 + 1.5)/2 = 1.5$, $\bar{X}(8, 8) = (8 + 8)/2 = 8, \cdots$. The values that the random variable $\bar{X}$ takes on are the set of values $\bar{x}$ such that $0 \leq \bar{x} \leq 8$. Another random variable, X_1, can be described as follows: For each ω in Ω, the random variable (numerically valued function) disregards the x_2 coordinate and transforms the x_1 coordinate into itself. This random variable, then, represents the arrival time of the first customer on the first day. Hence, $X_1(1, 2) = 1$, $X_1(1.6, 1.8) = 1.6$, $X_1(1.5, 1.5) = 1.5$, $X_1(8, 8) = 8$. The values the random variable X_1 takes on are the set of values x_1 such that $0 \leq x_1 \leq 8$. In a similar manner, the random variable X_2 can be described as representing the arrival time of the first customer on the second day. A third random variable, S^2, can be described as follows: For each ω in Ω, the random variable computes the sum of squares of the deviations of the coordinates about their average, i.e., $S^2(\omega) = S^2(x_1, x_2) = (x_1 - \bar{x})^2 + (x_2 - \bar{x})^2$. Hence $S^2(1, 2) = (1 - 1.5)^2 + (2 - 1.5)^2 = 0.5$, $S^2(1.6, 1.8) = (1.6 - 1.7)^2 + (1.8 - 1.7)^2 = 0.02$, $S^2(1.5, 1.5) = (1.5 - 1.5)^2 + (1.5 - 1.5)^2 = 0$, $S^2(8, 8) = (8 - 8)^2 + (8 - 8)^2 = 0, \cdots$. It is evident that the values the random variable S^2 takes on are the set of values s^2 such that $0 \leq s^2 \leq 32$.

All of the random variables just described are called continuous random variables since they take on a continuum of values. Discrete random variables are those which take on a finite or denumerable set of values.[5] An example of a discrete random variable can be obtained by referring to the experiment dealing with the measurement of demand. Let the discrete random variable X be defined as the demand during the month. (The experiment consists of measuring the demand for one month.) Thus, $X(0) = 0, X(1) = 1, X(2) = 2, \cdots$, so that the random variable takes on the set of values consisting of the integers. Note that Ω and the set of values the random variable takes on are identical so that this random variable is just the identity function.

From the above paragraphs, it is evident that any function of a random variable is itself a random variable since a function of a function is also a function. Thus, in the previous examples, $\bar{X} = (X_1 + X_2)/2$ and $S^2 = (X_1 - \bar{X})^2 + (X_2 - \bar{X})^2$ can also be recognized as random variables by noting that they are functions of the random variables X_1 and X_2.

This text is concerned with random variables that are real valued functions defined over the real line or a subset of the real line.

3.4 PROBABILITY AND PROBABILITY DISTRIBUTIONS

Returning to the example of the demand for a product during a month, note that the actual demand is not a constant; instead, it can be expected to exhibit some "variation." In particular, this variation can be described by introducing the concept of probability defined over events in the sample space. For example, if the event is the set E_1, where E_1 is $\{\omega = 0, \omega = 1, \omega = 2, \cdots, \omega = 10\}$, then intuitively one can speak of $P(E_1)$, where $P(E_1)$ is the probability of having a demand of 10 or less units. If $P(E)$ is known for all sets E in the sample space, then some "information" is available about the demand that can be expected to occur. To define the concept of probability rigorously is beyond the scope of this text. However, the following properties of probability that seem to be reasonable can be described.

(1) $0 \leq P\{E\} \leq 1$. This implies that the probability of an event is always non-negative and can never exceed 1.
(2) If E_0 is an event which cannot occur in the sample space, e.g., a demand of -7 units, then $P\{E_0\} = 0$.
(3) $P\{\Omega\} = 1$. If the event is the entire sample space, the probability of having some demand between 0 and N is certain.
(4) If E_1 and E_2 are disjoint (mutually exclusive) events in Ω, then $P\{E_1 + E_2\} = P\{E_1\} + P\{E_2\}$, where $\{E_1 + E_2\}$ is the event E_1 *or* E_2. Thus, if E_1 is the event of a demand of 0 or 1 and E_2 is the event of

[5] A denumerable set of values is a set whose elements can be put into one-to-one correspondence with the set of positive integers.

a demand of 4 or 5, then the probability of having a demand of 0, 1, 4, or 5, i.e., $\{E_1 + E_2\}$, is given by $P\{E_1\} + P\{E_2\}$.

Although these properties are rather formal, they do conform to one's intuitive notion about probability. A usual interpretation of probability is the frequency interpretation. This may be stated precisely as follows. Denote by n the number of times an experiment is performed, and by m the number of successful occurrences of the event E in the n trials. Then $P(E)$ can be defined as

$$P(E) = \lim_{n \to \infty} \frac{m}{n},$$

assuming the limit exists for such a phenomena. The ratio m/n does fulfill the conditions for probability, i.e.,

(1) $0 \leq m/n \leq 1$
(2) $0/n = 0$ (If the event E cannot occur, then $m = 0$.)
(3) $n/n = 1$ (If the event E must occur every time the experiment is performed, then $m = n$.)
(4) $(m_1 + m_2)/n = m_1/n + m_2/n$ if E_1 and E_2 are disjoint events. (If the event E_1 occurs m_1 times in the n trials and the event E_2 occurs m_2 times in the n trials, and E_1 and E_2 are disjoint, then the total number of successful occurrences of the event E_1 *or* E_2 is just $m_1 + m_2$.)

If these properties are true for a finite n, then we would expect them to be true for

$$P(E) = \lim_{n \to \infty} \frac{m}{n}.$$

The trouble with the frequency interpretation as a definition of probability is that it is not possible to actually determine the probability of an event E, since the question "How large must n be?" cannot be answered. Furthermore, such a definition does not permit a logical development of the theory of probability. However, a rigorous definition of probability, or finding methods for determining probabilities of events, is not of prime importance here.

We see that we can postulate the existence of probabilities, defined over events E in the sample space. However, we have already indicated that random variables may be of interest, and finding the relation between probabilities associated with events in the sample space and "probabilities" associated with random variables is quite important.

Associated with every random variable is a cumulative distribution function (C.D.F.). In order to define a C.D.F., it is necessary to introduce some additional notation. Define the symbol $E_b = \{X(\omega) \leq b\}$ (or, equivalently, $\{X \leq b\}$) as the set of outcomes ω in the sample space forming the event E_b such that the random variable X takes on values less than or equal to b. Then $P\{E_b\}$ is just the probability of this event. Note that this probability is well defined since E_b is an event in the sample space, and this event depends upon the random variable that is of interest. For example, suppose the experiment which measures the demand for a product during a month is performed. Let $N = 99$ and assume that the events $\{0\}$, $\{1\}$, $\{2\}, \cdots,$ $\{99\}$ each has probability equal to $1/100$, i.e., $P\{0\} = P\{1\} = P\{2\} = \cdots = P\{99\} = 1/100$. Let the random variable X be the square of the demand. Hence,

$$\{X \leq 150\}$$

is the set $E_b = \{0, 1, 2, 3, 4, 5, 6, 7, 8, 9, 10, 11, 12\}$ (since the square of these numbers is less than 150). Furthermore,

$$P\{E_b\} = \frac{1}{100} + \frac{1}{100} + \frac{1}{100} + \frac{1}{100} + \frac{1}{100} + \frac{1}{100} + \frac{1}{100} + \frac{1}{100} + \frac{1}{100} + \frac{1}{100} + \frac{1}{100} + \frac{1}{100} + \frac{1}{100} = \frac{13}{100}.$$

Thus, $P(E_b) = P\{X \leq b\} = 13/100$. For a given random variable X, $P\{X \leq b\}$ is denoted by $F_X(b)$, is called the cumulative distribution function (C.D.F.) of the random variable X, and is defined for all real values of b. Where there is no ambiguity, the C.D.F. will be denoted by $F(b)$. Hence, each random variable has a cumulative distribution function associated with it. This is not an arbitrary function, but is induced by the probabilities associated with events defined over the sample space Ω such that $\{X(\omega) \leq b\}$. The C.D.F. of a random variable is a numerically valued function defined for all b, $-\infty \leq b \leq \infty$, having the following properties:

(1) $F_X(b)$ is a nondecreasing function of b,

(2) $\lim_{b \to -\infty} F_X(b) = F_X(-\infty) = 0,$

(3) $\lim_{b \to +\infty} F_X(b) = F_X(+\infty) = 1.$

Using the definition of the event E_b, events of the form

$$\{a < X \leq b\}$$

can be described as the set of outcomes ω in the sample space such that the random variable X takes on values greater than a but not exceeding b. Thus, $P\{a < X \leq b\}$ can easily be seen to be

$$F_X(b) - F_X(a)\,.$$

As another example, consider the experiment which measures the times of the arrival of the first customer on each of two days. Ω consists of all points (x_1, x_2) such that $0 \leq x_1, x_2 \leq 8$, where x_1 represents the time the first customer arrives on the first day, and x_2 represents the time the first customer arrives on the second day. Consider all events associated with this experiment and assume that the probabilities of such events can be obtained. Suppose $\bar{X}$, the average of the two arrival times, is chosen as the random variable of interest, and that E_b is again the set of outcomes ω in

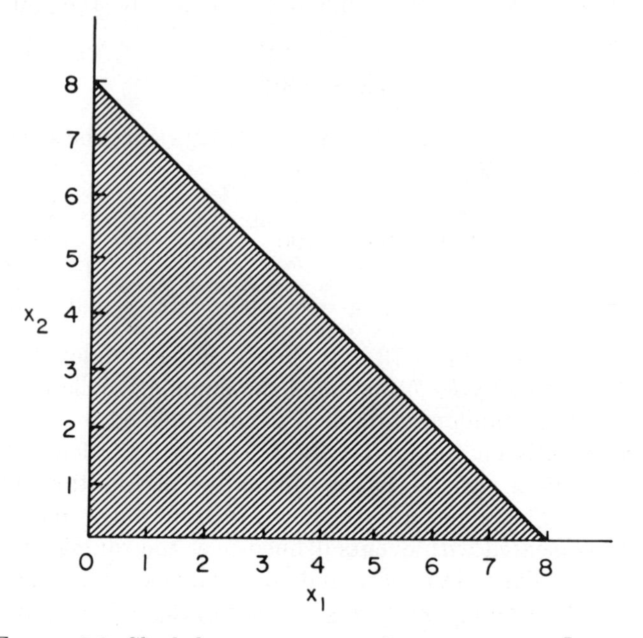

FIGURE 3.2. Shaded area represents the event $E_b = \{\bar{X} \leq 4\}$.

the sample space forming the event E_b such that $\bar{X} \leq b$. Hence, $F_{\bar{X}}(b) = P\{E_b\} = P\{\bar{X} \leq b\}$. To illustrate how this can be evaluated, suppose that $b = 4$ hours. All the values of x_1, x_2 are sought such that $(x_1 + x_2)/2 \leq 4$ or $x_1 + x_2 \leq 8$. This is shown by the shaded area in Fig. 3.2. Hence, $F_{\bar{X}}(b)$ is just the probability of a successful occurrence of the event given by the shaded area in Fig. 3.2. Presumably $F_{\bar{X}}(b)$ can be evaluated if probabilities of such events in the sample space are known.

Another random variable associated with this experiment is X_1, the time of the arrival of the first customer on the first day. Thus, $F_{X_1}(b) = P\{X_1 \leq b\}$, which can be obtained simply if probabilities of events over the sample space are given.

There is a simple frequency interpretation for the cumulative distribution function of a random variable. Suppose an experiment is repeated n times and the random variable X is observed each time. Denote by

$x_1, x_2, \cdots, x_n$ the outcomes of these n trials. Order these outcomes, letting $x_{(1)}$ be the smallest observation, $x_{(2)}$ the second smallest, $\cdots$, $x_{(n)}$ the largest. Plot the following step function $F_n(x)$:

For $x < x_{(1)}$, let $F_n(x) = 0$.
For $x_{(1)} \leq x < x_{(2)}$, let $F_n(x) = 1/n$.
For $x_{(2)} \leq x < x_{(3)}$, let $F_n(x) = 2/n$.

$\cdot$
$\cdot$
$\cdot$

For $x_{(n-1)} \leq x < x_{(n)}$, let $F_n(x) = (n-1)/n$.
For $x \geq x_n$, let $F_n(x) = n/n = 1$.

Such a plot is given in Fig. 3.3 and is seen to "jump" at the values that the random variable takes on.

$F_n(x)$ can be interpreted as the fraction of outcomes of the experiment less than or equal to x, and is called the sample cumulative distribution function. It can be shown that as the number of repetitions, n, of the experiment gets large, the sample C.D.F. approaches the C.D.F. of the random variable X.

In most problems encountered in practice, one is not concerned with

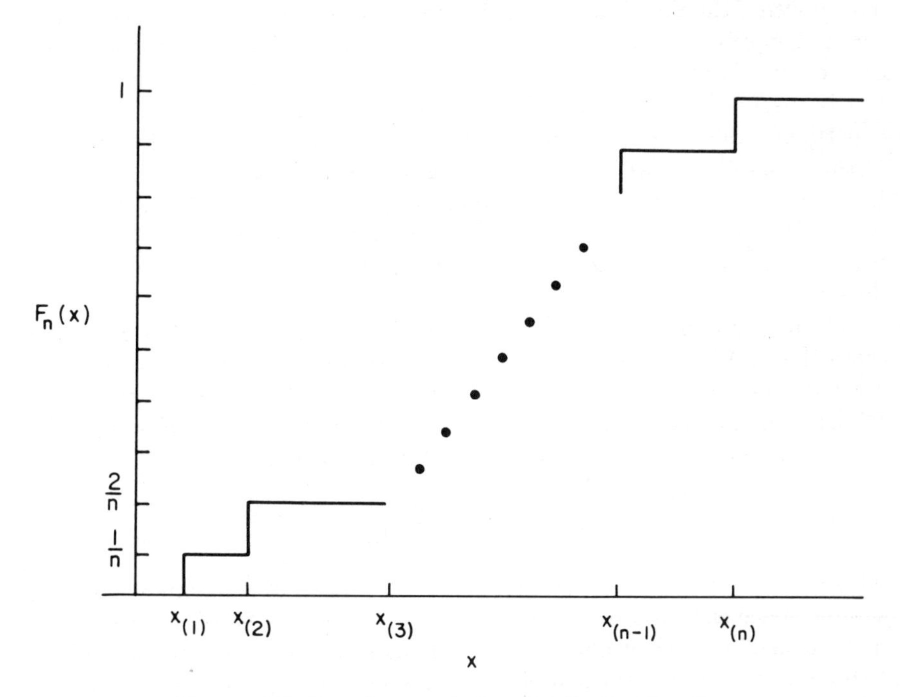

FIGURE 3.3. Sample cumulative distribution function.

events in the sample space and their associated probabilities. Instead, interest is focused on random variables and their associated cumulative distribution functions. Generally, a random variable (or random variables) is chosen and some assumption is made about the form of the C.D.F. or about the random variable. For example, the random variable X_1, the time of the first arrival on the first day, may be of interest, and an assumption may be made that the form of its C.D.F. is exponential. Similarly, the same assumption about X_2, the time of the first arrival on the second day, may also be made. If these assumptions are valid, then the C.D.F. of the random variable $\bar{X} = (X_1 + X_2)/2$ can be derived. Of course, these assumptions about the form of the C.D.F. are not arbitrary and really imply assumptions about probabilities associated with events in the sample space. Hopefully, they can be substantiated by either empirical evidence or theoretical considerations.

3.5 CONDITIONAL PROBABILITY AND INDEPENDENT EVENTS

Often experiments are performed so that some results are obtained early in time and some later in time. This is the case, for example, when the experiment consists of measuring the demand for a product during each of two months; the demand during the first month is observed at the end of the first month. Similarly, the arrival times of the first two customers on each of two days are observed sequentially in time. This early information can be useful in making predictions about the subsequent results of the experiment. Such information need not necessarily be associated with time. If the demand for two products during a month is investigated, knowing the demand of one of them may be useful in assessing the demand for the other. In order to utilize this information the concept of "conditional probability," defined over events occurring in the sample space, is introduced.

Consider two events in the sample space, E_1 and E_2, where E_1 represents the event that has occurred, and E_2 represents the event whose occurrence or non-occurrence is of interest. Furthermore, assume that $P\{E_1\} > 0$. The conditional probability of the occurrence of the event E_2, given that the event E_1 has occurred, $P\{E_2|E_1\}$ is defined to be

$$P\{E_2|E_1\} = \frac{P\{E_1 \cap E_2\}}{P\{E_1\}},$$

where $\{E_1 \cap E_2\}$ represents the event consisting of all points ω in the sample space common to *both* E_1 and E_2. For example, consider the experiment which consists of observing the demand for a product over each of two months. Suppose the sample space Ω consists of all points $\omega = (x_1, x_2)$, where x_1 represents the demand during the first month, and x_2 represents the demand during the second month, $x_1, x_2 = 0, 1, 2, \cdots, 99$. Furthermore, it is known that the demand for the first month has been 10. Hence, the event E_1, which consists of the points (10, 0), (10, 1), (10, 2), $\cdots$, (10, 99), has occurred. Consider the event E_2 which represents a demand for the product in the second month that does not exceed one unit. This event consists of the points (0, 0), (1, 0), (2, 0), $\cdots$, (10, 0), $\cdots$, (99, 0), (0, 1), (1, 1), (2, 1), $\cdots$, (10, 1), $\cdots$, (99, 1). The event $\{E_1 \cap E_2\}$ consists of the points (10, 0) and (10, 1). Hence, the probability of a demand which does not exceed one unit in the second month, given that a demand of 10 units occurred during the first month, i.e., $P\{E_2|E_1\}$, is given by

$$P\{E_2|E_1\} = \frac{P\{E_1 \cap E_2\}}{P\{E_1\}}$$

$$= \frac{P\{\omega = (10, 0), \omega = (10, 1)\}}{P\{\omega = (10, 0), \omega = (10, 1), \cdots, \omega = (10, 99)\}}.$$

The definition of conditional probability can be given a frequency interpretation. Denote by n the number of times an experiment is performed, and let n_1 be the number of times the event E_1 has occurred. Let n_{12} be the number of times that the event $E_1 \cap E_2$ has occurred in the n trials. n_{12}/n_1 is the proportion of times that the event E_2 occurs when E_1 has also occurred, i.e., n_{12}/n_1 is the conditional relative frequency of E_2, given that E_1 has occurred. This relative frequency n_{12}/n_1 is then equivalent to $(n_{12}/n)/(n_1/n)$. Using the frequency interpretation of probability for large n, n_{12}/n is approximately $P\{E_1 \cap E_2\}$, and n_1/n is approximately $P\{E_1\}$, so that the conditional relative frequency of E_2, given E_1, is approximately $P\{E_1 \cap E_2\}/P\{E_1\}$.

In essence, if one is interested in conditional probability, he is working with a reduced sample space, i.e., from Ω to E_1, modifying other events accordingly. Also note that conditional probability has the four properties described in Sec. 3.4, i.e.,

(1) $0 \leq P\{E_2|E_1\} \leq 1$.
(2) If E_2 is an event which cannot occur, then $P\{E_2|E_1\} = 0$.
(3) If the event E_2 is the entire sample space Ω, then $P\{\Omega|E_1\} = 1$.
(4) If E_2 and E_3 are disjoint events in Ω, then

$$P\{E_2 + E_3|E_1\} = P\{E_2|E_1\} + P\{E_3|E_1\}.$$

If $P\{E_2\} > 0$, then $P\{E_1|E_2\} = P\{E_1 \cap E_2\}/P\{E_2\}$ can also be defined.

The concept of conditional probability was introduced so that advantage could be taken of information about the occurrence or non-occurrence of events. It is conceivable that information about the occurrence of the event E_1 yields no information about the occurrence or non-occurrence of the event E_2. If $P\{E_2|E_1\} = P\{E_2\}$, or $P\{E_1|E_2\} = P\{E_1\}$, then E_1 and E_2 are said to be independent events. It then follows that if E_1 and E_2 are independent and $P\{E_1\} > 0$, then $P\{E_2|E_1\} = P\{E_1 \cap E_2\}/P\{E_1\} = P\{E_2\}$, so that $P\{E_1 \cap E_2\} = P\{E_1\}\,P\{E_2\}$. This can be taken as an alternative definition of independence of the events E_1 and E_2. It is usually difficult to show that events are independent by using the definitions of independence. Instead, it is generally simpler to use the information available about the experiment to postulate whether events are independent. This is usually based upon physical considerations. For example, if the demand for a product during a month is "known" *not* to affect the demand in subsequent months, then the events E_1 and E_2 defined previously can be said to be independent. In this case,

$$\begin{aligned} P\{E_2|E_1\} &= \frac{P\{E_1 \cap E_2\}}{P\{E_1\}} \\ &= \frac{P\{\omega = (10, 0), \omega = (10, 1)\}}{P\{\omega = (10, 0), \omega = (10, 1), \cdots, \omega = (10, 99)\}}, \\ &= \frac{P\{E_1\}\,P\{E_2\}}{P\{E_1\}} = P\{E_2\}, \\ &= P\{\omega = (0, 0), \omega = (1, 0), \cdots, \omega = (99, 0), \omega = (0, 1), \\ &\qquad \omega = (1, 1), \cdots, \omega = (99, 1)\}. \end{aligned}$$

The definition of independence can be extended to any number of events. $E_1, E_2, \cdots, E_n$ are said to be independent events if for *every* subset of these events $E_1^*, E_2^*, \cdots, E_k^*$,

$$P\{E_1^* \cap E_2^* \cap \cdots \cap E_k^*\} = P\{E_1^*\}\,P\{E_2^*\} \cdots P\{E_k^*\}.$$

Intuitively, this implies that knowledge of the occurrence of any of these events has no effect on the probability of occurrence of any other event.

3.6 DISCRETE PROBABILITY DISTRIBUTIONS

It has been pointed out that one is usually concerned with random variables and their associated probability distributions, and discrete random variables are those which take on a finite or denumerable set of values. The C.D.F. for a discrete random variable, $F_X(b)$, is given by

$$F_X(b) = P\{X(\omega) \le b\} = \sum_{\text{all } x_i \le b} P\{X(\omega) = x_i\},$$

where $\{X(\omega) = x_i\}$ is the set of outcomes ω in the sample space such that the random variable X takes on the value x_i. Since x_i represents a finite or denumerable set of numbers, the notation can be simplified by actually describing the numerical values of x_i. For example, in Sec. 3.4 the discrete random variable X, which represented the square of the demand, was considered. Since the possible demand was truncated, i.e., $N = 99$, the random variable may take on any one of the numbers 0, 1, 4, 9, $\cdots$, $(98)^2$, $(99)^2$. It follows that $x_0 = 0$, $x_1 = 1$, $x_2 = 4$, $x_3 = 9, \cdots, x_{98} = (98)^2$, $x_{99} = (99)^2$, and that $\{X(\omega) = x_0\} = \{X(\omega) = 0\}$, $\{X(\omega) = x_1\} = \{X(\omega) = 1\}$, $\{X(\omega) = x_2\} = \{X(\omega) = 4\}$, $\{X(\omega) = x_3\} = \{X(\omega) = 9\}, \cdots, \{X(\omega) = x_{98}\} = \{X(\omega) = (98)^2\}$, $\{X(\omega) = x_{99}\} = \{X(\omega) = (99)^2\}$. Thus, an equivalent characterization of $\{X(\omega) = x_i\}$ for all x_i, i.e., $x_0, x_1, x_2, \cdots, x_{99}$, is given by $\{X(\omega) = k\}$ for $k = 0, 1, 4, 9, \cdots, (98)^2, (99)^2$. Hence,

$$F_X(150) = \sum_{\text{all } x_i \leq 150} P\{X(\omega) = x_i\} = P\{X(\omega) = x_0\} + P\{X(\omega) = x_1\}$$

$$+ P\{X(\omega) = x_2\} + \cdots + P\{X(\omega) = x_{12}\}$$

$$= P\{X(\omega) = 0\} + P\{X(\omega) = 1\} + P\{X(\omega) = 4\} + \cdots + P\{X(\omega) = 144\}$$

$$= \sum_{\text{all } k \leq 150} P\{X(\omega) = k\} .$$

In general then, it is seen that

$$F_X(b) = \sum_{\text{all } x_i \leq b} P\{X(\omega) = x_i\} = \sum_{\text{all } k \leq b} P\{X(\omega) = k\} .$$

Furthermore, $P\{X(\omega) = k\}$ will be denoted by $P_X(k)$, so that

$$F_X(b) = \sum_{\text{all } k \leq b} P_X(k) .$$

The $P_X(k)$ are called the probability distribution of the discrete random variable X. When no ambiguity exists, $P_X(k)$ may be denoted by $P(k)$.

As an example, consider the discrete random variable which represents the demand for a product in a given month. Again let $N = 99$. $P_X(k) = P\{X = k\} = 1/100$ for all $k = 0, 1, \cdots, 99$, then the C.D.F. for this discrete random variable is given in Fig. 3.4. The probability distribution of this discrete random variable is shown in Fig. 3.5.

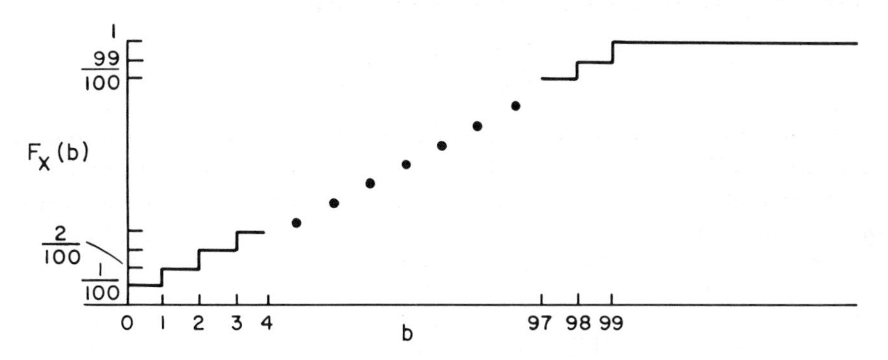

FIGURE 3.4. C.D.F. of a discrete random variable.

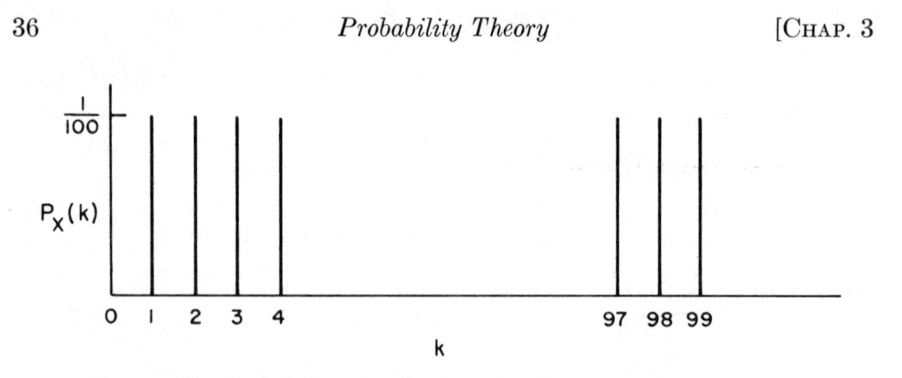

FIGURE 3.5. Probability distribution of a discrete random variable.

Of course, the heights of the vertical lines in Fig. 3.5 are all equal because $P_X(0) = P_X(1) = P_X(2) = \cdots = P_X(99)$ in this case. For other random variables X, the $P_X(k)$ need not be equal, and hence, the vertical lines will not be constant. In fact, all that is required for the $P_X(k)$ to form a probability distribution is that $P_X(k)$ be non-negative and

$$\sum_{\text{all } k} P_X(k) = 1 .$$

There are several important discrete probability distributions used in operations research work. The remainder of this section is devoted to a study of these distributions.

3.6.1 Binomial Distribution

A random variable X is said to have a binomial distribution if its probability distribution can be written as

$$P\{X = k\} = P_X(k) = \frac{n!}{k!(n-k)!} p^k(1-p)^{n-k} ,$$

where p is a constant lying between zero and one, n is any positive integer, and k is also an integer such that $0 \leq k \leq n$. It is evident that $P_X(k)$ is always non-negative, and it is easily proven that

$$\sum_{k=0}^{n} P_X(k) = 1 .$$

Note that this distribution is a function of the two parameters n and p. The probability distribution of this random variable is shown in Fig. 3.6. An interesting interpretation of the binomial distribution is obtained when $n = 1$. In this case

$$P\{X = 0\} = P_X(0) = 1 - p ,$$

and

$$P\{X = 1\} = P_X(1) = p .$$

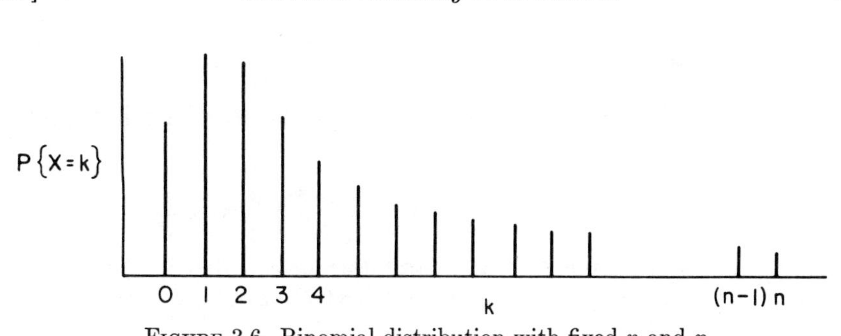

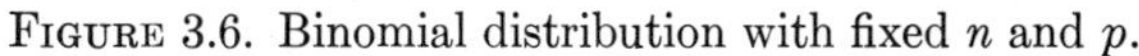

FIGURE 3.6. Binomial distribution with fixed n and p.

Such a random variable is said to have a Bernoulli distribution. Thus, if a random variable takes on two values, say, 0 or 1, with probability $1 - p$ or p, respectively, we have a Bernoulli random variable. The upturned face of a flipped coin is such an example. If a head is denoted by assigning it the number 0, and a tail by assigning it a 1, and if the coin is "fair" (the probability that a head will appear is 1/2), the upturned face is a Bernoulli random variable with parameter $p = 1/2$. Another example of a Bernoulli random variable is the quality of an item. If a defective item is denoted by 1 and a nondefective item by 0, and if p represents the probability of an item being defective, and $1 - p$ represents the probability of an item being nondefective, then the "quality" of an item (defective or nondefective) is a Bernoulli random variable.

If $X_1, X_2, \cdots, X_n$ are independent[6] Bernoulli random variables each with parameter p, then it can be shown that the random variable

$$X = X_1 + X_2 + \cdots + X_n$$

is a binomial random variable with parameters n and p. Thus, if a fair coin is flipped 10 times, then the total number of tails X, which is equivalent to $X_1 + X_2 + \cdots + X_{10}$, has a binomial distribution with parameters 10 and 1/2, i.e.,

$$P\{X = k\} = \frac{10!}{k!(10-k)!}\left(\frac{1}{2}\right)^k \left(\frac{1}{2}\right)^{10-k}.$$

Similarly, if the quality characteristics (defective or non-defective) of 50 items are independent Bernoulli random variables with parameter p, the total number of defective items in the 50 sampled, i.e., $X = X_1 + X_2 + \cdots + X_{50}$, has a binomial distribution with parameters 50 and p, so that

$$P\{X = k\} = \frac{50!}{k!(50-k)!}\, p^k(1-p)^{50-k}.$$

[6] The concept of independent random variables is introduced in Sec. 3.13. For the present purpose, random variables can be considered independent if their outcomes do not affect the outcomes of the other random variables.

3.6.2 **Poisson Distribution**

A random variable X is said to have a Poisson distribution if its probability distribution can be written as

$$P\{X = k\} = P_X(k) = \frac{\lambda^k e^{-\lambda}}{k!},$$

where λ is a positive constant (the parameter of this distribution), and k is any non-negative integer. It is evident that $P_X(k)$ is non-negative, and it is easily shown that

$$\sum_{k=0}^{\infty} \frac{\lambda^k e^{-\lambda}}{k!} = 1$$

An example of a probability distribution of a Poisson random variable is shown in Fig. 3.7. The C.D.F. of the Poisson random variable is tabulated in Table A5.4 of Appendix 5.

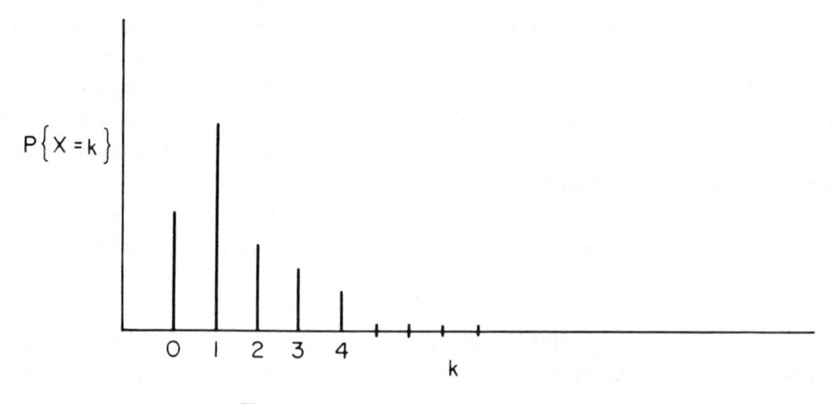

FIGURE 3.7. Poisson distribution.

In operations research, the Poisson distribution is often used. Heuristically speaking, this distribution is appropriate in many situations where an "event" occurs over a period of time, like the arrival of a customer; when it is as likely that this "event" will occur in one interval as in any other; also the occurrence of an event has no effect on whether or not another occurs. Then the number of customer arrivals in a fixed time is often assumed to have a Poisson distribution. Similarly, the demand for a given product is also often assumed to have this distribution.

3.6.3 **Geometric Distribution**

A random variable X is said to have a geometric distribution if its probability distribution can be written as

$$P\{X = k\} = P_X(k) = p(1 - p)^{k-1},$$

where the parameter p is a constant lying between 0 and 1, and k takes on the values 1, 2, 3, $\cdots$. It is clear that $P_X(k)$ is non-negative, and it is easy to show that

$$\sum_{k=1}^{\infty} p(1 - p)^{k-1} = 1.$$

The geometric distribution is useful in the following situation. Suppose an experiment is performed that leads to a sequence of independent[7] Bernoulli random variables each with parameter p, i.e., $P\{X_i = 1\} = p$ and $P\{X_i = 0\} = 1 - p$ for all i. The random variable X, which is the number of trials occurring until the first Bernoulli random variable takes on the value 1, has a geometric distribution with parameter p.

3.7 CONTINUOUS PROBABILITY DISTRIBUTIONS

In Sec. 3.3 continuous random variables are defined as those random variables which take on a continuum of values. The C.D.F. for a continuous random variable, $F_X(b)$, can usually be written as

$$F_X(b) = P\{X(\omega) \leq b\} = \int_{-\infty}^{b} f_X(y)dy,$$

where $f_X(y)$ is known as the density function of the random variable X. From a notational standpoint, the subscript X is used to indicate the random variable that is under consideration. When there is no ambiguity, this subscript may be deleted, and $f_X(y)$ will be denoted by $f(y)$. A knowledge of the density function enables one to calculate all sorts of probabilities, e.g.,

$$P\{a < X \leq b\} = F(b) - F(a) = \int_{a}^{b} f_X(y)dy.$$

Note that, strictly speaking, the symbol $P\{a < X \leq b\}$ relates to the probability that the outcome ω of the experiment belongs to a particular event in the sample space, namely, that event such that $X(\omega)$ is between a and b whenever ω belongs to the event. However, the reference to the event will be suppressed, and the symbol P will be used to refer to the probability that X falls between a and b. Hence, if the density function is known, it will be said that the probability distribution of the random variable is determined. Naturally, the density function can be obtained from the C.D.F. by using the relation

$$\frac{dF_X(y)}{dy} = \frac{d}{dy}\int_{-\infty}^{y} f_X(t)dt = f_X(y).$$

[7] The concept of independent random variables is introduced in Sec. 3.13. For the present purpose, random variables can be considered independent if their outcomes do not affect the outcomes of the other random variables.

A typical density function is given in Fig. 3.8, where the area under the entire density function is always taken to be one.

It is evident that the area under the density function between a and b is just

$$P\{a \leq X \leq b\} .$$

Note that when $a = b$, the area under the curve is zero, and hence, $P\{a \leq X \leq b\} = P\{X = a\} = 0$. Therefore, for continuous random variables, and any a and b,

$$P\{a \leq X \leq b\} = P\{a < X \leq b\} = P\{a \leq X < b\} = P\{a < X < b\} .$$

Of course, this is not true for discrete random variables.

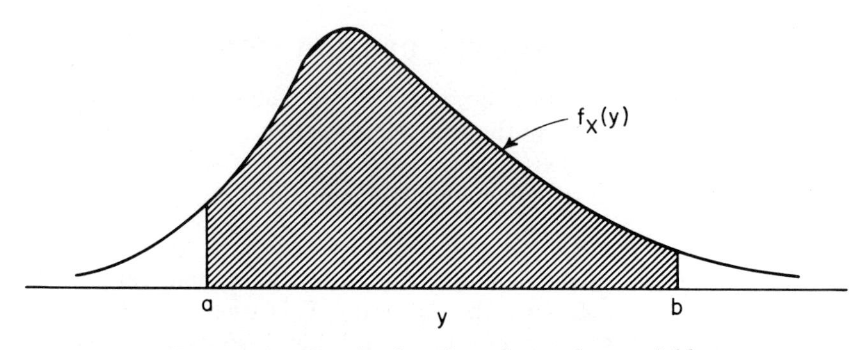

FIGURE 3.8. Density function of a random variable.

In defining the C.D.F. for continuous random variables, it was implied that $f_X(y)$ was defined for values of y from minus infinity to plus infinity since

$$F_X(b) = \int_{-\infty}^{b} f_X(y)dy .$$

This causes no difficulty, even for random variables which cannot take on negative values or are restricted to other regions (e.g., the arrival time of the first customer) since $f_X(y)$ can be zero over part of the interval from $-\infty$ to $+\infty$. In fact, the only requirements of a density function are that

(1) $f_X(y)$ be non-negative, and

(2) $\int_{-\infty}^{\infty} f_X(y)dy = 1$.

It has already been pointed out that $f_X(y)$ cannot be interpreted as $P\{X = y\}$ since this probability is always zero. However, $f_X(y)\,dy$ can be interpreted as the probability that the random variable X lies in the infinitesimal interval $(y, y + dy)$ so that, loosely speaking, $f_X(y)$ is a measure of the frequency with which the random variable will fall into a "small" interval near y.

There are several important continuous probability distributions that one uses in operations research work. The remainder of this section is devoted to a study of these distributions.

3.7.1 The Exponential Distribution

A continuous random variable whose density is given by

$$f_X(y) = \begin{cases} \dfrac{1}{\theta} e^{-y/\theta}, & \text{for } y \geq 0 \\ 0, & \text{for } y < 0 \end{cases}$$

is known as an exponentially distributed random variable. The exponential distribution is a function of the single parameter θ, where θ is any positive constant. $f_X(y)$ is a density function since it is non-negative, and integrates to one, i.e.,

$$\int_{-\infty}^{\infty} f_X(y)dy = \int_0^{\infty} \frac{1}{\theta} e^{-y/\theta}\, dy = -e^{-y/\theta}\Big|_0^{\infty} = 1\,.$$

The exponential density function is shown in Fig. 3.9.

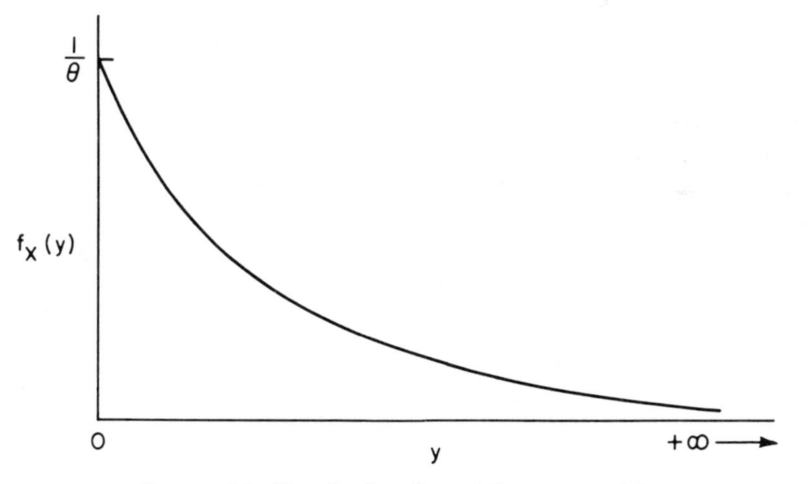

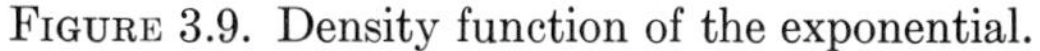
FIGURE 3.9. Density function of the exponential.

The C.D.F. of an exponentially distributed random variable $F_X(b)$ is given by

$$F_X(b) = \int_{-\infty}^{b} f_X(y)dy$$

$$= \begin{cases} 0, & \text{for } b < 0 \\ \displaystyle\int_0^b \frac{1}{\theta} e^{-y/\theta}\, dy = 1 - e^{-b/\theta}, & \text{for } b \geq 0\,, \end{cases}$$

and is shown in Fig. 3.10.

The exponential distribution has had widespread use in operations research. The time between customer arrivals, the length of time of telephone conversations, and the life of electronic components are often assumed to have an exponential distribution. Such an assumption has the important implication that the random variable does not "age." For example, suppose that the life of a vacuum tube is assumed to have an exponential distribution. If the tube has lasted 1000 hours, the probability of lasting an additional 50 hours is the same as the probability of lasting an additional 50 hours given that the tube has lasted 2000 hours. In other words, a brand new tube is no "better" than one which has lasted 1000 hours. This implication of the exponential is quite important and is often overlooked in practice.

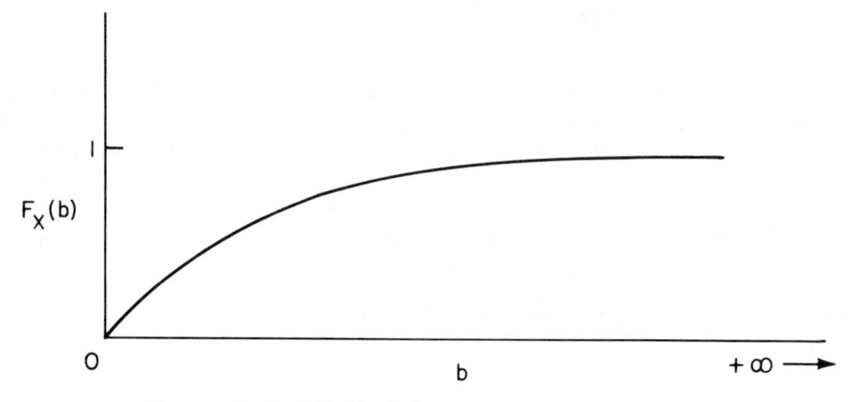

FIGURE 3.10. C.D.F. of the exponential distribution.

3.7.2 The Gamma Distribution

A continuous random variable whose density is given by

$$f_X(y) = \begin{cases} \dfrac{1}{\Gamma(\alpha)\beta^{\alpha}} y^{(\alpha-1)} e^{-y/\beta}, & \text{for } y \geq 0 \\ 0, & \text{for } y < 0 \end{cases}$$

is known as a gamma distributed random variable. This density is a function of the two parameters, α and β, both of which are positive constants. $\Gamma(\alpha)$ is defined as

$$\Gamma(\alpha) = \int_0^\infty t^{\alpha-1} e^{-t}\, dt, \qquad \text{for all } \alpha > 0\,.$$

If α is an integer, then repeated integration by parts yields

$$\Gamma(\alpha) = (\alpha - 1)! = (\alpha - 1)(\alpha - 2)(\alpha - 3) \cdots 3 \cdot 2 \cdot 1\,.$$

A graph of a typical gamma density function is given in Fig. 3.11.

A random variable having a gamma density is useful in its own right as a mathematical representation of physical phenomena, or it may arise as follows: Suppose a customer's service time has an exponential distribu-

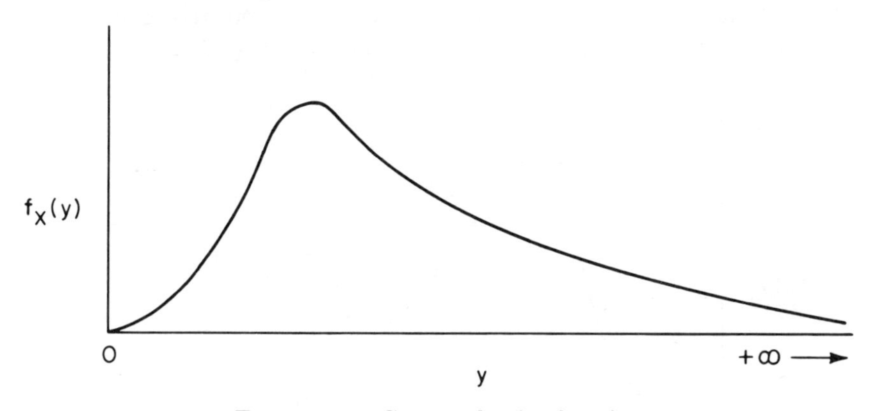

FIGURE 3.11. Gamma density function.

tion with parameter θ. The random variable T, the total time to service n customers, then has a gamma distribution with parameters n and θ (replacing α and β, respectively), i.e.,

$$P\{T < t\} = \int_0^t \frac{1}{\Gamma(n)\theta^n} y^{(n-1)} e^{-y/\theta}\, dy\,.$$

Note that when $n = 1$ (or $\alpha = 1$), the gamma density becomes the density function of an exponential random variable. Thus, sums of independent, exponentially distributed random variables have a gamma distribution.

Another important distribution, the chi-square distribution, is related to the gamma distribution. If X is a random variable having a gamma distribution with parameters $\beta = 1$ and $\alpha = \nu/2$ (ν is a positive integer), then a new random variable $Z = 2X$ is said to have a chi-square distribution with ν degrees of freedom. The density function is given in Table 3.1 (p. 52). The percentage points of the chi-square distribution are given in Table A5.3 of Appendix 5. Percentage points of the distribution of a random variable Z are the values z_α such that

$$P\{Z > z_\alpha\} = \alpha\,.$$

z_α is said to be the 100α percentage point of the distribution of the random variable Z.

3.7.3 The Beta Distribution

A continuous random variable whose density function is given by

$$f_X(y) = \begin{cases} \dfrac{\Gamma(\alpha+\beta)}{\Gamma(\alpha)\Gamma(\beta)} y^{(\alpha-1)}(1-y)^{(\beta-1)}, & \text{for } 0 \le y \le 1 \\ 0, & \text{elsewhere} \end{cases}$$

is known as a beta distributed random variable. This density is a function of the two parameters α and β, both of which are positive constants. A graph of a typical beta density function is given in Fig. 3.12.

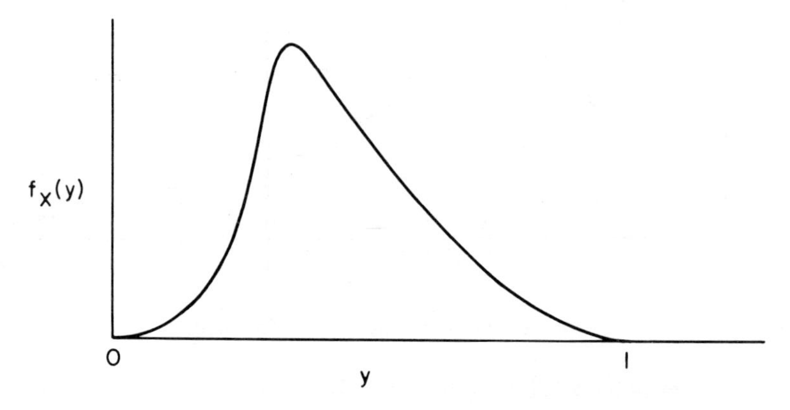

FIGURE 3.12. Beta density function.

Beta distributions form a useful class of distributions when a random variable is restricted to the unit interval. In particular, when $\alpha = \beta = 1$, the beta distribution is called the *uniform distribution* over the unit interval. Its density function is shown in Fig. 3.13, and it can be interpreted as having all the values between 0 and 1 equally likely to occur.

The C.D.F. for this random variable is given by

$$F_X(b) = \begin{cases} 0, & \text{for } b < 0 \\ b, & \text{for } 0 \le b \le 1 \\ 1, & \text{for } b > 1\,. \end{cases}$$

If the density function is to be constant over some other interval such as the interval $[c, d]$, a uniform distribution over this interval can also be obtained.[8] The density function is given by

[8] The beta distribution can also be generalized by defining the density function over some fixed interval, other than the unit interval.

$$f_X(y) = \begin{cases} \dfrac{1}{d-c}, & \text{for } c \le y \le d \\ 0, & \text{otherwise}. \end{cases}$$

Although such a random variable is said to have a uniform distribution over the interval $[c, d]$, it is no longer a special case of the beta distribution.

Another important distribution, Students t-distribution, is related to the beta distribution. If X is a random variable having a beta distribution with parameters $\alpha = 1/2$ and $\beta = \nu/2$ (ν is a positive integer), then a new random variable $Z = \sqrt{\nu x/(1 - x)}$ is said to have a Students t- (or t) distribution with ν degrees of freedom. The percentage points of the t-distribution are given in Table A5.2 of Appendix 5.

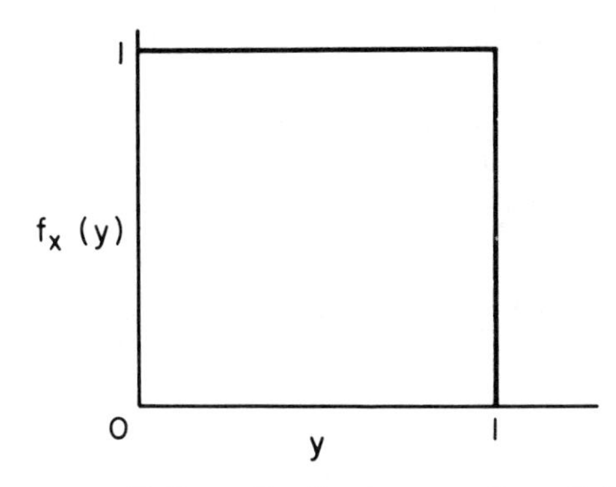

FIGURE 3.13. Uniform distribution over the unit interval.

3.7.4 The Normal Distribution

One of the most important distributions in operations research is the normal distribution. A continuous random variable whose density function is given by

$$f_X(y) = \frac{1}{\sqrt{2\pi}\,\sigma} e^{-\frac{(y-\mu)^2}{2\sigma^2}}, \qquad \text{for } -\infty < y < \infty$$

is known as a normally distributed random variable. The density is a function of the two parameters μ and σ, where μ is any constant and σ is positive. A graph of a typical normal density function is given in Fig. 3.14. This density function is a bell-shaped curve that is symmetric around μ. The C.D.F. for a normally distributed random variable is given by

$$F_X(b) = \int_{-\infty}^{b} \frac{1}{\sqrt{2\pi}\,\sigma} e^{-\frac{(y-\mu)^2}{2\sigma^2}}\, dy\,.$$

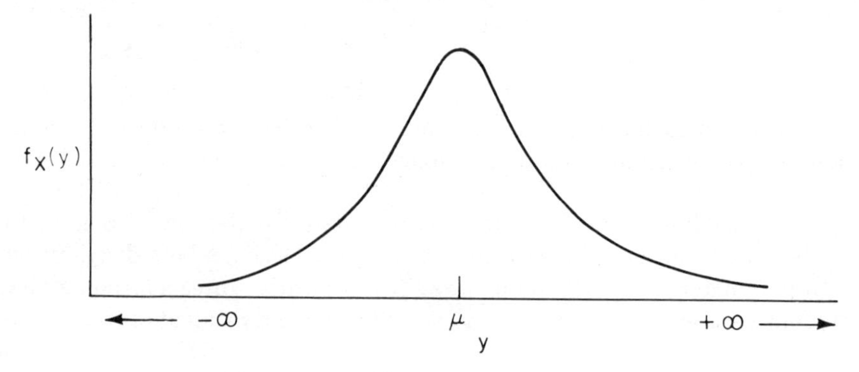

FIGURE 3.14. Normal density function.

By making the transformation $z = (y - \mu)/\sigma$, the C.D.F. can be written as

$$F_X(b) = \int_{-\infty}^{(b-\mu)/\sigma} \frac{1}{\sqrt{2\pi}} e^{-z^2/2} dz .$$

Hence, although this function is not integrable, it is easily tabulated. Table A5.1 presented in Appendix 5 is a tabulation of

$$\alpha = \int_{K_\alpha}^{\infty} \frac{1}{\sqrt{2\pi}} e^{-z^2/2} dz$$

as a function of K_α. Hence, to find $F_X(b)$ (and any probability derived from it) Table A5.1 is entered with $K_\alpha = (b - \mu)/\sigma$, and

$$\alpha = \int_{K_\alpha}^{\infty} \frac{1}{\sqrt{2\pi}} e^{-z^2/2} dz$$

is read from it. $F_X(b)$ is then just $1 - \alpha$. Thus, if $P\{14 < X \leq 18\} = F_X(18) - F_X(14)$ is desired, where X has a normal distribution with $\mu = 10$ and $\sigma = 4$, Table A5.1 is entered with $(18 - 10)/4 = 2$, and $1 - F_X(18) = .0228$ is obtained. The table is then entered with $(14 - 10)/4 = 1$, and $1 - F_X(14) = .1587$ is read. From these figures $F_X(18) - F_X(14) = .1359$ is found. If K_α is negative, use can be made of the symmetry of the normal distribution since

$$F_X(b) = \int_{-\infty}^{(b-\mu)/\sigma} \frac{1}{\sqrt{2\pi}} e^{-z^2/2} dz = \int_{-(b-\mu)/\sigma}^{\infty} \frac{1}{\sqrt{2\pi}} e^{-z^2/2} dz .$$

In this case, $-(b - \mu)/\sigma$ is positive, and $F_X(b) = \alpha$ is thereby read from the table by entering it with $-(b - \mu)/\sigma$. Thus, suppose it is desired to evaluate the expression

$$P\{2 < X \leq 18\} = F_X(18) - F_X(2) .$$

$F_X(18)$ has already been shown to be equal to $1 - .0228 = .9772$. To find $F_X(2)$ it is first noted that $(2 - 10)/4 = -2$ is negative. Hence, Table A5.1 is entered with $K_\alpha = +2$, and $F_X(2) = .0228$ is obtained. Thus,

$$F_X(18) - F_X(2) = .9772 - .0228 = .9544 .$$

As indicated previously, the normal distribution is a very important one. In particular, it can be shown that if $X_1, X_2, \cdots, X_n$ are independent,[9] normally distributed random variables with parameters (μ_1, σ_1), (μ_2, σ_2), $\cdots$, (μ_n, σ_n), respectively, then $X = X_1 + X_2 + \cdots + X_n$ is also a normally distributed random variable with parameters

$$\sum_{i=1}^{n} \mu_i$$

and

$$\sqrt{\sum_{i=1}^{n} \sigma_i^2} .$$

In fact, even if $X_1, X_2, \cdots, X_n$ are not normal, then under very weak conditions,

$$X = \sum_{i=1}^{n} X_i$$

tends to be normally distributed as n gets large. This is discussed further in Sec. 3.15.

Finally, if C is any constant and X is normal with parameters μ and σ, then the random variable CX is also normal with parameters $C\mu$ and $C\sigma$. Hence, it follows that if $X_1, X_2, \cdots, X_n$ are independent, normally distributed random variables each with parameters μ and σ, the random variable

$$\bar{X} = \sum_{i=1}^{n} X_i/n$$

is also normally distributed with parameters μ and $\sigma/\sqrt{n}$.

3.8 EXPECTATION

Although knowledge of the probability distribution of a random variable enables one to make all sorts of probability statements, a single value which may characterize the random variable and its probability distribution

[9] The concept of independent random variables is introduced in Sec. 3.13. For the present purpose, random variables can be considered independent if their outcomes do not affect the outcomes of the other random variables.

is often desirable. Such a quantity is the *expected value* of the random variable. One may speak of the expected value of the demand for a product, or the expected value of the time of the first customer arrival. In the experiment where the arrival time of the first customer on two successive days was measured, the expected value of the average arrival time of the first customers on two successive days may be of interest.

Formally, the expected value of a random variable X is denoted by $E(X)$ and is given by

$$E(X) = \begin{cases} \sum_{\text{all } k} kP\{X = k\} = \sum_{\text{all } k} kP_X(k), & \text{if } X \text{ is a discrete random variable} \\ \int_{-\infty}^{\infty} yf_X(y)dy, & \text{if } X \text{ is a continuous random variable}. \end{cases}$$

For a discrete random variable it is seen that $E(X)$ is just the sum of the products of the possible values the random variable X takes on and their respective associated probabilities. In the example of the demand for a product where $k = 0, 1, 2, \cdots, 98, 99$ and $P_X(k) = 1/100$ for all i, the expected value of the demand is

$$E(X) = \sum_{k=0}^{99} kP_X(k) = \sum_{k=0}^{99} k\frac{1}{100} = 49.5 .$$

Note that $E(X)$ need not be a value that the random variable can take on.

If X is a binomial random variable with parameters n and p, the expected value of X is given by

$$E(X) = \sum_{k=0}^{n} k\frac{n!}{k!(n-k)!}p^k(1-p)^{n-k}$$

and can be shown to equal np.

If the random variable X has a Poisson distribution with parameter λ,

$$E(X) = \sum_{k=0}^{\infty} k\frac{\lambda^k e^{-\lambda}}{k!}$$

and can be shown to equal λ.

Finally, if the random variable X has a geometric distribution with parameter p,

$$E(X) = \sum_{k=1}^{\infty} kp(1-p)^{k-1}$$

and can be shown to equal $1/p$.

For continuous random variables, the expected value can also be obtained easily. If X has an exponential distribution with parameter θ, the expected value is given by

$$E(X) = \int_{-\infty}^{\infty} y f_X(y) dy = \int_0^{\infty} y \frac{1}{\theta} e^{-y/\theta} dy .$$

This integral is easily evaluated to be

$$E(X) = \theta .$$

If the random variable X has a gamma distribution with parameters α and β, the expected value of X is given by

$$\int_{-\infty}^{\infty} y f_X(y) dy = \int_0^{\infty} y \frac{1}{\Gamma(\alpha)\beta^{\alpha}} y^{(\alpha-1)} e^{-y/\beta} dy = \alpha\beta .$$

If the random variable X has a beta distribution with parameters α and β, the expected value of X is given by

$$\int_{-\infty}^{\infty} y f_X(y) dy = \int_0^1 y \frac{\Gamma(\alpha + \beta)}{\Gamma(\alpha)\Gamma(\beta)} y^{(\alpha-1)} (1 - y)^{(\beta-1)} dy = \frac{\alpha}{\alpha + \beta} .$$

Finally, if the random variable X has a normal distribution with parameters μ and σ, the expected value of X is given by

$$\int_{-\infty}^{\infty} y f_X(y) dy = \int_{-\infty}^{\infty} y \frac{1}{\sqrt{2\pi}\, \sigma} e^{-(y-\mu)^2/2\sigma^2} dy = \mu .$$

The expectation of a random variable is quite useful in that, not only does it provide some characterization of the distribution, but it also has meaning in terms of the average of a sample. In particular, if a random variable is observed again and again, and the arithmetic mean $\bar{X}$ is computed, then $\bar{X}$ tends to the expectation of the random variable X as the number of trials becomes large. A precise statement of this property is given in Sec. 3.14. Thus, if the demand for a product takes on the values $k = 0, 1, 2, \cdots, 98, 99$, each with $P_X(k) = 1/100$ for all k, and if demands of $x_1, x_2, \cdots, x_n$ are observed on successive days, then the average of these values, $(x_1 + x_2 + \cdots + x_n)/n$, should be close to $E(X) = 49.5$ if n is sufficiently large.

It is not necessary to confine the discussion of expectation to discussion of that of a random variable X. If Z is some function of X, say, $Z = g(X)$, then $g(X)$ is also a random variable. The expectation of $g(X)$ can be defined as

$$E[g(X)] = \begin{cases} \displaystyle\sum_{\text{all } k} g(k) P\{X = k\} = \sum_{\text{all } k} g(k) P_X(k), & \text{if } X \text{ is a discrete random variable} \\ \displaystyle\int_{-\infty}^{\infty} g(y) f_X(y) dy, & \text{if } X \text{ is a continuous random variable .} \end{cases}$$

An interesting theorem, known as the "Theorem of the Unconscious Statistician,"[10] states that if X is a continuous random variable having density $f_X(y)$ and $Z = g(X)$ is a function of X having density $h_Z(y)$, then

$$E(Z) = \int_{-\infty}^{\infty} y h_Z(y)\, dy = \int_{-\infty}^{\infty} g(y) f_X(y)\, dy\,.$$

Thus, the expectation of Z can be found by using its definition in terms of the density of Z or, alternatively, by using its definition as the expectation of a function of X with respect to the density function of X. The identical theorem is true for discrete random variables.

3.9 MOMENTS

If the function g described in the previous section is given by

$$Z = g(X) = X^j,$$

where j is a positive integer, then the expectation of X^j is called the jth moment about the origin of the random variable X and is given by

$$E(X^j) = \begin{cases} \displaystyle\sum_{\text{all } k} k^j P_X(k), & \text{if } X \text{ is a discrete random variable} \\ \displaystyle\int_{-\infty}^{\infty} y^j f_X(y)\, dy, & \text{if } X \text{ is a continuous random variable.} \end{cases}$$

Note that when $j = 1$, the first moment coincides with the expectation of X. This is usually denoted by the symbol μ and is often called the mean or average of the distribution.

Using the "Theorem of the Unconscious Statistician," the expectation of $Z = g(X) = CX$ can easily be found, where C is a constant. If X is a continuous random variable, then

$$E[CX] = \int_{-\infty}^{\infty} Cy f_X(y)\, dy = C \int_{-\infty}^{\infty} y f_X(y)\, dy = CE(X)\,.$$

Thus, the expectation of a constant times a random variable is just the constant times the expectation of the random variable. This is also true for discrete random variables.

If the function g described in the previous section is given by $Z = g(X) = (X - E(X))^j = (X - \mu)^j$, where j is a positive integer, then the expectation of $(X - \mu)^j$ is called the jth moment about the mean of the random variable X and is given by

[10] The name for this theorem is motivated by the fact that a statistician often uses its conclusions without consciously worrying about whether the theorem is true.

$$E(X - E(X))^j = E(X - \mu)^j = \begin{cases} \sum_{\text{all } k} (k - \mu)^j P_X(k), & \text{if } X \text{ is a discrete random variable} \\ \int_{-\infty}^{\infty} (y - \mu)^j f_X(y)\, dy, & \text{if } X \text{ is a continuous random variable}. \end{cases}$$

Note that if $j = 1$, then $E(X - \mu) = 0$. If $j = 2$, then $E(X - \mu)^2$ is called the variance of the random variable X and is often denoted by σ^2. The square root of the variance, σ, is called the standard deviation of the random variable X. It is easily shown, in terms of definitions, that $\sigma^2 = E(X - \mu)^2 = E(X^2) - \mu^2$, i.e., the variance can be written as the second moment about the origin minus the square of the mean.

It has already been shown that if $Z = g(X) = CX$, then $E[CX] = CE(X) = C\mu$, where C is any constant and μ is $E(X)$. The variance of the random variable $Z = g(X) = CX$ is also easily obtained. By definition, if X is a continuous random variable, the variance of Z is given by

$$E(Z - E(Z))^2 = E(CX - CE(X))^2 = \int_{-\infty}^{\infty} (Cy - C\mu)^2 f_X(y)\, dy$$
$$= C^2 \int_{-\infty}^{\infty} (y - \mu)^2 f_X(y)\, dy = C^2\sigma^2.$$

Thus, the variance of a constant times a random variable is just the square of the constant times the variance of the random variable. This is also true for discrete random variables. Finally, the variance of a constant is easily seen to be zero.

It has already been shown that if the demand for a product takes on the values $0, 1, 2, \cdots, 99$, each with probability $1/100$, then $E(X) = \mu = 49.5$. Similarly,

$$\sigma^2 = \sum_{k=0}^{99} (k - \mu)^2 P_X(k) = \sum_{k=0}^{99} k^2 P_X(k) - \mu^2$$
$$= \sum_{k=0}^{99} k^2/(100) - (49.5)^2 = 833.25.$$

Table 3.1 gives the means and variances of the random variables which are often useful in operations research. Note that for some random variables a single moment, the mean, provides a complete characterization of the distribution, e.g., the Poisson random variable. For some random variables the mean and variance provide a complete characterization of the distribution, e.g., the normal. In fact, if all of the moments of a probability

TABLE 3.1. Table of Common Distributions

Distribution of random variable X	*Form*	*Para-meters*	*Expected value*	*Variance*	*Range of random variable*
Binomial	$P_X(k) = \frac{n!}{k!(n-k)!} p^k(1-p)^{n-k}$	n, p	np	$np(1-p)$	$0, 1, 2, \cdots, n$
Poisson	$P_X(k) = \frac{\lambda^k e^{-\lambda}}{k!}$	λ	λ	λ	$0, 1, 2, \cdots.$
Geometric	$P_X(k) = p(1-p)^{k-1}$	p	$\frac{1}{p}$	$\frac{1-p}{p^2}$	$1, 2, \cdots.$
Exponential	$f_X(y) = \frac{1}{\theta} e^{-y/\theta}$	θ	θ	θ^2	$(0, \infty)$
Gamma	$f_X(y) = \frac{1}{\Gamma(\alpha)\beta^\alpha} y^{(\alpha-1)} e^{-y/\beta}$	α, β	$\alpha\beta$	$\alpha\beta^2$	$(0, \infty)$
Beta	$f_X(y) = \frac{\Gamma(\alpha+\beta)}{\Gamma(\alpha)\Gamma(\beta)} y^{(\alpha-1)}(1-y)^{(\beta-1)}$	α, β	$\frac{\alpha}{\alpha+\beta}$	$\frac{\alpha\beta}{(\alpha+\beta)^2(\alpha+\beta+1)}$	$(0, 1)$
Normal	$f_X(y) = \frac{1}{\sqrt{2\pi}\sigma} e^{-\frac{1}{2}\frac{(y-\mu)^2}{\sigma^2}}$	μ, σ	μ	σ^2	$(-\infty, \infty)$
Students-t	$f_X(y) = \frac{1}{\sqrt{\pi\nu}} \frac{\Gamma([\nu+1]/2)}{\Gamma(\nu/2)} (1 + y^2/\nu)^{-(\nu+1)/2}$	ν	$0 (\text{for } \nu > 1)$	$\nu/(\nu-2) (\text{for } \nu > 2)$	$(-\infty, \infty)$
Chi Square	$f_X(y) = \frac{1}{2^{\nu/2}\Gamma(\nu/2)} y^{(\nu-2)/2} e^{-y/2}$	ν	ν	2ν	$(0, \infty)$

distribution are known, this is usually equivalent to specifying the entire distribution.

It has been seen that the mean and variance may be sufficient to completely characterize a distribution, e.g., the normal. However, what can be said, in general, about a random variable whose mean μ and variance σ^2 are known, but nothing else about the form of the distribution is specified? This can be expressed in terms of *Tchebycheff's inequality*, which states that

$$P\{\mu - C\sigma < X < \mu + C\sigma\} \geq 1 - \frac{1}{C^2},$$

where X is any random variable having mean μ and variance σ^2. For example, if $C = 3$, it follows that $P\{\mu - 3\sigma < X < \mu + 3\sigma\} \geq 1 - \frac{1}{9} = .8889$. However, if X is known to have a normal distribution, then $P\{\mu - 3\sigma < X < \mu + 3\sigma\} = .9973$. Note that the Tchebycheff inequality only gives a lower bound on the probability (usually a very conservative one) so there is no contradiction here.

3.10 BIVARIATE PROBABILITY DISTRIBUTION

Thus far, the discussion has been concerned with the probability distribution of a single random variable, e.g., the demand for a product during the first month, or the demand for a product during the second month. In an experiment which measures the demand during the first two months, it may well be important to look at the probability distribution of the vector random variable, (X_1, X_2), the demand during the first month, and the demand during the second month, respectively.

Define the symbol

$$E_{b_1,b_2} = \{X_1(\omega) \leq b_1, X_2(\omega) \leq b_2\}$$

(or, equivalently, $\{X_1 \leq b_1, X_2 \leq b_2\}$) as the set of outcomes ω in the sample space forming the event E_{b_1,b_2} such that the random variable X_1 takes on values less than or equal to b_1, *and* X_2 takes on values less than or equal to b_2. Then $P\{E_{b_1,b_2}\}$ denotes the probability of this event. In the above example of the demand for a product during the first two months, suppose that the sample space Ω consists of the set of all possible points ω where ω represents a pair of non-negative integer values (x_1, x_2). Assume that x_1 and x_2 are bounded by 99. Thus, there are $(100)^2$ ω points in Ω. Suppose further that each point ω has associated with it a probability equal to $1/(100)^2$ except for the points $\omega = (0, 0)$ and $\omega = (99, 99)$. The probability associated with the event $\{0, 0\}$ will be $1.5/(100)^2$, i.e., $P\{0, 0\} = 1.5/(100)^2$, and the probability associated with the event $\{99, 99\}$ will be $0.5/(100)^2$, i.e., $P\{99, 99\} = 0.5/(100)^2$. Thus, if there is interest in the "bivariate" random variable (X_1, X_2), the demand during the first and second months, respectively, then the event

$$\{ X_1 \leq 1, X_2 \leq 3 \}$$

is the set

$$E_{b_1,b_2} = \{(0, 0), (0, 1), (0, 2), (0, 3), (1, 0), (1, 1), (1, 2), (1, 3)\} .$$

Furthermore,

$$P\{E_{b_1,b_2}\} = \frac{1.5}{(100)^2} + \frac{1}{(100)^2} + \frac{1}{(100)^2} + \frac{1}{(100)^2} + \frac{1}{(100)^2} + \frac{1}{(100)^2} + \frac{1}{(100)^2} + \frac{1}{(100)^2}$$

$$= \frac{8.5}{(100)^2},$$

so that

$$P\{X_1 \leq 1, X_2 \leq 3\} = P\{E_{1,3}\} = \frac{8.5}{(100)^2} \cdot$$

A similar calculation can be made for any value of b_1 and b_2.

For any given bivariate random variable, (X_1, X_2), $P\{X_1 \leq b_1, X_2 \leq b_2\}$ is denoted by $F_{X_1X_2}(b_1, b_2)$, and is called the joint cumulative distribution function (C.D.F.) of the bivariate random variable (X_1, X_2) and is defined for all real values of b_1 and b_2. Where there is no ambiguity, the joint C.D.F. may be denoted by $F(b_1, b_2)$. Thus, attached to every bivariate random variable is a joint C.D.F. This is not an arbitrary function, but is induced by the probabilities associated with events defined over the sample space Ω such that $\{X_1(\omega) \leq b_1, X_2(\omega) \leq b_2\}$.

The joint C.D.F. of a random variable is a numerically valued function defined for all b_1, b_2, such that $-\infty \leq b_1, b_2 \leq \infty$, having the following properties:

(1) $F_{X_1X_2}(b_1, \infty) = P\{X_1 \leq b_1, X_2 \leq \infty\} = P\{X_1 \leq b_1\} = F_{X_1}(b_1)$, where $F_{X_1}(b_1)$ is just the C.D.F. of the univariate random variable X_1.
(2) $F_{X_1X_2}(\infty, b_2) = P\{X_1 \leq \infty, X_2 \leq b_2\} = P\{X_2 \leq b_2\} = F_{X_2}(b_2)$, where $F_{X_2}(b_2)$ is just the C.D.F. of the univariate random variable X_2.
(3) $F_{X_1X_2}(b_1, -\infty) = P\{X_1 \leq b_1, X_2 \leq -\infty\} = 0$,
$F_{X_1X_2}(-\infty, b_2) = P\{X_1 \leq -\infty, X_2 \leq b_2\} = 0$.

Using the definition of the event E_{b_1,b_2}, events of the form

$$\{a_1 < X_1 \leq b_1, a_2 < X_2 \leq b_2\}$$

can be described as the set of outcomes ω in the sample space such that the bivariate random variable, (X_1, X_2), takes on values such that X_1 is greater than a_1 but does not exceed b_1, *and* X_2 is greater than a_2 but does not exceed b_2. $P\{a_1 < X_1 \le b_1,\ a_2 < X_2 \le b_2\}$ can easily be seen to be

$$F_{X_1X_2}(b_1, b_2) - F_{X_1X_2}(b_1, a_2) - F_{X_1X_2}(a_1, b_2) + F_{X_1X_2}(a_1, a_2)\,.$$

It has already been seen that single random variables have been characterized as discrete or continuous random variables. A bivariate random variable can be characterized in a similar manner. A bivariate random variable, (X_1, X_2), is called a discrete bivariate random variable if X_1 and X_2 each can take on only a finite or denumerable set of values. Similarly, a bivariate random variable, (X_1, X_2), is called a continuous bivariate random variable if X_1 and X_2 each can take on a continuum of values. Of course, bivariate random variables can exist which are neither discrete or continuous, but these will not be important in this book.

The joint C.D.F. for a discrete random variable, $F_{X_1X_2}(b_1, b_2)$, is given by

$$\begin{aligned} F_{X_1X_2}(b_1, b_2) &= P\{X_1(\omega) \le b_1,\ X_2(\omega) \le b_2\} \\ &= \sum_{\text{all } k \le b_1} \sum_{\text{all } l \le b_2} P\{X_1(\omega) = k,\ X_2(\omega) = l\} \\ &= \sum_{\text{all } k \le b_1} \sum_{\text{all } l \le b_2} P_{X_1X_2}(k, l)\,, \end{aligned}$$

where $\{X_1(\omega) = k,\ X_2(\omega) = l\}$ is the set of outcomes ω in the sample space such that the random variable X_1 takes on the value k, and the variable X_2 takes on the value l; and $P\{X_1(\omega) = k,\ X_2(\omega) = l\} = P_{X_1X_2}(k, l)$ denotes the probability of this event. The $P_{X_1X_2}(k, l)$ are called the joint probability distribution of the discrete bivariate random variable (X_1, X_2). Thus, in the previous example, $P_{X_1X_2}(k, l) = 1/(100)^2$ for all k, l which are integers between 0 and 99, except for $P_{X_1X_2}(0, 0) = 1.5/(100)^2$ and $P_{X_1X_2}(99, 99) = 0.5/(100)^2$.

For a continuous random variable, the joint C.D.F., $F_{X_1X_2}(b_1, b_2)$, can usually be written as

$$F_{X_1X_2}(b_1, b_2) = P\{X_1(\omega) \le b_1,\ X_2(\omega) \le b_2\} = \int_{-\infty}^{b_1} \int_{-\infty}^{b_2} f_{X_1X_2}(s, t)\,ds\,dt\,,$$

where $f_{X_1X_2}(s, t)$ is known as the joint density function of the bivariate random variable (X_1, X_2). A knowledge of the joint density function enables one to calculate all sorts of probabilities, e.g.,

$$P\{a_1 < X_1 \le b_1,\ a_2 < X_2 \le b_2\} = \int_{a_1}^{b_1} \int_{a_2}^{b_2} f_{X_1X_2}(s, t)\,ds\,dt\,.$$

Hence, if the density function is known, it is said that the probability distribution of the random variable is determined. The joint density function can be viewed as a surface in three dimensions, where the volume under this surface over regions in the s, t plane correspond to probabilities. Naturally, the density function can be obtained from the C.D.F. by using the relation

$$\frac{\partial^2 F_{X_1X_2}(s, t)}{\partial s\, \partial t} = \frac{\partial^2}{\partial s\, \partial t} \int_{-\infty}^{s} \int_{-\infty}^{t} f_{X_1X_2}(u, v)du\, dv = f_{X_1X_2}(s, t) .$$

In defining the joint C.D.F. for a bivariate random variable, it was implied that $f_{X_1X_2}(s, t)$ was defined over the entire plane since

$$F_{X_1X_2}(b_1, b_2) = \int_{-\infty}^{b_1} \int_{-\infty}^{b_2} f_{X_1X_2}(s, t)ds\, dt$$

(which is analogous to what was done for a univariate random variable). This causes no difficulty, even for bivariate random variables having one or more components which cannot take on negative values or are restricted to other regions. In this case, $f_{X_1X_2}(s, t)$ can be defined as zero over part of the plane. In fact, the only requirements for a function to be a bivariate density function are that

(1) $f_{X_1X_2}(s, t)$ be non-negative, and

(2) $\int_{-\infty}^{\infty} \int_{-\infty}^{\infty} f_{X_1X_2}(s, t)ds\, dt = 1$.

3.11 MARGINAL AND CONDITIONAL PROBABILITY DISTRIBUTIONS

In the previous section the discussion was concerned with the joint probability distribution of a bivariate random variable, (X_1, X_2). However, there may also be interest in the probability distribution of the random variables, X_1 and X_2, considered separately. It has already been shown that if $F_{X_1X_2}(b_1, b_2)$ represents the joint C.D.F. of (X_1, X_2), then $F_{X_1}(b_1) = F_{X_1X_2}(b_1, \infty) = P\{X_1 \leq b_1, X_2 \leq \infty\} = P\{X_1 \leq b_1\}$ is the C.D.F. for the univariate random variable X_1, and $F_{X_2}(b_2) = F_{X_1X_2}(\infty, b_2) = P\{X_1 \leq \infty, X_2 \leq b_2\} = P\{X_2 \leq b_2\}$ is the C.D.F. for the univariate random variable X_2.

If the bivariate random variable (X_1, X_2) is discrete, it has been noted that the

$$P_{X_1X_2}(k, l) = P\{X_1(\omega) = k, X_2(\omega) = l\}$$

describe its joint probability distribution. The probability distribution of X_1 individually is given by

$$P_{X_1}(k) = P\{X_1(\omega) = k\} = \sum_{\text{all } l} P_{X_1X_2}(k, l)$$

and is called the marginal probability distribution of the discrete random variable X_1. Similarly, the marginal probability distribution of the discrete random variable X_2 is given by

$$P_{X_2}(l) = P\{X_2(\omega) = l\} = \sum_{\text{all } k} P_{X_1X_2}(k, l) .$$

If the experiment described previously which measures the demand for a product during the first two months is considered, it is seen that the marginal distribution of X_1 is given by

$$P_{X_1}(0) = \sum_{\text{all } l} P_{X_1X_2}(0, l) = P_{X_1X_2}(0, 0) + P_{X_1X_2}(0, 1) + \cdots + P_{X_1X_2}(0, 99)$$
$$= \frac{1.5}{(100)^2} + \frac{1}{(100)^2} + \cdots + \frac{1}{(100)^2} = \frac{100.5}{(100)^2},$$

$$P_{X_1}(1) = P_{X_1}(2) = \cdots = P_{X_1}(98) = \sum_{\text{all } l} P_{X_1X_2}(k, l),\ k = 1, 2, \cdots, 98$$
$$= \frac{100}{(100)^2},$$

$$P_{X_1}(99) = \sum_{\text{all } l} P_{X_1X_2}(99, l) = P_{X_1X_2}(99, 0) + P_{X_1X_2}(99, 1) + \cdots$$
$$+ P_{X_1X_2}(99, 99) = \frac{1}{(100)^2} + \frac{1}{(100)^2} + \cdots + \frac{0.5}{(100)^2} = \frac{99.5}{(100)^2} .$$

Note that this is, indeed, a probability distribution in that

$$P_{X_1}(0) + P_{X_1}(1) + \cdots + P_{X_1}(99) = \frac{100.5}{(100)^2} + \frac{100}{(100)^2} + \cdots + \frac{99.5}{(100)^2} = 1 .$$

Similarly, the marginal distribution of X_2 is given by

$$P_{X_2}(0) = \sum_{\text{all } k} P_{X_1X_2}(k, 0) = P_{X_1X_2}(0, 0) + P_{X_1X_2}(1, 0) + \cdots + P_{X_1X_2}(99, 0)$$
$$= \frac{1.5}{(100)^2} + \frac{1}{(100)^2} + \cdots + \frac{1}{(100)^2} = \frac{100.5}{(100)^2},$$

$$P_{X_2}(1) = P_{X_2}(2) = \cdots = P_{X_2}(98) = \sum_{\text{all } k} P_{X_1X_2}(k, l),\ l = 1, 2, \cdots, 98$$
$$= \frac{100}{(100)^2},$$

$$P_{X_2}(99) = \sum_{\text{all } k} P_{X_1X_2}(k, 99) = P_{X_1X_2}(0, 99) + P_{X_1X_2}(1, 99) + \cdots$$

$$+ P_{X_1X_2}(99, 99) = \frac{1}{(100)^2} + \frac{1}{(100)^2} + \cdots + \frac{.5}{(100)^2} = \frac{99.5}{(100)^2}.$$

If the bivariate random variable (X_1, X_2) is continuous, then $f_{X_1X_2}(s, t)$ represents the joint density. The density function of X_1 individually is given by

$$f_{X_1}(s) = \int_{-\infty}^{\infty} f_{X_1X_2}(s, t)dt$$

and is called the marginal density function of the continuous random variable X_1. Similarly, the marginal density function of the continuous random variable X_2 is given by

$$f_{X_2}(t) = \int_{-\infty}^{\infty} f_{X_1X_2}(s, t)ds .$$

Note that the marginal density functions of X_1 and X_2 are equivalent to the density functions of the univariate random variables X_1 and X_2 defined previously, i.e.,

$$\begin{aligned} P\{a_1 < X_1 \le b_1\} &= P\{a_1 < X_1 \le b_1, -\infty < X_2 \le \infty\} \\ &= \int_{a_1}^{b_1} \int_{-\infty}^{\infty} f_{X_1X_2}(s, t)ds\, dt \\ &= \int_{a_1}^{b_1} f_{X_1}(s)ds . \end{aligned}$$

As indicated in Section 3.5, experiments are often performed where some results are obtained early in time and further results later in time. For example, in the previously described experiment which measures the demand for a product during the first two months, the demand for the product during the first month is observed at the end of the first month. This information can be utilized in making probability statements about the demand during the second month. In particular, if the bivariate random variable (X_1, X_2) is discrete, the conditional probability distribution of X_2, given X_1, can be defined as

$$P_{X_2|X_1=k}(l) = P\{X_2(\omega) = l|X_1(\omega) = k\} = \frac{P_{X_1X_2}(k, l)}{P_{X_1}(k)}, \text{ if } P_{X_1}(k) > 0 ,$$

and the conditional probability distribution of X_1, given X_2, as

$$P_{X_1|X_2=l}(k) = P\{X_1(\omega) = k|X_2(\omega) = l\} = \frac{P_{X_1X_2}(k, l)}{P_{X_2}(l)}, \text{ if } P_{X_2}(l) > 0 .$$

Note that, for a given $X_2(\omega) = l$, $P_{X_1|X_2=l}(k)$ satisfies all of the conditions for a probability distribution for a discrete random variable. $P_{X_1|X_2=l}(k)$ is non-negative and, furthermore,

$$\sum_{\text{all } k} P_{X_1|X_2=l}(k) = \sum_{\text{all } k} \frac{P_{X_1X_2}(k, l)}{P_{X_2}(l)} = \frac{P_{X_2}(l)}{P_{X_2}(l)} = 1 .$$

Again, returning to the demand for a product during the first two months, if it were known that there was no demand during the first month, then

$$P_{X_2|X_1=0}(l) = P\{X_2(\omega) = l|X_1(\omega) = 0\} = \frac{P_{X_1X_2}(0, l)}{P_{X_1}(0)} = \frac{P_{X_1X_2}(0, l)}{100.5/(100)^2} .$$

Hence,

$$P_{X_2|X_1=0}(0) = \frac{P_{X_1X_2}(0, 0)}{(100.5)/(100)^2} = \frac{1.5}{100.5} ,$$

and

$$P_{X_2|X_1=0}(l) = \frac{1}{100.5} \qquad l = 1, 2, \cdots, 99 .$$

If the bivariate random variable (X_1, X_2) is continuous with joint density function $f_{X_1X_2}(s, t)$, and the marginal density function of X_1 is given by $f_{X_1}(s)$, then the conditional density function of X_2, given $X_1 = s$, is defined as

$$f_{X_2|X_1=s}(t) = \frac{f_{X_1X_2}(s, t)}{f_{X_1}(s)} , \text{ if } f_{X_1}(s) > 0 .$$

Similarly, if the marginal density function of X_2 is given by $f_{X_2}(t)$, then the conditional density function of X_1, given $X_2 = t$, is defined as

$$f_{X_1|X_2=t}(s) = \frac{f_{X_1X_2}(s, t)}{f_{X_2}(t)} , \text{ if } f_{X_2}(t) > 0 .$$

Note that, given $X_1 = s$ and $X_2 = t$, the conditional density functions, $f_{X_2|X_1=s}(t)$ and $f_{X_1|X_2=t}(s)$, respectively, satisfy all of the conditions for a density function. They are non-negative and, furthermore,

$$\begin{aligned}\int_{-\infty}^{\infty} f_{X_2|X_1=s}(t)dt &= \int_{-\infty}^{\infty} \frac{f_{X_1X_2}(s, t)dt}{f_{X_1}(s)} \\ &= \frac{1}{f_{X_1}(s)} \int_{-\infty}^{\infty} f_{X_1X_2}(s, t)dt = \frac{f_{X_1}(s)}{f_{X_1}(s)} = 1 ,\end{aligned}$$

and

$$\begin{aligned}\int_{-\infty}^{\infty} f_{X_1|X_2=t}(s)ds &= \int_{-\infty}^{\infty} \frac{f_{X_1X_2}(s, t)ds}{f_{X_2}(t)} \\ &= \frac{1}{f_{X_2}(t)} \int_{-\infty}^{\infty} f_{X_1X_2}(s, t)ds = \frac{f_{X_2}(t)}{f_{X_2}(t)} = 1 .\end{aligned}$$

As an example of the use of these concepts for a continuous bivariate random variable, consider an experiment which measures the time of the first arrivals at a store on each of two consecutive days. Suppose that the joint density function for the random variable (X_1, X_2), which represent the arrival time on the first and second days, respectively, is given by

$$f_{X_1X_2}(s, t) = \begin{cases} \frac{1}{\theta^2} e^{-(s+t)/\theta}, & \text{for } s, t \geq 0 \\ 0, & \text{otherwise.} \end{cases}$$

The marginal density function of X_1 is given by

$$f_{X_1}(s) = \begin{cases} \int_0^\infty \frac{1}{\theta^2} e^{-(s+t)/\theta}\, dt = \frac{1}{\theta} e^{-s/\theta}, & \text{for } s \geq 0 \\ 0, & \text{otherwise,} \end{cases}$$

and the marginal density function of X_2 is given by

$$f_{X_2}(t) = \begin{cases} \int_0^\infty \frac{1}{\theta^2} e^{-(s+t)/\theta}\, ds = \frac{1}{\theta} e^{-t/\theta}, & \text{for } t \geq 0 \\ 0, & \text{otherwise.} \end{cases}$$

If it is announced that the arrival time of the first customer on the first day occurred at time s, the conditional density of X_2, given $X_1 = s$, is given by

$$f_{X_2 \mid X_1 = s}(t) = \frac{f_{X_1X_2}(s, t)}{f_{X_1}(s)} = \frac{\frac{1}{\theta^2} e^{-(s+t)/\theta}}{\frac{1}{\theta} e^{-s/\theta}} = \frac{1}{\theta} e^{-t/\theta}.$$

It is interesting to note at this point that the conditional density of X_2, given $X_1 = s$, is independent of s and, furthermore, is the same as the marginal density of X_2.

3.12 EXPECTATIONS FOR BIVARIATE DISTRIBUTIONS

In Sec. 3.8 the expectation of a function of a univariate random variable was defined. The expectation of a function of a bivariate random variable (X_1, X_2) may be defined in a similar manner. Let $g(X_1, X_2)$ be a function of the bivariate random variable (X_1, X_2). Let

$$P_{X_1X_2}(k, l) = P\{X_1 = k, X_2 = l\}$$

denote the joint probability distribution if (X_1, X_2) is a discrete random variable, and let $f_{X_1X_2}(s, t)$ denote the joint density function if (X_1, X_2) is a continuous random variable. The expectation of $g(X_1, X_2)$ is now defined as

$$E[g(X_1, X_2)] = \begin{cases} \sum_{\text{all } k,l} g(k, l)P_{X_1X_2}(k, l), & \text{if } X_1, X_2 \text{ is a discrete random variable} \\ \int_{-\infty}^{\infty}\int_{-\infty}^{\infty} g(s, t)f_{X_1X_2}(s, t)ds\,dt, & \text{if } X_1, X_2 \text{ is a continuous random variable.} \end{cases}$$

An alternate definition can be obtained by recognizing that $Z = g(X_1, X_2)$ is itself a univariate random variable and, hence, has a density function if Z is continuous and a probability distribution if Z is discrete. The expectation of Z for these cases has already been defined in Sec. 3.8. Of particular interest here is the extension of the "Theorem of the Unconscious Statistician" which states that if (X_1, X_2) is a continuous random variable and if Z has a density function $h_Z(y)$, then

$$E(Z) = \int_{-\infty}^{\infty} yh_Z(y)dy = \int_{-\infty}^{\infty}\int_{-\infty}^{\infty} g(s, t)f_{X_1X_2}(s, t)ds\,dt\,.$$

Thus, the expectation of Z can be found by using its definition in terms of the density of the univariate random variable Z or, alternatively, by use of its definition as the expectation of a function of the bivariate random variable (X_1, X_2) with respect to its joint density function. The identical theorem is true for a discrete bivariate random variable, and, of course, both results are easily extended to n variate random variables.

There are several important functions g that should be considered. All the results will be stated for continuous random variables, but equivalent results also hold for discrete random variables.

If $g(X_1, X_2) = X_1$, it is easily seen that

$$E(X_1) = \int_{-\infty}^{\infty}\int_{-\infty}^{\infty} sf_{X_1X_2}(s, t)ds\,dt = \int_{-\infty}^{\infty} sf_{X_1}(s)ds\,.$$

Note that this is just the expectation of the univariate random variable X_1 with respect to its marginal density. In a similar manner, if $g(X_1, X_2) = [X_1 - E(X_1)]^2$, then

$$\begin{aligned} E[X_1 - E(X_1)]^2 &= \int_{-\infty}^{\infty}\int_{-\infty}^{\infty} [s - E(X_1)]^2 f_{X_1X_2}(s, t)ds\,dt \\ &= \int_{-\infty}^{\infty} [s - E(X_1)]^2 f_{X_1}(s)ds\,, \end{aligned}$$

which is just the variance of the univariate random variable X_1 with respect to its marginal density.

If $g(X_1, X_2) = [X_1 - E(X_1)][X_2 - E(X_2)]$, then $E[g(X_1, X_2)]$ is called the covariance of the random variable (X_1, X_2), i.e.,

$$E[X_1 - E(X_1)][X_2 - E(X_2)] = \int_{-\infty}^{\infty}\int_{-\infty}^{\infty} [s - E(X_1)][t - E(X_2)]f_{X_1X_2}(s, t)ds\,dt .$$

An easy computational formula is provided by the identity

$$E[X_1 - E(X_1)][X_2 - E(X_2)] = E(X_1X_2) - E(X_1)E(X_2) .$$

The correlation coefficient between X_1 and X_2 is defined to be

$$\rho = \frac{E[X_1 - E(X_1)][X_2 - E(X_2)]}{\sqrt{E[X_1 - E(X_1)]^2 E[X_2 - E(X_2)]^2}} .$$

It is easily shown that $-1 \leq \rho \leq +1$.

The final results pertain to a linear combination of random variables. Let $g(X_1, X_2) = C_1X_1 + C_2X_2$, where C_1 and C_2 are constants. Then

$$\begin{aligned} E[g(X_1, X_2)] &= \int_{-\infty}^{\infty}\int_{-\infty}^{\infty} (C_1s + C_2t)f_{X_1X_2}(s, t)ds\,dt , \\ &= C_1\int_{-\infty}^{\infty} sf_{X_1}(s)ds + C_2\int_{-\infty}^{\infty} tf_{X_2}(t)dt, \\ &= C_1E(X_1) + C_2E(X_2) . \end{aligned}$$

Thus, the expectation of a linear combination of univariate random variables is just the sum of the respective coefficient times the expectations of the random variables. It easily follows that

$$E[C_1X_1 + C_2X_2 + \cdots + C_nX_n] = C_1E(X_1) + C_2E(X_2) + \cdots + C_nE(X_n) .$$

If

$$g(X_1, X_2) = [C_1X_1 + C_2X_2 - \{C_1E(X_1) + C_2E(X_2)\}]^2 ,$$

then

$$\begin{aligned} E[g(X_1, X_2)] &= \text{variance of } g(X_1, X_2), \\ &= C_1^2E[X_1 - E(X_1)]^2 + C_2^2E[X_2 - E(X_2)]^2 \\ &\qquad + 2C_1C_2E[X_1 - E(X_1)][X_2 - E(X_2)] , \\ &= C_1^2 \text{ variance } X_1 + C_2^2 \text{ variance } X_2 \\ &\qquad + 2C_1C_2 \text{ covariance } X_1X_2 . \end{aligned}$$

For n univariate random variables, the variance of a linear combination, $C_1X_1 + C_2X_2 + \cdots + C_nX_n$, is given by

$$\sum_{i=1}^{n} C_i^2 \text{ variance } X_i + 2\sum_{j=i+1}^{n}\sum_{i=1}^{n} C_iC_j \text{ covariance } X_iX_j .$$

3.13 INDEPENDENT RANDOM VARIABLES AND RANDOM SAMPLES

The concept of independent events has already been defined, i.e., E_1 and E_2 are independent events if, and only if,

$$P\{E_1 \cap E_2\} = P\{E_1\}P\{E_2\} .$$

From this definition the very important concept of independent random variables can be introduced. The random variables, X_1 and X_2, are said to be independent if events of the form $\{X_1(\omega) \leq b_1\}$ and $\{X_2(\omega) \leq b_2\}$ are independent events for all b_1 and b_2. Using the definition of independent events, then, the random variables X_1 and X_2 are called independent random variables if

$$P\{X_1 \leq b_1, X_2 \leq b_2\} = P\{X_1 \leq b_1\}P\{X_2 \leq b_2\}$$

for all b_1 and b_2. Thus, X_1 and X_2 are independent if

$$\begin{aligned} F_{X_1X_2}(b_1, b_2) &= P\{X_1 \leq b_1, X_2 \leq b_2\} = P\{X_1 \leq b_1\}P\{X_2 \leq b_2\} \\ &= F_{X_1}(b_1)F_{X_2}(b_2) . \end{aligned}$$

Thus, the independence of the random variables X_1 and X_2 implies that the joint C.D.F. factors into the product of the C.D.F.'s of the individual random variables. Furthermore, it is easily shown that if (X_1, X_2) is a discrete bivariate random variable, then X_1 and X_2 are independent random variables if, and only if, $P_{X_1X_2}(k, l) = P_{X_1}(k)P_{X_2}(l)$, i.e., $P\{X_1(\omega) = k, X_2(\omega) = l\} = P\{X_1(\omega) = k\}P\{X_2(\omega) = l\}$, for all k and l. Similarly, if (X_1, X_2) is a continuous bivariate random variable, then X_1 and X_2 are independent random variables if, and only if,

$$f_{X_1X_2}(s, t) = f_{X_1}(s)f_{X_2}(t) ,$$

for all s and t. Thus, if X_1, X_2 are to be independent random variables, the joint density (or probability) function must factor into the product of the marginal density functions of the random variables. Using this result, it is easily seen that if X_1, X_2 are independent random variables, then the covariance of X_1, X_2 must be zero. Hence, the results on the variance of linear combinations of random variables given in Sec. 3.12 can be simplified when the random variables are independent, i.e.,

$$\text{variance} \sum_{i=1}^{n} C_iX_i = \sum_{i=1}^{n} C_i^2 \text{ variance } X_i$$

when the X_i are independent.

Another interesting property of independent random variables can be deduced from the factorization property. If X_1, X_2 is a discrete bivariate random variable, then X_1 and X_2 are independent if, and only if,

$$P_{X_1|X_2=l}(k) = P_{X_1}(k), \qquad \text{for all } k \text{ and } l.$$

Similarly, if X_1, X_2 is a continuous bivariate random variable, then X_1 and X_2 are independent if, and only if,

$$f_{X_1|X_2=t}(s) = f_{X_1}(s), \qquad \text{for all } s \text{ and } t.$$

In other words, if X_1 and X_2 are independent, a knowledge of the outcome of one, say, X_2, gives no information about the probability distribution of the other, say, X_1. It has been noted that, in the example in Sec. 3.11 on the time of first arrivals, the conditional density of the arrival time of the first customer on the second day, given that the first customer on the first day arrived at time s, was equal to the marginal density of the first customer on the second day. Hence, X_1 and X_2 were independent random variables. In the example of the demand for a product during two consecutive months it was seen that

$$P_{X_2|X_1=0}(0) = \frac{1.5}{100.5} \neq P_{X_2}(0) = \frac{100.5}{(100)^2}.$$

Hence, the demands during each month were dependent (not independent) random variables.

The definition of independent random variables generally does not lend itself to determine whether or not random variables are independent in a probabilistic sense by looking at their outcomes. Instead, by analyzing the physical situation, the experimenter usually is able to make a judgment about whether the random variables are independent by ascertaining if the outcome of one will affect the probability distribution of the other.

The definition of independent random variables is easily extended to three or more random variables. For example, if the joint C.D.F. of the n dimensional random variable, $X_1, X_2, \cdots, X_n$, is given by $F_{X_1X_2\cdots X_n}(b_1, b_2, \cdots, b_n)$ and $F_{X_1}(b_1), F_{X_2}(b_2), \cdots, F_{X_n}(b_n)$ represents the C.D.F.'s of the univariate random variables, $X_1, X_2, \cdots, X_n$, respectively, then $X_1, X_2, \cdots, X_n$ are independent random variables if, and only if,

$$F_{X_1X_2\cdots X_n}(b_1, b_2, \cdots, b_n) = F_{X_1}(b_1)F_{X_2}(b_2)\cdots F_{X_n}(b_n) \qquad \text{for all } b_1, b_2, \cdots, b_n.$$

Having defined the concept of independent random variables, the term *random sample* can now be introduced. A random sample simply means a sequence of independent and identically distributed random variables. Thus, $X_1, X_2, \cdots, X_n$ constitute a random sample of size n if the X_i are independent and identically distributed random variables. For example, in Sec. 3.6 it was pointed out that if $X_1, X_2, \cdots, X_n$ are independent Bernoulli random variables each with parameter p(i.e., if the X's are a random sample), then the random variable,

$$X = \sum_{i=1}^{n} X_i,$$

has a binomial distribution with parameters n and p.

3.14 LAW OF LARGE NUMBERS

In Sec. 3.8, it was pointed out that the mean of a random sample tends to converge to the expectation of the random variables as the sample size increases. In particular, suppose the random variable X, the demand for a product, may take on one of the possible values $k = 0, 1, 2, \cdots, 98, 99$, each with $P_X(k) = 1/100$ for all k. Then $E(X)$ is easily seen to be 49.5. If a random sample of size n is taken, i.e., the demands are observed for n days, with each day's demand being independent and identically distributed random variables, it was pointed out that the random variable $\bar{X}$ should take on a value close to 49.5 if n is large. This result can be stated precisely as the Law of Large Numbers.

Law of Large Numbers

Let the random variables $X_1, X_2, \cdots X_n$ be independent identically distributed random variables (a random sample of size n) each having mean μ. Consider the random variable which is the sample mean, $\bar{X}$,

$$\bar{X} = \frac{X_1 + X_2 + \cdots + X_n}{n}.$$

Then for any constant $\epsilon > 0$,

$$\lim_{n \to \infty} P\{|\bar{X} - \mu| > \epsilon\} = 0.$$

The interpretation of the law of large numbers is that as the sample size increases, the probability is "close" to one that $\bar{X}$ is "close" to μ. Assuming that the variance of each X_i is $\sigma^2 < \infty$, this result is easily proved by using Tchebycheff's inequality (stated in Sec. 3.9). Since each X_i has mean μ and variance σ^2, $\bar{X}$ also has mean μ, but its variance is σ^2/n. Hence, applying Tchebycheff's inequality to the random variable $\bar{X}$, it is evident that

$$P\left\{\mu - \frac{C\sigma}{\sqrt{n}} < \bar{X} < \mu + \frac{C\sigma}{\sqrt{n}}\right\} \geq 1 - \frac{1}{C^2}.$$

This is equivalent to

$$P\left\{|\bar{X} - \mu| > \frac{C\sigma}{\sqrt{n}}\right\} \leqslant \frac{1}{C^2}.$$

Let $C\sigma/\sqrt{n} = \epsilon$, so that $C = \epsilon\sqrt{n}/\sigma$. Thus,

$$P\{\bar{X} - \mu| > \epsilon\} \leqslant \frac{\sigma^2}{\epsilon^2 n},$$

so that

$$\lim_{n \to \infty} P\{|\bar{X} - \mu| > \epsilon\} = 0,$$

as was to be proved.

3.15 CENTRAL LIMIT THEOREM

In Sec. 3.7 it was pointed out that sums of independent normally distributed random variables are themselves normally distributed. Furthermore, it was also indicated that even if the random variables are *not* normally distributed, the distribution of their sum still tends toward normality. This latter statement can be made precise by means of the Central Limit Theorem.

Central Limit Theorem: Let the random variables $X_1, X_2, \cdots, X_n$ be independent with means $\mu_1, \mu_2, \cdots, \mu_n$, respectively, and variance σ_1^2, $\sigma_2^2, \cdots, \sigma_n^2$, respectively. Consider the random variable Z_n,

$$Z_n = \frac{\sum_{i=1}^{n} X_i - \sum_{i=1}^{n} \mu_i}{\sqrt{\sum_{i=1}^{n} \sigma_i^2}}.$$

Then, under certain regularity conditions, Z_n is approximately normally distributed with zero mean and unit variance in the sense that

$$\lim_{n \to \infty} P\{Z_n \leq b\} = \int_b^{\infty} \frac{1}{\sqrt{2\pi}} e^{-y^2/2}\, dy.$$

Note that if the X_i form a random sample with each X_i having mean μ and variance σ^2, then $Z_n = (\bar{X} - \mu)\sqrt{n}/\sigma$.[11] Hence, sample means from random samples tend toward normality in the sense just described by the Central Limit Theorem even if the X_i are not normally distributed.

It is difficult to give sample sizes beyond which the Central Limit Theorem applies, and approximate normality can be assumed for sample means. This, of course, does depend upon the form of the underlying dis-

[11] Under these conditions, the Central Limit Theorem actually holds without assuming any other regularity conditions.

tribution. From a practical point of view, moderate sample sizes, like 10, are often sufficient.

3.16 FUNCTIONS OF RANDOM VARIABLES

In Sec. 3.8 the "Theorem of the Unconscious Statistician" was introduced, and it was pointed out that if a function $Z = g(X)$ of a continuous random variable is considered, its expectation can be taken with respect to the density function $f_X(y)$ of X, or the density function $h_Z(y)$ of Z. In discussing this choice, it was implied that the density function of Z was known. In general, then, given the cumulative distribution function, $F_X(b)$, of a random variable X there may be interest in obtaining the cumulative distribution function, $H_Z(b)$, of a random variable $Z = g(X)$. Of course, it is always possible to go back to the sample space and determine $H_Z(b)$ directly from probabilities associated with the sample space. However, alternate methods for doing this are desirable.

If X is a discrete random variable, the values k that the random variable X takes on and the associated $P_X(k)$ are known. If $Z = g(X)$ is also discrete, denote by m the values that Z takes on. The probabilities $Q_Z(m) = P\{Z = m\}$ for all m are required. The general procedure is to enumerate for each m all of the values of k such that

$$g(k) = m .$$

$Q_Z(m)$ is then determined as

$$Q_Z(m) = \sum_{\substack{\text{all } k \\ \text{such that} \\ g(k)=m}} P_X(k) .$$

To illustrate, consider again the example involving the demand for a product in a single month. Let this random variable be noted by X, and let $k = 0, 1, \cdots, 99$ with $P_X(k) = 1/100$ for all k. Consider a new random variable Z which takes on the value of 0 if there is no demand and 1 if there is *any* demand. This random variable may be useful for determining whether anyone is needed for shipping. The probabilities,

$$Q_Z(0) \text{ and } Q_Z(1) ,$$

are required. If $m = 0$, the only value of k such that $g(k) = 0$ is $k = 0$. Hence,

$$Q_Z(0) = \sum_{\substack{\text{all } k \\ \text{such that} \\ g(k)=0}} P_X(k) = P_X(0) = \frac{1}{100} .$$

If $m = 1$, the values of k such that $g(k) = 1$ are $k = 1, 2, 3, \cdots, 98, 99$. Hence,

$$Q_Z(1) = \sum_{\substack{\text{all } k \\ \text{such that} \\ g(k)=1}} P_X(k) = P_X(1) + P_X(2) + P_X(3) + \cdots + P_X(98) + P_X(99) = \frac{99}{100}.$$

If X is a continuous random variable, then both the C.D.F., $F_X(b)$, and the density function, $f_X(y)$ may be assumed to be known. If $Z = g(X)$ is also a continuous random variable, either the C.D.F., $H_Z(b)$, or the density function, $h_Z(y)$, is sought. To find $H_Z(b)$, note that

$$H_Z(b) = P\{Z \leq b\} = P\{g(X) \leq b\} = P\{A\},$$

where A consists of all points such that $g(X) \leq b$. Thus, $P\{A\}$ can be determined from the density function or C.D.F. of the random variable X. For example, suppose that the C.D.F. for the time of the first arrival in a store is given by

$$F_X(b) = \begin{cases} 1 - e^{-b/\theta}, & \text{for } b \geq 0 \\ 0, & \text{for } b < 0, \end{cases}$$

where $\theta > 0$. Suppose further that the random variable $Z = g(X) = X + 1$, which represents an hour after the first customer arrives, is of interest, and the C.D.F. of Z, $H_Z(b)$ is desired. To find this C.D.F. note that

$$H_Z(b) = P\{Z \leq b\} = P\{X + 1 \leq b\} = P\{X \leq b - 1\}$$
$$= \begin{cases} 1 - e^{-(b-1)/\theta}, & \text{for } b \geq 1 \\ 0, & \text{for } b < 1. \end{cases}$$

Furthermore, the density can be obtained by differentiating the C.D.F., i.e.,

$$h_Z(y) = \begin{cases} \dfrac{1}{\theta} e^{-(y-1)/\theta}, & \text{for } y \geq 1 \\ 0, & \text{for } y < 1. \end{cases}$$

Another technique can be used to find the density function directly if $g(X)$ is monotone and differentiable. In this case, it can be shown that

$$h_Z(y) = f_X(s)\left|\frac{ds}{dy}\right|,$$

where s is expressed in terms of y. In the example, $Z = g(X) = X + 1$, so that y, the value the random variable Z takes on, can be expressed in terms of s, the value the random variable X takes on, i.e., $y = g(s) = s + 1$. Thus, $s = y - 1$, $f_X(s) = \frac{1}{\theta} e^{-s/\theta} = \frac{1}{\theta} e^{-(y-1)/\theta}$, and $ds/dy = 1$. Hence, $h_Z(y) = \frac{1}{\theta} e^{-(y-1)/\theta}|1| = \frac{1}{\theta} e^{-(y-1)/\theta}$, which is the result previously obtained.

All of the discussion in this section concerned functions of a single random variable. If X_1, X_2 is a bivariate random variable, there may be interest in the probability distribution of such functions as $X_1 + X_2$, X_1X_2, X_1/X_2, etc. If X_1X_2 is discrete, the technique for single random variables is easily extended. A detailed discussion of the techniques available for continuous bivariate random variables is beyond the scope of this text. However, a few notions related to independent random variables will be discussed.

If X_1, X_2 is a continuous bivariate random variable, and X_1 and X_2 are independent, then its joint density is given by

$$f_{X_1X_2}(s, t) = f_{X_1}(s)f_{X_2}(t) .$$

Consider the function

$$Z = g(X_1, X_2) = X_1 + X_2 .$$

The C.D.F. for Z can be expressed as $H_Z(b) = P\{Z \leq b\} = P\{X_1 + X_2 \leq b\}$. This can be evaluated by integrating the bivariate density over the region such that $s + t \leq b$, i.e.,

$$H_Z(b) = \iint\limits_{s+t\leq b} f_{X_1}(s)f_{X_2}(t)ds\, dt ,$$

$$= \int_{-\infty}^{\infty} \int_{-\infty}^{b-t} f_{X_1}(s)f_{X_2}(t)ds\, dt .$$

Differentiating with respect to b yields the density function

$$h_Z(y) = \int_{-\infty}^{\infty} f_{X_2}(t)f_{X_1}(y - t)dt .$$

This can also be written alternately as

$$h_Z(y) = \int_{-\infty}^{\infty} f_{X_1}(s)f_{X_2}(y - s)ds .$$

Note that the integrand may be zero over part of the range of the variable, as shown in the following example.

Suppose that the times of the first arrival on two successive days, X_1 and X_2, are independent, identically distributed random variables having density

$$f_{X_1}(s) = \begin{cases} \dfrac{1}{\theta} e^{-s/\theta}, & \text{for } s \geq 0 \\ 0, & \text{otherwise} . \end{cases}$$

$$f_{X_2}(t) = \begin{cases} \dfrac{1}{\theta} e^{-t/\theta}, & \text{for } t \geq 0 \\ 0, & \text{otherwise} . \end{cases}$$

To find the density of $Z = X_1 + X_2$, note that

$$f_{X_1}(s) = \begin{cases} \frac{1}{\theta} e^{-s/\theta}, & \text{for } s \geq 0 \\ 0, & \text{for } s < 0, \end{cases}$$

and

$$f_{X_2}(y - s) = \begin{cases} \frac{1}{\theta} e^{-(y-s)/\theta}, & \text{if } y - s \geq 0 \text{ so that } s \leq y \\ 0, & \text{if } y - s < 0 \text{ so that } s > y. \end{cases}$$

Hence,

$$f_{X_1}(s) f_{X_2}(y - s) = \begin{cases} \frac{1}{\theta} e^{-s/\theta} \frac{1}{\theta} e^{-(y-s)/\theta} = \frac{1}{\theta^2} e^{-y/\theta}, & \text{if } 0 \leq s \leq y \\ 0, & \text{otherwise}. \end{cases}$$

Hence,

$$h_Z(y) = \int_{-\infty}^{\infty} f_{X_1}(s) f_{X_2}(y - s) ds = \int_0^y \frac{1}{\theta^2} e^{-y/\theta} ds$$
$$= \frac{y}{\theta^2} e^{-y/\theta}.$$

Note that this is just a gamma distribution with parameters $\alpha = 2$ and $\beta = \theta$. Hence, as indicated in Sec. 3.7, the sum of two independent, exponentially distributed random variables has a gamma distribution. This example illustrates how to find the density function for finite sums of independent random variables. Combining this result with those for univariate random variables leads to easily finding the density function of linear combinations of independent random variables.

SELECTED REFERENCES

1. Cramer, H., *The Elements of Probability Theory and Some of its Applications*, Wiley, New York, 1955.
2. Derman, C., and Klein, M., *Probability and Statistical Inference for Engineers*, Oxford University Press, New York, 1959.
3. Feller, W., *An Introduction to Probability Theory and its Applications*, Vol. 1, 2nd ed., Wiley, New York, 1957.
4. Meyer, P. L., *Introductory Probability and Statistical Applications*, Addison-Wesley, Reading, Mass., 1965.
5. Parzen, E., *Modern Probability Theory and Its Applications*, Wiley, New York, 1960.

PROBLEMS

1. A cube has its six sides colored red, white, blue, green, yellow and violet. It is assumed that these six sides are equally likely to show when the cube is tossed. The cube is tossed once.

(a) Describe the sample space.
(b) Consider the random variable that assigns the number 1 to red and white, the number 2 to green and blue, and the number 3 to yellow and violet. What is the distribution of this random variable?
(c) Let $Y = (X - 1)^2$ where X is the random variable in part (b). Find $E(Y)$.

2. Suppose the sample space S consists of the four points

$$\omega_1,\ \omega_2,\ \omega_3,\ \omega_4,$$

and the associated probabilities over the events are given by

$$P\{\omega_1\} = \frac{1}{3},\ P\{\omega_2\} = \frac{1}{3},\ P\{\omega_3\} = \frac{1}{6},\ P\{\omega_4\} = \frac{1}{6}.$$

Define the random variable X_1 by

$$\begin{aligned} X_1(\omega_1) &= 1\,, \\ X_1(\omega_2) &= 1\,, \\ X_1(\omega_3) &= 4\,, \\ X_1(\omega_4) &= 5\,, \end{aligned}$$

and the random variable X_2 by

$$\begin{aligned} X_2(\omega_1) &= 1\,, \\ X_2(\omega_2) &= 1\,, \\ X_2(\omega_3) &= 1\,, \\ X_2(\omega_4) &= 5\,. \end{aligned}$$

(a) Find the probability distribution of X_1, i.e., $P_{X_1}(i)$.
(b) Find $E(X_1)$.
(c) Find the probability distribution of the random variable $X_1 + X_2$, i.e., $P_{X_1+X_2}(i)$.
(d) Find $E(X_1 + X_2)$ and $E(X_2)$.
(e) Find $F_{X_1X_2}(b_1, b_2)$.
(f) Compute the correlation coefficient between X_1 and X_2.
(g) Compute $E[2X_1 - 3X_2]$.

3. During the course of a day a machine turns out two items, one in the morning and one in the afternoon. The quality of each item is measured as good (G), mediocre (M), or bad (B). The long-run fraction of good items the machine produces is $\frac{1}{2}$, the fraction of mediocre items is $\frac{1}{3}$, and the fraction of bad items is $\frac{1}{6}$.

(a) In a column write down the sample space for the experiment which consists of observing the day's production.
(b) Assume a good item returns a profit of \$2, a mediocre item a profit of \$1, and a bad item yields nothing. Let X be the random variable describing the total profit for the day. In a column adjacent to the column in part (a), write down the value of this random variable corresponding to each point in the sample space.
(c) Assuming that the qualities of the morning and afternoon items are independent, associate with every point in the sample space a probability for that point, in a third column.
(d) Write down the set of all possible outcomes for the random variable X. Give the probability distribution function for the random variable.
(e) What is the expected value of the day's profit?

4. The random variable X has density function f given by

$$f_X(y) = \begin{cases} \theta, & \text{for } 0 \leq y \leq \theta \\ K, & \text{for } \theta < y \leq 1 \\ 0, & \text{elsewhere}\,. \end{cases}$$

(a) Determine K in terms of θ.
(b) Find $F_X(b)$, the C.D.F. of X.
(c) Find $E(X)$.
(d) Suppose $\theta = \frac{1}{2}$. Is $P\{X - \frac{1}{2} < a\} = P\{-(X - \frac{1}{2}) < a\}$?

5. Let X be a discrete random variable with probability distribution

$$P\{X = x_1\} = \tfrac{1}{3}$$

and

$$P\{X = x_2\} = \tfrac{2}{3}\,.$$

(a) Determine x_1 and x_2 so that

$$E(X) = 0 \text{ and variance } (X) = 8\,.$$

(b) Sketch the C.D.F. of X.

6. The life X, in hours, of a certain kind of radio tube has a probability density function given by

$$f_X(y) = \begin{cases} \dfrac{100}{y^2}, & \text{for } y \geq 100 \\ 0, & \text{for } y < 100\,. \end{cases}$$

(a) What is the probability that a tube will survive 150 hours of operation?
(b) Find the expected value of the random variable.

7. The random variable X can take only the values 0, ± 1, ± 2, and

$$P\{-1 < X < 2\} = .4\,, \qquad P\{X = 0\} = .2\,,$$
$$P\{|X| \leq 1\} = .6\,, \qquad P\{X \geq 2\} = P\{X = 1 \text{ or } -1\}\,.$$

(a) Find the probability distribution of X.
(b) Graph the C.D.F. of X.
(c) Compute $E(X)$.

8. Let X be a random variable with density

$$f_X(y) = \begin{cases} K(1 - y^2), & \text{for } -1 < y < 1 \\ 0, & \text{otherwise}\,. \end{cases}$$

(a) What value of K will make $f_X(y)$ a true density?
(b) What is the C.D.F. of X?
(c) Find $E(2X - 1)$.
(d) Find variance (X).
(e) Find the approximate value of $P\{\bar{X} > .05\}$, where $\bar{X}$ is the sample mean from a random sample of size $n = 100$ from the above distribution. Hint: Note that n is "large."

9. The distribution of X, the life of a transistor, in hours, is approximated by a triangular distribution as follows:

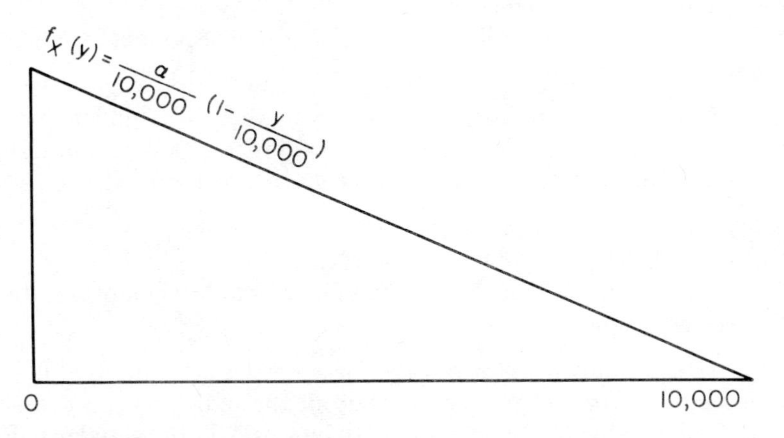

(a) What is the value of α?
(b) Find the expected value of the life of transistors.
(c) Find the C.D.F., $F_X(b)$, for this density. Note that this must be defined for all b between plus and minus infinity.

(d) If X represents the random variable, the life of a transistor, let $Z = 2X$ be a new random variable. Using the results of (*c*), find the C.D.F. of Z.

10. The number of orders per week, X, for radios can be assumed to have a Poisson distribution with parameter $\lambda = 20$.

(a) Find $P\{X \geq 20\}$ and $P\{X = 14\}$.
(b) If the number of radios in the inventory is 25, what is the probability of a shortage occurring in a week?

11. Consider the following game. Player A flips a fair coin until a head appears. He pays player B 2^n dollars, where n is the number of tosses required until a head appears. For example, if a head appears on the first trial, player A pays player B 2 dollars. If the game results in 4 tails followed by a head, player A pays player B $2^5 = 32$ dollars. Therefore, the payoff to player B is a random variable which takes on the values 2^n for $n = 1, 2, \cdots$ and whose probability distribution is given by $(1/2)^n$ for $n = 1, 2, \cdots$, i.e., if X denotes the payoff to player B

$$P(X = 2^n) = \left(\frac{1}{2}\right)^n \text{ for } n = 1, 2, \cdots.$$

The usual definition of a fair game between two players is for each player to have equal expectation for the amount to be won.

(a) How much should player B pay to player A so that this game will be fair?
(b) What is the variance of X?
(c) What is the probability of player B winning no more than \$16 in one play of the game?

12. The demand, D, for a product in a week is a random variable taking on the values of $-1, 0, 1$ with probabilities $1/6$, $3/6$, and $C/6$, respectively. A demand of -1 implies that an item is returned.

(a) Find C, $E(D)$, and variance D.
(b) Find $E(e^{D^2})$.
(c) Sketch the C.D.F. of the random variable D, labeling all the necessary values.

13. In a certain chemical process three bottles of a standard fluid are emptied into a larger container. A study of the individual bottles shows that the mean value of the contents is 16 ounces, and the standard deviation is 0.07 ounces. If three bottles form a random sample:

(a) Find the expected value and the standard deviation of the volume of liquid emptied into the larger container.

(b) If the content of the individual bottles is normally distributed, what is the probability that the volume of liquid emptied into the larger container will be in excess of 48.25 ounces?

14. Consider the density function of a random variable X defined by

$$f_X(y) = \begin{cases} 0, & \text{for } \quad y < 0 \\ 6y(1-y), & \text{for } 0 \leq y \leq 1 \\ 0, & \text{for } \quad 1 < y\,. \end{cases}$$

(a) Find the C.D.F. corresponding to this density function. (Be sure you describe it completely.)
(b) Calculate the mean and variance.
(c) What is the probability that a random variable having this density will exceed .75?
(d) Consider the experiment where five independent random variables are observed, each random variable having the density function given above. What is the expected value of the sample mean of these observations?
(e) What is the variance of the sample mean described in part (d)?

15. A transistor radio operates on 3 size $D1\frac{1}{2}$ volt batteries so that nominally it operates on $4\frac{1}{2}$ volts. Suppose the actual voltage of a single new battery is normally distributed with mean $1\frac{1}{2}$ volts and variance .04. The radio will not operate "properly" at the outset if the voltage falls outside the range 4–5 volts.

(a) What is the probability that the radio will not operate "properly"?
(b) Suppose that the assumption of normality is not valid. Give a bound on the probability that the radio will not operate "properly."

16. The life of electric light bulbs is known to be a normally distributed random variable with unknown mean μ and standard deviation 200 hours. The value of a lot of 1000 bulbs is $(1000)(1/5000)\ \mu$ dollars. A random sample of n bulbs is to be drawn by a prospective buyer and $1000(1/5000)\ \bar{X}$ dollars paid to the manufacturer. How large should n be so that the probability is .95 that the buyer does not overpay or underpay the manufacturer by more than \$20?

17. A joint random variable (X_1, X_2) is said to have a bivariate normal distribution if its joint density is given by

$$f_{X_1,X_2}(s,t) = \frac{1}{2\pi\sigma_{X_1}\sigma_{X_2}\sqrt{1-\rho^2}} \exp\left\{-\frac{1}{2(1-\rho^2)}\left[\left(\frac{s-\mu_{X_1}}{\sigma_{X_1}}\right)^2 - 2\rho\frac{(s-\mu_{X_1})(t-\mu_{X_2})}{\sigma_{X_1}\sigma_{X_2}} + \left(\frac{t-\mu_{X_2}}{\sigma_{X_2}}\right)^2\right]\right\}$$

for $-\infty < s < \infty$ and $-\infty < t < \infty$.

(a) Show that $E(X_1) = \mu_{X_1}$ and $E(X_2) = \mu_{X_2}$.
(b) Show that variance $(X_1) = \sigma^2_{X_1}$, variance $(X_2) = \sigma^2_{X_2}$, and the correlation coefficient is ρ.
(c) Show that marginal distributions of X_1 and X_2 are normal.
(d) Show that the conditional distribution of X_1, given $X_2 = x_2$, is normal with mean

$$\mu_{X_1} + \rho \frac{\sigma_{X_1}}{\sigma_{X_2}} (x_2 - \mu_{X_2})$$

and variance $\sigma^2_{X_1}(1 - \rho^2)$.

18. The joint demand for a product over two months is a continuous random variable (X_1, X_2) having a joint density given by

$$f_{X_1,X_2}(s, t) = \begin{cases} c, & \text{if } 1000 \leq s \leq 1500, \text{ and } 500 \leq t \leq 1000 \\ 0, & \text{otherwise}. \end{cases}$$

(a) Find c.
(b) Find $F_{X_1X_2}(b_1, b_2)$, $F_{X_1}(b_1)$, and $F_{X_2}(b_2)$.
(c) Find $f_{X_2|X_1=s}(t)$.

19. Two machines produce a certain item. The capacity, per day, of machine 1 is 1 unit and that of machine 2 is 2 units. Let (X_1, X_2) be the discrete random variable which measures the actual production on each machine per day. Each entry in the table below represents the joint probability, e.g., $P_{X_1X_2}(0, 0) = \frac{1}{8}$.

X_2 \ X_1	0	1
0	$\frac{1}{8}$	0
1	$\frac{1}{4}$	$\frac{1}{4}$
2	$\frac{1}{8}$	$\frac{1}{4}$

(a) Find the marginal distributions of X_1 and X_2.
(b) Find the conditional distribution of X_1, given $X_2 = 2$.
(c) Are X_1 and X_2 independent random variables?
(d) Find $E(X_1)$, $E(X_2)$, variance (X_1), and variance (X_2).
(e) Find the probability distribution of $(X_1 + X_2)$.

CHAPTER 4

Statistical Inference and Decision Theory

4.1 INTRODUCTION

In the previous chapter, the basic notions of probability theory were introduced. Little mention was made of decision-making since the discussion was concerned with describing natural phenomena in terms of a probabilistic model. Random variables and their associated probability distributions were always assumed to be completely specified. Even in this situation, and in the absence of sample data, decisions may be required.

A more common occurrence involves decision-making when sample data are available; this is the concern of statistics. Statistics is a science which deals with making decisions from observed data in the face of uncertainty. This chapter presents a framework for making decisions both when sample data are available and unavailable.

4.2 DECISION-MAKING WITHOUT OBSERVED DATA

Consider the following inventory problem. A new type of airplane is to be purchased by the Air Force, and the number of spare engines accompanying the order must be determined. The Air Force must order these spare engines in batches of 5 and can only choose among 15, 20, or 25 spares. The supplier of these engines has two plants, and the Air Force must make its decision prior to knowing which plant will be used. From past experience it is known that the number of spare engines required when production takes place at plant A is approximated by a Poisson distribution with parameter $\lambda = 21$, whereas the number of spare engines required when production takes place at plant B is approximated by a Poisson distribution with parameter $\lambda = 24$. The cost of a spare engine purchased now is \$250,000, whereas the cost of purchasing a spare engine at a later date will be $500,000. Holding costs and interest charges are to be neglected. Spares must always be supplied if they are demanded, and unused engines will be scrapped when the airplanes become obsolete.

Before seeking a solution to this problem, it is worthwhile to formulate a general framework for decision-making. The decision-maker must choose an action a from a set A of possible actions. In the inventory example, the set A consists of three points, a_1, a_2, a_3, corresponding to ordering 15, 20, or 25 spare engines, respectively. In taking an action, the decision-maker must be aware of its consequences, which will be a function of the "state of nature." A "state of nature," θ, is a representation of a possible situation to which the action will apply. Generally, the "state of nature" is a representation of the probabilistic model of the physical phenomenon being studied and is characterized by the parameter of a family of probability distributions. The set of possible values that θ can assume will be denoted by Θ. In the inventory example Θ consists of two points, θ_1 and θ_2, which can be $\lambda = 21$ and $\lambda = 24$, the parameters of two possible Poisson distributions. In order to measure the consequences of a decision-maker's action, it will be assumed that there exists a *loss function* $l(a, \theta)$ which reflects the loss from taking action a when the state of nature is θ, and which is defined for each combination of a and θ. If the problem is formulated in terms of gains, a gain can be termed as a negative loss. The loss function is generally measured in monetary terms, although other "utility" functions can be used. Note that $l(a, \theta)$ is assumed to be a function only of a and θ. The interpretation of the loss function requires further explanation. In the inventory example, the "cost" incurred when, say, action a_2 is taken and the state of nature is θ_1 (when 15 spares are ordered and $\lambda = 21$) depends upon the number of spare engines actually required. The number of spare engines actually required is a random variable whose probability distribution is a function of $\lambda = 21$. In this situation, the loss is measured as the *expected* "cost" and is a function of a_2 and θ_1. Thus, in general, when "costs" associated with a and θ are random variables, the loss function is measured as the *expected* "cost."

TABLE 4.1. Loss Table for the Inventory Problem

action \ state of nature	$\theta_1:\lambda = 21$	$\theta_2:\lambda = 24$
a_1: order 15	6.8265×10^6	8.265×10^6
a_2: order 20	6.178×10^6	7.270×10^6
a_3: order 25	6.514×10^6	7.002×10^6

For the inventory example, Table 4.1, the loss table for the inventory problem, can now be computed.

An entry in the table, e.g., the entry corresponding to taking action a_2 when the true state of nature is θ_1, is computed as follows. Let the random variable Z represent the total cost of spare engines purchased, which is a function of the demand. Thus, when action a_2 is taken, and the true state of nature is $\theta_1 = 21$ ($\theta_1 = 21$ is written in place of $\theta_1: \lambda = 21$ for economy of notation), then

$$Z(D) = \begin{cases} (250{,}000)(20) + (500{,}000)(D\text{–}20), & \text{for } D > 20\,, \\ (250{,}000)(20), & \text{for } D \leq 20\,, \end{cases}$$

where D, the number of spare engines required, is a random variable having a Poisson distribution with parameter $\lambda = 21$.

As mentioned above, the expected total cost of spare engines purchased is required for completion of the loss table. By applying the material in Secs. 3.6.2 and 3.8, the expected value of the total cost of spare engines purchased, $E(Z)$, can be calculated as

$$E(Z) = \sum_{k=0}^{\infty} Z(k)P_D(k) = \sum_{k=0}^{20} Z(k)P_D(k) + \sum_{k=21}^{\infty} Z(k)P_D(k)$$

$$= \sum_{k=0}^{20} 5{,}000{,}000P_D(k) + \sum_{k=21}^{\infty} [5{,}000{,}000 + 500{,}000k - 10{,}000{,}000]P_D(k)$$

$$= 5{,}000{,}000P\{D \leq 20\} - 5{,}000{,}000P\{D > 20\} + 500{,}000 \sum_{k=21}^{\infty} kP_D(k)$$

$$= -5{,}000{,}000 + 10{,}000{,}000P\{D \leq 20\} + 500{,}000 \sum_{k=21}^{\infty} \frac{k(21)^k e^{-21}}{k!}\,,$$

where $P\{D \leq 20\}$ is the probability that a Poisson random variable with parameter $\lambda = 21$ is less than or equal to 20. By referring to Table A5.4 of Appendix 5, it is seen that

$$P\{D \leq 20\} = 0.471$$

and that

$$\sum_{k=21}^{\infty} \frac{k(21)^k e^{-21}}{k!} = 21 \sum_{k=21}^{\infty} \frac{(21)^{k-1} e^{-21}}{(k-1)!}$$

$$= 21 \sum_{j=20}^{\infty} \frac{(21)^j e^{-21}}{j!}$$

$$= 21(1 - 0.384) = 12.936\,.$$

Hence, $E(Z) = -5{,}000{,}000 + 4{,}710{,}000 + 6{,}468{,}000 = 6{,}178{,}000$, and the entry is obtained. Similar calculations are made for the other five entries in the table. Although the calculations required are tedious, this table may now be assumed to be given, i.e., the loss function $l(a, \theta)$ is well defined for all θ and a.

From the foundations of utility theory, the regret function is an alternative to the loss function in measuring the consequences of taking an action a when the true state of nature is θ. The *regret function* $r(a, \theta)$ is defined to be

$$r(a, \theta) = l(a, \theta) - \min_{a \in A} l(a, \theta) ,$$

i.e., the regret for all a and θ is obtained by subtracting the minimum loss for this θ from the loss for this particular a and θ. The loss function and the

TABLE 4.2. Regret Table for the Inventory Problem

action \ state of nature	$\theta_1 : \lambda = 21$	$\theta_2 : \lambda = 24$
a_1: order 15	$.6485 \times 10^6$	1.263×10^6
a_2: order 20	0	$.268 \times 10^6$
a_3: order 25	$.336 \times 10^6$	0

regret function generally are not equivalent. The philosophy for using regret instead of loss can be summarized as follows. If the true state of nature is known, and the decision-maker takes the best action, he still incurs a loss, although through no fault of his own since he took the best possible action. Therefore, instead of penalizing him by this quantity, it is subtracted from each loss incurred by actions taken under this state of nature. The difference $r(a, \theta)$ is called the regret and represents the loss which could have been avoided had the best action for that state of nature been taken. Thus, a regret table always has a zero entry as one of its entries for a given state of nature. In the inventory example, the regret table is given in Table 4.2.

If the true state of nature is $\theta_1 = 21$, the best action to take is a_2, order 20 items. If action a_3 is taken, and 25 are ordered, a cost of $.336 \times 10^6$ is "regretted."

In some formulations, losses are stated in terms of regret immediately. If the best action is taken for a given state of nature, the loss is often assumed to be zero for this combination. In fact, in later sections, such situations are studied extensively.

4.2.1 **Minimax Criterion**

If the true state of nature were known, it would be simple to choose the correct action, i.e., that action which has minimum loss or regret. Unfortunately, the true state of nature is not generally known, and choosing a "correct action" is not simple. In the inventory example, if $\theta = 21$, the best action is to purchase 20 spare engines, whereas, if $\theta = 24$, the best action is to purchase 25 spare engines. This decision theory formulation has the appearance of game theory described in detail in Chapter 9, with the two players being the decision-maker and nature. The "actions" correspond to the pure strategies of the decision-maker, and the states of nature correspond to the pure strategies of nature. The payoff matrix in game theory is analogous to the loss table or regret table. An approach for obtaining solutions to game theory problems is through the minimax principle. This principle tells the decision-maker to find the maximum loss for each of his actions and choose that action which has the smallest maximum loss. Similarly, the decision-maker's opponent, nature in this case, should find the minimum loss to the decision-maker for each one of his possible states of nature, and present to the decision-maker that state of nature which maximizes this minimum loss. If these loss values are equal, the game is said to have a "value." If a game has a "value," and each player follows his optimal strategy, the decision-maker can guarantee that his loss will never exceed the "value." Furthermore, if the decision-maker follows his optimal strategy, and nature deviates from his, the loss to the decision-maker can only be decreased. Unfortunately, in this context a value does not always exist. However, it does exist in the inventory example. By using the minimax criterion the decision-maker should choose action a_3, and guarantee that his loss will not exceed 6.982×10^6. Similarly, nature should choose state $\theta = 24$ and can guarantee that the decision-maker's loss will be at least 6.982×10^6. Thus, this "game" does indeed have a value, and the minimax strategy for the decision-maker is to order 25 spare engines.

A fundamental theorem in the theory of games states that if mixed strategies are allowed, and the minimax principle followed, the game always has a "value." A mixed strategy for the decision-maker is a probability distribution defined over the action space. The actual choice of strategy is dependent upon the outcome of a random device having the probability distribution associated with the action space. Thus, choosing a mixed strategy is equivalent to choosing a probability distribution. Similarly, a mixed strategy for nature is a probability distribution defined over the possible states of nature. Pure strategies are just special cases of mixed strategies where the probability assigned to the chosen action is 1 and 0 to the others. Since both the action and the state of nature are random variables, the loss incurred is also a random variable, and again "expected loss" is the criterion.

However, even though the minimax principle has some attractive properties, it is seldom used in games against nature since it is an extremely conservative criterion in this context. The actions taken using this principle assume that nature is a conscious opponent who wishes to inflict on the decision-maker as much "damage" as possible. Generally, nature is not a malevolent opponent, and it is unlikely that the decision-maker has to guard against such an occurrence.

The minimax principle can be applied to the regret function, and all of the previous comments are applicable, although the minimax strategies using regret will generally be different from those using loss.

4.2.2 Bayes Criterion

In the previous section, it was pointed out that the minimax principle says to proceed as if nature will select a probability distribution, defined over the possible states of nature, which is "least favorable" to the decision-maker. It was also noted that this is a very conservative approach since there is no reason to expect nature to use this distribution. As a matter of fact, in some situations the decision-maker will actually have some advance information about θ that contradicts this assumption about what nature will do. When this happens, the decision-maker certainly should take this information into account. Such information can usually be translated into a probability distribution, acting as though the state of nature is a random variable, in which case this distribution is referred to as a *prior* distribution. Prior distributions are often subjective in that they may depend upon the experience or intuition of an individual.

For example, in the inventory problem, the Air Force may know from past experience that $\frac{2}{3}$ of all types of airplane engines are produced in plant A, and only $\frac{1}{3}$ in plant B. Hence, the prior distribution for θ may be assumed to be

$$\begin{aligned} P\{\theta = 21\} &= P_\theta(21) = \tfrac{2}{3}, \\ P\{\theta = 24\} &= P_\theta(24) = \tfrac{1}{3}. \end{aligned}$$

A procedure for utilizing the prior distribution to aid in the selection of an action is the Bayes criterion. The *Bayes principle* tells the decision-maker to select that action (called the *Bayes decision procedure*) which minimizes the expected loss. The expected loss is evaluated with respect to the prior distribution which is defined over the possible states of nature. Thus, for the inventory problem, the expected loss, $E[l(a)]$, for each action is given by:

$$\begin{aligned} E[l(a_1)] &= (6.8265 \times 10^6)(\tfrac{2}{3}) = (8.265 \times 10^6)(\tfrac{1}{3}) = 7.306 \times 10^6, \\ E[l(a_2)] &= (6.178 \times 10^6)(\tfrac{2}{3}) + (7.270 \times 10^6)(\tfrac{1}{3}) = 6.542 \times 10^6, \\ E[l(a_3)] &= (6.514 \times 10^6)(\tfrac{2}{3}) + (7.002 \times 10^6)(\tfrac{1}{3}) = 6.677 \times 10^6. \end{aligned}$$

Hence, the Bayes principle leads to selecting action a_2, i.e., purchasing 20 spares, and the associated expected loss is 6.542×10^6. It is interesting to speculate on whether the decision-maker could have improved upon this expected loss by making use of a mixed strategy rather than a pure strategy (since nature is using the mixed strategy specified by the prior distribution). It can be shown that the decision-maker cannot improve his position by using mixed strategies so that it is sufficient for him to consider only pure strategies.

The above discussion has been concerned with loss functions. If a regret function is substituted for the loss function, the *same* Bayes procedure will always be obtained. Thus, in the inventory example, if Table 4.2 (the regret table) is used, the Bayes procedure still will be to order 20 spare engines.

An interesting comment pertaining to the inventory example can be made with respect to the action a_1, ordering 15 spare engines. In looking at the loss table or the regret table, it is clear that the decision-maker should never take this action. No matter what the state of nature is, a_2 and a_3 have smaller losses or regrets associated with them, and so are said to dominate action a_1. Hence, the action a_1 could have been discarded early in the analysis.

4.3 DECISION-MAKING WITH DATA

The previous sections assumed that the decision-maker was to make his decision without experimentation. However, if some experimentation is possible (possibly at a cost), the data derived from this experimentation should be incorporated into the decision-making process. For example, returning to the inventory example, suppose that the following information is made available to the Air Force. A similar type of engine was produced for an earlier version of the current airplane under consideration. The order size for this earlier type was the same as for the current model. Furthermore, its non-obsolete life is identical with that planned for the present version. The engine for the current order will be produced in the same plant as the previous model, although the Air Force is not aware of which of the two plants this is. The reason for this lack of knowledge is due to the haste in which the spare engine decision must be made. The Air Force has access to the data on the number of spares actually required for the older version (which had a Poisson distribution), but it does not have time to determine the production location. Intuitively, it would seem advantageous to incorporate this available information into the decision-making process. Before proceeding with the example, a general method for incorporating data will be discussed.

Let X denote the information made available by experimentation obtained from a random sample. X is then a random variable and may be viewed as a function of the sample data, e.g., X may denote a sample mean, the maximum of the sample, a vector of the sample observations, the third observation in a sample, etc. The decision-maker is to choose a decision function, or strategy, which is a function of X, and which tells him what action to take for each possible value that X may take on. Denote this function to be chosen as $d(x)$, so that if the random variable X takes on the value x, then $a = d(x)$ would be the action to be taken. The decision-maker, then, is interested in choosing an "optimal" function d from among the many possible decision functions. In order to evaluate a decision function, its consequences must be explored. Since the action taken, a, is a function of the outcome of the random variable X, the loss associated with that action also depends upon the outcome of this random variable. An appropriate measure of the consequences of taking action $a = d(x)$, when the true state of nature is θ, is then given by the expected value of the loss. This quantity will be known as the *risk function*, $R(d, \theta)$, i.e.,

$$R(d, \theta) = E[l(d, \theta)] ,$$

where the expectation is taken with respect to the probability distribution of the random variable X.

Now consider how to apply this approach to the example. Suppose the following decision rule d_1 is to be evaluated. If the number of spare engines required for the old version were greater than 23, order 25 spare engines for the new plane; otherwise order 20 spares. Thus, action a_2 is taken if X, the number of spares required on the older version, is 23 or fewer; action a_3 is taken if X exceeds 23, i.e.,

$$\begin{aligned} a_2 &= d_1(x), \qquad \text{for } x \leq 23 , \\ a_3 &= d_1(x), \qquad \text{for } x > 23 . \end{aligned}$$

Therefore,

$$\begin{aligned} R(d_1, 21) &= E[l(d_1, 21)] \\ &= (6.178 \times 10^6)\, P\{X \leq 23\} \\ &\qquad + (6.514 \times 10^6)\, P\{X > 23\} = 6.27 \times 10^6 , \end{aligned}$$

where X is a Poisson random variable with parameter 21.

$$\begin{aligned} R(d_1, 24) &= E[l(d_1, 24)] \\ &= (7.270 \times 10^6)\, P\{X \leq 23\} \\ &\qquad + (7.002 \times 10^6)\, P\{X > 23\} = 7.13 \times 10^6 , \end{aligned}$$

where X is a Poisson random variable with parameter 24. Thus, it is evident how the risk function for a given decision function is evaluated. An "optimal" decision function can be defined as one which will minimize the risk for every value of θ. It is evident that an optimal decision function (in this sense) may not always exist, and, in fact, it does not exist in most cases. Hence, another criterion for selecting optimal procedures is considered in the next section.

In some of the statistical literature, the term risk is used to denote the expected value of the regret, i.e.,

$$R(d, \theta) = E[r(d, \theta)] .$$

In many cases, the loss function is already expressed as a regret function, so the corresponding risk functions would be the same. The remainder of this chapter considers the regret function as the loss function, and, hence, the risk function denotes the expected value of the regret. Using regret in the inventory example,

$$\begin{aligned} R(d_1, 21) &= E[r(d_1, 21)] \\ &= (0)\, P\{X \leq 23\} + (.336 \times 10^6)\, P\{X > 23\} = .0954 \times 10^6\,, \end{aligned}$$

and

$$\begin{aligned} R(d_1, 24) &= E[r(d_1, 24)] \\ &= (.268 \times 10^6)\, P\{X \leq 23\} + (0)\, P\{X > 23\} = .127 \times 10^6\,. \end{aligned}$$

4.3.1 **Bayes Procedures**

Even when data are available, there is no best approach for selecting "*optimal* procedures." With data, it is still possible to use a minimax criterion, or a minimax decision function, but it, too, suffers from the same disadvantages as when no data are available, i.e., it assumes that nature will act as a conscious opponent and confront the decision-maker with the least favorable distribution of θ.

If the decision-maker has some advance information about the states of nature which can be described in terms of a prior distribution, then the Bayes principle can be applied to the risk function. If the states of nature are discrete, the Bayes risk corresponding to a prior probability distribution of θ, $P_\theta(k)$, is given by

$$B(d) = \sum_{\text{all } k} R(d, k) P_\theta(k)\,.$$[12]

If the states of nature are continuous, the Bayes risk corresponding to a prior probability density function of θ, $P_\theta(y)$, is given by

$$B(d) = \int_{-\infty}^{\infty} R(d, y) P_\theta(y)\, dy\,.$$[13]

The *Bayes principle* tells the decision-maker to select that function d (called the *Bayes decision procedure*) which minimizes $B(d)$. A method for finding Bayes decision procedures is presented below.

When no data were available, the Bayes procedure selected that action which minimized the expected loss; this expectation was evaluated with respect to the prior distribution of θ. Now that data are available, additional

[12] Observe that the notation established in Chapter 3 is being used to represent the possible values that θ can take on.

[13] Observe that the notation established in Chapter 3 is being used. The variable of integration, y, represents the possible values that θ can take on.

information is available about the state of nature. For example, in the inventory example, if the earlier version required 30 spare engines, this is "evidence" about whether the engines were produced in plant A or plant B (whether λ is 21 or 24). After observing these data, the prior distribution should be updated using more timely information about the probability distribution of the state of nature. Such updated information is called the *posterior distribution* of θ, given the prior distribution and the data $X = x$. The posterior distribution of θ is just the conditional distribution of θ, given $X = x$. If θ is discrete, the posterior distribution will be denoted by $h_{\theta|X=x}(k)$, and if θ is continuous, the posterior distribution will be denoted by $h_{\theta|X=x}(y)$. The method for calculating the posterior distribution is given later. However, if the method used for calculating the Bayes procedure when no data are available is followed (selecting that action which minimizes the *expected loss*), with this expectation now evaluated with respect to the *posterior distribution* of θ, given $X = x$, this decision procedure minimizes $B(d)$. Hence, it is the Bayes procedure. This is not an obvious statement, but it can easily be proved. Thus, in order to find the Bayes procedure, the decision-maker computes the posterior distribution of θ, given $X = x$. He then chooses that action which minimizes the expected loss (note that loss is used rather than risk), with this expectation evaluated with respect to the *posterior* distribution of θ, given $X = x$.

In Secs. 3.10 and 3.11, bivariate probability distributions and marginal and conditional probability distributions were introduced. In the context of the present section, (θ, X) is a bivariate random variable having a joint probability distribution. Consider the case where (θ, X) is a discrete bivariate random variable with joint probability distribution given by $P_{\theta X}(k, j)$. The random variables θ and X each have marginal distributions. In fact, $P_\theta(k)$, the prior distribution of θ, is the marginal distribution of θ. The usual expression given as the probability distribution of the random variable X actually corresponds to the conditional probability distribution of X, given θ. For example, if X has a Poisson distribution with parameter $\lambda = 24$, then $e^{-24}24^j/j!$ is just the conditional probability distribution function of X, given $\lambda = 24$. To indicate that this is a "conditional distribution" the notation

$$Q_{X|\theta=k}(j) = P\{X = j|\theta = k\}$$

is introduced. Thus,

$$Q_{X|\theta=24}(j) = P\{X = j|\theta = 24\} = \frac{e^{-24}24^j}{j!}$$

represents the conditional probability distribution of X, given that $\theta = 24$, and has the form of a Poisson distribution with parameter $\lambda = 24$.

If the joint distribution of (θ, X) is of interest, the expression

$$P_{\theta X}(k, j) = Q_{X|\theta=k}(j)P_\theta(k)$$

can be used to evaluate it. $Q_X(j)$, the marginal distribution of X, can also be obtained, i.e.,

$$Q_X(j) = \sum_{\text{all } k} P_{\theta X}(k, j) = \sum_{\text{all } k} Q_{X|\theta=k}(j) P_\theta(k) .$$

Finally, the only remaining probability distribution that has not been discussed is the conditional distribution of θ, given $X = x$, i.e., the posterior distribution of θ, given $X = x$, $h_{\theta|X=x}(k)$. An alternative expression for the joint probability distribution of (θ, X) is given by

$$P_{\theta X}(k, j) = h_{\theta|X=x}(k) Q_X(j) .$$

Equating the two expressions for $P_{\theta X}(k, j)$ leads to the important result from which the posterior distribution can be calculated, i.e.,

$$h_{\theta|X=x}(k) = \frac{Q_{X|\theta=k}(j) P_\theta(k)}{Q_X(j)} .$$

Thus, in summary, the posterior distribution can be calculated using the above expression. $P_\theta(k)$ is the prior distribution. $Q_{X|\theta=k}(j)$ is the ordinary expression for the probability distribution of the random variable X, but it is written in this form to show the dependence on the value of the parameter θ. The function $Q_X(j)$ is the marginal distribution of the random variable X and is obtained from

$$Q_X(j) = \sum_{\text{all } k} Q_{X|\theta=k}(j) P_\theta(k) .$$

Returning to the inventory example, suppose that 30 spare engines were required for the earlier version of the airplane. Recall that the prior distribution of θ is assumed to be

$$P\{\theta = 21\} = P_\theta(21) = \tfrac{2}{3} ,$$
$$P\{\theta = 24\} = P_\theta(24) = \tfrac{1}{3} .$$

It is necessary to evaluate the expressions $h_{\theta|X=30}(21)$ and $h_{\theta|X=30}(24)$, where

$$h_{\theta|X=30}(21) = \frac{Q_{X|\theta=21}(30) P_\theta(21)}{Q_X(30)}$$

and

$$h_{\theta|X=30}(24) = \frac{Q_{X|\theta=24}(30) P_\theta(24)}{Q_X(30)} .$$

In this case,

$$Q_{X|\theta=21}(30) = P\{X = 30|\theta = 21\}$$

and

$$Q_{X|\theta=24}(30) = P\{X = 30|\theta = 24\}$$

are just the probabilities that a Poisson random variable takes on the value 30 when the parameter is 21 and 24, respectively. These probabilities are easily obtained from the tables of the Poisson distribution given in Table A5.4 of Appendix 5 by using the relation

$$P\{X = 30\} = \sum_{k=0}^{30} P_X(k) - \sum_{k=0}^{29} P_X(k) .$$

Hence,

$$Q_{X|\theta=21}(30) = .013$$

and

$$Q_{X|\theta=24}(30) = .036 .$$

Thus,

$$Q_X(30) = Q_{X|\theta=21}(30)P_\theta(21) + Q_{X|\theta=24}(30)P_\theta(24) = (.013)(\tfrac{2}{3}) + (.036)(\tfrac{1}{3}) = .02067$$

so that

$$h_{\theta|X=30}(21) = \frac{(.013)(2/3)}{.02067} = .420 ,$$

$$h_{\theta|X=30}(24) = \frac{(.036)(1/3)}{.02067} = .580 .$$

It is now seen that, as a result of observing some data (a previous demand for 30 spare engines), the prior probability that plant A ($\theta = 21$) was used to produce the spare engines has decreased from $\frac{2}{3}$ to the posterior probability of .420. Similarly, the prior probability that plant B ($\theta = 24$) was used to produce the spare engines has increased from $\frac{1}{3}$ to the posterior probability of .580. To obtain the Bayes procedure the expected loss is computed with respect to the posterior distribution of θ for each of the actions as follows.

$$\begin{aligned} E[l(a_1)] &= (.6485 \times 10^6)(.42) + (1.263 \times 10^6)(.58) = 1.005 \times 10^6 , \\ E[l(a_2)] &= (0)(.42) + (.268 \times 10^6)(.58) = .155 \times 10^6 , \\ E[l(a_3)] &= (.336 \times 10^6)(.42) + (0)(.58) = .141 \times 10^6 . \end{aligned}$$

The Bayes procedure selects action a_3 (since this minimizes the expected loss) which implies that 25 spares would be ordered. Thus, it is seen that the experimental data changes the action of the decision-maker. Without data, the Bayes procedure was to order 20 spares, whereas the information obtained from the data leads the decision-maker to order 25 spare engines. As noted before, this Bayes procedure would have been the same had "loss" been used instead of "regret."

This method of computing Bayes procedures has the important advantage that it is only necessary to compute $d(x)$ for the single point corresponding to the outcome of the experiment. Using the basic formula for $B(d)$ to find the Bayes procedure requires the determination of the entire function $d(x)$, which is generally more difficult.

The expression for the posterior distribution has been given where θ and X are both discrete random variables. If θ is discrete and X is continuous, the posterior distribution, $h_{\theta|X=x}(x)$, is given by

$$h_{\theta|X=x}(k) = \frac{f_{X|\theta=k}(x)P_\theta(k)}{f_X(x)},$$

where $P_\theta(k)$ is the prior distribution of θ, and $f_{X|\theta=k}(x)$ is the ordinary expression for the density function of the random variable X, but it is written in this form to show the dependence on the value of the parameter θ. The function $f_X(x)$ is the marginal density of the random variable X and is obtained from

$$f_X(x) = \sum_{\text{all } k} f_{X|\theta=k}(x)P_\theta(k).$$

If both θ and X are continuous, the posterior distribution, $h_{\theta|X=x}(y)$, is given by

$$h_{\theta|X=x}(y) = \frac{f_{X|\theta=y}(x)P_\theta(y)}{f_X(x)},$$

where $P_\theta(y)$ is the prior density function of θ. The function $f_{X|\theta=y}(x)$ has been defined previously. $f_X(x)$ is the marginal density of the random variable X and is obtained from

$$f_X(x) = \int_{-\infty}^{\infty} f_{X|\theta=y}(x)P_\theta(y)dy.$$

Finally, if θ is continuous and X is discrete, the posterior distribution, $h_{\theta|X=x}(y)$, is given by

$$h_{\theta|X=x}(y) = \frac{Q_{X|\theta=y}(j)P_\theta(y)}{Q_X(j)},$$

where $P_\theta(y)$ is the prior density function of θ. The function $Q_{X|\theta=y}(j)$ is the ordinary expression for the probability distribution of the random variable X, i.e., $P\{X = j|\theta = y\}$, but it is written in this form to show the dependence on the value of the parameter θ. $Q_X(j)$ is the marginal distribution of the random variable X and is obtained from

$$Q_X(j) = \int_{-\infty}^{\infty} Q_{X|\theta=y}(j)P_\theta(y)dy.$$

4.4 TESTS OF HYPOTHESIS

The previous sections formulated a decision theory framework for making decisions, using a minimax or Bayes criterion for choosing decision rules. This section is concerned with exploring other criteria for decision-making when there are only two actions, a_1 and a_2, open to the decision-maker, and decisions are to be based upon the outcome of a random sample. The decisions will still be related to making statements about the states of nature. The objective will be to partition Θ, the set of all possible values of the states of nature, into two mutually exclusive sets, Ω_1 and Ω_2, having the following property. If θ is in Ω_1, the action a_1 is the preferred action, whereas, if θ is in Ω_2, the action a_2 is the preferred action. The loss incurred when action a is taken and the state of nature is θ is denoted by $l(a, \theta)$, and it is assumed that

$$\begin{aligned} l(a_1, \theta) &= 0, \qquad \text{if } \theta \text{ is in } \Omega_1, \\ l(a_2, \theta) &= 0, \qquad \text{if } \theta \text{ is in } \Omega_2, \end{aligned}$$

i.e., the loss function is a regret function. A decision function, d, is a function which assigns either action a_1 or a_2 for each possible sample vector $(x_1, x_2, \cdots, x_n)$.

Since this type of problem has been studied extensively in the statistical literature, its own terminology has evolved. Statements that θ is contained in a subset of Θ are said to be hypotheses about nature. When the subset consists of a single point, an assertion about the state is called a *simple hypothesis*. A statement about a subset containing more than one simple hypothesis is called a *composite hypothesis*.

A composite hypothesis is said to be true if one of the simple hypotheses that constitute the composite hypothesis is the true state of nature. The set Ω_1 is associated with the hypothesis H_1: θ is in Ω_1. The set Ω_2 is associated with the alternative hypothesis H_2: θ is in Ω_2. The action a_1 is called accepting the hypothesis H_1, and the action a_2 is called rejecting the hypothesis H_1 (which implies accepting the alternative hypothesis H_2). The decision function d leads to accepting or rejecting the hypothesis H_1 and is called a test of the hypothesis. Actually, the decision function partitions the sample space into two disjoint parts, those points which lead to accepting H_1, and those points which lead to rejecting H_1 (and consequently accepting H_2). The set of points in the sample space which leads to rejection of H_1 is called a "critical region" of the test. Thus, if a sample point falls into the critical region, action a_2 is taken and the hypothesis, H_1: θ is in Ω_1, is rejected. If the sample point falls outside the critical region, action a_1 is taken and the hypothesis, H_1: θ is in Ω_1, is accepted. Therefore, choosing a critical region is equivalent to choosing a decision function or test, and conversely.

It is often possible to show that "optimal" tests depend on the sample only through a function T of the random sample. Such a function of the random sample is called a test statistic. The decision function is then of the form $d(T)$. Again, the decision function partitions the range of values of T into two disjoint parts, those points which lead to accepting H_1, and those points which lead to rejecting H_1. Those points which lead to rejecting H_1 are again called the critical region of the test. Henceforth, the critical region of a test will be labeled C, and will denote the set of sample points, or the set of values of the test statistic T, which lead to rejection of H_1.

4.4.1 **Type I and Type II Errors**

As noted previously, there is no loss incurred when action a_1 is taken and θ is in Ω_1, or when action a_2 is taken and θ is in Ω_2. This is then equivalent to incurring no loss when the hypothesis H_1 is accepted when the true state of nature is in Ω_1, or when the hypothesis H_1 is rejected when the true state of nature is in Ω_2. When the hypothesis H_1 is rejected (action a_2 is taken) and the true state of nature is in Ω_1, the loss $l(a, \theta)$ will be denoted by $\epsilon_1(\theta)$, and it is called the *type I error*. When the hypothesis H_1 is accepted (action a_1 is taken) and the true state of nature is in Ω_2, the loss $l(a, \theta)$ will be denoted by $\epsilon_2(\theta)$, and it is called the *type II error*. Thus, the loss function can be written as

$$l(a_1, \theta) = \begin{cases} 0, & \text{if } \theta \text{ is in } \Omega_1 \\ \epsilon_2(\theta), & \text{if } \theta \text{ is in } \Omega_2 \end{cases}$$

and

$$l(a_2, \theta) = \begin{cases} \epsilon_1(\theta), & \text{if } \theta \text{ is in } \Omega_1 \\ 0, & \text{if } \theta \text{ is in } \Omega_2\,. \end{cases}$$

For a given decision rule, or critical region C, the risk function $R(C, \theta)$ can be evaluated as follows.

$$R(C, \theta) = \begin{cases} \epsilon_1(\theta)P(C|\theta), & \text{if } \theta \text{ is in } \Omega_1 \\ \epsilon_2(\theta)P(\bar{C}|\theta), & \text{if } \theta \text{ is in } \Omega_2\,, \end{cases}$$

where $P(C|\theta)$ is the probability that the sample point or the test statistic, whichever is appropriate, falls into the critical region C when θ is in Ω_1, and $P(\bar{C}|\theta)$ is the probability that the sample point or the test statistic, whichever is appropriate, falls outside the critical region C when θ is in Ω_2.

A good decision rule is sought which will minimize the risk for every value of θ in Θ. As noted earlier, this is not generally possible, so that additional criteria or measures must be introduced. Other problems may also arise in using the risk as the appropriate measure. In many of the problems that the decision-maker faces in the context of testing hypotheses, the loss function is not known (or not known with sufficient accuracy) to merit its use. In this case, a reasonable decision rule will be one which, in some sense, minimizes $P(C|\theta)$ and $P(\bar{C}|\theta)$. The usual method is to choose a value α, and then find the decision procedure (if one exists) which minimizes $P(\bar{C}|\theta)$ for all θ in Ω_2 subject to $P(C|\theta) \leq \alpha$. Note that $P(C|\theta)$ is just the probability of rejecting the hypothesis when it is in fact true and is called the probability of the type I error. This probability is also known as the *level of significance* and is often denoted by α. $P(\bar{C}|\theta)$ is the probability of accepting the hypothesis when it is in fact false and is called the probability of the type II error. It is often denoted by β [or $\beta(\theta)$].

As an example of the material presented on tests of hypotheses, return to the inventory problem. The hypothesis to be tested is H_1: the true state of nature is $\theta = 21$, and the alternative to the hypothesis is H_2: the true state of nature is $\theta = 24$.[14] Thus, Ω_1 consists of the single point, $\theta = 21$, and Ω_2 consists of the single point, $\theta = 24$. As was pointed out earlier, the action a_1 (order 15 spares) can be neglected. Hence, there are only two remaining actions, a_2 and a_3, i.e., order 20 and 25 spares, respectively. Relabel a_2 by a_1' and a_3 by a_2'. Then a_1' denotes the action that accepts H_1, the hypothesis that $\theta = 21$, which implies the ordering of 20 spare engines; a_2' denotes the action which accepts H_2, the alternative to the hypothesis, which implies the ordering of 25 spare engines. The losses are given in Table 4.3.

TABLE 4.3. Loss Table for a Test of Hypothesis for the Inventory Problem

Action \ State of nature	H_1 true $\theta = 21$	H_2 true $\theta = 24$
a_1': accept H_1	0	$.268 \times 10^6$
a_2': reject H_1 (accept H_2)	$.336 \times 10^6$	0

Thus,

$$\epsilon_2(\theta) = .268 \times 10^6 ,$$

and

$$\epsilon_1(\theta) = .336 \times 10^6 .$$

Suppose that the data on the previous model airplane are available, and the decision-maker uses the decision rule to accept the hypothesis if the number of spare engines demanded does not exceed 23. The critical region C is given by the set of points $\{24, 25, 26, \cdots\}$. Hence,

[14] The hypothesis and alternative can be interchanged without changing the problem.

$$P(C|\theta = 21) = \sum_{k=24}^{\infty} P_X(k) ,$$

where X is a Poisson random variable with parameter $\theta = \lambda = 21$. From A5.4 of Appendix 5, $P(C|\theta = 21)$ is seen to equal .284.

$$P(\bar{C}|\theta = 24) = \sum_{k=0}^{23} P_X(k) ,$$

where again X is a Poisson random variable, now with parameter $\theta = \lambda = 24$. Thus, $P(\bar{C}|\theta = 24) = .473$.

The risk is given by

$$R(C, \theta) = \begin{cases} (.336 \times 10^6)(.284) = .0954 \times 10^6 , & \text{if } \theta = 21 \\ (.268 \times 10^6)(.473) = .127 \times 10^6 , & \text{if } \theta = 24 . \end{cases}$$

It can now be concluded that, if the loss function is not known, and this decision procedure is used, the probability of type I error is $\alpha = .284$, and the probability of type II error is $\beta = .473$. If this type I error is satisfactory, the optimal decision procedure would be that rule which had a value of α of .284 or less, and which minimized β. It can be shown that the decision rule presented is this optimal decision function.

By choosing a critical region which minimizes $P(\bar{C}|\theta)$ for all θ in Ω_2 subject to $P(C|\theta) \leq \alpha$ as a criterion for optimality, optimal decision rules can often be derived. Once the form of these rules is known, the probability of accepting the hypothesis H_1 can be plotted against the true state of nature. Such a plot is known as an *Operating Characteristic* (O. C.) curve. This O. C. curve is a function of the sample size as well as the decision functions. The decision-maker usually chooses an O. C. curve which reflects his attitudes toward the allowable probability of type I and type II errors, and and then he chooses his sample size to guarantee that his errors will not exceed these allowances.

4.5 POINT ESTIMATION

In many decision-making problems, the decision-maker is willing to assume that the observations obtained come from a family of distributions completely specified except for the parameters. For example, the decision-maker may be willing to assume that the time between arrivals of customers to a store follows an exponential distribution. This implies that the density function of the random variable, time, is given by

$$f_X(y) = \begin{cases} \dfrac{1}{\theta} e^{-y/\theta}, & \text{if } y \geq 0 \\ 0, & \text{if } y < 0 , \end{cases}$$

where θ is the unknown parameter of this distribution. The general problem to be considered here is how a decision-maker should estimate such a parameter θ on the basis of observing a random sample, $X_1, X_2, \cdots, X_n$. The decision function he chooses associates with each sample point an action, the action being an estimate, $\hat{\theta}$, of the parameter θ. Thus,

$$\hat{\theta} = d(x_1, x_2, \cdots, x_n)$$

and is called an *estimator* of θ. The function $\hat{\theta}$ is an estimator, and the value the function takes on (after the experiment) is called an *estimate* of θ. A reasonable loss function used in problems concerned with point estimation is given by

$$l(\hat{\theta}, \theta) = K(\theta)(\hat{\theta} - \theta)^2 ,$$

where $K(\theta) > 0$ for all values of $\hat{\theta}$. This quadratic loss function has the desirable property that the loss increases quite rapidly as $|\hat{\theta} - \theta|$ increases. Furthermore, many smooth functions which are 0 at $\hat{\theta} = \theta$ can be reasonably approximated by this quadratic function for $\hat{\theta}$ near θ. A possible disadvantage of using such a loss function is the determination of $K(\theta)$. Many real world problems are solved by assuming that $K(\theta) = 1$, in which case the quadratic loss function is called the squared error loss function. Note that the loss and regret are the same when the quadratic loss function is used.

In order to compare estimators, it is necessary to compute their risks. If $\hat{\theta}_1 = d(x_1, x_2, \cdots, x_n)$ is an estimator, the risk is given by

$$R(d, \theta) = E[l(\hat{\theta}, \theta)] .$$

A convenient way of comparing two estimators, $\hat{\theta}_1$ and $\hat{\theta}_2$, is to examine the ratio of their risks,

$$R(d_1, \theta)/R(d_2, \theta) ,$$

for the various values of θ. This ratio is known as the *relative efficiency* of $\hat{\theta}_1$ with respect to $\hat{\theta}_2$. Thus, if squared error is used (as assumed in the remaining sections of this chapter), the relative efficiency is given by

$$R(d_1, \theta)/R(d_2, \theta) = E(\hat{\theta}_1 - \theta)^2/E(\hat{\theta}_2 - \theta)^2 ,$$

where $E[\hat{\theta}_i - \theta]^2$ is called the mean square error for the estimator $\hat{\theta}_i$. If the relative efficiency is greater than 1 for all θ, it is said that $\hat{\theta}_2$ is a "better" estimator than $\hat{\theta}_1$. Similarly, if the relative efficiency is smaller than 1 for all θ, then $\hat{\theta}_1$ is a better estimator than $\hat{\theta}_2$. If an estimator, $\hat{\theta}_0$, exists that has risk no greater than that associated with any other estimator for every value of θ, then $\hat{\theta}_0$ is said to be an optimal estimator. Unfortunately, optimal estimators do not exist for many problems.

Continuing with the example of the exponential density function for the time between arrivals, suppose that a random sample is taken. Let $\hat{\theta} = \bar{X}$ be the estimator of θ. The mean square error is given by

$$R(\hat{\theta}, \theta) = E[\bar{X} - \theta]^2 .$$

Before evaluating this expression, it is worthwhile determining $E(X)$. This expectation is given by

$$E(X) = \int_0^\infty y \frac{1}{\theta} e^{-y/\theta} \, dy = \theta .$$

Hence, $E(\bar{X})$ also equals θ, so that the mean square error coincides with the variance of $\bar{X}$. Furthermore, the variance of $\bar{X}$ is just the variance of X divided by the sample size. It then follows that

$$R(\hat{\theta}, \theta) = \text{variance } (X)/n .$$

The variance of X is easily evaluated to be θ^2 so that

$$R(\hat{\theta}, \theta) = \theta^2/n .$$

4.5.1 Unbiased Estimators

In addition to looking at the risk of an estimator, a decision-maker seeks other properties that may be desirable. One such property is unbiasedness. An estimator $\hat{\theta}$ is said to be unbiased if

$$E(\hat{\theta}) = \theta \qquad \text{for all } \theta .$$

If an estimator is unbiased, the mean square error is equivalent to the variance so that

$$R(\hat{\theta}, \theta) = \text{variance } (\hat{\theta}) .$$

If $\hat{\theta}$ is not unbiased, the difference between $E(\hat{\theta})$ and θ is called the bias, i.e.,

$$\text{bias} = E(\hat{\theta}) - \theta .$$

Such an estimator is called a biased estimator. In the above example involving the time between customer arrivals, $\bar{X}$ is an unbiased estimator of θ. Furthermore, the risk, θ^2/n, is the variance of $\bar{X}$. There are many unbiased estimators, e.g., the first observation X_1 is one. Note that $\bar{X}$ is a better estimator than X_1 for all n in the sense of relative efficiency in that

$$\frac{R(\bar{X}, \theta)}{R(X_1, \theta)} = \frac{\theta^2/n}{\theta^2} = \frac{1}{n}$$

is always less than 1.

Although an unbiased estimator is intuitively appealing, it should be noted that a biased estimator can sometimes be better in the sense of having a lower mean square error.

4.5.2 Consistent Estimators

Intuitively, another desirable property for estimators to possess is that the risk becomes small as the sample size increases or, equivalently, as the sample size n gets large, $\hat{\theta}_n$ (the estimator based upon a sample of size n) should tend to θ. A precise statement is as follows: let $\hat{\theta}_1, \hat{\theta}_2, \cdots, \hat{\theta}_n, \cdots$ be a sequence of estimators of θ. This sequence of estimators is said to be consistent if for every $\epsilon > 0$

$$\lim_{n \to \infty} P\{\theta - \epsilon < \hat{\theta}_n < \theta + \epsilon\} = 1$$

for each value of θ. In the current example, it is easily shown that $\bar{X}$ is a consistent estimator of θ.

4.5.3 Efficient Unbiased Estimators

A useful lower bound on the variance of an unbiased estimator of a parameter θ is known as the Cramer–Rao inequality. Let $\hat{\theta}$ be an unbiased estimator based upon a random sample of size n. The Cramer–Rao inequality states (assuming some regularity conditions hold) that

$$\text{variance }(\hat{\theta}) \geq \frac{1}{nE\left\{\left[\frac{\partial}{\partial\theta} \log f_X(X, \theta)\right]^2\right\}},$$

where $f_X(X, \theta)$ is the density function (probability distribution if X is discrete) of the random variable X. Thus, if an unbiased estimator can be found which achieves this lower bound, it must be the "optimal" estimator among the class of all unbiased estimators.

To illustrate, consider again the exponential distribution so that

$$\log f_X(X, \theta) = \log\left[\frac{1}{\theta} e^{-X/\theta}\right] = -\log \theta - X/\theta .$$

Furthermore,

$$\frac{\partial}{\partial\theta}[-\log \theta - X/\theta] = -\frac{1}{\theta} + \frac{X}{\theta^2},$$

and its square is given by

$$\frac{1}{\theta^2} - \frac{2X}{\theta^3} + \frac{X^2}{\theta^4}.$$

Hence,

$$E\left\{\left[\frac{\partial}{\partial\theta} \log f_X(X, \theta)\right]^2\right\} = \frac{1}{\theta^2} - \frac{2E(X)}{\theta^3} + \frac{E(X^2)}{\theta^4} = \frac{1}{\theta^2}$$

so that

$$\text{variance }(\hat{\theta}) \geq \theta^2/n .$$

Since it has been shown that the variance of $\bar{X}$ equals θ^2/n, it follows that $\bar{X}$ must be the "optimal" estimator among the class of all unbiased estimators.

However, it often happens that an unbiased estimator cannot be exhibited which achieves the Cramer–Rao lower bound.

4.5.4 Estimators Determined by the Method of Moments

In the previous sections, properties of estimators were discussed, but methods for obtaining estimators were not presented. The oldest, and perhaps simplest method is the *method of moments*. Suppose that there are k parameters to be estimated for a density function, $f_X(y, \theta_1, \theta_2, \cdots, \theta_k)$. Let $\mu_1', \mu_2', \cdots, \mu_k'$ denote the first, second, $\cdots$, kth moment about the origin of the random variable X, respectively, i.e.,

$$\mu_i' = \int_{-\infty}^{\infty} y^i f_X(y, \theta_1, \theta_2, \cdots, \theta_k) dy .$$

These moments will, in general, be a function of the k parameters, $\theta_1, \theta_2, \cdots, \theta_k$. Let $X_1, X_2, \cdots, X_n$ be a random sample of size n. Denote by m_1', $m_2', \cdots, m_k'$ the first, second, $\cdots$, kth sample moment, i.e.,

$$m_i' = \sum_{j=1}^{n} X_j^i/n .$$

Let $\hat{\theta}_1, \hat{\theta}_2, \cdots, \hat{\theta}_k$ be the solution to the following k simultaneous equations in k unknowns,

$$\mu_i' = m_i', \qquad \text{for } i = 1, 2, \cdots, k .$$

These solutions represent the method of moments estimators. For the exponential distribution, there is only one parameter θ and $\mu_1' = \theta$. Furthermore, $m_1' = \bar{X}$ so that $\bar{X}$ is the method of moments estimator of θ.

A more complicated example concerns the normal distribution. The two parameters are μ and σ^2, the mean and variance, respectively. Furthermore,

$$\begin{aligned} \mu_1' &= \mu , \\ \mu_2' &= \sigma^2 + \mu^2 . \end{aligned}$$

Also,

$$\begin{aligned} m_1' &= \bar{X} , \\ m_2' &= \Sigma X_i^2/n . \end{aligned}$$

Hence, the two equations are

$$\begin{aligned} \bar{X} &= \mu , \\ \Sigma X_i^2/n &= \sigma^2 + \mu^2 . \end{aligned}$$

Solving these equations simultaneously leads to

$$\hat{\theta}_1 = \bar{X} ,$$
$$\hat{\theta}_2 = \Sigma X_i^2/n - \bar{X}^2 .$$

Under quite general conditions, the method of moments can be shown to lead to estimates which are consistent. Furthermore, their distributions tend to be normal as the sample size gets large.

4.5.5 Estimators Determined by the Method of Maximum Likelihood

The reliability at time t of a piece of complex electronic equipment is defined as the probability that it will perform successfully until at least time t. Suppose that 20 pieces are tested, and all that is measured is whether or not the equipment failed before time t. If the equipment performs successfully, record a 1. If it fails, record a zero. This can be represented in terms of a mathematical model as drawing a random sample of size 20 from a Bernoulli distribution with parameter p (Sec. 3.6.1), i.e., $X_1, X_2, \cdots, X_{20}$ are random variables with

$$\left.\begin{aligned} P\{X_i = 1\} &= P_{X_i}(1) = p \\ P\{X_i = 0\} &= P_{X_i}(0) = 1 - p \end{aligned}\right\} \text{for } i = 1, 2, \cdots, 20 .$$

An equivalent way of describing this probability distribution is given by the expression

$$P\{X_i = x_i\} = p^{x_i} (1 - p)^{1-x_i} , \qquad x_i = 0, 1, \qquad \text{and } i = 1, 2, \cdots, 20 .$$

The reliability at time t is then

$$P_X(1) = p .$$

In general, let $X_1, X_2, \cdots, X_n$ be a random sample from a discrete probability distribution $P_X(k)$. Define the *likelihood function*, L, by

$$L = P\{X_1 = x_1\}P\{X_2 = x_2\} \cdots P\{X_n = x_n\} ,$$

where x_i represents the actual outcome of the random variable X_i. Therefore, L is just the probability of obtaining the observed sample and is a function of the parameters of the probability distribution. Thus, for the reliability example,

$$\begin{aligned} L &= [p^{x_1} (1 - p)^{1-x_1}][p^{x_2} (1 - p)^{1-x_2}] \cdots [p^{x_n} (1 - p)^{1-x_n}] \\ &= p^{\Sigma x_i} (1 - p)^{n-\Sigma x_i} . \end{aligned}$$

The principle of maximum likelihood says to find that value of the parameter θ which maximizes the likelihood function, and call this value the maximum likelihood estimate of θ. Thus, the likelihood function can be viewed as only a function of the parameter θ (the x_i are now fixed constants), and the value of θ is sought which maximizes the probability of obtaining this particular sample.

Often it is easier to maximize the logarithm of the likelihood function rather than the likelihood function itself. This is permissible since the logarithm is a monotonic function, so these two maxima will occur at the same place. The logarithm of the likelihood function will be denoted by $\mathfrak{L}$. Thus, in the reliability example,

$$\mathfrak{L} = \Sigma x_i \log p + (n - \Sigma x_i) \log (1 - p) .$$

To maximize this function, it is necessary to solve the following equation for p:

$$\frac{d\mathfrak{L}}{dp} = \frac{\Sigma x_i}{p} - \frac{(n - \Sigma x_i)}{(1 - p)} = 0 .$$

The solution is $\hat{p} = \Sigma x_i/n = \bar{x}$. Hence, the maximum likelihood estimator is the total number of pieces of equipment which do not fail before time t divided by the number tested.

In general then, to find maximum likelihood estimators, it is necessary to find that value of θ which satisfies the equation

$$\frac{dL}{d\theta} = 0$$

or, equivalently,

$$\frac{d\mathfrak{L}}{d\theta} = 0 .$$

Of course, it is necessary to show that this leads to a maximum and not a minimum or point of inflection (see Appendix 2).

For the case of a continuous random variable, maximizing the probability of obtaining the observed sample leads to difficulties since such a probability is zero. However, if the "probability of obtaining the observed sample" is interpreted as the probability of each random variable falling into its interval $(x_i, x_i + dx_i)$, with the length of the interval suppressed, then the interpretation given previously is applicable. Hence the likelihood function, L, is defined as

$$L = f_{X_1}(x_1, \theta) f_{X_2}(x_2, \theta) \cdots f_{X_n}(x_n, \theta) ,$$

where $f_{X_i}(x_i, \theta)$ is the value of the density function of the random variable X_i at the sample point x_i, given that the value of the parameter is θ. The principle of maximum likelihood says to find that value of the parameter θ which maximizes the likelihood function. Call this value the maximum likelihood estimate of θ. Returning to the exponential distribution,

$$L = \frac{1}{\theta} e^{-x_1/\theta} \frac{1}{\theta} e^{-x_2/\theta} \cdots \frac{1}{\theta} e^{-x_n/\theta}$$
$$= \frac{1}{\theta^n} e^{-\Sigma x_i/\theta} .$$

Again, it is easier to work with $\mathcal{L} = \log L$. Hence,

$$\mathcal{L} = -n \log \theta - \Sigma x_i/\theta .$$

In order to find the value of θ which maximizes $\mathcal{L}$, it is necessary to solve the equation

$$\frac{dL}{d\theta} = -\frac{n}{\theta} + \frac{\Sigma x_i}{\theta^2} = 0 .$$

$\hat{\theta} = \Sigma x_i/n$ is the value of θ which maximizes $\mathcal{L}$, and hence is the maximum likelihood *estimate* of θ. The maximum likelihood *estimator* is then

$$\hat{\theta} = \Sigma X_i/n ,$$

which coincides with the method of moments estimator.

If the likelihood function contains k parameters, i.e.,

$$L = f_{X_1}(x_1, \theta_1, \theta_2, \cdots, \theta_k) f_{X_2}(x_2, \theta_1, \theta_2, \cdots, \theta_k) \cdots f_{X_n}(x_n, \theta_1, \theta_2, \cdots, \theta_k) ,$$

then the maximum likelihood estimators of $\theta_1, \theta_2, \cdots, \theta_k$ are the values $\hat{\theta}_1, \hat{\theta}_2, \cdots, \hat{\theta}_k$ which maximize L. These are often obtained as the simultaneous solution to the equations

$$\frac{\partial L}{\partial \theta_1} = \frac{\partial L}{\partial \theta_2} = \cdots = \frac{\partial L}{\partial \theta_k} = 0 .$$

(See Appendix 2 on maximizing functions of several variables.)

Maximum likelihood estimators are the most commonly used estimators in practice. They are often easy to obtain, and have many other desirable properties (in addition to maximizing the likelihood function). In particular, maximum likelihood estimators, though often biased, are consistent. They are also asymptotically efficient in that $\sqrt{n}\hat{\theta}$ has a variance which achieves the Cramer–Rao lower bound, i.e.,

$$\text{variance}\,(\sqrt{n}\hat{\theta}) \to \frac{1}{E\left\{\left[\frac{\partial}{\partial \theta} \log f_X(X, \theta)\right]^2\right\}} ,$$

as n gets large. Furthermore, the random variable $\sqrt{n}(\hat{\theta} - \theta)$ approaches the normal distribution with zero mean and the variance given above. Finally, maximum likelihood estimators possess the property of invariance. That is, if $\hat{\theta}$ is the maximum likelihood estimator of θ, and $h(\theta)$ is a function of θ, with a single inverse, then the maximum likelihood estimator of $h(\theta)$ is $h(\hat{\theta})$.

4.5.6 **Bayes Estimators**

In Sec. 4.3.1, Bayes procedures were discussed. In particular, if the decision-maker has some advance information about the states of nature, say, described in terms of a prior distribution, the Bayes principle can be applied to the risk function. If the states of nature are continuous, the Bayes risk corresponding to probability density function $p_\theta(y)$ of θ is given by

$$B(d) = \int_{-\infty}^{\infty} R(d, y)p_\theta(y)dy .$$

The Bayes principle tells the decision-maker to select that function d, the Bayes decision procedure, which minimizes $B(d)$. It was also pointed out that if the action taken minimizes the expected loss (evaluated with respect to the *posterior* distribution of θ), then this decision procedure minimizes $B(d)$, and hence is the Bayes procedure. The expression for the posterior density of θ, $h_{\theta|X=x}(y)$ is also given in Sec. 4.3.1.

Given a mean square error loss function, i.e., $(\hat{\theta} - \theta)^2$, the posterior expected loss is $E[\hat{\theta} - \theta]^2$, where the expectation is taken with respect to the posterior distribution of θ. However, $E[\hat{\theta} - \theta]^2 = E[\theta - \hat{\theta}]^2$ is the second moment of the "random variable" θ and is known to be a minimum if it is taken about $E(\theta)$. Hence, the expected value of θ (evaluated with respect to the posterior distribution of θ) is, therefore, the Bayes action, i.e.,

$$\hat{\theta} = E(\theta) = \int_{-\infty}^{\infty} y h_{\theta|X=x}(y)dy .$$

As an example, return to the reliability problem. Assume that there exists a prior distribution of p which is uniform over the interval [0, 1]. The posterior distribution of p, given k success, can be computed from the results in Sec. 4.3.1, which yields

$$h_{p|X=k}(y) = \binom{n}{k}(n + 1)y^k(1 - y)^{n-k} .$$

Therefore, when $n = 20$, the Bayes action (Bayes estimator of p) is given by

$$E(p) = \int_0^1 y \binom{20}{k}(21)y^k(1 - y)^{20-k}\, dy = \frac{k+1}{22} \cdot$$

Thus, the Bayes estimator of p does not coincide with the maximum likelihood estimator of p. (Sec. 4.5.5 showed the latter estimate is given by $k/20$.)

Under quite general conditions, Bayes estimators corresponding to any given prior distribution can be shown to be consistent, asymptotically efficient, and asymptotically normally distributed. In fact, Bayes estimators and maximum likelihood estimators differ only slightly when n is large.

4.6 INTERVAL ESTIMATION

The preceding section indicated that certain kinds of point estimates have many desirable properties. Unfortunately, they also have the undesirable property of usually being incorrect! For example, if the estimator $\hat{\theta}$ is a continuous random variable, then the probability is zero that it equals the parameter θ being estimated. Hence, an estimate of a parameter that is accompanied by some interval around this estimate is desirable, together with some measure of assurance that the interval includes the true parameter. This kind of approach is described below.

4.6.1 Confidence Interval Estimation

A technique for finding intervals as described above is available. Such intervals are known as *confidence intervals*, and the measure of assurance is given by a *confidence coefficient*. To illustrate how to obtain them, suppose that the daily demand for a given product can be approximated by a normally distributed random variable having unknown mean, but known standard deviation, say, 20. Suppose that a random sample of 25 days is to be taken, and an interval estimate of the mean demand μ is desired. Let the random variable $\bar{X}$ be the sample mean. Hence, $\bar{X}$ is also normally distributed with mean μ, and its standard deviation is $20/5 = 4$. Thus,

$$P\left\{-K_{\alpha/2} \leq \frac{\bar{X} - \mu}{4} \leq K_{\alpha/2}\right\} = 1 - \alpha$$

so that

$$P\{\bar{X} - 4K_{\alpha|2} \leq \mu \leq \bar{X} + 4K_{\alpha|2}\} = 1 - \alpha ,$$

where $K_{\alpha|2}$ is the 100 $\alpha/2$ percentage point of the normal distribution. $\bar{X} - 4K_{\alpha|2}$ is called the lower confidence limit, $\bar{X} + 4K_{\alpha|2}$ is called the upper confidence limit, and $(\bar{X} - 4K_{\alpha|2}, \bar{X} + 4K_{\alpha|2})$ is known as the confidence interval. $(1 - \alpha)$ is called the confidence coefficient. For example, if, after the experiment, $\bar{X}$ takes on the value 93 and α is chosen to be $.05(K_{\alpha|2} = 1.96)$, then the lower confidence limit is given by $93 - 7.84 = 85.16$ and the upper confidence limit is given by $93 + 7.84 = 100.84$. The confidence coefficient is .95. The decision-maker can then make the following announcement: *μ lies in the interval (85.16, 100.84), and this statement is made with confidence .95*. The meaning of this assertion must be examined carefully. If the decision-maker is going to make such statements about 100 (independent) products using the above method (correcting for the proper standard deviations), and if he later became aware of the correct means, he would have found that, on the average, 95 of the 100 intervals would have included the true values of μ. Since μ, in this context, is not to be interpreted as a random variable, the statement,

$$P\{85.16 \leq \mu \leq 100.84\} = .95 ,$$

has no meaning. (This probability is either one or zero, depending upon whether the mean is in *this* interval or not.) The assertion of "confidence

.95" means that *before* the sample was drawn, the probability was .95 that the interval to be constructed would include the true mean.

The general expression for finding a confidence interval for μ with confidence coefficient $1 - \alpha$ when σ is known is given by

$$(\bar{X} - K_{\alpha/2}\sigma/\sqrt{n}, \bar{X} + K_{\alpha/2}\sigma/\sqrt{n}) .$$

A useful method for constructing confidence intervals for any single parameter θ is as follows. Let $\hat{\theta}$ be an estimator of θ whose distribution depends on θ. Find a function of $\hat{\theta}$ and θ, say, $Z(\hat{\theta}, \theta)$, which has a distribution independent of θ and any other (nuisance) parameters present. Then a probability statement of the form

$$P\{c \leq Z \leq d\} = 1 - \alpha$$

can be inverted to obtain an equivalent inequality of the form

$$P\{g(Z) \leq \theta \leq h(Z)\} = 1 - \alpha .$$

The random variables $g(Z)$ and $h(Z)$ are the lower and upper confidence limits, respectively. These limits are random variables; sometimes they include θ, and sometimes they exclude θ. The probability is $(1 - \alpha)$ that they include θ.

As an example, a confidence interval can be obtained for the mean, μ, of a normal distribution when the variance, σ^2, is unknown. Let $\bar{X}$ be the random variable, the sample mean, obtained from a random sample of size n. It can be shown that

$$Z = \frac{(\bar{X} - \mu)\sqrt{n}}{s}$$

has a t distribution (see the end of Section 3.7.3) with $(n - 1)$ degrees of freedom, where

$$s^2 = \sum_{i=1}^{n} (X_i - \bar{X})^2/(n - 1) .$$

Thus, $\bar{X}$ is an estimator of μ whose distribution depends on μ. However, Z has a distribution independent of μ, so that

$$P\left\{-t_{\alpha/2;n-1} \leq \frac{(\bar{X} - \mu)\sqrt{n}}{s} \leq t_{\alpha/2;n-1}\right\} = 1 - \alpha ,$$

where $t_{\alpha/2;n-1}$ is the 100 $\alpha/2$ percentage point of the t distribution with $(n - 1)$ degrees of freedom, as given in Table A5.2. Inverting this inequality leads to

$$P\left\{\bar{X} - t_{\alpha/2;n-1}\frac{s}{\sqrt{n}} \leq \mu \leq \bar{X} + t_{\alpha/2;n-1}\frac{s}{\sqrt{n}}\right\} = 1 - \alpha ,$$

so that the random variables

$$g(Z) = \bar{X} - t_{\alpha/2;n-1}\frac{s}{\sqrt{n}}$$

and

$$h(Z) = \bar{X} + t_{\alpha/2;n-1}\frac{s}{\sqrt{n}}$$

are the lower and upper confidence limits, respectively.

This method is often applicable to real world problems. However, there are certain cases where it is not possible to find functions of the desired form which have distributions independent of the parameters. In these cases, other methods must be applied.

4.6.2 Posterior Distributions

An alternative to constructing a confidence interval can be obtained by using a Bayesian framework. If some information about the parameter θ is available, and the decision-maker is willing to translate this information into a prior distribution for θ, then the posterior distribution given the sample data can be used to make probability statements about the parameter. In fact, probability statements relative to the posterior distribution of θ can be used as an alternative to the confidence statements. Of course, such probability statements depend upon the prior distribution chosen. It is interesting to note that when the mean μ of a normal distribution with known standard deviation is assumed to have a uniform prior weighting, the confidence interval with confidence coefficient $(1 - \alpha)$ coincides with the $(1 - \alpha)$ probability interval for μ relative to the posterior distribution. For other prior distributions, this is not necessarily true, nor is it generally true for other parameters using uniform prior distributions.

4.7 LINEAR REGRESSION

Statistical problems often are concerned with data where there exists a relationship between two variables. This section highlights the results when the relationship is linear. For example, suppose that a publisher of textbooks is concerned about the initial production run for his books. He sells books both through bookstores and through direct mail orders. This latter method comes about after an extensive advertising campaign through publishing media and direct mail. The advertising campaign is conducted prior to the publication of the book. The sales manager has noted that there is a rather interesting linear relationship that exists between the number of mail orders and the number sold through bookstores during the first year. He suggested that this relationship be exploited for use in setting the initial production run for his subsequent books.

Thus, if the number of mail order sales for a book is denoted by X, and the number of bookstore sales by Y, then the random variables X and Y exhibit "a degree of association." There is no functional relationship between these two random variables, i.e., given the number of mail order sales, one does not expect to determine *exactly* the number of bookstore sales. Note that for any given number of mail order sales there is a range of possible bookstore sales, and vice versa. This variation may be partially due to measurement errors (incorrect counts, for example), but it can be attributed primarily to individual variation among published books. Thus, no unique functional relationship between mail order sales and bookstore sales can be expected. However, it is anticipated that bookstore sales, for a given observed mail order sales, increase as mail order sales increase. If this is so, what then is meant by the statement, "The sales manager has noted that there is a rather interesting linear relationship that exists between the number of mail orders and the number sold through bookstores during the first year"? Such a statement implies that the *expected value* of the number of bookstore sales is linear with respect to the number of mail order sales, i.e.,

$$E[Y|X = x] = \alpha + \beta x .$$

Thus, if the number of mail order sales is x for many different books, the average number of corresponding bookstore sales would tend to be approximately $\alpha + \beta x$.

Other examples of this "degree of association model" can easily be found. An educator may be interested in the relationship between a student's performance on the college entrance examination and his subsequent performance in college. An engineer may be interested in the relationship between tensile strength and hardness of a material. An economist may wish to predict a measure of inflation as a function of the cost of living index, etc.

The "degree of association model" is not the only model of interest. In some cases, there exists a functional relationship between two variables, possibly linearly linked. For example, Ohm's law, which is extremely useful in the design and analysis of electrical circuits, is of this form. The algebraic expression of Ohm's law is given by

$$I = V/R ,$$

where I is the current measured in amperes, R is the resistance in ohms, and V is the potential difference in volts. If an experiment were run, holding R fixed (perhaps unknown), and plotting I against V, these points *should* fall on a straight line through the origin with slope $1/R$. However, the points will not lie exactly on a straight line due to errors of measurement. Generally one of the two variables is assumed to be known without error, and this variable will be denoted by x. (In practice, the error in x may not be exactly zero, but will be assumed to be negligible compared to the error in Y.) Other examples occur in calibration problems in engineering, and bioassay in medicine. In the calibration of an instrument, the instrument is usually calibrated to some standard (which is known exactly) over a wide range of values; the resultant plot (the calibration curve) is often linear. An example of a bioassay is an assay for immunoglobulins in human sera. Human serum contains three known antibodies (gamma globulins): γ_A, γ_G, and γ_M. These are often routinely assayed by the method of radial immunodiffusion. A fixed amount of human serum is placed on a special plate, and a ring forms. The diameter of the ring is a function of the concentration of the immunoglobulin in the serum. Standard dilutions of immunoglobulin can be placed on these special plates, and pairs of points plotted. The ring size diameter plotted against the logarithm of the concentration of the standard is a linear function.

Calling these plots linear functions does not imply that each point falls on the line. Again, due to measurement errors in Y, all that can be said is that

$$E[Y|x] = \alpha + \beta x ,$$

i.e., the expected value of Y, given x, is linear. Such a statement is equivalent to saying that a linear regression exists. Note that both the "degree of association" and "exact functional relationship" models lead to the same linear regression, and their subsequent treatment is almost identical. Hence, the bookstore example will be explored further to illustrate how to treat both kinds of models.

4.7.1 **Method of Least Squares**

Suppose that bookstore sales and mail order sales are given for 15 books. These data appear in Table 4.4, and the resulting plot is given in Fig. 4.1.

It is evident that the points in Fig. 4.1 do not lie on a straight line. Hence, it is not clear where the line should be drawn to show the linear relationship. Suppose that an arbitrary line, given by the expression $\tilde{y} = a + bx$, is drawn through the data. A measure of how well this line fits the data can be obtained by computing the sum of squares of the vertical deviations of the actual points from the fitted line. Thus, let y_i represent the bookstore sales of the ith book, and x_i the corresponding mail order sales. Denote by $\tilde{y}_i$ the point on the fitted line corresponding to the mail order sales of x_i. The proposed measure of fit is then given by

$$Q = (y_1 - \tilde{y}_1)^2 + (y_2 - \tilde{y}_2)^2 + \cdots + (y_{15} - \tilde{y}_{15})^2 = \sum_{i=1}^{15} (y_i - \tilde{y}_i)^2 .$$

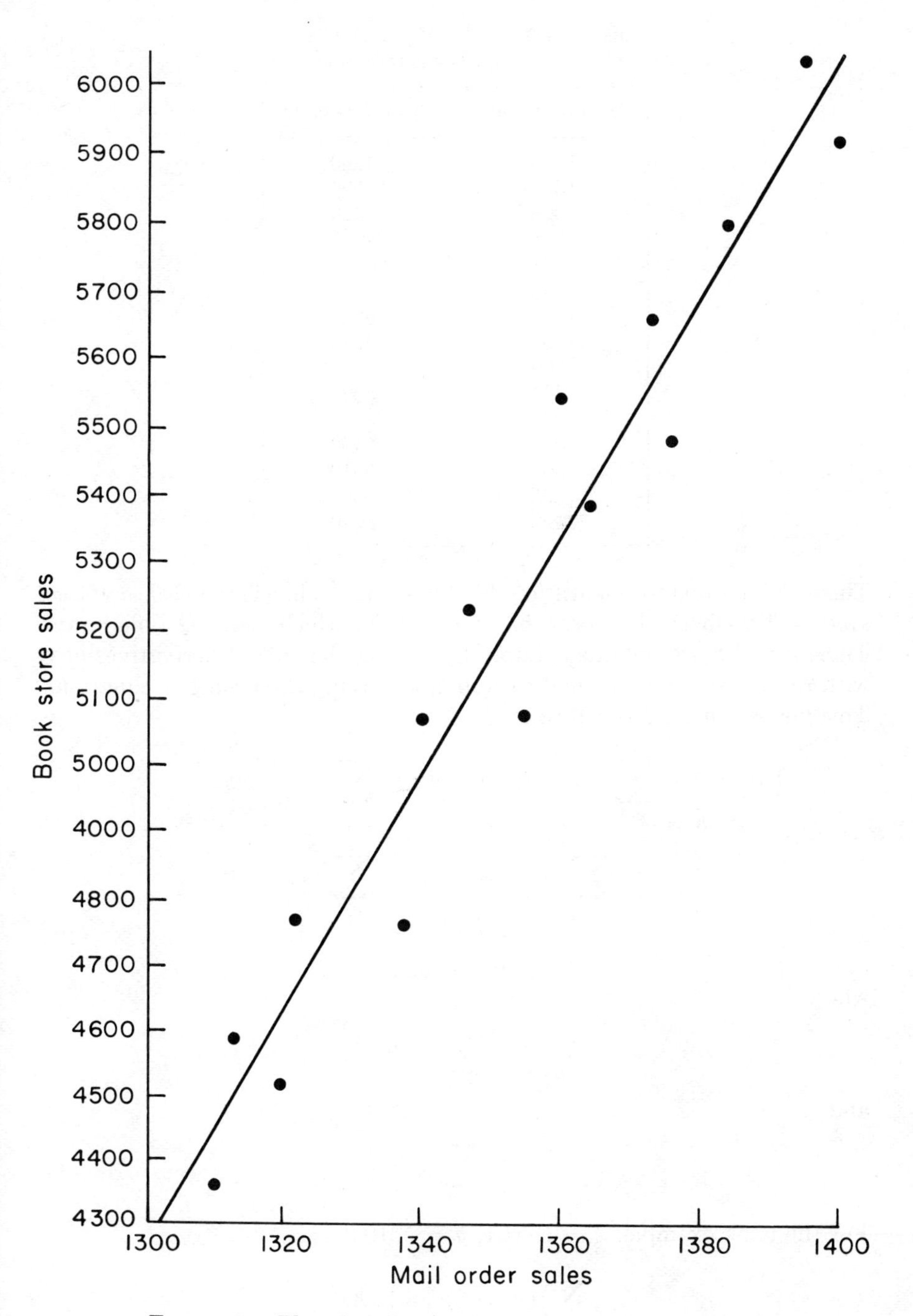

FIGURE 4.1. Plot of mail order sales versus bookstore sales.

TABLE 4.4. Table of Mail Order and Bookstore Sales

Mail order sales	*Bookstore sales*
1310	4360
1313	4590
1320	4520
1322	4770
1338	4760
1340	5070
1347	5230
1355	5080
1360	5550
1364	5390
1373	5670
1376	5490
1384	5810
1395	6060
1400	5940

The usual method for identifying the "best" fitted line is the *method of least squares*. This method chooses that line, $a + bx$, which makes Q a minimum. Thus, a and b are obtained simply by setting the partial derivatives of Q with respect to a and b equal to zero, and solving the resultant equations. This yields the desired solution,

$$b = \frac{\sum_{i=1}^{n} (x_i - \bar{x})(y_i - \bar{y})}{\sum_{i=1}^{n} (x_i - \bar{x})^2} = \frac{\sum_{i=1}^{n} (x_i - \bar{x})y_i}{\sum_{i=1}^{n} (x_i - \bar{x})^2},$$

and

$$a = \bar{y} - b\bar{x},$$

where

$$\bar{x} = \sum_{i=1}^{n} x_i/n$$

and

$$\bar{y} = \sum_{i=1}^{n} y_i/n .$$

For the book example, $\bar{x} = 1353.1$, $\bar{y} = 5219.3$,

$$\sum_{i=1}^{15} (x_i - \bar{x})^2 = 11966,$$

and $a = -19041.9$, $b = 17.930$. Hence, the least squares estimate of the bookstore sales $\tilde{y}$, when the mail order sales is x, is given by

$$\tilde{y} = -19041.9 + 17.930\, x\,,$$

and this line is drawn in Fig. 4.1.

4.7.2 **Properties of Least Squares Estimates**

Although the method of least squares is intuitively appealing, it appears to be based on a rather arbitrary criterion. In fact, one can think of many other competitive measures, such as the "sum of the absolute deviations," "sum of the perpendicular devations," etc. However, there are three properties of least squares that make it a particularly appealing measure. These are stated below.

(1) Gauss–Markov Property

Suppose that the underlying model of the relationship between the two variables is given by

$$E(Y_i|x_i) = \alpha + \beta x_i\,,$$

where the x_i are viewed as constants, and the Y_i are random variables having mean $E(Y_i|x_i)$ and variance σ^2 which is independent of i. A random sample of n pairs, (x_1, Y_1), (x_2, Y_2), $\cdots$, (x_n, Y_n) is taken. The line, $\alpha + \beta x$, is to be estimated by a line $\tilde{y} = a + bx$, where a is to be an estimate of α, and b is to be an estimate of β. The Gauss–Markov theorem states that a and b, the least squares estimate of α and β, respectively, are the minimum variance unbiased estimates of these parameters among the class of all linear estimates, i.e., estimates of the form

$$\sum_{i=1}^{n} c_i y_i\,.$$

Note that since the x_i are assumed to be fixed constants, the least squares estimates are indeed linear functions of the y_i.

(2) Maximum Likelihood Property

If the above assumptions for Y_i still hold, i.e., the Y_i are random variables having mean $E(Y_i|x) = \alpha + \beta x_i$ and variance σ^2 independent of i, and if, in addition, the Y_i are normally distributed, then the least squares estimates for α and β (based upon a random sample of size n) coincide with the maximum likelihood estimates. Furthermore, the probability distributions of these estimates are normally distributed.

(3) EXTENSION TO NON-LINEAR REGRESSION

The third property is that, even if the underlying relationship between the two variables is not linear, the method of least squares generalizes easily to the problem of estimating the nonlinear relationship.

For the remainder of this section on linear regression, it will be assumed that

(i) A random sample of n pairs $(x_1, Y_1), (x_2, Y_2), \cdots, (x_n, Y_n)$ is to be taken.
(ii) The Y_i are normally distributed with mean, $\alpha + \beta x_i$, and variance σ^2 (independent of i).

Assumption (ii) is worth exploring. The procedures to be presented are "robust" in the sense that the assumption of normality is not crucial for obtaining good estimates. However, the assumption of constant variance is quite important.

Under assumptions (i) and (ii) the least squares estimate of the intercept α and the slope β, given by a and b, respectively,

(1) coincide with the maximum likelihood estimates,
(2) are linear combinations of the y's (x's are assumed to be fixed constants),
(3) are unbiased, i.e., $E(a) = \alpha$ and $E(b) = \beta$,
(4) are the minimum variance unbiased estimates among the class of all linear estimates with

$$\text{variance}(a) = \sigma^2 \left[\frac{1}{n} + \frac{\bar{x}^2}{\sum_{i=1}^{n} (x_i - \bar{x})^2} \right],$$

$$\text{variance}(b) = \sigma^2 / \sum_{i=1}^{n} (x_i - \bar{x})^2 ,$$

(5) are normally distributed with parameters as given in (3) and (4).

Finally, an unbiased estimate of σ^2 is given by $s^2_{y|x}$, where

$$s^2_{y|x} = \sum_{i=1}^{n} (y_i - \tilde{y}_i)^2/(n - 2) .$$

Furthermore, $(n - 2)s^2_{y|x}/\sigma^2$ has a chi-square distribution with $(n - 2)$ degrees of freedom (see Chapter 3) and is independent of the random variables, a, b, and $\tilde{y}$. This result can be used to help derive tests of hypothesis about α, β, and σ^2.

4.7.3 Confidence Interval Estimation of $E(Y|x = x_*)$

A very important reason for obtaining the linear relationship between two variables is to use the line for future decision-making. From the regression line, it is possible to estimate $E(Y|x)$ by a point estimate and a confidence interval. For example, the book publisher might want to use this approach to estimate the expected number of bookstore sales corresponding to a mail order sale of, say, 1400 by both a point estimate and confidence interval estimate. He may be interested in this for sales projections. A point estimate corresponding to $x = x_*$ is given by

$$\tilde{y}_* = a + bx_* .$$

The end points of a $(100)(1 - \alpha)$ percent confidence interval are given by

$$a + bx_* - t_{\alpha/2;n-2}s_{y|x}\sqrt{\left[\frac{1}{n} + \frac{(x_* - \bar{x})^2}{\Sigma(x_i - \bar{x})^2}\right]},$$

and

$$a + bx_* + t_{\alpha/2;n-2}s_{y|x}\sqrt{\left[\frac{1}{n} + \frac{(x_* - \bar{x})^2}{\Sigma(x_i - \bar{x})^2}\right]},$$

where $s^2_{y|x}$ is the estimate of σ^2, and $t_{\alpha/2;n-2}$ is the $100\alpha/2$ percentage point of the t-distribution with $n - 2$ degrees of freedom (see Table A5.2 of Appendix 5). It should be noted that the interval is most narrow where $x_* = \bar{x}$, and becomes wider as x_* departs from the mean.

In the book example, $s^2_{y|x}$ is computed from the data in Table 4.4 to be 17,030. If a 95% confidence interval is required, Table A5.2 gives $t_{.025;13} =$ 2.160. The results derived in the preceding section yield 6060 as the point estimate of $E(Y|1400)$. Hence, the lower confidence limit corresponding to a mail order of 1400 is 5918, and the upper confidence limit is 6202. The fact that the confidence interval was obtained at a data point ($x = 1400$) is purely coincidental.

4.7.4 Predictions

The confidence interval statement for the expected number of bookstore sales corresponding to a mail order of 1400 may be useful for budgeting purposes, but it is not too useful for making decisions about the *actual* number of books to be printed. Instead of obtaining bounds on the *expected* number of bookstore sales, this kind of decision requires bounds on what the *actual* bookstore sales will be, i.e., a *prediction interval* on the value that the random variable (bookstore sales) can take on. The two end points of such an interval are given *by* the expressions

$$a + bx_+ - t_{\alpha/2;n-2}s_{y|x}\sqrt{\left[1 + \frac{1}{n} + \frac{(x_+ - \bar{x})^2}{\sum_{i=1}^{n}(x_i - \bar{x})^2}\right]},$$

$$a + bx_+ + t_{\alpha/2;n-2}s_{y|x}\sqrt{\left[1 + \frac{1}{n} + \frac{(x_+ - \bar{x})^2}{\sum_{i=1}^{n}(x_i - \bar{x})^2}\right]}.$$

For a given value x_+, the probability is $1 - \alpha$ that the value of the future Y_+ associated with the x_+ will fall in this interval. Thus, if x_+ is 1400, then the corresponding 95% prediction interval for the number of bookstore sales is given by 6060 ± 316, which is naturally wider than the confidence interval for the expected number of bookstore sales.

Whereas, the book publisher can find an interval which will contain bookstore sales corresponding to a particular mail order sale with probability $1 - \alpha$, he is unable to use this type of result over and over and still maintain a measure for making correct statements. The reason is that these statements would all be based upon the same statistical data, so that they would not be statistically independent. If the statements are independent, and k future bookstore sales are to be predicted with each statement being made with probability $1 - \alpha$, then the probability is $(1 - \alpha)^k$ that *all* k predictions of future bookstore sales are correct. However, if k is large or possibly unknown, even this technique based upon the (incorrect) assumption of independence would be useless. A solution to this problem can be obtained by using *simultaneous tolerance intervals*. Using this technique, the book publisher can take the mail order sales of any book, find an interval (based on the previously determined fitted line) that will contain the actual bookstore sales with probability at least $1 - \alpha$, and can repeat this for any number of books having the same or different mail order sales. Furthermore, the probability is P that all of these predictions are correct. An alternative interpretation is as follows. If every book publisher followed this procedure, each using his own fitted line, then 100 P percent of the book publishers (on the average) would find that at least $100(1 - \alpha)$ percent of the bookstore sales of his books would fall into the predicted intervals. The expression for the end points of each such interval is given by

$$a + bx_+ - c^{**}s_{y|x}\sqrt{\left[\frac{1}{n} + \frac{(x_+ - \bar{x})^2}{\sum_{i=1}^{n}(x_i - \bar{x})^2}\right]}$$

and

$$a + bx_+ + c^{**}s_{y|k}\sqrt{\left[\frac{1}{n} + \frac{(x_+ - \bar{x})^2}{\sum_{i=1}^{n}(x_i - \bar{x})^2}\right]},$$

where c^{**} is given in Table 4.5. c^{**} is clearly a function of n, P, and α.

Thus, the book publisher can state that the bookstore sales corresponding to a known mail order sales will fall in the interval constructed using the expressions given above. Such statements can be made for as many books as the publisher desires. Furthermore, the probability is P that at least

TABLE 4.5. Values[a] of c^{**}

n	$P = 0.50$	$P = 0.75$	$P = 0.90$	$P = 0.95$	$P = 0.99$	$P = 0.999$
			$\alpha = 0.10$			
4	7.471	10.160	13.069	14.953	18.663	23.003
6	5.380	7.453	9.698	11.150	14.014	17.363
8	5.037	7.082	9.292	10.722	13.543	16.837
10	4.983	7.093	9.366	10.836	13.733	17.118
12	5.023	7.221	9.586	11.112	14.121	17.634
14	5.101	7.394	9.857	11.447	14.577	18.232
16	5.197	7.586	10.150	11.803	15.057	18.856
18	5.300	7.786	10.449	12.165	15.542	19.484
20	5.408	7.987	10.747	12.526	16.023	20.104
			$\alpha = 0.05$			
4	10.756	14.597	18.754	21.445	26.760	32.982
6	6.652	9.166	11.899	13.669	17.167	21.266
8	5.933	8.281	10.831	12.484	15.750	19.568
10	5.728	8.080	10.632	12.286	15.553	19.369
12	5.684	8.093	10.701	12.391	15.724	19.619
14	5.711	8.194	10.880	12.617	16.045	20.050
16	5.771	8.337	11.107	12.898	16.431	20.559
18	5.848	8.499	11.357	13.204	16.845	21.097
20	5.937	8.672	11.619	13.521	17.272	21.652
			$\alpha = 0.01$			
4	24.466	33.019	42.398	48.620	60.500	74.642
6	10.444	14.285	18.483	21.215	26.606	32.920
8	8.290	11.453	14.918	17.166	21.652	26.860
10	7.567	10.539	13.796	15.911	20.097	24.997
12	7.258	10.182	13.383	15.479	19.579	24.403
14	7.127	10.063	13.267	15.355	19.485	24.316
16	7.079	10.055	13.306	15.410	19.582	24.467
18	7.074	10.111	13.404	15.552	19.794	24.746
20	7.108	10.198	13.566	15.745	20.065	25.122

[a] Reprinted by permission from "Simultaneous Tolerance Intervals in Regression," by G. J. Lieberman and R. G. Miller, *Biometrika*, **50,** 1 and 2, 164 (1963).

$100(1 - \alpha)$ percent of the bookstore sales corresponding to the mail order sales will fall in these intervals. If P is chosen as .75, and $\alpha = .05$, the appropriate value of c^{**} is 8.265. Hence, the number of bookstore sales corresponding to a mail order sales of 1400 books will fall in the interval 6060 ± 540. If another book had a mail order sales of 1353, the bookstore sales would fall in the interval, 5258 ± 278, etc. 95% of the bookstore sales will fall into their predicted intervals, and these statements are made with confidence 0.75.

4.8 CHOICE OF DISTRIBUTION FUNCTIONS

One of the most important problems in statistics, and one of the most difficult, is the choice of the parametric form of a probability distribution. It is especially important because the assumption made about the form of the probability distribution is usually quite critical in determining the decision rules to be used. Such an assumption often must be made in the absence of any data. Sometimes it may be possible to use large sample properties of the decision rules such as obtained, e.g., by invoking the central limit theorem. An alternative approach is to base the decisions upon procedures which do not use any information about the probability distribution (nonparametric procedures).

When sample data are available the decision-maker has both subjective and objective procedures available to aid him in his choice. In the category of subjective procedures are analyses made by plotting histograms and sample cumulative distribution functions. Objective procedures are obtained by using Goodness of Fit Tests.

4.8.1 Histograms and Sample Cumulative Distribution Functions

Suppose that the unknown density function of a continuous random variable is under consideration. Empirical frequencies obtained from sample data can be related to density functions as follows. Suppose a random sample of size n is obtained. Let $x_1, x_2, \cdots, x_n$ denote the values that the random variable in this random sample takes on. Divide the abscissa between the largest and smallest x's into k equal intervals. Let $f_1, f_2, \cdots, f_k$ denote the proportion (relative frequency) of the values, $x_1, x_2, \cdots, x_n$, that fall into the first, second, $\cdots$, kth interval, respectively. Plot a bar graph such as that shown in Figure 4.2, where the height of the ith bar is determined so that its area is f_i. This plot is called a *histogram*, and the total area of the histogram is one.

As the sample size gets large, and the intervals small, the histogram tends to be similar in shape to that of the density function of X. Hence, by looking at a histogram, one can assess visually whether it seems to possess the characteristics of a presumed density function. For example, the histogram may suggest whether or not the underlying density is symmetric, unimodal, etc.

In Sec. 3.4, the sample cumulative distribution function $F_n(x)$ was defined, and such a plot appears in Fig. 3.3. $F_n(x)$ can be interpreted as the fraction of outcomes of the experiment less than or equal to x. It can be shown that as n (the number of repetitions of the experiment) gets large, the sample cumulative distribution function approaches the cumulative

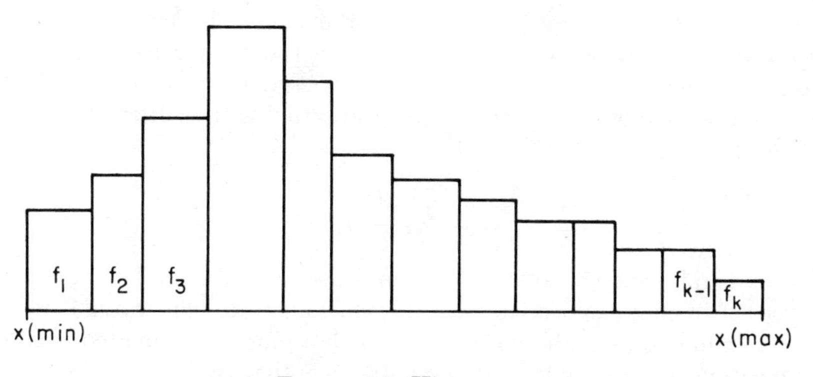

FIGURE 4.2. Histogram.

distribution function of the random variable X. Again then, by looking at a sample cumulative distribution function, one can assess visually whether it seems to possess the characteristics of a presumed distribution function. In this case, however, additional aid is available.

There exists graph paper known as normal probability paper. By properly choosing the scale of the ordinate, the cumulative distribution function of the normal distribution plots as a straight line. Normal probability paper is a graph paper possessing such a special grid for the ordinate. Hence, the cumulative distribution function of a normally distributed random variable will plot as a straight line on this paper, where the mean is the abscissa corresponding to the .50 ordinate, and the standard deviation is the distance between the abscissa of the .8413 point and the abscissa of the .50 point. Hence, if a plot of the *sample* cumulative distribution function appears to be nearly a straight line on normal probability paper, this would suggest that the probability distribution is indeed normal. Similar paper can be constructed for other distribution functions.

Both of the above techniques suffer from the fact that many different distributions may sometimes yield random samples that have an indistinguishable appearance when they are plotted on either a histogram or on probability paper. Thus, it often is not possible to identify objectively a particular probability distribution on the basis of a random sample. Therefore, objective procedures for doing this are of interest, and two such procedures are described in the next section.

4.8.2 Chi-Square Goodness of Fit and Kolmogorov-Smirnov

One objective procedure for verifying whether or not a probability distribution has a specified form is the chi-square goodness of fit test. This test compares a set of sample frequencies with a set of frequencies that would be expected on the basis of some hypothesis. If this comparison is favorable, the hypothesis is accepted; otherwise it is rejected. The test procedure is as follows: let $f_1, f_2, \cdots, f_k$ be the sample frequencies of k classes, and let $f_1^o, f_2^o, \cdots, f_k^o$ be the frequencies that would be expected if the hypothesis about the form of the distribution is true. If the hypothesis is true, then

$$\chi^2 = \sum_{i=1}^{k} \frac{(f_i - f_i^o)^2}{f_i^o}$$

will tend to have a chi-square distribution as k gets large. The number of degrees of freedom associated with this chi-square random variable will be $(k - 1)$ minus the number of parameters that must be estimated from the sample data. For example, if the hypothesis is that the distribution is normal with mean 7 and variance 6, the degrees of freedom are just $(k - 1)$. On the other hand, if the hypothesis is that the distribution is normal without specifying its mean and variance, then in order to obtain f_i^o, the mean and variance must be estimated from the data (usually by the method of maximum likelihood), and the degrees of freedom become $k - 3$.

The choice of k is rather arbitrary, but a good rule of thumb indicates that k should be chosen so that each $f_i^o \geq 5$. The test of the hypothesis is carried out by comparing the value that the random variable χ^2 takes on, with a selected critical value of the chi-square distribution (chosen from the table of the percentage points of the chi-square distribution given in Table A5.3 of Appendix 5). The hypothesis is rejected if χ^2 exceeds this critical value. If the critical value chosen corresponds to the α percentage point, then the probability of accepting the hypotheses when it is true is approximately $(1 - \alpha)$.

The Kolmogorov–Smirnov test is a competitor of the chi-square goodness of fit whenever the hypothesized form of the distribution is completely specified (including the values of all parameters). In fact, it is a more powerful test and so should be used in this situation. This test compares the sample cumulative distribution function $F_n(x)$ with the hypothesized cumulative distribution function $F(x)$. In particular, define the random variable D_n as

$$D_n = \max_{\text{all } x} |F_n(x) - F(x)| .$$

The distribution of D_n is independent of $F(x)$. It has been computed for various sample sizes and can be found in most elementary textbooks on mathematical statistics. If $D_n^*(\alpha)$ is the α percentage point of the distribution of D_n, and if the hypothesis that $F(x)$ is the appropriate cumulative distribution function is rejected when $D_n > D_n^*(\alpha)$, then the probability is $(1 - \alpha)$ of accepting the hypothesis when it is indeed true.

SELECTED REFERENCES

1. Chernoff, H., and Moses, L., *Elementary Decision Theory*, Wiley, New York, 1959.
2. Freund, J. E., *Mathematical Statistics*, Prentice-Hall, Englewood Cliffs, N. J., 1962.
3. Hogg, R., and Craig, A., *Introduction to Mathematical Statistics*, 2nd ed., Macmillan, New York, 1965.
4. Lindgren, B. W., *Statistical Theory*, Macmillan, New York, 1960.
5. Mood, A. M., and Graybill, F. A., *Introduction to the Theory of Statistics*, 2nd ed., McGraw-Hill, New York, 1963.
6. Schlaifer, R., *Probability and Statistics for Business Decisions*, McGraw-Hill, New York, 1959.

PROBLEMS

1. Assume that there are two weighted coins. Coin 1 has a probability of .3 of turning up heads, and coin 2 has a probability of .6 of turning up heads. The decision-maker must decide which coin was tossed. The probability that coin 1 was tossed is .6, and the probability that coin 2 was tossed is .4. The loss matrix is given below.

	Coin 1 tossed	Coin 2 tossed
a_1: say coin 1 tossed	0	1
a_2: say coin 2 tossed	1	0

(a) What is the Bayes procedure (action) before the coin is tossed?
(b) What is the Bayes procedure if the coin is tossed once, and the outcome is heads? What if it is tails?

2. In the manufacture of a certain type of fabric the finished width is the dimension of interest. The supplier states that the average width is $3\frac{1}{2}$ inches. The consumer, being a skeptic, will run an experiment to decide whether to accept or reject the lot. It is well known that the true width is a random variable which is normally distributed with a known standard deviation of $\frac{1}{16}$ inches. The consumer knows that the average width is either $3\frac{1}{2}$, $3\frac{33}{64}$, or $3\frac{17}{32}$. The loss in dollars is given by the following table.

	Average width $3\frac{1}{2}$	$3\frac{33}{64}$	$3\frac{17}{32}$
Accept	0	1000	2000
Reject	4000	500	0

Furthermore, each of the three states is known to be equally likely to occur.

(a) Without sampling, what is the Bayes decision rule?
(b) A sample of size 10 is taken and $\bar{x} = 3\frac{17}{32}$. What is the Bayes decision rule?

3. Repeat problem 2 when the loss matrix is modified as follows. Let X be the random variable which denotes the actual width of the material. When the material is accepted, the loss is equal to $64000\ (X - 3\frac{1}{2})$. When the material is rejected, the loss is equal to $800{,}000\ (X - 3\frac{17}{32})^2$.

4. It is alleged that students at a certain university today are brighter by three units than they were in the past. Over the years a special examination in statistics has been given, and it was determined that the average grade was 74 units. This procedure has been discontinued, but the same examination is once again to be offered to determine if the above allegation is true. Assume that the test scores are independent, normally distributed random variables with common mean and standard deviation equal to 3 units.

The loss table is given as follows:

Action μ	74	77
Say students are brighter	0	1
Say students are not brighter	1	0

Suppose a random sample of size 50 is given the examination, and the posterior probabilities are computed and found to be $\frac{3}{4}$ for $\mu = 74$ and $\frac{1}{4}$ for $\mu = 77$. What is the Bayes action that should be taken?

5. A new type of film for ordinary 35-millimeter cameras has been developed. It is packaged in sets of 5 sheets, each sheet providing an instantaneous snapshot. Since this is a new process, the manufacturer has attached an additional sheet to the package so that the store may test one before the package of 5 is sold. In promoting the film, an offer to refund the entire purchase price of the film if one of the five is defective has been made. This refund must be paid by the camera store, and the selling price has been fixed at \$1.00 if this guarantee is to be valid. The camera store may sell the film for 50 cents if the above guarantee is replaced by one which pays 10 cents for each defective sheet. The cost of the film to the camera store is 25 cents and is not returnable. The store may take 3 actions:

a_1: scrap the film,
a_2: sell the film for \$1.00,
a_3: sell the film for 50 cents.

(a) If the six states of nature correspond to 0, 1, 2, 3, 4, 5 defective sheets in the package, complete the following loss table.

a \ θ	0	1	2	3	4	5
a_1	.25					
a_2	$-.75$		.25			
a_3	$-.25$	$-.15$		.05		

(b) Suppose that a model for the process is that the quality of each sheet has a Bernoulli distribution with parameter $p = .05$. The prior distribution of the states of nature is then binomial with parameter $n = 5$ and $p = .05$, i.e., if θ denotes the number of defective sheets, then

$$P\{\theta = k\} = P_\theta(k) = \binom{5}{k}(.05)^k\,(.95)^{5-k}\,.$$

What is the Bayes procedure (before testing the attached sheet).
(c) After testing the attached sheet, what is the Bayes procedure if the print is good? What is it if it is bad?

6. Suppose X_1 and X_2 form a random sample of size 2 from a distribution such that

$$E(X) = \mu$$

and

$$E(X - \mu)^2 = \sigma^2\,.$$

Two estimators of μ are

$$T_1 = \frac{X_1 + X_2}{2} = \bar{X}\,,$$

and

$$T_2 = \frac{X_1 + 2X_2}{3}\,.$$

Which is a better estimate?

7. The probability density function of a certain random variable X is given by

$$f_X(y) = \begin{cases} 2y/\theta^2, & \text{for } 0 \leq y \leq \theta \\ 0, & \text{otherwise}, \end{cases}$$

where θ is a parameter of the density.

Consider the problem of estimating θ from a random sample $X_1, \cdots, X_n$ of n observations from the given density. Two methods for forming such estimates are the method of maximum likelihood and the method of moments. For this problem, the maximum likelihood estimator, denoted by T_1, is the largest of the values $X_1, X_2, \cdots, X_n$; the method of moments estimator, T_2, is three halves of the sample mean. Some information about these estimates is:

$$\begin{aligned} T_1 &= \max\{X_1, X_2, \cdots, X_n\}, \\ E(T_1) &= \frac{2n}{2n+1}\theta, \\ \text{variance } (T_1) &= \frac{n}{(n+1)(2n+1)^2}\theta^2, \\ T_2 &= \left(\frac{3}{2}\right)\bar{X} = \frac{3(X_1 + \cdots + X_n)}{2n}, \\ E(T_2) &= \theta, \\ \text{variance } (T_2) &= \frac{\theta^2}{8n}. \end{aligned}$$

Compute the mean square error for both estimates. Using mean square error as a criterion, which estimate is better if $n = 2$? If $n = 3$, which is better?

8. Consider the function

$$f_X(y) = \begin{cases} \dfrac{K}{\theta}\left(1 - \dfrac{1}{\theta}y\right), & 0 \leq y \leq \theta \\ 0, & y < 0 \text{ and } y > \theta. \end{cases}$$

(a) What value(s) of K and θ make $f_X(y)$ a bona-fide probability density function?
(b) Find $E(X)$.
Consider the class of all estimators of θ of the form $C\bar{X}$ (where C is a constant and $\bar{X}$ is computed from a sample of size n).
(c) What value of C makes $C\bar{X}$ an unbiased estimator of θ?
(d) Find the minimum mean square error estimator in the class $C\bar{X}$.
(e) Show that the minimum mean square error estimator approaches the unbiased estimator for large n.

9. Suppose X_1 and X_2 are independent observations having a common distribution with mean $= \mu$ and variance $= 1$. Consider point estimates of μ of the following form:

$$\hat{\mu} = \lambda X_1 + (1 - \lambda)X_2 ,$$

where $0 \leq \lambda \leq 1$.

(a) For what values of λ is μ unbiased?
(b) Noting that $\hat{\mu} - \mu = \lambda(X_1 - \mu) + (1 - \lambda)(X_2 - \mu)$, compute the expected squared error of $\hat{\mu}$. Is there a value of λ which yields a uniformly best estimate of this type?

10. A radio manufacturer wishes to test the reliability of radios. Let p be the probability that a radio functions properly when turned on, and let $(1 - p)$ be the probability that the radio fails when turned on. Suppose that radios are tested as follows: The radio is turned on and off repeatedly until failure occurs. Let N be the number of the trial at which the first failure occurs. (Each turn-on constitutes a trial.) Then N is a discrete random variable with the distribution

$$P\{N = n\} = (1 - p)\, p^{n-1}, \qquad \text{for } n = 1, 2, 3, \cdots .$$

Suppose a random sample of r radios is taken, and each radio is tested by the above procedure. Let N_i denote the outcome of testing the ith radio.

(a) Find the maximum likelihood estimate of p.
(b) The reliability $R(n_0)$ of a radio is defined to be the probability that the radio will not fail in the first n_0 trials.

$$R(n_0) = P\{N > n_0\} = 1 - P\{N \leq n_0\} = 1 - \sum_{n=1}^{n_0} (1 - p)p^{n-1} .$$

Find the maximum likelihood estimate of $R(n_0)$.

11. A buyer of lots of material notes that the incoming quality P has density given by

$$f_P(y) = \theta y^{\theta-1}, \qquad \text{for } 0 < y < 1, \text{ and for } 0 < \theta < \infty .$$

Suppose that a random sample of n lots is screened and $p_1, p_2, \cdots, p_n$ obtained.

(a) Find $\hat{\theta}$, the maximum likelihood estimate of θ.
(b) Find the asymptotic variance of $\sqrt{n}\hat{\theta}$.
(c) Using the asymptotic properties of $\hat{\theta}$, find a lower 95% confidence bound for θ.

12. Let $X_1, \cdots, X_n$ be a random sample of size n from a Poisson distribution with parameter λ, i.e.,

$$P_X(k) = \frac{\lambda^k e^{-\lambda}}{k!} \cdot$$

Let λ be considered as a random variable having a prior density function

$$f_\lambda(y) = \begin{cases} e^{-y}, & \text{for } 0 < y < \infty \\ 0, & \text{otherwise} . \end{cases}$$

The loss function to be considered is

$$(\hat{\lambda} - \lambda)^2 .$$

(a) Let $T = \Sigma X_i$, and noting that the sum of n independent Poisson random variables, each with parameter λ, is also distributed as a Poisson random variable but with parameter $n\lambda$, show that the posterior distribution of λ, given $T = t$, is given by

$$h_{\lambda|T=t}(y) = \frac{y^t e^{-(n+1)y}(n+1)^{t+1}}{\Gamma(\theta + 1)} \cdot$$

(b) Show that the Bayes estimator is given by

$$(T + 1)/(n + 1) .$$

(c) Find the maximum likelihood estimator.

13. Let $X_1, X_2, \cdots, X_n$ be a random sample of size n from a normal distribution with parameters μ and σ^2. Let μ be considered as a random variable having a prior distribution which is also normal but with parameters ν, γ^2. The loss function to be considered is

$$(\hat{\mu} - \mu)^2 .$$

(a) Show that the posterior distribution of μ, given $\bar{X} = \bar{x}$, is normal.
(b) Find the Bayes estimator for μ.

14. The following data relate road width x and accident frequency Y. Road width (in feet) was treated as a constant; and values of the random variable Y, in accidents per 10^8 vehicle miles, were observed.

Number of observations = 7.

$$\sum_{i=1}^{7} x_i = 354 \qquad \sum_{i=1}^{7} Y_i = 481$$

$$\sum_{i=1}^{7} x_i^2 = 19956 \qquad \sum_{i=1}^{7} Y_i^2 = 35451$$

$$\sum_{i=1}^{7} x_i Y_i = 22200$$

x	y
26	92
30	85
44	78
50	81
62	54
68	51
74	40

Assume that Y is normally distributed with mean $\alpha + \beta x$ and constant variance for all x, and that the sample is random.

(a) Fit a least squares line to the data.
(b) Construct a 95% prediction interval for Y_+, a future observation of Y, corresponding to $x_+ = 55$ feet.
(c) Suppose that two future observations on Y, both corresponding to $x_+ = 55$ feet, are to be made. Construct prediction intervals for both of these observations so that the probability is *at least* 95% that *both* future values of Y will fall into them simultaneously.
Hint: If k predictions are to be made [such as given in (*d*)], each with probability $1 - \alpha$, then the probability is *at least* $1 - k\alpha$ that all k future observations will fall into their respective intervals.
(d) Construct a simultaneous tolerance interval for the future value of Y corresponding to $x_+ = 55$ feet with $P = .90$ and $1 - \alpha = .95$.

15. The data below are observations on a dependent random variable Y taken at various levels of an independent variable x. [It is to be assumed that $E(Y_i|x_i) = \alpha + \beta x_i$, and Y_i are independent normal random variables with mean 0 and variance σ^2.] Suppose the data are as follows.

x_i	0	2	4	6	8
y_i	0	4	7	13	16

(a) Estimate the linear relationship by the method of least squares.
(b) Find a 95% confidence interval for the expected value of Y at $x_* = 10$.
(c) Find a 95% prediction interval for a future observation to be taken at $x_+ = 10$.
(d) Obtain an upper 95% confidence limit for σ^2.
(e) Prove that

$$a + bx_+ \pm t_{\alpha/2;n-2}s_{y|x}\sqrt{\left[\frac{1}{N} + \frac{1}{n} + \frac{(x_+ - \bar{x})^2}{\Sigma(x_i - \bar{x})^2}\right]}$$

is a $100(1 - \alpha)$% prediction interval for the arithmetic mean $\overline{Y}_+$ of N future observations to be taken at x_+.
(f) For $x_+ = 10$, $P = .90$, and $(1 - \alpha) = .95$, find a simultaneous tolerance interval for the future value of Y_+.

16. If a particle is dropped at time $t = 0$, physical theory indicates that the relationship between r, the distance traveled, and t, the time elapsed, is $r = gt^k$ for some positive constants g and k. A transformation to linearity can be obtained by taking logarithms:

$$\log r = \log g + k \log t\,.$$

Letting $y = \log r$, $A = \log g$, and $x = \log t$, this relation becomes $y = A + kx$. Due to random error in measurement, however, it can only be stated that $E(Y|x) = A + kx$. Assume Y is normally distributed with mean $A + kx$ and variance σ^2.

A physicist who wishes to estimate k and g performs the following experiment: At time 0 the particle is dropped. At time t the distance r is measured. He performs this experiment 5 times, obtaining the following data:

y = *logarithm* r	x = *logarithm* t
−3.95	−2.0
−2.12	−1.0
0.08	0.0
2.20	+1.0
3.87	+2.0

(a) Obtain least squares estimates for k and $\log g$.
(b) Find a 95% confidence interval for $E(\log r|x)$ when $x_* = 0$.
(c) Find a 95% prediction interval for r when $x_+ = 0$.

The following data has been calculated:

$$\bar{y} = .016$$

$$\Sigma(x_i - \bar{x})^2 = 10$$

$$\Sigma(x_i - \bar{x})(y_i - \bar{y}) = 19.96$$

$$\Sigma(y_i - \tilde{y}_i)^2 = .0858$$

$$\frac{s_{y|x}}{\sqrt{\Sigma(x_i - \bar{x})^2}} = .053$$

$$s_{y|x}\sqrt{\frac{1}{5}} = .076 .$$

Note: All logarithms are to the base 10.

17. Suppose that the relation between Y and x is given by

$$E(Y|x) = \beta x ,$$

where Y is assumed to be normally distributed with mean βx and *known* variance σ^2. n independent pairs of observations are taken and are denoted by $x_1, y_1; x_2, y_2; \cdots; x_n, y_n$.

(a) Find the least squares estimate of β.
(b) Find the variance of the least squares estimate of β.
(c) For $X = x_*$, find a 95% two-sided confidence interval for

$$E(Y|X = x_*) .$$

Part III

TECHNIQUES: MATHEMATICAL PROGRAMMING

CHAPTER 5

Linear Programming

5.1 INTRODUCTION

Linear programming deals with the problem of allocating limited resources among competing activities in an optimal manner. This problem of allocation can arise whenever one must select the level of certain activities which must compete for certain scarce resources necessary to perform those activities. The great variety of situations to which linear programming can be applied is indeed remarkable. It ranges from the allocation of production facilities to products to the allocation of airplane fuel to bomber runs, from portfolio selection to the selection of shipping patterns, from production scheduling to the solution of parlor games, and so on almost ad infinitum. However, the one common ingredient in each of these situations is the necessity for allocating resources to activities.

Linear programming uses a mathematical model to describe the problem of concern. The adjective "linear" means that all the mathematical functions in this model are required to be linear functions. The word "programming" is essentially a synonym for planning. Thus, linear programming involves the planning of activities in order to obtain an "optimal" result, i.e., a result which reaches the specified goal best (according to the mathematical model) among all feasible alternatives.

5.2 THE LINEAR PROGRAMMING MODEL

The mathematical statement of a general form of the linear programming problem is the following. Find $x_1, x_2, \cdots, x_n$ which maximizes the linear function,

$$Z = c_1x_1 + c_2x_2 + \cdots + c_nx_n ,$$

subject to the restrictions,

$$\begin{aligned} a_{11}x_1 + a_{12}x_2 + \cdots + a_{1n}x_n &\leq b_1 \\ a_{21}x_1 + a_{22}x_2 + \cdots + a_{2n}x_n &\leq b_2 \\ &\cdot \\ &\cdot \\ &\cdot \\ a_{m1}x_1 + a_{m2}x_2 + \cdots + a_{mn}x_n &\leq b_m \end{aligned}$$

and

$$x_1 \geq 0,\ x_2 \geq 0, \cdots, x_n \geq 0\,,$$

where the a_{ij}, b_i, and c_j are given constants. The function being maximized is called the objective function. The restrictions are also referred to as constraints or restraints. The variables being solved for are called decision variables.

The linear programming model is easily interpreted in terms of the discussion of the previous section. Given n competing activities, the decision variables, $x_1, x_2, \cdots, x_n$, represent the levels of these activities. For example, if each activity is the production of a certain product, then x_j would be the number of units of the jth product to be produced during a given period of time. Z is the chosen over-all measure of effectiveness, e.g., profit over the given time period. c_j is the increase in the over-all measure of effectiveness that would result from each unit increase in x_j. The number of relevant scarce resources is m, so that each of the first m linear inequalities corresponds to a restriction on the availability of one of these resources. b_i is the amount of resource i available to the n activities. a_{ij} is the amount of resource i consumed by each unit of activity j. Therefore, the left side of these inequalities is the total usage of the respective resources. The nonnegativity restrictions ($x_j \geq 0$) rule out the possibility of negative activity levels.

This elementary form of the linear programming model, together with the assumption that the $b_i > 0$, is used as a basis for presenting the solution procedure in Sec. 5.5. However, it should be noted that this model can also be written in other forms that can be solved, as indicated in Sec. 5.6. For example, it creates no new complications to minimize Z instead of maximizing Z, or for the inequalities to be "greater than or equal" instead of "less than or equal." Furthermore, the case where some of the restrictions involve equalities instead of inequalities, or where $b_i \leq 0$ for some i, can be solved.

One key to the successful application of linear programming is the ability to recognize when a problem can be solved by linear programming and to formulate the corresponding model. Several illustrative examples are presented in the next section. Section 5.4 then discusses the underlying assumptions of linear programming in detail in order to further clarify when it is or is not applicable.

5.3 EXAMPLES

Example 1

A manufacturing firm has discontinued production of a certain unprofitable product line. This created considerable excess production capacity. Management is considering devoting this excess capacity to one or more of three products; call them products 1, 2, and 3. The available capacity on the machines which might limit output is summarized in the following table.

Machine type	*Available time (in machine hours per week)*
Milling machine	200
Lathe	100
Grinder	50

The number of machine hours required for each unit of the respective products is given below.

Productivity
(in machine hours per unit)

Machine type	*Product 1*	*Product 2*	*Product 3*
Milling machine	8	2	3
Lathe	4	3	
Grinder	2		1

The sales department indicates that the sales potential for products 1 and 2 exceeds the maximum production rate and that the sales potential for product 3 is 20 units per week.

The unit profit would be \$20, \$6, and \$8, respectively, on products 1, 2, and 3.

The problem is to formulate a linear programming model for determining how much of each product the firm should produce in order to maximize profit.

Formulation of Example 1

Let x_i $(i = 1, 2, 3)$ be the number of units of product i produced per week. Since profit has been chosen as the measure of effectiveness, the object is to maximize

$$Z = 20x_1 + 6x_2 + 8x_3 ,$$

subject to the restrictions developed below.

The "limited resources" in this situation are the available capacity of the three machine groups and the sales potential for product 3. Therefore, a mathematical constraint must be developed to describe each of these resource restrictions. The first restriction is that no more than 200 milling machine hours per week can be allocated to the activities, the production of the three products. The number of milling machine hours actually allocated is $8x_1 + 2x_2 + 3x_3$. Therefore, the mathematical statement of the first restriction is

$$8x_1 + 2x_2 + 3x_3 \leq 200 .$$

Similarly, the other two capacity restrictions are

$$\begin{aligned} 4x_1 + 3x_2 &\leq 100 \\ 2x_1 + x_3 &\leq 50 . \end{aligned}$$

The mathematical statement of the sales potential restriction obviously is

$$x_3 \leq 20 .$$

Finally, there are the non-negativity restrictions.

Therefore, in summary, the linear programming model for this problem is the following. Maximize

$$Z = 20x_1 + 6x_2 + 8x_3 ,$$

subject to the restrictions,

$$\begin{aligned} 8x_1 + 2x_2 + 3x_3 &\leq 200 \\ 4x_1 + 3x_2 &\leq 100 \\ 2x_1 + x_3 &\leq 50 \\ x_3 &\leq 20 \end{aligned}$$

and

$$x_1 \geq 0, \ x_2 \geq 0, \ x_3 \geq 0 .$$

Example 2

One of the classic problems of linear programming is the diet problem. The objective is to ascertain the quantities of certain foods that should be eaten to meet certain nutritional requirements at a minimum cost. Assume that consideration is limited to milk, beef, and eggs, and to vitamins A, C, and D. Suppose that the number of milligrams of each of these vitamins contained within a unit of each food is as given below.

Vitamin	*Gallon of milk*	*Pound of beef*	*Dozen of eggs*	*Minimum daily requirements*
A	1	1	10	1 mg.
C	100	10	10	50 mg.
D	10	100	10	10 mg.
Cost	\$1.00	\$1.10	\$0.50	

What is the linear programming formulation for this problem?

Formulation of Example 2

Let x_M, x_B, and x_E be the number of gallons of milk, pounds of beef, and dozens of eggs, respectively, in the daily diet. The objective is to minimize cost, and the resource restrictions are in the form of lower bounds rather than upper bounds. Therefore, the linear programming model for this problem is the following. Minimize

$$Z = 1.0x_M + 1.1x_B + 0.5x_E ,$$

subject to the restrictions,

$$\begin{aligned} x_M + \quad x_B + 10x_E &\geq 1 \\ 100x_M + \ 10x_B + 10x_E &\geq 50 \\ 10x_M + 100x_B + 10x_E &\geq 10 \end{aligned}$$

and

$$x_M \geq 0,\ x_B \geq 0,\ x_E \geq 0 .$$

In Section 5.6 it is shown that this type of linear programming model can easily be converted into the form presented in Section 5.2.

Example 3

Consider a product mix problem within the context of a simplified oil refinery situation. Suppose that the refinery wishes to blend four petroleum constituents into three grades of gasoline, *A*, *B*, and *C*. The problem is to determine the mix of the four constituents that will maximize profit.

The availability and costs of the four constituents are given below.

Constituent	*Maximum quantity available in barrels per day*	*Cost per barrel*
1	3,000	\$3
2	2,000	\$6
3	4,000	\$4
4	1,000	\$5

To maintain the required quality for each grade of gasoline it is necessary to specify certain maximum or minimum percentages of the constituents in each blend. These are given below, along with the selling price for each grade.

Grade	*Specification*	*Selling price per barrel*
A	Not more than 30% of 1 Not less than 40% of 2 Not more than 50% of 3	$5.50
B	Not more than 50% of 1 Not less than 10% of 2	$4.50
C	Not more than 70% of 1	$3.50

Assume that all other cash flows are fixed so that the "profit" to be maximized is total sales income minus the total cost of the constituents.

Set up a linear programming model for determining the amount and blend of each grade of gasoline.

Formulation of Example 3

Before attempting to write down a linear programming model, careful consideration should always be given to the proper definition of the decision variables. Although this is often obvious, it sometimes becomes the crux of the entire problem. After clearly identifying what information is really desired and the most convenient form for conveying this information by means of decision variables, it is usually easy to write down the objective function and the restrictions on the values of these decision variables.

In this particular problem, the decisions to be made are well defined, but the proper means of conveying this information may require a little thought. Since the amounts of the various gasolines are desired, it would seem natural to define one set of decision variables accordingly. Proceeding tentatively along this line, define $y_i (i = A, B, C)$ as the number of barrels of gasoline grade i produced per day. The blend of each grade is identified by the proportion of each constituent in the gasoline. Therefore, one's first reaction might be to define a set of decision variables, $z_{ij} (i = A, B, C; j = 1, 2, 3, 4)$, as the proportion of constituent j in gasoline grade i. However, recall that both the cost and the availability of the constituents are by quantity, and that this information must be recorded in the objective function and the constraints, respectively. The total quantity of constituent 1 used, for example, is $z_{A1}y_A + z_{B1}y_B + z_{C1}y_C$. But this is definitely not a linear function since it involves products of variables. Therefore, a *linear* programming model cannot be constructed with these decision variables. How can the linearity be restored? Merely by replacing each product of the old decision variables by a single variable! In other words, define $x_{ij} = z_{ij}y_i$ (for $i = A, B, C; j = 1, 2, 3, 4$), and then let the x_{ij} be the decision variables. Thus, x_{ij} is the total number of barrels of constituent j allocated to gasoline grade i per day. The total amount of gasoline grade i produced per day is then $x_{i1} + x_{i2} + x_{i3} + x_{i4}$. The proportion of constituent j in gasoline grade i is $x_{ij}/(x_{i1} + x_{i2} + x_{i3} + x_{i4})$. Therefore, this choice of decision variables conveys all the necessary information and appears to be well-suited to the construction of a linear programming model.

The total profit Z is given by

$$\begin{aligned} Z = 5.5(x_{A1} + x_{A2} + x_{A3} + x_{A4}) + 4.5(x_{B1} + x_{B2} + x_{B3} + x_{B4}) \\ + 3.5(x_{C1} + x_{C2} + x_{C3} + x_{C4}) - 3(x_{A1} + x_{B1} + x_{C1}) \\ - 6(x_{A2} + x_{B2} + x_{C2}) - 4(x_{A3} + x_{B3} + x_{C3}) - 5(x_{A4} + x_{B4} + x_{C4}) . \end{aligned}$$

Thus,

$$\begin{aligned} Z = 2.5x_{A1} - 0.5x_{A2} + 1.5x_{A3} + 0.5x_{A4} + 1.5x_{B1} - 1.5x_{B2} + 0.5x_{B3} \\ - 0.5x_{B4} + 0.5x_{C1} - 2.5x_{C2} - 0.5x_{C3} - 1.5x_{C4} . \end{aligned}$$

Hence, the model is to maximize Z, subject to the restrictions imposed by the availability of constituents and the blend requirements, and by the restrictions that $x_{ij} \geq 0$ for $i = A, B, C$, and $j = 1, 2, 3, 4$. The availability restrictions clearly are

$$\begin{aligned} x_{A1} + x_{B1} + x_{C1} &\leq 3000 \\ x_{A2} + x_{B2} + x_{C2} &\leq 2000 \\ x_{A3} + x_{B3} + x_{C3} &\leq 4000 \\ x_{A4} + x_{B4} + x_{C4} &\leq 1000 . \end{aligned}$$

The blend restrictions for gasoline grade A are

$$\begin{aligned} x_{A1} &\leq 0.3(x_{A1} + x_{A2} + x_{A3} + x_{A4}) \\ x_{A2} &\geq 0.4(x_{A1} + x_{A2} + x_{A3} + x_{A4}) \\ x_{A3} &\leq 0.5(x_{A1} + x_{A2} + x_{A3} + x_{A4}) . \end{aligned}$$

However, these restrictions are not in a convenient form for a linear programming model, so they should be rewritten as

$$\begin{aligned} 0.7x_{A1} - 0.3x_{A2} - 0.3x_{A3} - 0.3x_{A4} &\leq 0 \\ -0.4x_{A1} + 0.6x_{A2} - 0.4x_{A3} - 0.4x_{A4} &\geq 0 \\ -0.5x_{A1} - 0.5x_{A2} + 0.5x_{A3} - 0.5x_{A4} &\leq 0 . \end{aligned}$$

Similarly, the final forms of the blend restrictions for gasoline grades B and C are

$$\begin{aligned} 0.5x_{B1} - 0.5x_{B2} - 0.5x_{B3} - 0.5x_{B4} &\leq 0 \\ -0.1x_{B1} + 0.9x_{B2} - 0.1x_{B3} - 0.1x_{B4} &\geq 0 \\ 0.3x_{C1} - 0.7x_{C2} - 0.7x_{C3} - 0.7x_{C4} &\leq 0 . \end{aligned}$$

Example 4

A certain farming organization operates three farms of comparable productivity. The output of each farm is limited both by the usable acreage and by the amount of water available for irrigation. The data for the upcoming season are the following.

Farm	*Usable acreage*	*Water available in acre feet*
1	400	1500
2	600	2000
3	300	900

The organization is considering three crops for planting which differ primarily in their expected profit per acre and in their consumption of water. Furthermore, the total acreage that can be devoted to each of the crops is limited by the amount of appropriate harvesting equipment available.

Crop	*Maximum acreage*	*Water consumption in acre feet per acre*	*Expected profit per acre*
A	700	5	$400
B	800	4	$300
C	300	3	$100

In order to maintain a uniform workload among the farms, it is the policy of the organization that the percentage of the usable acreage planted must be the same at each farm. However, any combination of the crops may be grown at any of the farms. The organization wishes to know how much of each crop should be planted at the respective farms in order to maximize expected profit. Formulate this as a linear programming problem.

Formulation of Example 4

It is quite clear that the decision variables, $x_{ij} (i = 1, 2, 3; j = A, B, C)$, should be the number of acres at the ith farm devoted to the jth crop. Therefore, the objective is to maximize

$$Z = 400(x_{1A} + x_{2A} + x_{3A}) + 300(x_{1B} + x_{2B} + x_{3B}) + 100(x_{1C} + x_{2C} + x_{3C}),$$

subject to $x_{ij} \geq 0$ (for $i = 1, 2, 3$ and $j = A, B, C$) and the restrictions developed below.

The restrictions on usable acreage at each farm are

$$\begin{aligned} x_{1A} + x_{1B} + x_{1C} &\leq 400 \\ x_{2A} + x_{2B} + x_{2C} &\leq 600 \\ x_{3A} + x_{3B} + x_{3C} &\leq 300\,. \end{aligned}$$

The restrictions on water availability are

$$\begin{aligned} 5x_{1A} + 4x_{1B} + 3x_{1C} &\leq 1500 \\ 5x_{2A} + 4x_{2B} + 3x_{2C} &\leq 2000 \\ 5x_{3A} + 4x_{3B} + 3x_{3C} &\leq \ \ 900\,. \end{aligned}$$

The crop restrictions on acreage are

$$\begin{aligned} x_{1A} + x_{2A} + x_{3A} &\leq 700 \\ x_{1B} + x_{2B} + x_{3B} &\leq 800 \\ x_{1C} + x_{2C} + x_{3C} &\leq 300\,. \end{aligned}$$

Because of the policy of a uniform workload, the equations,

$$\begin{aligned} \frac{x_{1A} + x_{1B} + x_{1C}}{400} &= \frac{x_{2A} + x_{2B} + x_{2C}}{600} \\ \frac{x_{2A} + x_{2B} + x_{2C}}{600} &= \frac{x_{3A} + x_{3B} + x_{3C}}{300} \\ \frac{x_{1A} + x_{1B} + x_{1C}}{400} &= \frac{x_{3A} + x_{3B} + x_{3C}}{300}\,, \end{aligned}$$

must be satisfied. Since the first two equations imply the third, the third equation can be omitted from the model. Furthermore, these equations are not yet in a convenient form for a linear programming model since all of the variables are not on the left-hand side. Hence, the final forms of the uniform workload restrictions are

$$\begin{aligned} 3(x_{1A} + x_{1B} + x_{1C}) - 2(x_{2A} + x_{2B} + x_{2C}) &= 0 \\ x_{2A} + x_{2B} + x_{2C} - 2(x_{3A} + x_{3B} + x_{3C}) &= 0\,. \end{aligned}$$

5.4 LIMITATIONS OF LINEAR PROGRAMMING

Having had a glimpse of the great variety of situations to which linear programming can be applied, it would now be well to survey the underlying assumptions of linear programming that limit its applicability.

5.4.1 **Proportionality**

A primary requirement of linear programming is that the objective function and every constraint function must be linear. This requires, in turn, that the measure of effectiveness and resource usage must be proportional to the level of each activity conducted individually. Programming problems which are non-linear because they lack proportionality arise quite frequently, but their solution is obtainable presently for only certain special cases. It is occasionally possible to reformulate a non-linear programming problem into the linear programming format so that the simplex method can be used, but this is the fortunate exception rather than the rule. This is discussed further in Chapter 17.

Even though it may appear that a problem is completely linear, appearances are sometimes deceiving. It is not always true that both the marginal measure of effectiveness and the marginal usage of each resource will be constants over the entire range of levels of each activity. For example, the unit profit or the number of man hours per unit of production will sometimes change if the production level changes. It is often justifiable to assume linearity as an approximation, but one should make this decision knowingly.

Another subtle type of non-linearity is known as the fixed charge problem. This arises whenever there is a "setup" charge associated with an activity. To illustrate, let x be the level of that activity, and let Δ denote the incremental measure of effectiveness or the incremental resource usage associated with x. Then

$$\Delta = \begin{cases} 0, & \text{if } x = 0 \\ K + cx, & \text{if } x > 0\,, \end{cases}$$

where K is the "fixed charge" associated with any positive level of the activity. Since Δ is not a linear function of x over its entire range (because of its "jump" at $x = 0$), it cannot be included in a linear programming model.

5.4.2 **Additivity**

Suppose that the measure of effectiveness and each resource usage are directly proportional to the level of each activity conducted individually. This is not sufficient to guarantee linearity. A special form of non-linearity will arise if there are joint interactions between some of the activities regarding the total measure of effectiveness or the total usage of some resource. Therefore, it is required that the activities be "additive" with respect to the measure of effectiveness and each resource usage. In other words, the total measure of effectiveness and each total resource usage resulting from the joint performance of the activities must equal the respective sums of these quantities resulting from each activity being conducted individually.

To illustrate, suppose a company is considering the production of two products which would have to compete for the same market. Suppose that the profit would be c_1x_1 if the first product is produced at the rate x_1, but the second product is not produced at all, and that c_2x_2 would be the profit from producing the second product at the rate x_2 if $x_1 = 0$. These two products are additive with respect to profits only if the total profit would be $c_1x_1 + c_2x_2$ when both $x_1 > 0$ and $x_2 > 0$. This would not be true, for example, if prices must be lowered in order to sell both x_1 and x_2 instead of just one or the other.

An example of two activities not additive with respect to resource usage would be where a by-product is produced with the scrap material from the primary product. This material would still have to be procured if only one of the two products were produced. However, the total material requirements if both are produced is less than the sum of the requirements if each were produced individually.

5.4.3 **Divisibility**

It is frequently the case that the decision variables would have physical significance only if they have integer values. However, there is no guarantee that the solution procedure presented in Sec. 5.5 will yield an integer solution. Therefore, another limitation of linear programming in obtaining an optimal solution is that fractional levels of the decision variables must be permissible.

Nevertheless, this solution procedure is often still used when an integer solution is required. If the optimal solution to the linear programming problem happens to include only integers, this is the desired solution to the problem of interest. Otherwise, a common procedure is to round down to the nearest integer. This procedure has two pitfalls. First, this integer solution need not be feasible. This may occur, for example, if some of the a_{ij} terms are negative. Second, even if it is feasible, this solution need not be too near optimality. Reaching the optimal integer solution may require a much more drastic realignment of the decision variable values than merely rounding off. Some progress has been made in recent years in developing solution procedures for finding an optimal integer solution. However, these procedures are not yet very efficient, and their use has been limited.

Integer linear programming is discussed further in Chapter 16.

5.4.4 **Deterministic**

All of the coefficients in the linear programming model (a_{ij}, b_i, and c_j) are assumed to be known constants. In reality, they are frequently neither known nor constants. Linear programming models are usually formulated in order to select some future course of action. Therefore, the coefficients used would be based on a prediction of future conditions. The information available may be inadequate to make a precise determination of the appropriate values for the coefficients. Furthermore, these coefficients may actually be random variables, each with an underlying probability distribution for the value that it will take on when the decision is implemented.

A number of approaches are sometimes used when some of the coefficients are not known constants. Some of these are discussed in Chapter 15, including sensitivity analysis, an extension of sensitivity analysis known as parametric linear programming, and the formal introduction of probabilistic elements into the formulation of the problem.

5.4.5 **Significance of Limitations**

In concluding this discussion of the limitations of linear programming, several points should be emphasized. A practical problem which completely satisfies all of the assumptions of linear programming is very rare indeed. However, the linear programming model is often the most accurate representation available of the problem, which will yield a reasonable recommendation for action before implementation is required. Nevertheless, the user should be fully aware of the assumptions and approximations involved, and should satisfy himself that they are justified before proceeding with a linear programming approach.

5.5 **THE SIMPLEX METHOD**

The "simplex method" is the name that has been attached to a method for solving any linear programming problem. This method is an algebraic procedure which progressively approaches the optimal solution through a well-defined iterative process until optimality is finally reached. The procedure is straightforward and requires only time and patience to execute it manually. However, it is well suited for an electronic computer and is usually done in that way.

The method is first motivated by an illustrative example. A summary outline is then given. The elementary form of the linear programming model presented in Sec. 5.2 is assumed throughout this section. It is also assumed that the b_i are positive. The next section discusses the modifications required for other forms of the model.

Consider the following linear programming model. Maximize

$$Z = 3x_1 + 5x_2 ,$$

subject to the restrictions,

$$\begin{aligned} x_1 &\leq 4 \\ x_2 &\leq 6 \\ 3x_1 + 2x_2 &\leq 18 \\ x_1 \geq 0,\ x_2 &\geq 0 . \end{aligned}$$

How can this problem be solved? For this very simple case where there are only two variables and therefore only two "dimensions" involved, a simple graphical method can be used. This method will also help to illustrate what the simplex method does.

The first step in the graphical method is to depict graphically the values of (x_1, x_2), which are permitted by the restrictions. This is done by drawing the lines which must border the region of permissible values. To begin, note that the restriction, $x_1 \leq 4$, means that (x_1, x_2) cannot lie to the right of the line $x_1 = 4$ in the following figure.

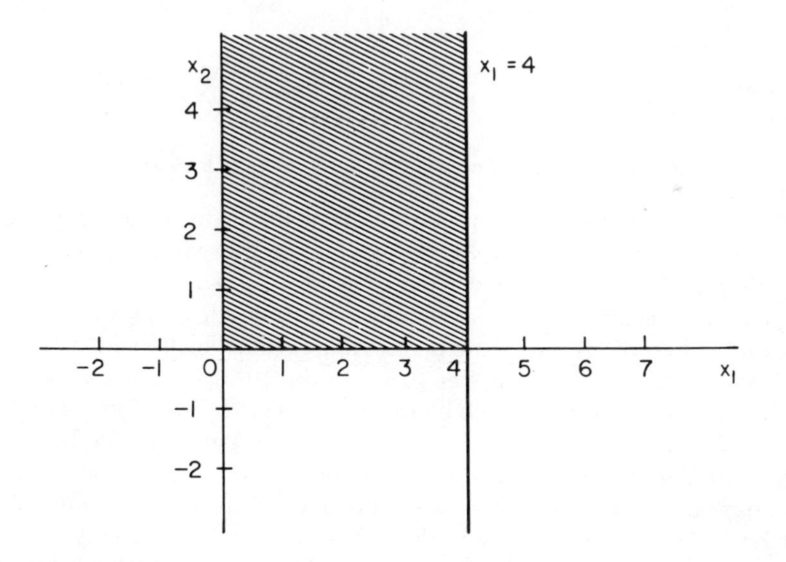

FIGURE 5.1. Shaded area shows permissible values of (x_1, x_2).

Adding the lines $x_2 = 6$, $3x_1 + 2x_2 = 18$, $x_1 = 0$, and $x_2 = 0$, the following region of permissible values of (x_1, x_2) is obtained.

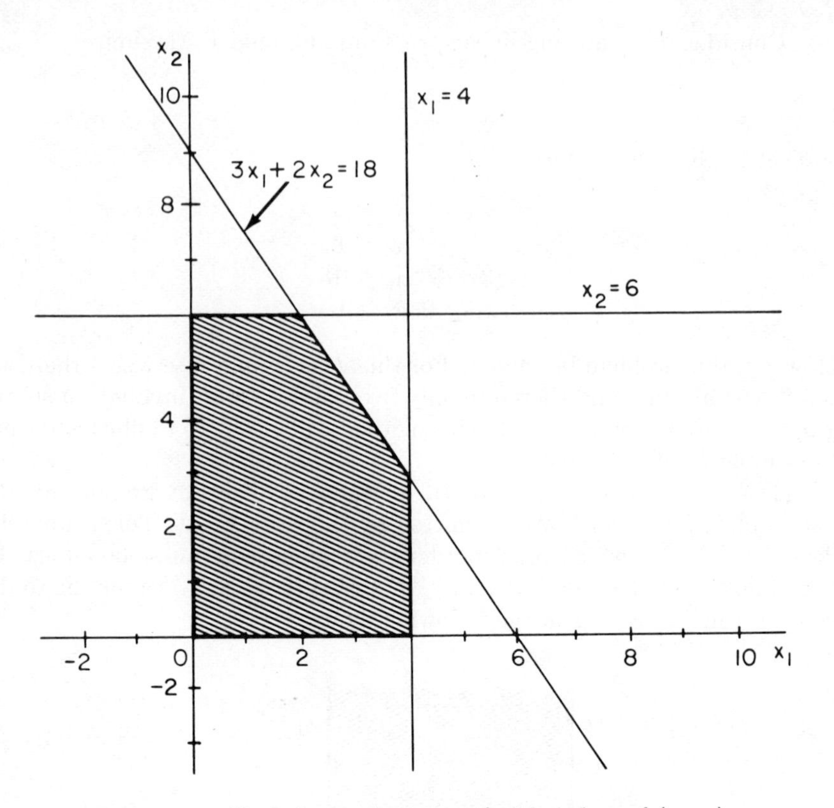

FIGURE 5.2. Shaded area shows permissible values of (x_1, x_2).

The second and final step is to pick out the point in this region which maximizes the value of $Z = 3x_1 + 5x_2$. This step becomes automatic after a little practice, but to discover the basis for it, it is instructive to proceed by trial and error. Try, for example, $Z = 10 = 3x_1 + 5x_2$ to see if there are any values of (x_1, x_2) in the permissible region which yield a value of Z as large as 10. Drawing the line $3x_1 + 5x_2 = 10$, it is seen that there are many points on this line which lie within the region. Therefore, try a larger value of Z, say $Z = 20 = 3x_1 + 5x_2$. Again, a segment of the line, $3x_1 + 5x_2 = 20$, lies within the region so that the maximum permissible value of Z must be at least 20. Notice that this line giving a larger value of Z is farther up and away from the origin than the first line. It may now have become clear that this trial and error procedure involves nothing more than drawing a family of parallel lines containing at least one point in the permissible region and selecting the line which is the greatest distance from the origin (in the direction of increasing values of Z). This line clearly passes through the point (2, 6), as indicated in the figure below, so that the equation is $3x_1 + 5x_2 = 3(2) + 5(6) = 36 = Z$.

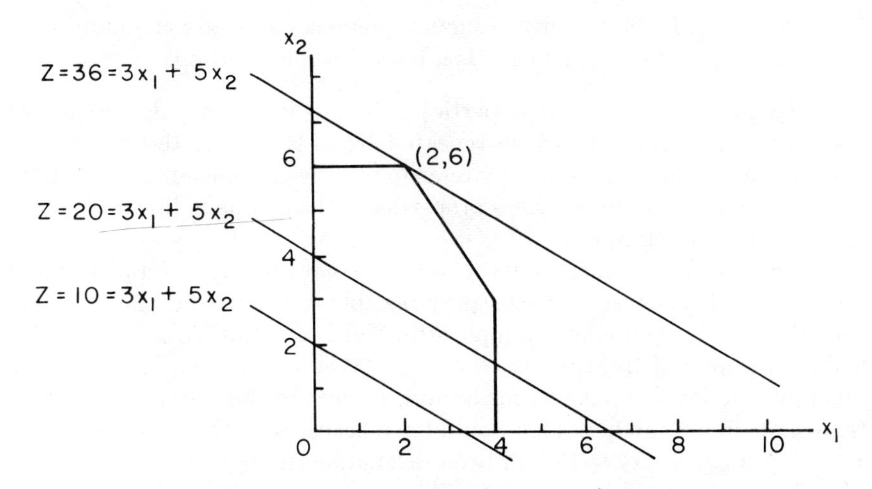

FIGURE 5.3. Value of (x_1, x_2) which maximizes $3x_1 + 5x_2$.

Hence, the desired solution is $x_1 = 2$, $x_2 = 6$.

Unfortunately, this graphical method cannot be used with more than two, or possibly three, variables (dimensions). However, it will help to illustrate the simplex method, which may be used with any number of variables. First, certain terminology should be introduced.

(1) *A feasible solution* is a value of $(x_1, x_2, \cdots, x_n)$ for which all of the restrictions are satisfied.

(2) *An optimal solution* is a feasible solution which maximizes the objective function.

These terms are easily interpreted in terms of the graphical presentation. The feasible solutions are the points within the permissible region, including the boundary points. The optimal solution in the example is $x_1 = 2$, $x_2 = 6$.

It is now possible to state the fundamental properties of linear programming upon which the simplex method is based.

Property 1: The collection of feasible solutions constitute a convex set.[15]

Property 2: If a feasible solution exists, a basic feasible solution[16] exists where the basic feasible solutions correspond to the extreme points[17] of the set of feasible solutions.

Property 3: There exists only a finite number of basic feasible solutions.

[15] See Appendix 1 for a definition and discussion of convex sets.

[16] An algebraic definition of basic feasible solution is given shortly, after the required concepts have been introduced.

[17] See Appendix 1 for the definition of an extreme point of a convex set. In the above example, the extreme points are the corner points, so the basic feasible solutions are (0, 0), (0, 6), (2, 6), (4, 3), and (4, 0).

Property 4: If the objective function possesses a finite maximum, then at least one optimal solution is a basic feasible solution.

The proofs that these properties hold are long; they are available elsewhere,[18] and so will not be repeated here. However, the reader can readily verify their plausibility by referring to the graphical representation. Note that a key reason for these properties is the complete linearity of the linear programming model.

The necessity for including the hypothesis of properties 2 and 4 should be clarified. There need not exist any feasible solutions. This would have been the case in the present example if the third constraint, $3x_1 + 2x_2 \leq 18$, had been replaced by, say, $3x_1 + 2x_2 \geq 100$. Furthermore, the objective function can have $+\infty$ as its maximum, subject to the restrictions, rather than some finite number. This would have occurred in the example if, say, $x_2 \leq 6$ and $3x_1 + 2x_2 \leq 18$ had been deleted, since $x_2 = +\infty$, and, therefore, $Z = +\infty$ would have been feasible according to the model.

The significance of property 1 is indicated later. However, the reader should make an immediate effort to understand the significance of the last three properties. Assume that a feasible solution exists and that the optimal value of Z is finite. Properties 2 and 3 indicate that the number of basic feasible solutions is strictly positive and finite. Property 4 indicates that only this finite number of solutions need be investigated in order to find an optimal solution. Thus, even though there is an infinite number of feasible solutions, attention can be limited to an identifiable finite number of them. Therefore, an optimal solution can always be found by examining each of the basic feasible solutions and selecting the one with the largest value of Z.

Applying this conclusion to the above example, the basic feasible solutions are the following: (0, 0) with $Z = 0$, (0, 6) with $Z = 30$, (2, 6) with $Z = 36$, (4, 3) with $Z = 27$, and (4, 0) with $Z = 12$. Therefore, since 36 is larger than the other values of Z, (2, 6) must be an optimal solution.

To digress for a moment, it should be pointed out that an optimal solution need not be a basic feasible solution. This can occur if a number of feasible solutions tie for the maximum feasible value of Z, since property 4 guarantees only that at least one of these will be a basic feasible solution. To illustrate, suppose that the objective function in the present example were changed to $Z = 3x_1 + 2x_2$. Then the two basic feasible solutions, (2, 6) and (4, 3), and all of the non-basic feasible solutions on the line segment between these two points would have been optimal solutions.

What does the simplex method do? It does not examine all of the basic feasible solutions, since the number of these tends to be huge (even though

[18] See W. W. Garvin, *Introduction to Linear Programming*, McGraw-Hill, New York, 1960, pp. 10–25.

finite) for large problems, and most of them are far from optimal. Instead, it looks at only a relatively few of the promising basic feasible solutions, and then stops when one of these is identified as being optimal. The procedure is to move repeatedly from an extreme point (basic feasible solution) along an "edge" to an adjacent extreme point having a larger value of Z. When no adjacent extreme point has a larger value of Z, an optimal solution has been reached and the procedure stops. Such a solution must be optimal primarily because of property 1 (as well as the linearity of the objective function), as the reader can verify by constructing a counter-example if non-convex sets were possible. Furthermore, an optimal solution must be reached within a finite number of steps (with the theoretically possible exception of degenerate cases, which are discussed in Sec. 5.6.7) for the following reasons. Since each successive extreme point must increase the value of Z, it is impossible to return to an extreme point previously reached. Hence, the number of steps (iterations) can be no greater than the number of extreme points, which is finite by property 3. While what the simplex method basically does may now be clear, the question of how it is done remains to be answered. It was pointed out earlier that the simplex method is an algebraic procedure, whereas the preceding discussion has discussed only geometrical concepts involving extreme points. How does one translate this conceptually geometrical procedure into a usable algebraic procedure?

The crux of the problem is to identify extreme points (basic feasible solutions) algebraically. The problem is complicated by the fact that the model involves inequations, which are much less amenable to algebraic manipulation than equations. Therefore, the first step is to use a trick to convert the model into an equivalent model containing no inequalities (except for the non-negativity constraints, which will cause no serious problems). This trick involves the use of "slack variables."

Consider the inequality $x_1 \leq 4$. How can one replace this inequation by an equivalent equation? Let

$$x_3 = 4 - x_1 ,$$

so that x_3 is just the slack between the two sides of the inequality; hence, x_3 is called a slack variable. Therefore,

$$x_1 + x_3 = 4 .$$

The original constraint, $x_1 \leq 4$, holds whenever $x_3 \geq 0$. Hence, $x_1 \leq 4$ is entirely equivalent to, and will be replaced by, the set of restrictions,

$$x_1 + x_3 = 4$$

and

$$x_3 \geq 0 .$$

Introducing slack variables in an identical fashion for the other restrictions (except for the non-negativity restrictions), the original linear programming model can now be replaced by the equivalent model, maximize

$$Z = 3x_1 + 5x_2,$$

subject to the restrictions,

$$\begin{aligned} x_1 \quad\quad + x_3 \quad\quad\quad &= 4 \\ x_2 \quad\quad + x_4 \quad &= 6 \\ 3x_1 + 2x_2 \quad\quad\quad + x_5 &= 18 \end{aligned}$$

and

$$x_j \geq 0 \quad \text{for} \quad j = 1, 2, \cdots, 5.$$

Although this program is identical to the original problem, this form for the statement of the problem is much more convenient for algebraic manipulation and for identification of basic feasible solutions.

A general algebraic definition of basic feasible solution can now be given.

Definitions: If there are m equations in n variables ($n > m$), a *basic solution* is one obtained by solving for m variables in terms of the remaining ($n - m$) variables, and setting these ($n - m$) variables equal to zero.[19] A *basic feasible solution* is a basic solution where all m of these variables are non-negative (≥ 0).[20] A *non-degenerate basic feasible solution* is a basic solution where these m variables are positive (>0).

The m variables are referred to as "basic" variables or as the variables in the "basis." The ($n - m$) variables are referred to as "non-basic" variables.

To illustrate these definitions, consider the current formulation of the example, which has three constraint equations in five variables. Suppose that x_1, x_2, and x_3 have been chosen as the basic variables, so that x_4 and x_5 are the non-basic variables. Therefore, by setting $x_4 = 0$ and $x_5 = 0$, and solving the three simultaneous equations for x_1, x_2, and x_3 (see Appendix 4 for a systematic way of doing this), it is easy to determine that $x_2 = 6$, $x_1 = 2$, and $x_3 = 2$. Thus, $(x_1, x_2, x_3, x_4, x_5) = (2, 6, 2, 0, 0)$ is a basic solution and, in fact, is a non-degenerate basic feasible solution which corresponds to the extreme point $(x_1, x_2) = (2, 6)$.

For the moment, only non-degenerate basic feasible solutions are to be considered. Degeneracy is discussed in Section 5.6.7.

Now that basic feasible solutions can be identified, it is time to explore how to obtain the initial basic feasible solution, and then how to obtain

[19] This assumes that such a solution exists and is unique. See Appendix 4 for the conditions under which this is true.

[20] A proof that this algebraic definition is equivalent (after dropping the slack variables) to the geometrical definition given earlier in terms of extreme points is given by W. W. Garvin, *op. cit.*, pp. 10 ff.

succeeding basic feasible solutions. As the definition indicates, one can obtain a basic solution in the present example by selecting any three variables and solving for them. However, this basic solution might not be feasible since some of the variables could be negative. Although one could proceed by trial and error to find a basic solution which was also feasible, a much more convenient procedure is used by the simplex method. In particular, the selection of the m slack variables as the initial basic variables always provides an obvious basic feasible solution, given the assumptions stated at the beginning of this section. (The next section discusses other cases.) Thus, applying the definition of basic solution,

$$x_3 = 4 - x_1$$
$$x_4 = 6 - x_2$$
$$x_5 = 18 - 3x_1 - 2x_2 ,$$

and the $(5 - 3)$ non-basic variables, x_1 and x_2, are set equal to zero. Therefore, the initial basic feasible solution is $x_1 = 0$, $x_2 = 0$, $x_3 = 4$, $x_4 = 6$, $x_5 = 18$. (Under the current assumptions, the initial basic feasible solution always is $x_j = 0$ for $j = 1, \cdots, n - m$ and $x_{n-m+i} = b_i$ for $i = 1, 2, \cdots, m$.) Referring back to the geometric approach, this procedure has selected the origin as the initial extreme point (basic feasible solution) so that $Z = 0$.

Given a basic feasible solution, the simplex method obtains the next one (or discovers that the present solution is optimal) by, in effect, selecting an adjacent extreme point which increases the value of Z. The algebraic analogue of an "adjacent" extreme point is a basic feasible solution with all but one of the same variables in the basis. Thus, finding the next basic feasible solution requires selecting one basic variable to leave the present basis and become non-basic, and selecting one non-basic variable to enter the basis as a replacement. How are the "leaving variable" and "entering variable" selected?

The entering variable is chosen by examining the objective function to estimate the effect of each alternative. To illustrate, the two candidates to enter the basis in this case are x_1 and x_2, and the objective function is

$$Z = 3x_1 + 5x_2 .$$

Since an entering variable is changed from a non-basic to a basic variable, its value would be increased from zero to some positive number (except in degenerate cases). Therefore, either x_1 and x_2 would increase Z by entering the basis. It can now be definitely concluded, therefore, that the initial basic feasible solution is not optimal and that one of these two variables should be chosen to enter the basis. A number of methods for choosing between x_1 and x_2 could be used. One is arbitrary selection. However, it would be desirable to have as few iterations as possible in order to decrease computational effort, and a judicious selection might help to move toward the maximum value of Z faster. Another alternative is to try both variables in the basis individually and see which one would increase Z more. The disadvantage is that this requires considerable extra computational effort on each iteration. The method actually used is a compromise that is both convenient and computationally efficient in practice. Without any extra computations, it selects the variable which appears most likely to increase Z by the greatest amount, namely, the one which increases Z at the fastest rate as that variable is increased. (This variable does not necessarily increase Z the most since the constraints may prevent it from becoming as large as some of the other non-basic variables could.) Since x_2 increases Z at the rate of 5 per unit increase in x_2, whereas the rate for x_1 is only 3, x_2 is chosen as the entering variable.

The candidates for the leaving variable are x_3, x_4, and x_5. The first result of a variable leaving the basis would be that the variable would decrease from its positive value to a value of zero. The variable chosen is the one which reaches zero first as the entering basic variable, x_2 in this case, is increased. This increases Z as much as is feasible by increasing x_2, since infeasible, negative-valued variables would result if x_2 were increased any further. This is illustrated by the following table.

Equation	Maximum increase in x_2
$x_3 = 4 - x_1$	no limit
$x_4 = 6 - x_2$	$x_2 \leq 6$
$x_5 = 18 - 3x_1 - 2x_2$	$x_2 \leq 9$

Therefore, x_4 must be chosen as the leaving variable, and x_2 takes on the value six.

The next step is to solve for the new values of the remaining basic variables. This is done by the Gauss–Jordan method of elimination described in Appendix 4, which involves algebraically manipulating the equations until the basic variables (and Z) can be expressed in terms of only the non-basic variables. This requires that each basic variable appear in exactly one equation and that this equation contain no other basic variable; Z plays the role of the basic variable in the objective function equation. To illustrate, consider the original set of equations, where the basic variables are shown in darker print.

$$
\begin{array}{llllll}
(0) & \mathbf{Z} - 3x_1 - 5x_2 & & & & = 0 \\
(1) & \quad x_1 & + \mathbf{x_3} & & & = 4 \\
(2) & \quad\quad x_2 & & + \mathbf{x_4} & & = 6 \\
(3) & \quad 3x_1 + 2x_2 & & & + \mathbf{x_5} & = 18\,.
\end{array}
$$

The variables in the new basis are x_2, x_3, and x_5. The new basic variable, x_2, has replaced x_4 as the basic variable in equation (2). However, x_2 must now be eliminated from the other equations in which it appears. This is done by adding or subtracting a proper multiple of equation (2) to or from the other equations. Thus, the new equation (3) is the old equation (3) minus two times equation (2), and the new equation (0) is the old equation (0) plus five times equation (2). This yields the second set of equations, which is completely equivalent algebraically to the first set, as given below.

$$\begin{array}{lllllll} (0) & \mathbf{Z} - 3x_1 & & & + 5x_4 & & = 30 \\ (1) & \quad\; x_1 & & + \mathbf{x}_3 & & & = 4 \\ (2) & & \mathbf{x}_2 & & + \;\; x_4 & & = 6 \\ (3) & \quad 3x_1 & & & - 2x_4 & + \mathbf{x}_5 & = 6\,. \end{array}$$

For purposes of illustration, exchange the location of x_2 and x_4

$$\begin{array}{lllllll} (0) & \mathbf{Z} - 3x_1 + 5x_4 & & & & = 30 \\ (1) & \quad\; x_1 & & + \mathbf{x}_3 & & & = \;\;4 \\ (2) & & x_4 & & + \mathbf{x}_2 & & = \;\;6 \\ (3) & \quad 3x_1 - 2x_4 & & & & + \mathbf{x}_5 & = \;\;6\,. \end{array}$$

It should now be clear that these manipulations have put the second set of equations into the same convenient form which immediately yielded a solution for the first set. The second basic feasible solution obviously is $x_1 = 0$, $x_2 = 6$, $x_3 = 4$, $x_4 = 0$, and $x_5 = 6$, which yields $Z = 30$.

Is this second basic feasible solution optimal? As before, the answer is obtained by an examination of the objective function. However, the objective function in its original form, $Z = 3x_1 + 5x_2$, can no longer be used! It is now possible to emphasize why the objective function, equation (0), was included in the above manipulations. Since the original form of the objective function now contains a basic variable, x_2, but not one of the non-basic variables, x_4, two things happen. First, it is no longer possible to use the objective function in this form to conclude that increasing the value of x_1 will increase the value of Z. The reason is that this change in x_1 might affect the value of x_2, since x_2 is now a basic variable rather than a non-basic variable fixed at zero. (Note, for example, that two of the original basic variables, x_4 and x_5, were affected by the last change in the basis.) Second, without x_4 in the objective function, no judgment can be made regarding its effect on Z resulting from the interactions of the constraints. Therefore, the objective function must be rewritten in terms of all of the non-basic variables, but none of the basic variables, before one can test for optimality and (if necessary) select an entering variable. This is exactly what was accomplished by the above manipulations of equation (0), which yielded $Z = 30 + 3x_1 - 5x_4$ as the objective function. This objective function is completely equivalent to the original one, in view of the constraints, but is in a form convenient for the present analysis. It can now be concluded that increasing the value of x_1 (with x_4 remaining non-basic and therefore equal to zero) does indeed increase the value of Z, so that the current basic feasible solution is not optimal. Therefore, at least one more iteration is required.

Before proceeding with the next iteration, it is now possible to give a meaningful summary of the simplex method.

SUMMARY OF SIMPLEX METHOD

First iteration: Introduce slack variables. If the model is not in the form being assumed in this section, see Sec. 5.6 for the necessary adjustments. Otherwise, select the slack variables to be the initial basic variables. Go to Step 3.

Step 1. Determine the new entering basic variable: Select the non-basic variable which, when increased, would increase Z at the fastest rate. This is done by checking the magnitude of the coefficients in the current objective function and selecting the non-basic variable whose coefficient is largest (or smallest, if the variables are on the left-hand side). (See Sec. 5.6.6 regarding ties.)

Step 2. Determine the new leaving basic variable: Select the basic variable which reaches zero first as the entering basic variable is increased. This is done by checking each equation to see how much the entering basic variable can be increased before the current basic variable in that equation reaches zero. A formal algebraic procedure for doing this is the following. Let e denote the subscript of the entering basic variable, let a'_{ie} denote its current coefficient in equation i, and let b'_i denote the current right-hand side for this equation ($i = 1, 2, \cdots, m$). Then the upper bound for x_e in equation i is

$$x_e \leq \begin{cases} +\infty, & \text{if } a'_{ie} \leq 0 \\ \dfrac{b'_i}{a'_{ie}}, & \text{if } a'_{ie} > 0 \,. \end{cases}$$

Therefore, determine the equation with the smallest such upper bound and select the current basic variable in that equation as the leaving basic variable. (See Sec. 5.6.7 regarding ties.)

Step 3. Determine the new basic feasible solution: Solve for the basic variables in terms of the non-basic variables by the Gauss–Jordan method of elimination (see Appendix 4), and set the non-basic variables equal to zero.

Step 4. Determine whether this solution is optimal: Check if Z can be increased by increasing any non-basic variable. This is done by eliminating the basic variables from the objective function and then checking the sign of the coefficient of each non-basic variable. If all of these coefficients are non-positive (or non-negative, if the variables are on the left-hand side), then this solution is optimal, so stop. (See Sec. 5.6.8 to interpret zero coefficients.) Otherwise, go to Step 1.

To illustrate, apply these four steps to the next iteration for the present example.

1. Since the current objective function is $Z = 30 + 3x_1 - 5x_4$, increasing only x_1 would increase Z, i.e., x_1 has the largest (and only) positive coefficient. Therefore, x_1 is chosen as the new entering basic variable.
2. The upper limits on x_1 before the basic variable in the respective equations reaches zero are as follows:

$$\text{equation } 1: x_1 \le 4 \text{ for } x_3 \ge 0 .$$
$$\text{equation } 2: \text{No limit on } x_1 \text{ for } x_2 \ge 0 .$$
$$\text{equation } 3: x_1 \le 2 \text{ for } x_5 \ge 0 .$$

   Therefore, x_5 must be chosen as the leaving basic variable.
3. After eliminating x_1 from all equations in the last set except equation (3), where x_1 replaces x_5 as the basic variable, the new set of equations is as follows.

$$\begin{array}{llcl}
(0) & \mathbf{Z} \qquad\qquad + 3x_4 + \ \ x_5 & = & 36 \\
(1) & \qquad\qquad \mathbf{x}_3 + \tfrac{2}{3}x_4 - \tfrac{1}{3}x_5 & = & 2 \\
(2) & \qquad\quad \mathbf{x}_2 \quad + \ x_4 & = & 6 \\
(3) & \quad \mathbf{x}_1 \qquad - \tfrac{2}{3}x_4 + \tfrac{1}{3}x_5 & = & 2
\end{array}$$

   Therefore, the next basic feasible solution is $x_1 = 2$, $x_2 = 6$, $x_3 = 2$, $x_4 = 0$, $x_5 = 0$; the corresponding value of Z is 36.
4. Since the new form of the objective function is $Z = 36 - 3x_4 - x_5$, so that the coefficient of neither non-basic variable is positive, the current basic feasible solution obtained above must be optimal. Therefore, the desired solution to the original form of the problem is $x_1 = 2$, $x_2 = 6$, which yields $Z = 36$.

Reference back to the geometric approach indicates that the simplex method examined three extreme points, (0, 0), (0, 6), and (2, 6), finding that the latter point is the optimal solution.

After a little practice to learn the hows and whys of the simplex method, the reader may then prefer to use a shorthand procedure. Instead of writing down the set of equations in full detail, this procedure involves using a "simplex tableau" to record only the essential information, namely the coefficients of the variables and the constants on the right-hand side of the equations. This saves writing down the symbols for the variables in each of the equations. The following is one form of the simplex tableau, as it would appear for the initial iteration of the example.

Basic variable	Equation number	Coefficient of Z	x_1	x_2	x_3	x_4	x_5	Right side of equation
Z	0	1	−3	−5	0	0	0	0
x_3	1	0	1	0	1	0	0	4
x_4	2	0	0	1	0	1	0	6
x_5	3	0	3	2	0	0	1	18

The basic procedure when using the simplex tableau is the same as before. The only change is that the relevant information is written more concisely. To illustrate this, consider how the four steps of the simplex method would be applied to obtain the next simplex tableau from the one shown above.

1. Consider "row" 0 of the tableau. The smallest coefficient in this row is -5, so x_2 would be chosen as the new entering basic variable.
2. Now consider the positive numbers in the column for x_2 (excluding row 0). Since $6/1 < 18/2$, the new leaving basic variable must be the current basic variable for row 2, namely, x_4.
3. Take these results into account by replacing x_4 by x_2 in the basic variable column. Since 1 is the current coefficient of x_2 in row 2, divide this entire row by 1. Then, since -5, 0, and 2 are the coefficients of x_2 in rows 0, 1, and 3, subtract (-5), 0, and 2 times row 2 from these rows, respectively. The resulting tableau is the following.

Basic variable	Equation number	Coefficient of Z	x_1	x_2	x_3	x_4	x_5	Right side of equation
Z	0	1	−3	0	0	5	0	30
x_3	1	0	1	0	1	0	0	4
x_2	2	0	0	1	0	1	0	6
x_5	3	0	3	0	0	−2	1	6

Thus, the new basic feasible solution is $x_3 = 4$, $x_2 = 6$, $x_5 = 6$, $x_1 = 0$, $x_4 = 0$, with $Z = 30$.

4. Consider row 0 again. Since one of the coefficients (-3) is negative, this solution cannot be optimal, so another iteration is required.

The next iteration is left to the reader as an exercise (see Problem 5).

5.6 COMPLICATIONS AND THEIR RESOLUTION

Thus far, the discussion of the simplex method has focused solely on the case where the linear programming model is in the form presented in Sec. 5.2. The present section discusses the adjustments required for other legitimate forms of the linear programming model. Various complications that can arise when using the simplex method are also discussed.

5.6.1 Minimization

It is common to want to minimize, instead of maximize, the objective function. This occurred, for example, in Example 3 of Sec. 5.3.

Minimization can be handled very easily in either of two ways. One is to make the following very minor changes in the simplex method. The new entering basic variable should be the non-basic variable which would *decrease*, rather than increase, Z at the fastest rate when this variable is increased. Similarly, the test for optimality should be whether Z can be *decreased*, rather than increased, by increasing any non-basic variable.

The second method of handling minimization is to convert the problem into an equivalent problem involving maximization, and then proceed as usual with the simplex method. This conversion consists of maximizing the negative of the original objective function. Minimizing any function $f(x_1, x_2, \cdots, x_n)$ subject to a set of restrictions is completely equivalent to maximizing $-f(x_1, x_2, \cdots, x_n)$ subject to the same set of restrictions.[21] Geometrically, this amounts to reversing directions twice and thereby ending up headed in the original direction. As an example, minimizing $(-3x_1 - 5x_2)$ subject to the set of restrictions for the illustrative problem of Sec. 5.5 is completely equivalent to that very problem, where the objective was to maximize $(3x_1 + 5x_2)$.

5.6.2 Inequality in the Wrong Direction

The direction of an inequality is always reversed when both sides are multiplied by (-1). Therefore, if a constraint (other than the non-negativity restrictions) is in the "wrong" direction $(\geq)$, it can be converted into an inequality in the desired direction $(\leq)$ by changing all of the signs on both sides.

To illustrate, consider the inequality $3x_1 + 2x_2 \geq 18$. This is completely equivalent to the inequality $-3x_1 - 2x_2 \leq -18$.

Unfortunately, it frequently happens that this procedure creates a non-positive value for b_i, as in the above example where $b_i = -18$. The significance of this and the adjustments required are discussed in the next section.

5.6.3 Non-Positive b_i

To illustrate the nature of the problem and its resolution, consider the example of Sec. 5.5 with the one revision that the third restriction is replaced by $-3x_1 - 2x_2 \leq -18$. This may be the original form of the re-

[21] This follows immediately from the facts that (1) $f = -(-f)$, and (2) the smaller f is, the larger $-f$ is, so that (3) minimum $f = -$maximum $(-f)$.

striction, or it may have evolved as illustrated in Sec. 5.6.2. At any rate, after proceeding in the usual manner, the initial set of equations becomes the following:

$$
\begin{array}{llr}
(0) & \mathbf{Z} - 3x_1 - 5x_2 & = 0 \\
(1) & x_1 + \mathbf{x}_3 & = 4 \\
(2) & x_2 + \mathbf{x}_4 & = 6 \\
(3) & -3x_1 - 2x_2 + \mathbf{x}_5 & = -18 .
\end{array}
$$

Continuing to proceed as usual by selecting the slack variables as the initial basic variables, the initial basic solution would be $x_1 = 0$, $x_2 = 0$, $x_3 = 4$, $x_4 = 6$, $x_5 = -18$. But this is not permissible. The solution is not feasible, since it is required that $x_5 \geq 0$.

Hence, the crux of the problem with negative b_i is that there is no longer an obvious initial basic feasible solution with which to start the simplex method. Fortunately, procedures for getting started are available, and are presented subsequently.

When some of the b_i equal zero, but none are negative, it is still possible to use the slack variables to obtain an initial basic feasible solution. However, it would be a degenerate one, which raises the problems to be discussed in Sec. 5.6.7. Fortunately, these problems are not particularly serious. Nevertheless, the option is available (although rarely exercised) to use the first procedure presented below in order to obtain an initial non-degenerate basic feasible solution.

One obvious procedure for trying to obtain an initial basic feasible solution with negative b_i is to select some set other than all of the slack variables as the basic variables, and to solve for them. However, this procedure has some disadvantages. One is that it requires extra algebraic manipulation outside the routine of the simplex method. More seriously, there is a good chance that some of the variables chosen to be basic will have negative values, so the basic solution obtained will still not be feasible. It then becomes a trial and error procedure to find a set of basic variables whose solution is positive.

The procedure which is commonly used instead involves subtracting an "artificial variable" from the left side of each equation with negative b_i, and then using this artificial variable as the initial basic variable for that equation. To illustrate, equation (3) becomes

$$-3x_1 - 2x_2 + x_5 - x_6 = -18 ,$$

which would then be rewritten as

$$3x_1 + 2x_2 - x_5 + x_6 = 18 .$$

The restriction that $x_6 \geq 0$ is also imposed, so that x_6 may henceforth be treated just like the other variables. The obvious initial basic feasible solution to this new problem then becomes $x_1 = 0$, $x_2 = 0$, $x_3 = 4$, $x_4 = 6$, $x_5 = 0$, $x_6 = 18$. Unfortunately, this is not a basic feasible solution to the right problem. The original problem has been considerably revised by the introduction of the artificial variable. Recall that the original third constraint was $-3x_1 - 2x_2 \leq -18$. By adding one variable and subtracting another, both of which can take on any non-negative value, this constraint has, in effect, been eliminated. Since the difference, $x_5 - x_6$, can take on any value, negative or positive, the "restriction" that $-3x_1 - 2x_2 + x_5 - x_6 = -18$ permits x_1 and x_2 to take on any value. In short, the effect of introducing the artificial variable has been to enlarge the original set of feasible solutions.

Now suppose that the simplex method is permitted to proceed and obtain an optimal solution for the revised problem, and that this solution also happens to be feasible for the original problem. What conclusions can be drawn about the original problem? Since the solution maximizes the objective function over a set of possible solutions which includes the entire set permitted by the original problem, this solution must also be optimal for the original problem.

Unfortunately, there is no guarantee that the optimal solution to the revised problem will also be feasible for the original problem. That is, there is no guarantee until another revision is made. This new revision amounts to assigning such an overwhelming penalty to being outside the original set of feasible solutions that the optimal solution to the revised problem must lie within this original set. Recall that the revised problem coincides with the original problem when $x_6 = 0$. Therefore, if the original objective function, $Z = 3x_1 + 5x_2$, is changed to $Z = 3x_1 + 5x_2 - Mx_6$, where M is some *very* large number, then the maximum value of Z must occur when $x_6 = 0$ (x_6 cannot be negative).

This method of driving an artificial variable to zero is known as the "Big M" method. Although this example involved only one artificial variable, any number of them would be handled in exactly the same way. When an electronic computer is to be used, M would be assigned some particular value, such as 9,999,999,999.

Since the artificial variables are used as initial basic variables, they must be removed from the objective function [equation (0)] algebraically before testing for optimality and selecting the entering variable for the first time. Thus, since equations (0) and (3) for the example are

$$(0) \quad Z - 3x_1 - 5x_2 \qquad + Mx_6 = 0$$

$$\vdots$$

$$(3) \qquad 3x_1 + 2x_2 - x_5 + x_6 = 18\,,$$

M times equation (3) should be subtracted from equation (0) to eliminate x_6 from the latter equation, which yields

$$(0) \quad Z + (-3M - 3)x_1 + (-2M - 5)x_2 + Mx_5 = -18M$$

Since two of these three non-basic variables have negative coefficients, the initial basic feasible solution is not optimal, so x_1 would be chosen as the entering basic variable.

An alternative to the Big M method for driving artificial variables to zero is the "two-phase" method. After introducing the artificial variables into the constraints in the same way as described above, this method would proceed as follows. In Phase I, replace the original objective function by the *sum of the artificial variables.* Thus, in the current example, the objective function becomes

$$W = x_6 .$$

Then *minimize* this objective function, subject to the same set of restrictions, by the simplex method. Since the artificial variables, like the other variables, must be non-negative, the minimum feasible value of W must be zero (with the one exception discussed in Section 5.6.9). Therefore, the optimal solution for Phase I must have all of the artificial variables equal to zero, so it must be a basic feasible solution for the original problem. "Phase II" then consists of solving the original problem by the simplex method, using the Phase I solution (without the artificial variables) as the initial basic feasible solution. (The one exception is when one or more of the artificial variables happen to be degenerate basic variables in the Phase I solution. In this case, these variables would be carried along in Phase II, but they would not be allowed to become positive.) As with the Big M method, all of the basic variables would be eliminated from equation (0) before it is used the first time.

Although it is not immediately obvious, the Big M method and the two-phase method always have the same sequence of basic feasible solutions (with the one possible exception of when a tie for the entering basic variable occurs in the two-phase method). Therefore, they are essentially equivalent from a computational viewpoint, so there is little basis for choosing between them. When a digital computer is to be used, the tendency has been to select the two-phase method merely to avoid round-off error caused by manipulating the large value assigned to M.

5.6.4 **Equalities**

Suppose that the example of Sec. 5.5 is modified so that the third constraint becomes an equality, $3x_1 + 2x_2 = 18$, instead of an inequality.

Since it is no longer necessary or meaningful to introduce a slack variable for this constraint, the original set of equations would be the following:

$$\begin{aligned}
&(0) \quad \mathbf{Z} - 3x_1 - 5x_2 &&= 0\\
&(1) \quad x_1 + \mathbf{x}_3 &&= 4\\
&(2) \quad x_2 + \mathbf{x}_4 &&= 6\\
&(3) \quad 3x_1 + 2x_2 &&= 18\,.
\end{aligned}$$

Unfortunately, these equations do not have an obvious initial basic feasible solution, since there is no longer a slack variable to use as the initial basic variable for equation (3). Three procedures are given for circumventing this problem.

One procedure is to make no adjustments and, instead, to solve for different basic solutions from this set of equations until one is found that is feasible. However, as with its twin in the preceding section, this procedure requires considerable computational effort and perhaps many futile attempts before a basic feasible solution is found. In the present example, the only sets of basic variables which yield feasible solutions are x_1, x_2, x_3, and x_1, x_2, x_4.

Another procedure is to replace each constraint involving an equality by two comparable constraints involving inequalities going in opposite directions. To illustrate, $3x_1 + 2x_2 = 18$ would be replaced by

$$3x_1 + 2x_2 \leq 18$$

and

$$3x_1 + 2x_2 \geq 18\,.$$

This is equivalent to the original constraint, and it is already known how to easily obtain an initial basic feasible solution beginning with a set of restrictions involving only inequalities. (The last two sections describe how to handle the greater-than-or-equal inequality.) When there is more than one equality constraint originally, this formulation can be streamlined somewhat by *adding* all of these greater-than-or-equal inequalities together to obtain just one such inequality. This one composite inequality plus the individual less-than-or-equal inequalities are sufficient to insure that all of the original equality constraints will hold.

A third procedure is conceptually similar to the main procedure presented in the preceding section. For each equality, it introduces one artificial variable as if it were a slack variable for an inequality. This revises the original problem by, in effect, replacing each equality by an inequality. After thereby obtaining an obvious initial basic feasible solution for the revised problem, either the Big M method or the two-phase method (described in Sec. 5.6.3) is then used to reach basic feasible solutions for the original problem. To illustrate for the present example, equation (3), $3x_1 + 2x_2 = 18$, is replaced by $3x_1 + 2x_2 + x_5 = 18$, where x_5 is the artificial variable introduced to provide an initial basic variable for that equation. The initial solution thus becomes $x_1 = 0$, $x_2 = 0$, $x_3 = 4$, $x_4 = 6$, $x_5 = 18$. With the Big M method, the objective function is also changed to $Z = 3x_1 + 5x_2 - Mx_5$, where M is a very large number in order to eventually force x_5 to zero. Hence, the original equation (0) is $Z - 3x_1 - 5x_2 + Mx_5 = 0$, although the basic variable x_5 must be removed algebraically (as in Sec. 5.6.3) by subtracting M times the new equation (3) before equation (0) is used.

This last procedure is the one generally used since it adds a minimum of effort to both the set-up and execution of the simplex method.

5.6.5 Variables Unconstrained in Sign

Although the decision variables must be restricted to non-negative values in most practical problems, this is not always the case. However, the simplex method assumes non-negative variables. Fortunately, it is possible to convert a problem involving variables unconstrained in sign into an equivalent problem involving only non-negative variables.

A variable unconstrained in sign can always be expressed as the difference of two non-negative variables. Thus, given that $y \geq 0$ and $z \geq 0$, then x can be expressed as $x = y - z$ by letting $y = x$, $z = 0$ when $x \geq 0$ and letting $z = -x$, $y = 0$ when $x \leq 0$. Therefore, one may replace each unconstrained variable in the model by the difference of two new non-negative variables. Since the simplex method only examines basic feasible solutions (extreme points), it will always have at least one of these two non-negative variables set equal to zero.

To illustrate, suppose that the example of Sec. 5.5 is modified by deleting the requirement that $x_1 \geq 0$. Letting $x_1 = y_1 - z_1$, where $y_1 \geq 0$, $z_1 \geq 0$, the model becomes the following. Maximize

$$Z = 3y_1 - 3z_1 + 5x_2,$$

subject to the restrictions,

$$\begin{aligned} y_1 - z_1 \qquad\quad &\leq 4 \\ x_2 &\leq 6 \\ 3y_1 - 3z_1 + 2x_2 &\leq 18 \end{aligned}$$

and

$$y_1 \geq 0,\ z_1 \geq 0,\ x_2 \geq 0\,.$$

When the original problem has more than one variable which is unconstrained in sign, this formulation may be streamlined somewhat by replacing each such variable x_j by $x_j = y_j - z$ instead, where $y_j \geq 0$ and $z \geq 0$ as before, but z is the *same* variable for all relevant j. The interpretation of z in this case is that $-z$ is the current value of the largest negative original variable, so that y_j is the amount by which x_j exceeds this value.

5.6.6 Tie for the Entering Basic Variable

It can easily occur by chance that two or more non-basic variables will share the maximum positive coefficient in the current form of the objective function. These non-basic variables would then be tied for the honor of becoming the next entering basic variable. This would occur, for example, if the current objective function were $Z = 2x_1 + 2x_2 + x_3$, since x_1 and x_2 would be tied. How should this tie be broken?

The answer is that the selection between the contenders may be made arbitrarily. The optimal solution will be reached eventually, regardless of the variable chosen, and there is no convenient method for predicting in advance which choice will lead there sooner.

5.6.7 Tie for the Leaving Basic Variable—Degeneracy

When several basic variables reach zero simultaneously as the entering basic variable is being increased, does it matter which one is chosen as the leaving basic variable? Theoretically, it does matter and in a very critical way. To illustrate the cause for concern, modify the example of Sec. 5.5 by replacing the third constraint, $3x_1 + 2x_2 \leq 18$, by $3x_1 + 2x_2 \leq 12$. The initial set of equations would then become the following:

$$
\begin{array}{lllllll}
(0) & \mathbf{Z} - 3x_1 - 5x_2 & & & & = & 0 \\
(1) & \quad x_1 & + \mathbf{x_3} & & & = & 4 \\
(2) & \quad\quad x_2 & & + \mathbf{x_4} & & = & 6 \\
(3) & \quad 3x_1 + 2x_2 & & & + \mathbf{x_5} & = & 12.
\end{array}
$$

As before, x_2 would be chosen as the next entering basic variable, but which variable should leave the basis? Both x_4 and x_5 reach zero simultaneously as x_2 is increased to six. Suppose that x_4 is chosen arbitrarily. The resulting set of equations is given below:

$$
\begin{array}{lllllll}
(0) & \mathbf{Z} - 3x_1 & & + 5x_4 & & = & 30 \\
(1) & \quad x_1 & + \mathbf{x_3} & & & = & 4 \\
(2) & \quad\quad \mathbf{x_2} & & + x_4 & & = & 6 \\
(3) & \quad 3x_1 & & - 2x_4 & + \mathbf{x_5} & = & 0.
\end{array}
$$

The corresponding basic feasible solution is $x_1 = 0$, $x_2 = 6$, $x_3 = 4$, $x_4 = 0$, $x_5 = 0$, which is degenerate since a basic variable, x_5, is zero. Since equation (0) indicates that this solution is not optimal, x_1 is chosen as the next entering basic variable. Since x_1 cannot be increased without driving x_5 negative, x_5 must be chosen as the leaving basic variable. This leads to the following set of equations:

$$
\begin{array}{lllllll}
(0) & \mathbf{Z} & & & + 3x_4 & + \ x_5 = & 30 \\
(1) & & & \mathbf{x}_3 & + \frac{2}{3}x_4 & - \frac{1}{3}x_5 = & 4 \\
(2) & & \mathbf{x}_2 & & + \ x_4 & = & 6 \\
(3) & \mathbf{x}_1 & & & - \frac{2}{3}x_4 & + \frac{1}{3}x_5 = & 0.
\end{array}
$$

Hence, the optimal solution for this problem is $x_1 = 0$, $x_2 = 6$, $x_3 = 4$, $x_4 = 0$, $x_5 = 0$, as obtained in the preceding iteration.

What were the significant implications in this example? Notice first that the tie for the leaving basic variable inevitably led immediately to a degenerate basic feasible solution, since the candidate(s) not chosen to leave the basis must still take on a value of zero. If such a variable is subsequently chosen to leave the basis before its value is changed, the corresponding entering basic variable must also remain zero, and the value of Z must remain unchanged. But if Z may remain the same rather than increase at each iteration, what is to prevent the simplex method from going round in a loop repeating the same sequence of solutions periodically rather than eventually increasing Z toward the optimal solution? This did not happen in the example where the optimal solution had already been reached, but other examples have been artificially constructed so that they do become entrapped in just such a perpetual loop.

Fortunately, although it has been shown that such a perpetual loop is theoretically possible, it has never been known to occur in practical problems. If a loop were to occur, one could always get out of it by changing the choice of the leaving basic variable. Furthermore, special rules[22] have been constructed for breaking ties so that such loops are always avoided. However, such rules have been virtually ignored in actual application without any mishaps, and they will not be repeated here.

5.6.8 **Multiple Solutions**

Suppose that the example of Sec. 5.5 is modified so that the objective function is $Z = 3x_1 + 2x_2$. Referring to the graphic presentation, it is clear that, although (2, 6) is still optimal, (4, 3) and the entire line segment between these two extreme points are also optimal. They all yield the maximum value of Z, which is 18. The existence of such multiple solutions would often be of interest. There may be qualitative factors not included in the model which would generate a preference for one or more of these multiple solutions over the others. However, the simplex method stops as soon as it finds one optimal solution. Does it also provide any clue as to the existence of other optimal solutions?

The answer is that it does. If the simplex method were applied to the

[22] See, for example, A. Charnes, "Optimality and Degeneracy in Linear Programming," *Econometrica*, **20**, 160–170 (1952).

present example, it would stop after obtaining the following third set of equations:

$$\begin{array}{llr}
(0) & \mathbf{Z} \quad + 0x_3 \qquad\quad + x_5 & = 18 \\
(1) & \quad \mathbf{x}_1 \; + \; x_3 & = 4 \\
(2) & \qquad\quad \tfrac{3}{2}x_3 + \mathbf{x}_4 - \tfrac{1}{2}x_5 & = 3 \\
(3) & \quad \mathbf{x}_2 - \tfrac{3}{2}x_3 \qquad + \tfrac{1}{2}x_5 & = 3\,.
\end{array}$$

Since Z cannot be increased any further, $x_1 = 4$, $x_2 = 3$, $x_3 = 0$, $x_4 = 3$, $x_5 = 0$ has been identified as an optimal solution. How does one know that there are other optimal solutions? Note that one of the non-basic variables, x_3, has a zero coefficient in the current objective function, $Z = 18 + 0x_3 - x_5$. Recall that each coefficient of a non-basic variable in the current objective function indicates the rate at which Z increases as that variable is increased. Therefore, bringing x_3 into the basis would neither increase nor decrease Z, so that the corresponding basic feasible solution must also be optimal. This solution may be completely identified by resuming the simplex method to obtain the next set of equations given below:

$$\begin{array}{llr}
(0) & \mathbf{Z} \qquad\quad + 0x_4 + \; x_5 & = 18 \\
(1) & \quad \mathbf{x}_1 \qquad - \tfrac{2}{3}x_4 + \tfrac{1}{3}x_5 & = 2 \\
(2) & \qquad\quad \mathbf{x}_3 + \tfrac{2}{3}x_4 - \tfrac{1}{3}x_5 & = 2 \\
(3) & \qquad \mathbf{x}_2 \quad + \; x_4 & = 6\,.
\end{array}$$

Hence, $x_1 = 2$, $x_2 = 6$, $x_3 = 2$, $x_4 = 0$, $x_5 = 0$ is the second optimal basic feasible solution. Since the current objective function, $Z = 18 + 0x_4 - x_5$, also has a zero coefficient for a non-basic variable, still another iteration could be executed, but this would only lead back to the identical set of equations obtained before. Therefore, there are only the two optimal basic feasible solutions in this case. However, any weighted average of optimal solutions must also be optimal, so that there is an infinite number of optimal non-basic feasible solutions. These correspond to the points on the line segment between the two optimal extreme points.

5.6.9 No Feasible Solution

Sections 5.6.3 and 5.6.4 were basically concerned with the problem of obtaining an initial basic feasible solution when an obvious one is not available. The procedures especially advocated involved constructing an artificial problem and finding an initial basic feasible solution for this revised problem instead. This enabled the simplex method to begin its pilgrimage toward the basic feasible solutions and ultimately the optimal solution for the original problem.

However, users of these procedures should be wary of a certain pitfall. If an initial basic feasible solution is not obvious, this may be the case for the very good reason that there are no feasible solutions at all! Nevertheless, by using these procedures to construct a fictitious "feasible" solution, there is nothing to stop the simplex method from proceeding as usual and ultimately reporting a supposedly optimal solution.

There are at least two ways in which the user can safeguard against being duped into adopting a solution that is infeasible. First, it would be well to satisfy himself that there must be some feasible solutions before incurring the time and expense of applying the simplex method. The model might have been improperly constructed or the constraints might be so restrictive (by necessity or by choice) that they are actually incompatible. Second, the solution reported by the simplex method should always be checked for feasibility. This can be done by checking each restriction to verify that it is satisfied. However, those procedures which use artificial variables provide their own signpost for checking feasibility. If there are no feasible solutions, then at least one of the artificial variables which were supposed to be driven to zero will instead appear as a positive basic variable in the solution purported to be optimal. Otherwise, they will all be zero.

5.6.10 Unbounded Optimal Solutions

Rather than having no feasible solutions, it is also possible that the restrictions, or lack of them, permit one or more variables to increase without limit and never violate feasibility. How does the simplex method handle this case? If one of these variables is ever selected as an entering basic variable, it can be increased indefinitely (and, therefore, Z as well) without driving any of the present basic variables negative. Hence, there would be no leaving basic variable, so the simplex method would then terminate with the information that the optimal solution is unbounded. (See Problem 10 for an illustration.) The theoretical solution would give that variable and Z a value of $+\infty$. However, if the problem has physical significance, it may well be that important constraints were omitted or that a computational mistake was made.

5.7 THEORY AND EXTENSIONS OF LINEAR PROGRAMMING

5.7.1 Duality Theory

One of the most important discoveries in the early development of linear programming was the concept of duality and its many important ramifications. This discovery revealed that every linear programming problem has associated with it another linear programming problem called the dual. Although it appears at first glance that there is only a superficial relationship between the dual problem and the original problem (called the primal), the relationship is actually a very intimate and useful one.

Consider any linear programming problem in the form exhibited in Sec. 5.2.

Primal Problem: Find $x_j \geq 0$ $(j = 1, 2, \cdots, n)$ in order to maximize

$$Z_x = c_1x_1 + c_2x_2 + \cdots + c_nx_n ,$$

subject to the restrictions,

$$\begin{aligned} a_{11}x_1 + a_{12}x_2 + \cdots + a_{1n}x_n &\leq b_1 \\ a_{21}x_1 + a_{22}x_2 + \cdots + a_{2n}x_n &\leq b_2 \\ &\vdots \\ a_{m1}x_1 + a_{m2}x_2 + \cdots + a_{mn}x_n &\leq b_m . \end{aligned}$$

The corresponding dual problem is obtained by transposing the rows and columns of constraint coefficients, transposing the coefficients of the objective function and the right-hand side of the constraints, reversing the inequalities, and minimizing instead of maximizing.

Dual Problem: Find $y_i \geq 0$ $(i = 1, 2, \cdots, m)$ in order to minimize

$$Z_y = b_1y_1 + b_2y_2 + \cdots + b_my_m ,$$

subject to the restrictions,

$$\begin{aligned} a_{11}y_1 + a_{21}y_2 + \cdots + a_{m1}y_m &\geq c_1 \\ a_{12}y_1 + a_{22}y_2 + \cdots + a_{m2}y_m &\geq c_2 \\ &\vdots \\ a_{1n}y_1 + a_{2n}y_2 + \cdots + a_{mn}y_m &\geq c_n . \end{aligned}$$

Thus, the coefficients in the jth constraint of the dual problem are the coefficients of x_j in the primal problem constraints, and vice versa; furthermore, the right-hand side of the jth dual problem constraint is the coefficient of x_j in the primal problem objective function, and vice versa. Hence, there is one dual variable for each primal constraint and one dual constraint for each primal variable.

To illustrate, consider the example of Sec. 5.5. Maximize

$$Z_x = 3x_1 + 5x_2 ,$$

subject to

$$\begin{aligned} x_1 \qquad &\leq 4 \\ x_2 &\leq 6 \\ 3x_1 + 2x_2 &\leq 18 \end{aligned}$$

and

$$x_j \geq 0 \ (j = 1, 2) .$$

The corresponding dual problem is to minimize

$$Z_y = 4y_1 + 6y_2 + 18y_3,$$

subject to

$$\begin{aligned} y_1 \qquad + 3y_3 &\geq 3 \\ y_2 + 2y_3 &\geq 5 \end{aligned}$$

and

$$y_i \geq 0 \qquad \text{for } i = 1, 2, 3.$$

A dual problem also exists for any linear programming problem that is not in the form considered above. In particular, suppose that the ith constraint is in the form of an equality instead of an inequality. The dual problem would then be constructed just as before, except that the ith dual variable would be unrestricted in sign rather than restricted to be non-negative. Similarly, if the non-negativity restriction is removed for the jth primal variable, the resulting change in the dual problem is that the jth constraint is in the form of an equation rather than an inequation.

The above rules, plus the tricks introduced in Secs. 5.6.1 and 5.6.2, make it possible to construct the dual problem corresponding to any linear programming problem. This then raises an interesting question. Since the dual problem is itself a linear programming problem, it, too, must have an associated dual problem. So what is the "dual of the dual"? As summarized in Theorem 5.1, the answer is that, given any primal problem and its dual problem, the dual problem for this dual problem coincides exactly with this primal problem.

Theorem 5.1: The dual of the dual is the primal.

The reader may find it instructive to prove this theorem himself (see Problem 12).

The theorem implies a completely symmetrical relationship between the primal and dual problems. In fact, it is immaterial which problem is called the primal and which is called the dual. Anything that can be said about one problem with respect to the other also holds in reverse.

The significance of the existence of the dual problem is now to be explored.

It will be helpful to introduce some new notation before stating the fundamental theorem of duality theory (known as the Dual Theorem) and related results. In general, let a variable with an asterisk in its exponent denote the optimal value of that variable.[23] Particular applications of this convention follow.

[23] When multiple optimal solutions exist, let "the" optimal solution or value refer to the one that would be initially obtained by the simplex method.

Definition: Let Z_x^*, Z_y^*, x_j^*, and y_i^* denote the optimal value of Z_x, Z_y, x_j, and y_i, respectively. Thus,

$$Z_x^* = \sum_{j=1}^{n} c_j x_j^* \quad \text{and} \quad Z_y^* = \sum_{i=1}^{m} b_i y_i^* .$$

Theorem 5.2 (Dual Theorem): Assume that finite feasible solutions exist for both the primal problem and the dual problem.[24] Then there exists a finite optimal solution for both problems and, furthermore,

$$Z_x^* = Z_y^* .$$

Restating the Dual Theorem verbally, the maximum feasible value of the primal objective function equals the minimum feasible value of the dual objective function. A proof is given in Chapter 15.

The relationship between the primal and dual problem is even more intimate than indicated by Theorems 5.1 and 5.2. A rigorous examination of this relationship is too advanced a topic to be covered in depth here, so it is postponed to Chapter 15. However, it would be worthwhile to summarize briefly the most important ideas, as follows.

First, it should be noted that the simplex method automatically solves both the primal problem and its dual problem simultaneously. In particular, the optimal value of the ith dual variable ($i = 1, 2, \cdots, m$) equals the coefficient of the ith slack variable in the final equation (0) obtained by the simplex method. To illustrate, consider the example given above. The final equation (0) for this primal problem was found in Sec. 5.5 to be $Z_x + 3x_4 + x_5 = 36$ (where x_3, x_4, and x_5 are the slack variables). Therefore, the optimal solution for the dual problem is $y_1 = 0$, $y_2 = 3$, $y_3 = 1$. (Note that the corresponding value of the dual objective function is $Z_y = 4y_1 + 6y_2 + 18y_3 = 36 = Z_x$, as indicated by the Dual Theorem.)

This relationship provided by the simplex method has a number of important implications. One is that, because of Theorem 5.1, the simplex method can be applied directly to whichever problem (the primal or the dual) appears to require less computational effort. Another is that alternate solution procedures can be devised that solve the primal problem by operating directly on the dual problem. One such procedure, called the dual simplex method, is described in detail in Chapter 15. Such a procedure is also extremely useful for conducting certain kinds of sensitivity analysis on the primal problem. Furthermore, duality relationships provide important insights when performing such an analysis.

[24] The Dual Theorem is stated in this form in order to focus attention on the primary result, namely, $Z_x^* = Z_y^*$. However, it should be noted that there is a slightly stronger form of the theorem which additionally states that if a finite feasible solution exists for one of the two problems (primal or dual), and if its optimal solution is finite, then a finite feasible solution exists for the other problem also.

Finally, the optimal dual solution provides a very useful economic interpretation of the primal problem. To indicate this, let y_i^* denote the optimal value of the ith dual variable $y_i (i = 1, 2, \cdots, m)$, and consider the corresponding ith constraint in the primal problem, $a_{i1}x_1 + a_{i2}x_2 + \cdots + a_{in}x_n \leq b_i$. Recall that, in Sec. 5.2, b_i was interpreted as the amount of resource i available, whereas, the optimal value of the objective function, $Z_x = Z_x^*$, might be interpreted as the total profit obtained by using the optimal solution. In this case, y_i^* indicates the rate at which profit would increase (decrease) if the amount of resource i available were increased (decreased) over a certain range. (This range is the range of b_i over which the original optimal basis is not changed.) Thus, y_i^* may be interpreted as the "marginal value" of resource i. For example, if one more unit of resource i were made available, the resulting increase in profit would be y_i^* (assuming that the optimal basis remains the same).

The ideas summarized above, and a number of related concepts, are discussed in more detail in Chapter 15.

5.7.2 Sensitivity Analysis

Practical problems that are formulated as linear programming problems are seldom completely "solved" as soon as the simplex method identifies the optimal solution for the model. The parameters of the model (c_j, a_{ij}, b_i) are seldom known with complete certainty. Therefore, it is usually advisable to perform a sensitivity analysis to determine the effect on the optimal solution if particular parameters take on other possible values. If the optimal value of the objective function is relatively sensitive to changes in certain parameters, special care should be taken in estimating these parameters and in selecting a solution which does well for most of their likely values. A second situation where additional computations are required is where changes must be made in the original model, either because errors and omissions were discovered or because new information indicates that the estimates of the parameter values should be revised.

Fortunately, it is not necessary to resolve the problem from the beginning each time a minor change is made in the model. Given the previous optimal solution and the corresponding set of equations, it is usually possible to check whether the same basis is optimal or not and, if not, to use it as a starting point to solve quickly for the new optimal solution.

To illustrate, consider the case where the coefficient of x_j in the objective function c_j is changed to a new value c_j' after the optimal solution to the original problem has been obtained. It is clear that this original optimal solution is still feasible since the constraints are unchanged. The question that needs to be answered is whether this solution is still optimal or not. To determine this, consider what the effect of changing this coefficient has been. A review of the simplex method indicates, if all of the calculations were to be repeated with c_j replaced by c_j', the only resulting change in the final set of equations is that the coefficient of x_j in the final equation (0) is reduced by $(c'_j - c_j)$. Therefore, if x_j is a *non-basic* variable in the original optimal solution, then this new equation (0) can now be checked in the usual way (i.e., by checking whether all of the coefficients of non-basic variables are non-negative) to determine whether this solution is optimal now. Actually, since only the coefficient of x_j has changed, it is only necessary to check whether this coefficient is still non-negative. Thus, if it is non-negative, the solution is still optimal; otherwise, it becomes necessary to make x_j an entering basic variable and to continue with the simplex method until the new optimal solution has been identified.

Now consider the case where x_j is a *basic* variable in the original optimal solution. For this case, it is necessary to interject one additional step in the above procedure before using the new equation (0) to test for optimality. Recall that this test (developed in Sec. 5.5) requires that all basic variables (other than Z) have been eliminated from equation (0). However, by changing c_j to c'_j, the coefficient of x_j in the final equation (0) has been changed from zero to $(c_j - c'_j)$. Therefore, the one additional step needed is that this non-zero coefficient must be eliminated in the usual way, i.e., by subtracting $(c_j - c'_j)$ times the final equation containing x_j as its basic variable from equation (0). After this is done, the test for optimality would be applied, and, if the solution is no longer optimal, then the simplex method would be resumed, starting with this basic feasible solution.

To demonstrate how this is done, consider the example used in Sec. 5.5. Suppose that, after obtaining the optimal solution shown there, the original objective function is changed from $Z = 3x_1 + 5x_2$ to $Z = 3x_1 + x_2$. Recall that the final equation (0), given in Sec. 5.5, is

$$(0) \quad Z + 3x_4 + x_5 = 36 .$$

Therefore, since the original equation (0) has been changed from $Z - 3x_1 - 5x_2 = 0$ to $Z - 3x_1 + (-5 + 4)x_2 = 0$, this final equation (0) is thereby changed to

$$(0) \quad Z + 4x_2 + 3x_4 + x_5 = 36 .$$

Since x_2 is a basic variable, it must then be eliminated from this equation (0) by subtracting 4 times equation (2) (which is $x_2 + x_4 = 6$ in the final set of equations), which yields

$$(0) \quad Z - x_4 + x_5 = 12 .$$

Since x_4 now has a negative coefficient, the original optimal solution ($x_1 = 2$, $x_2 = 6$, $x_3 = 2$, $x_4 = 0$, $x_5 = 0$) is no longer optimal, and x_4 is chosen as the new entering basic variable. One more iteration of the simplex method then yields the solution, $x_1 = 4$, $x_2 = 3$, $x_3 = 0$, $x_4 = 3$, $x_5 = 0$, which proves to be the new optimal solution.

Other kinds of changes in the original model can also be tested in a fairly similar manner. In particular, changes in b_i or a_{ij} (as given in Section 5.2), or the addition of a new constraint or variable, can be handled. However, most of these changes require a somewhat more sophisticated analysis than did a change in c_j, so a description is deferred until Chapter 15.

Finally, it should be noted that this kind of analysis can still be used when a number of changes are being made simultaneously. Furthermore, there even exist systematic procedures (called "parametric linear programming") for studying the effect of simultaneous changes as the magnitude of these changes increases. This, too, is presented in Chapter 15.

5.7.3 Generalizations of Linear Programming

The linear programming model may be generalized in several ways by dropping certain of the underlying assumptions presented in Sec. 5.4. For example, suppose that the "proportionality" and "additivity" assumptions are dropped, so that the objective function and constraint functions may be non-linear. This leads to the general area of "non-linear programming," which is presented in Chapter 17. As indicated there, no satisfactory procedure exists for solving the general non-linear programming problem. However, if it is at least assumed that the constraint functions are convex[25] and the objective function is concave,[25] then there are several practical solution procedures available. As might be expected, these procedures tend to be much less efficient than the simplex method, except for special cases.

Another generalization is where the "divisibility" assumption is dropped instead, so that the decision variables can only have, say, integer values. This leads to the general area of "integer linear programming," presented in Chapter 16. Although solution procedures have been developed for this problem, they generally are computationally feasible only for relatively small problems.

Finally, suppose that the "deterministic" assumption is dropped instead, so that some or all of the parameters of the linear programming model may be random variables rather than constants. This leads to the general area of "linear programming under risk," included in Chapter 15. Several fairly reasonable approaches are available for formulating such a problem and for solving certain special cases.

SELECTED REFERENCES

1. Dantzig, George B., *Linear Programming and Extensions,* Princeton University Press, Princeton, N.J., 1963.

[25] See Appendix 1 for a definition of convex function and concave function.

2. Garvin, Walter W., *Introduction to Linear Programming,* McGraw-Hill, New York, 1960.
3. Hadley, G., *Linear Programming,* Addison-Wesley, Reading, Mass., 1962.
4. Vazsonyi, Andrew, *Scientific Programming in Business and Industry,* Wiley, New York, 1958.

PROBLEMS

1. An airlines company is considering the purchase of new long-range, medium-range, and short-range jet passenger airplanes. The purchase price would be $6,700,000 for each long-range plane, $5,000,000 for each medium-range plane, and $3,500,000 for each short-range plane. The Board of Directors has authorized a maximum commitment of $150,000,000 for these purchases. Regardless of which airplanes are purchased, air travel of all distances is expected to be sufficiently large that these planes would be utilized at essentially maximum capacity. It is estimated that the net annual profit (after subtracting capital recovery costs) would be $420,000 per long-range plane, $300,000 per medium-range plane, and $230,000 per short-range plane.

It is predicted that enough trained pilots will be available to the company to man 30 new airplanes. If only short-range planes were purchased, the maintenance facilities would be able to handle 40 new planes. However, each medium-range plane is equivalent to $1\frac{1}{3}$ short-range planes, and each long-range plane is equivalent to $1\frac{2}{3}$ short-range planes in terms of their use of the maintenance facilities.

The information given above was obtained by a preliminary analysis of the problem. A more detailed analysis will be conducted subsequently. However, using the above data as a first approximation, management wishes to know how many planes of each type should be purchased in order to maximize profit. Formulate the linear programming model for this problem. (Ignore the fact that the number of airplanes must be an integer. Integer programming is discussed in Chapter 16.)

2. A certain corporation has three branch plants with excess production capacity. All three plants have the capability for producing a certain product, and management has decided to use some of the excess production capacity in this way. This product can be made in three sizes—large, medium, and small—which yield a net unit profit of $12, $10, and $9, respectively. Plants 1, 2, and 3 have the excess manpower and equipment capacity to produce 500, 600, and 300 units per day of this product, respectively, regardless of the size or combination of sizes involved. However, the amount of available in-process storage space also imposes a limitation on the production rates. Plants 1, 2, and 3 have 9000, 8000, and

3500 square feet of in-process storage space available for this product. Each unit of the large, medium, and small sizes produced per day requires 20, 15, and 12 square feet, respectively.

Sales forecasts indicate that 600, 800, and 500 units of the large, medium, and small sizes, respectively, can be sold per day.

In order to maintain a uniform workload among the plants and to retain some flexibility, management has decided that the additional production assigned to each plant must use the same percentage of the excess manpower and equipment capacity.

Management wishes to know how much of each of the sizes should be produced by each of the plants in order to maximize profit. Formulate the linear programming model for this problem.

3. An investor has money-making activities A and B available at the beginning of each of the next five years. Each dollar invested in A at the beginning of one year returns \$1.40 (a profit of \$0.40) two years later (in time for immediate reinvestment). Each dollar invested in B at the beginning of one year returns \$1.70 three years later.

In addition, money-making activities C and D will each be available at one time in the future. Each dollar invested in C at the beginning of the second year hence returns \$2.00 four years later. Each dollar invested in D at the beginning of the fifth year hence returns \$1.30 one year later.

The investor begins with \$10,000. He wishes to know which investment plan maximizes the amount of money he can accumulate by the beginning of the sixth year hence. Formulate the linear programming model for this problem.

4. Consider the following linear programming problem. Maximize

$$Z = 2x_1 + x_2 ,$$

subject to the restrictions,

$$\begin{aligned} x_1 + 4x_2 &\leq 24 \\ x_1 + 2x_2 &\leq 14 \\ 2x_1 - x_2 &\leq 8 \\ x_1 - x_2 &\leq 3 \\ x_1 \geq 0, \; x_2 &\geq 0 . \end{aligned}$$

(a) Find all of the basic solutions for this problem, and indicate which ones are basic feasible solutions. Use this information to identify the optimal solution.

(b) Solve this problem graphically.

(c) Solve this problem algebraically by the simplex method.

5. Consider the example introduced in Sec. 5.5. Beginning with the second simplex tableau given at the end of that section, execute another iteration of the simplex method and thereby obtain the final tableau for the problem.

6. Consider the example introduced in Sec. 5.6.3.

(a) Use the Big M method to solve this problem by the simplex method.
(b) Use the two-phase method to solve this problem by the simplex method.

7. Consider the example introduced in Sec. 5.6.4.

(a) Use the Big M method to solve this problem by the simplex method.
(b) Use the two-phase method to solve this problem by the simplex method.

8. Consider the following mathematical model. Minimize

$$Z = 2x_1 + x_2 - 6x_3 - x_4 ,$$

subject to

$$\begin{aligned} 3x_1 + x_4 &\leq 25 \\ x_1 + x_2 + x_3 + x_4 &= 20 \\ 4x_1 + 6x_3 &\geq 5 \\ 2 \leq 2x_2 + 3x_3 + 2x_4 &\leq 30 \end{aligned}$$

and

$$x_1 \geq 0,\ x_2 \geq 0,\ x_3 \geq 0$$

(x_4 unconstrained in sign).

(a) Reformulate this model into an equivalent linear programming model having the same form (except for the equality constraint) as presented in Sec. 5.2. Then make the necessary adjustments (introducing slack variables, artificial variables, etc.) in preparation for applying the simplex method.
(b) Using the Big M method, execute the first two complete iterations of the simplex method, i.e., obtain the next two sets of equations (after the initial set) and the corresponding (artificial) basic feasible solutions. Do not solve further.
(c) Using the two-phase method instead, execute the first two complete iterations of the simplex method. Do not solve further.

9. Consider the following problem. Maximize

$$Z = 2x_1 + 3x_2 + 5x_3 ,$$

subject to

$$\begin{aligned} 3x_1 + 10x_2 + 5x_3 &\leq 15 \\ 33x_1 - 10x_2 + 9x_3 &\leq 33 \\ x_1 + 2x_2 + x_3 &\geq 4 \end{aligned}$$

and

$$x_1 \geq 0,\ x_2 \geq 0,\ x_3 \geq 0 .$$

Use the simplex method to demonstrate that this problem does not possess any feasible solutions.

10. Consider the following problem. Maximize

$$Z = 4x_1 + x_2 + 3x_3 + 5x_4 ,$$

subject to

$$\begin{aligned} -4x_1 + 6x_2 + 5x_3 - 4x_4 &\leq 20 \\ 3x_1 - 2x_2 + 4x_3 + x_4 &\leq 10 \\ 8x_1 - 3x_2 + 3x_3 + 2x_4 &\leq 20 \end{aligned}$$

and

$$x_1 \geq 0,\ x_2 \geq 0,\ x_3 \geq 0,\ x_4 \geq 0 .$$

Use the simplex method to demonstrate that this problem has an unbounded optimal solution.

11. Consider the following linear programming problem. Maximize

$$Z = 3x_1 + x_2 + 4x_3 ,$$

subject to

$$\begin{aligned} 6x_1 + 3x_2 + 5x_3 &\leq 25 \\ 3x_1 + 4x_2 + 5x_3 &\leq 20 \end{aligned}$$

and

$$x_1 \geq 0,\ x_2 \geq 0,\ x_3 \geq 0 .$$

The corresponding *final* set of equations yielding the optimal solution is

$$\begin{aligned} &(0) \quad Z + 2x_2 + \frac{1}{5}x_4 + \frac{3}{5}x_5 = 17 \\ &(1) \quad x_1 - \frac{1}{3}x_2 + \frac{1}{3}x_4 - \frac{1}{3}x_5 = \frac{5}{3} \\ &(2) \quad x_2 + x_3 - \frac{1}{5}x_4 + \frac{2}{5}x_5 = 3 . \end{aligned}$$

(a) Construct the dual problem for this problem.

(b) Identify the optimal solution for this problem and the optimal solution for its dual problem.

(c) Suppose that the objective function is now changed to $Z = 3x_1 + 4x_2 + 4x_3$. Without redoing the simplex method, determine if the previous optimal solution is still optimal. If it is not, adjust the final set of equations and determine the new optimal solution.

(d) Suppose that the objective function is changed instead to $Z = 3x_1 + x_2 + x_3$. Check to see if the previous optimal solution is still optimal, and, if it is not, find the new optimal solution directly.

(e) Suppose that the objective function is changed instead to $Z = 2x_1 + 2x_2 + 3x_3$. Check to see if the previous optimal solution is still optimal, and, if it is not, find the new optimal solution directly.

12. Consider Theorem 5.1 given in Sec. 5.7.1.

(a) Prove this theorem when the primal problem is in the form given at the beginning of Sec. 5.7.1.
(b) Extend this proof to include the possibility of equality constraints and variables unconstrained in sign in the primal problem.

13. Construct the dual problem corresponding to the model given in Problem 8.

CHAPTER 6

Special Types of Linear Programming Problems

6.1 INTRODUCTION

As was suggested in the early part of Chapter 5, a very broad class of practical problems can be formulated as linear programming problems. Since the simplex method is powerful enough to solve all of these problems, it is only to be expected that this general method is not the most efficient one for solving certain simple special types of linear programming problems. One such special type is known as the "transportation problem," although it is also applicable in certain situations not involving transportation. Another is an extension of the transportation problem called the "transhipment problem." A third special type is the so-called "assignment problem." These three problems, and their streamlined solution procedures, are described in the following sections.

6.2 THE TRANSPORTATION PROBLEM

6.2.1 Nature of the Problem

The transportation problem received its name because it arises very naturally in the context of determining optimal shipping patterns. However, many problems having nothing to do with transportation fit the mathematical model for the transportation problem and can, therefore, be solved by one of its simple and efficient solution procedures.

To illustrate a prototype of the transportation problem, suppose that m factories supply n warehouses with a certain product. Factory $i(i = 1, 2, \cdots, m)$ produces a_i units (total or per unit time), and warehouse $j(j = 1, 2, \cdots, n)$ requires b_j units. Suppose that the cost of shipping from factory i to warehouse j is directly proportional to the amount shipped, and that the unit cost is c_{ij}. Let the decision variables, x_{ij}, be the amount shipped from factory i to warehouse j. What shipping pattern (values of x_{ij}) minimizes total transportation cost?

The corresponding mathematical model for the transportation problem is the following. Find x_{ij} ($i = 1, 2, \cdots, m$; $j = 1, 2, \cdots, n$) in order to minimize

$$\sum_{i=1}^{m} \sum_{j=1}^{n} c_{ij} x_{ij} ,$$

subject to the restrictions,

$$\sum_{j=1}^{n} x_{ij} = a_i, \qquad \text{for } i = 1, 2, \cdots, m$$

$$\sum_{i=1}^{m} x_{ij} = b_j, \qquad \text{for } j = 1, 2, \cdots, n$$

$$x_{ij} \geq 0, \qquad \text{for all } i \text{ and } j .$$

It is the simple structure of this model, particularly that all of the constraint coefficients equal either zero or one, which permits the use of much more efficient solution procedures than the complete simplex method. The basic procedure of examining a sequence of constantly improving, basic feasible solutions until an optimal one is reached is the same as with the simplex method, but it can now be done more simply.

It should be carefully noted that the model has feasible solutions only if

$$\sum_{i=1}^{m} a_i = \sum_{j=1}^{n} b_j .$$

This may be verified by observing that the restrictions require that both

$$\sum_{i=1}^{m} a_i \text{ and } \sum_{j=1}^{n} b_j \text{ equal } \sum_{i=1}^{m} \sum_{j=1}^{n} x_{ij} .$$

This condition that the total supply must equal the total demand merely requires that the system be in balance. If the problem has physical significance and this condition is not met, it usually means that either a_i or b_j actually represents a bound rather than an exact requirement. If this is the case, a fictitious "factory" or "warehouse" can be introduced to take up the slack in order to convert the inequalities into equalities and satisfy the feasibility condition. This is illustrated subsequently.

If x_{ij} represents a total amount to be shipped rather than a shipping rate, it may have physical significance only for integer values. Fortunately, because of the simple structure of the model, it can be shown that there must exist an optimal solution involving only integers if all the a_i and b_j are integers.

Rather than writing all of the equations involved, the model for a transportation problem is usually written in a concise tabular form, as illustrated below.

		Destination				
		1	2	⋯	n	*Supply*
Source	1	c_{11}	c_{12}	⋯	c_{1n}	a_1
	2	c_{21}	c_{22}	⋯	c_{2n}	a_2
	⋮	⋮	⋮		⋮	⋮
	m	c_{m1}	c_{m2}	⋯	c_{mn}	a_m
Demand		b_1	b_2	⋯	b_n	

This cost and requirements table is sufficient to completely specify a transportation problem preparatory to its solution. The actual calculations are made directly on the "transportation array" below, which gives the current trial solution.

		Destination				
		1	2	⋯	n	*Supply*
Source	1	x_{11}	x_{12}	⋯	x_{1n}	a_1
	2	x_{21}	x_{22}	⋯	x_{2n}	a_2
	⋮	⋮	⋮		⋮	⋮
	m	x_{m1}	x_{m2}	⋯	x_{mn}	a_m
Demand		b_1	b_2		b_n	

These two tables are often combined by inserting c_{ij} into a corner of the respective cells.

6.2.2 EXAMPLES

Example 1

A manufacturer must produce a certain product in sufficient quantity to meet contracted sales in the next four months. The production facilities available for this product are limited, but by different amounts in the respective months. The unit cost of production also varies according to the facilities and personnel available. The product may be produced in one month and then held for sale in a later month, but at an estimated storage cost of $1 per unit per month. No storage cost is incurred for goods sold in the same month in which they are produced. There is presently no inventory of this product, and none is desired at the end of the four months. Given the data in the following table, how much should be produced in each of the four months in order to minimize total cost?

Month	*Contracted sales*	*Maximum production*	*Unit cost of production*	*Unit storage cost per month*
1	20	40	14	1
2	30	50	16	1
3	50	30	15	1
4	40	50	17	1

It is apparent that this particular problem can be readily formulated as a general linear programming problem. Letting the decision variables, $x_i (i = 1, 2, 3, 4)$, be the production in month i, the model is the following. Minimize

$$Z = 14x_1 + 16x_2 + 15x_3 + 17x_4 + (x_1 - 20) + (x_1 + x_2 - 50) + (x_1 + x_2 + x_3 - 100) = 17x_1 + 18x_2 + 16x_3 + 17x_4 - 170\,,$$

subject to the restrictions,

$$\begin{aligned} x_1 &\leq 40\,, \\ x_2 &\leq 50\,, \\ x_3 &\leq 30\,, \\ x_4 &\leq 50\,, \\ x_1 &\geq 20\,, \\ x_1 + x_2 &\geq 50\,, \\ x_1 + x_2 + x_3 &\geq 100\,, \\ x_1 + x_2 + x_3 + x_4 &= 140\,, \\ x_1 \geq 0,\ x_2 \geq 0,\ x_3 &\geq 0,\ x_4 \geq 0\,. \end{aligned}$$

However, it may not be so readily apparent that this problem can be formulated in alternative ways which will yield a solution with much less effort. Nevertheless, this can indeed be done by recasting the problem as a transportation problem.[26]

[26] An even simpler solution procedure than those for the transportation problem is also available for this particular production scheduling problem. See E. M. L. Beale, G. Morton, and A. H. Land, "Solution of a Purchase-Storage Programme," *Operational Research Quarterly*, **9**, 174–197 (1958).

In order to develop this formulation, it is necessary to identify the "sources" and "destinations," as well as x_{ij}, c_{ij}, a_i, and b_j. It would be instructive for the reader to attempt to identify as many of these items as he can before reading further. After some thought, the following conclusions may have been drawn.

$$\begin{aligned}
\text{Source } i &= \text{production in month } i \ (i = 1, 2, 3, 4). \\
\text{Destination } j &= \text{sales in month } j \ (j = 1, 2, 3, 4). \\
x_{ij} &= \text{amount produced in month } i \text{ for sale in month } j. \\
c_{ij} &= \text{unit cost associated with } x_{ij} \\
&= \begin{cases} \text{production plus storage cost, if } i \leq j \\ ?, \quad \text{if } i > j \end{cases} \\
a_i &= ? \\
b_j &= \text{contracted sales in month } j.
\end{aligned}$$

The corresponding cost and requirements table is given below.

		Destination				
		1	2	3	4	*Supply*
Source	1	14	15	16	17	?
	2	?	16	17	18	?
	3	?	?	15	16	?
	4	?	?	?	17	?
Demand		20	30	50	40	

Thus, it remains to identify the missing costs and the supplies.

It is obviously impossible to produce items in one month for sale in an earlier month, so that x_{ij} must be zero if $i > j$. Therefore, there is no real cost that can be associated with x_{ij} for $i > j$. Nevertheless, unless the solution procedure is to be executed manually with the prohibited allocations excluded from consideration, it is necessary to assign some value for the unidentified costs. Fortunately, the Big M method introduced in Section 5.6.3 may be used to do this. Thus, a very large number (denoted by M for convenience) is assigned to the unidentified entries in the cost table in order to force the corresponding values of x_{ij} to be zero in the final solution.

The numbers to insert into the supply column are not obvious because the "supplies," the amount produced in the respective months, are not fixed quantities. In fact, the objective is to solve for the most desirable values of these production quantities. Nevertheless, it is necessary to assign some definite number to every entry in the table, including those in the supply column. A clue is provided by the fact that, although the supply constraints are not present in the usual form, these constraints do exist in the form of upper bounds on the amount that can be supplied. Their mathematical description is the following:

$$\begin{aligned} x_{11} + x_{12} + x_{13} + x_{14} &\leq 40\,, \\ x_{21} + x_{22} + x_{23} + x_{24} &\leq 50\,, \\ x_{31} + x_{32} + x_{33} + x_{34} &\leq 30\,, \\ x_{41} + x_{42} + x_{43} + x_{44} &\leq 50\,. \end{aligned}$$

The only change from the standard model is that these constraints are in the form of inequalities instead of equations. To convert them to equations, the trick employed in Section 5.5 of introducing slack variables should be used. In this context, the slack variables are allocations to a fictitional or dummy destination representing the unused production capacity in the respective months. This permits the "supply" to be the total production capacity in the given month. Furthermore, since the demand for the dummy destination is the total unused capacity, the sum of the supplies equals the sum of the demands, so that a feasible solution is obtainable. The cost entries associated with the dummy destination should be zero since there is no cost incurred by a fictional allocation.

Therefore, the final cost and requirements table is the following.

		Destination					
		1	2	3	4	5	*Supply*
Source	1	14	15	16	17	0	40
	2	M	16	17	18	0	50
	3	M	M	15	16	0	30
	4	M	M	M	17	0	50
Demand		20	30	50	40	30	

A solution procedure is presented subsequently.

Example 2

A company has decided to initiate the production of some or all of five new products at three branch plants with excess production capacity. These products sell by their weight. However, to simplify the discussion, let one unit of each product refer to the amount of that product which would sell for $100. The production effort required for one unit of each product is quite comparable. The available production capacity per unit time at each of the plants is given below.

Plant	*Available capacity in total number of units*
1	40
2	60
3	90

Marketing research has provided the following estimates of the potential sales per unit time for the respective products.

Product	*Potential sales in units*
1	30
2	40
3	70
4	40
5	60

Plant 3 cannot produce product 5. The variable costs per unit for the other combinations of plants and products are given below.

		1	2	3	4	5
Plant	1	20	19	14	21	16
	2	15	20	13	19	16
	3	18	15	18	20	X

What quantity of the respective products should be produced at each of the plants?

To formulate this situation as a transportation problem, the plants would be the sources, and the products (or their buyers) may be considered the destinations. The decision variables, $x_{ij}(i = 1, 2, 3; j = 1, 2, 3, 4, 5)$, would be the production quantity of product j by plant i. The associated unit costs are given in the preceding table. The supplies are the available production capacity at the plants. Since it is desired to use all available capacity, the supplies should be considered as fixed requirements. The demands are the potential sales of the products. Since these potential sales exceed total available production capacity, these "demands" must be considered as upper bounds rather than fixed requirements. Therefore, it is necessary to introduce a dummy plant (source) to fictionally provide the slack between what is actually supplied and what is "demanded." The resulting final cost and requirements table is given below.

		Destination					
		1	2	3	4	5	*Supply*
Source	1	20	19	14	21	16	40
	2	15	20	13	19	16	60
	3	18	15	18	20	M	90
	4	0	0	0	0	0	50
Demand		30	40	70	40	60	

This problem is used to illustrate solution procedures in subsequent sections.

6.2.3 IDENTIFYING BASIC FEASIBLE SOLUTIONS

Basic feasible solutions are defined in exactly the same way for the transportation problem as for the general linear programming problem. However, the solution procedure is executed directly on the transportation array rather than with the original set of equations. Therefore, it is necessary to be able to identify basic feasible solutions as they would appear in the transportation array.

Since there are m sources and n destinations, the original mathematical model contained $(m + n)$ equations. One might, therefore, jump to the conclusion that a non-degenerate basic feasible solution must have $(m + n)$ strictly positive variables, i.e., $(m + n)$ non-zero allocations (entries) in the transportation array. However, an examination of the constraint equations reveals that one of them is redundant. Since

$$\sum_{i=1}^{m} a_i = \sum_{i=1}^{m} \sum_{j=1}^{n} x_{ij} = \sum_{j=1}^{n} b_j ,$$

any one of the equations can be derived from the rest of them. Hence, there are only $(m + n - 1)$ linearly independent equations, so that a non-degenerate basic feasible solution must have exactly $(m + n - 1)$ non-zero allocations in the transportation array. [A degenerate basic feasible solution would have less than $(m + n - 1)$ non-zero allocations. Degeneracy is discussed in Section 6.2.6.] In order to be feasible, a solution must, of course, have no negative values and must also satisfy all of the supply and demand requirements exactly. While these are the obvious requirements for non-degenerate basic feasible solutions, there remains one additional requirement. To illustrate, consider the following non-basic feasible solution.

		Destination					
		1	2	3	4	5	*Supply*
Source	1				20	20	40
	2				20	40	60
	3		20	70			90
	4	30	20				50
Demand		30	40	70	40	60	

(*Note:* Zero entries are omitted in the above transportation array.)

The signpost that reveals that this solution is not basic is the "closed loop" connecting cells (1, 4), (1, 5), (2, 5), and (2, 4). In other words, by tracing with a pencil through the array, it is possible to move from any one of these four cells back to itself by drawing a sequence of horizontal and vertical lines to cells containing non-zero allocations without either retracing or lifting the pencil.

The significance of such a closed loop is that it indicates that the solution is actually a weighted average of two basic feasible solutions. Geometrically, the solution must lie on the segment between two extreme points. To motivate the reason for this, consider a general linear programming model such that one of its equations is $x_1 + x_2 = 2$, and these variables appear in no other constraint equations. Since any equation must have exactly one basic variable, any basic feasible solution must include either $x_1 = 0$, $x_2 = 2$, or $x_1 = 2$, $x_2 = 0$. Any solution which includes $x_1 = 1$, $x_2 = 1$ must be non-basic since, by the geometric definition given in Section 5.5 and Appendix 1, no basic feasible solution (extreme point) can be a weighted average of other feasible solutions. The same is true of the transportation problem example. Adding 20 to cells (1, 5) and (2, 4) and then subtracting 20 from cells (1, 4) and (2, 5) uncover one basic feasible solution. A second is provided by alternately adding and subtracting 20 from cells (1, 4), (1, 5), (2, 5), and (2, 4), respectively, instead. The original solution happened to lie exactly midway between these two basic feasible solutions. It did not have more than $(m + n - 1)$, i.e., $4 + 5 - 1 = 8$, non-zero allocations because these two basic solutions happen to be degenerate.

Any non-basic feasible solution can be reduced to a basic feasible solution by the process of eliminating all closed loops as illustrated above. A set of allocations is said to be in "independent positions" if it is impossible to form any closed loops through these allocations. Thus, a solution is a non-degenerate basic feasible solution if it has the following properties:

(1) Feasibility.
(2) Exactly $(m + n - 1)$ strictly positive allocations.
(3) Allocations in independent positions.

6.2.4 FINDING AN INITIAL BASIC FEASIBLE SOLUTION

One very simple procedure for obtaining an initial basic feasible solution is the following:

(1) Start with the cell in the upper left-hand corner.
(2) Allocate the maximum feasible amount.
(3) Move one cell to the right if there is any remaining supply. Otherwise, move one cell down. If both are impossible, stop. Otherwise, go to step (2).

This procedure is known as the "Northwest Corner Rule" because it starts with the cell in the "northwest" corner of the array. (Actually, since the ordering of the rows and columns is arbitrary, there is nothing sacred about starting with the northwest corner, and many other valid procedures could be used instead.) Applying it to Example 2 of Section 6.2.2, the following solution is obtained.

		Destination					
		1	2	3	4	5	*Supply*
Source	1	30	10				40
	2		30	30			60
	3			40	40	10	90
	4					50	50
Demand		30	40	70	40	60	

This is obviously a basic feasible solution. [It is feasible, that is, for the revised problem which permits a non-zero allocation in the (3, 5) cell, but at such a high cost (M) that the optimal solution would have no such allocation.]

It is easy to verify that the northwest corner rule must always yield an initial basic feasible solution for a properly formulated problem. It observes demand and supply requirements throughout the procedure and stops when both are satisfied simultaneously. Since it moves only to the right and down, no closed loops can be formed. It moves $(n - 1)$ steps to the right and m steps down, so no more than $(m + n - 1)$ non-zero allocations can be made. In fact, the only complication that can arise is that it can make less than $(m + n - 1)$ non-zero allocations, thereby yielding a degenerate basic feasible solution. This would occur if both a supply and a demand are simultaneously exhausted at any intermediate iteration. The reader can illustrate this by exchanging the demands for destinations 2 and 3. However, obtaining a degenerate basic feasible solution does not create any serious problems, as will be discussed later.

Unfortunately, there is no reason to expect the basic feasible solution provided by the northwest corner rule to be particularly close to the optimal solution. Therefore, it may be worthwhile to expend a little more effort on obtaining a promising initial basic feasible solution in order to reduce the number of iterations required to reach the optimal solution. One procedure which is designed to do this is "Vogel's Approximation Method."

Vogel's approximation method is based on the use of the "difference" associated with each row and column in the table giving c_{ij}, the unit costs. A row or column "difference" is defined here as the arithmetic difference between the smallest and next-to-the-smallest element in that row or column. This quantity provides a measure of the proper priorities for making allocations to the respective rows and columns, since it indicates the minimum unit penalty incurred by failing to make an allocation to the smallest cost cell in that row or column. Thus, this procedure repeatedly makes the maximum feasible allocation in the smallest cost cell of the remaining row or column with the largest difference. It never changes an allocation previously made, so the procedure stops as soon as the total demand and supply are exhausted. The detailed steps involved in Vogel's approximation method are summarized below.

(1) Construct the cost and requirements table, and then go to step (3).
(2) Use the cost and requirements table for the problem that remains after the previously assigned allocations (both zero and positive) have been made.
(3) Calculate each row difference and column difference.
(4) Select the row or column with the largest difference. (Ties may be broken arbitrarily.)
(5) Allocate as much as possible to the smallest cost cell in that row or column.
(6) Allocate zero elsewhere in the row or column where the supply or demand is exhausted.
(7) Make the only feasible allocation in any rows or columns having only one cell without an allocation.
(8) Eliminate all fully allocated rows and columns from further consideration. Stop if no rows and columns remain. Otherwise, go to step (2).

Applying Vogel's approximation method to Example 2, the first table looks as follows.

		Destination						*Row*
		1	2	3	4	5	*Supply*	*difference*
Source	1	20	19	14	21^0	16	40	2
	2	15	20	13	19^0	16	60	2
	3	18	15	18	20^0	M	90	3
	4	0	0	0	0^{40}	0	50	0
Demand		30	40	70	40	60		
Column difference		15	15	13	19	16		

Since column 4 has the largest difference, its smallest cost cell, (4, 4), is selected for a positive allocation. The supply is 50, but the demand is only 40, so 40 is allocated to (4, 4). (Allocations are indicated by the superior numbers.) Since this exhausts the demand, the other cells in column 4 must have zero allocations. Column 4 can now be eliminated from further consideration, so it is deleted from subsequent tables. The supply for source 4 must also be reduced to 10. Everything is now ready for the second iteration.

		Destination 1	2	3	5	Supply	Row difference
Source	1	20	19	14	16	40	2
	2	15	20	13	16	60	2
	3	18	15	18	M	90	3
	4	0^0	0^0	0^0	0^{10}	10	0
Demand		30	40	70	60		
Column difference		15	15	13	16		

Proceeding as before, the smallest cost cell for destination 5, (4, 5), is selected for the positive allocation. However, since the supply for source 4 becomes exhausted before the demand for destination 5, the zero allocations must be made in the rest of row 4 in this case. A demand of 50 remains for future allocations in column 5. The subsequent tables and their allocations are obtained in a similar manner, as shown below.

		Destination 1	2	3	5	Supply	Row difference
Source	1	20	19^0	14	16	40	2
	2	15	20^0	13	16	60	2
	3	18	15^{40}	18	M	90	3
Demand		30	40	70	50		
Column difference		3	4	1	0		

		Destination 1	3	5	Supply	Row difference
Source	1	20^0	14	16	40	2
	2	15^{30}	13	16	60	2
	3	18^0	18	M	50	0
Demand		30	70	50		
Column difference		3	1	0		

		Destination 3	5	Supply	Row difference
Source	1	14	16	40	2
	2	13	16	30	3
	3	18^{50}	M^0	50	M − 18
Demand		70	50		
Column difference		1	0		

		Destination 3	5	*Supply*	*Row difference*
Source	1	14^{0}	16^{40}	40	2
	2	13^{20}	16^{10}	30	3
Demand		20	50		
Column difference		1	0		

Combining all of these allocations onto a single transportation array gives the following initial basic feasible solution (where the allocations from the dummy source—source 4—are fictional).

		Destination 1	2	3	4	5	*Supply*
Source	1					40	40
	2	30		20		10	60
	3		40	50			90
	4				40	10	50
Demand		30	40	70	40	60	

After a little practice, the user probably would want to execute this entire procedure on the original cost and requirements table. He would need merely to cross out rows and columns as they are completed and revise the supplies, demands, and differences as required.

Although ties for the largest difference may be broken arbitrarily, a number of reasonable guidelines have been suggested for breaking them. Some of these should become apparent to the user as they are needed.

6.2.5 MOVING TOWARD OPTIMALITY

Given an initial non-degenerate basic feasible solution, the next question is how to find successively better basic feasible solutions. Just as for the simplex method (see Section 5.5), this boils down to selecting the appropriate entering and leaving basic variables and identifying the corresponding solution.

Selecting an entering basic variable in this context amounts to selecting a new cell in which to make a non-zero allocation in the transportation array. The criterion of selecting the variable which improves the value of the objective function at the fastest rate is still applicable. Thus, it is desired to select that unoccupied cell which would decrease total cost by the greatest amount when an allocation of $+1$ is made there (and the changes required to maintain feasibility are made elsewhere). The change in total cost caused by the introduction of an allocation of +1 to a particular cell can be found very easily. To illustrate, suppose that an allocation of +1 in the (1, 1) cell is added to the initial basic feasible solution found at the end of the last section.

		Destination 1	2	3	4	5	*Supply*
Source	1	+1				40	40
	2	30		20		10	60
	3		40	50			90
	4				40	10	50
Demand		30	40	70	40	60	

This new allocation violates the supply and demand requirements for source 1 and destination 1, respectively, so changes are required elsewhere in order to restore feasibility. Notice that the new allocation has created a closed loop with cells (1, 1), (1, 5), (2, 5), and (2, 1) at the corners. Furthermore, alternately subtracting and adding the amount of the new allocation to these other cells is precisely the chain of events which will successfully restore feasibility. This is illustrated below.

		Destination 1	2	3	4	5	*Supply*
Source	1	+1				40 − 1	40
	2	30 − 1		20		10 + 1	60
	3		40	50			90
	4				40	10	50
Demand		30	40	70	40	60	

Since the unit costs for these cells in the loop are 20, 16, 16, and 15, respectively, it should be apparent that the change in total cost must be $+20 - 16 + 16 - 15 = +5$. Therefore, x_{11} cannot be a candidate for the entering basic variable since it would increase cost rather than decrease it.

The reaction to introducing a new allocation to a non-degenerate basic feasible solution is always similar to that illustrated above. It always creates a unique closed loop. The unique chain reaction which will restore feasibility without involving other new basic variables is to alternately subtract and add the amount of the new allocation to the respective end points of the segments of the closed loop. (This always works, provided the new allocation is not so large that it drives other allocations negative.) The consequent change in total cost is easily calculated from the corresponding unit costs.

The closed loop created by a new allocation is not always quite as evident as in the case just considered. For example, suppose that the new allocation of +1 is made in the (1, 2) cell instead. The resulting chain reaction is illustrated below.

		Destination 1	2	3	4	5	*Supply*
Source	1		+1			40 − 1	40
	2	30		20 − 1		10 + 1	60
	3		40 − 1	50 + 1			90
	4				40	10	50
Demand		30	40	70	40	60	

Referring to the cost and requirements table which indicates that $c_{12} = 19$, $c_{15} = 16$, $c_{25} = 16$, $c_{23} = 13$, $c_{33} = 18$, $c_{32} = 15$, it is clear that the change in total cost is $+19 - 16 + 16 - 13 + 18 - 15 = +9$. Therefore, the (1, 2) cell also is not a candidate for the new basic feasible solution.

One could continue in this way to seek candidates for the entering basic variable. If none are found, the present solution would be optimal. Otherwise, the candidate which decreases cost at the fastest rate would be chosen. However, this process of testing each unoccupied cell individually would be rather long and tedious. Fortunately, a procedure is available for obtaining the same information with much less computational effort. This procedure amounts to examining the objective function where all of the basic variables have been eliminated, just as was done for the general linear programming problem. Recall that the objective is to minimize

$$Z = \sum_{i=1}^{m} \sum_{j=1}^{n} c_{ij}x_{ij} .$$

The restrictions (other than the non-negativity restrictions) can be written as

$$0 = a_i - \sum_{j=1}^{n} x_{ij}, \qquad \text{for } i = 1, 2, \cdots, m ,$$

$$0 = b_j - \sum_{i=1}^{m} x_{ij}, \qquad \text{for } j = 1, 2, \cdots, n .$$

Any multiple of each of these equations can be legitimately added to the objective function to try to eliminate the basic variables. Denote these multiples by u_i ($i = 1, 2, \cdots, m$) and v_j ($j = 1, 2, \cdots, n$), respectively. Therefore,

$$Z = \sum_{i=1}^{m}\sum_{j=1}^{n} c_{ij}x_{ij} + \sum_{i=1}^{m} u_i\left(a_i - \sum_{j=1}^{n} x_{ij}\right) + \sum_{j=1}^{n} v_j\left(b_j - \sum_{i=1}^{m} x_{ij}\right)$$

$$= \sum_{i=1}^{m}\sum_{j=1}^{n} (c_{ij} - u_i - v_j)x_{ij} + \sum_{i=1}^{m} u_i a_i + \sum_{j=1}^{n} v_j b_j .$$

Thus, in order to have a coefficient of zero, it is necessary that

$$c_{rs} = u_r + v_s$$

for each basic variable x_{rs}, i.e., for each occupied cell (r, s). There are $(m + n - 1)$ occupied cells and, therefore, $(m + n - 1)$ of these equations. Since there are $(m + n)$ unknowns (the u_i and v_j), one of these variables can be assigned a value arbitrarily, and the rest of them can then be solved algebraically. Fortunately, this can be done very quickly and easily, as will be demonstrated shortly.

Once all of the u_i and v_j have been determined, the entering basic variable (if any) can be immediately identified by calculating $c_{ij} - (u_i + v_j)$ for each vacant cell. If $c_{ij} - (u_i + v_j) \geq 0$ in every case, then the solution must be optimal since no non-basic variable can decrease Z. Otherwise, the cell with the smallest (largest negative) value of $[c_{ij} - (u_i + v_j)]$ is chosen to receive the new allocation, since this non-basic variable decreases Z at the fastest rate.

Applying this procedure to the initial basic feasible solution found by Vogel's approximation method, one begins by filling in the values of c_{ij} for only the occupied cells.

				16
15		13		16
	15	18		
			0	0

Since any one of the u_i or v_j can be assigned a value arbitrarily, it would be well to select a convenient variable and a convenient value. One reasonable rule, which will be adopted here, is to select the u_i which has the largest number of allocations in its row and assign it the value of zero. Since $c_{ij} = u_i + v_j$, this immediately yields v_j for the columns containing those allocations.

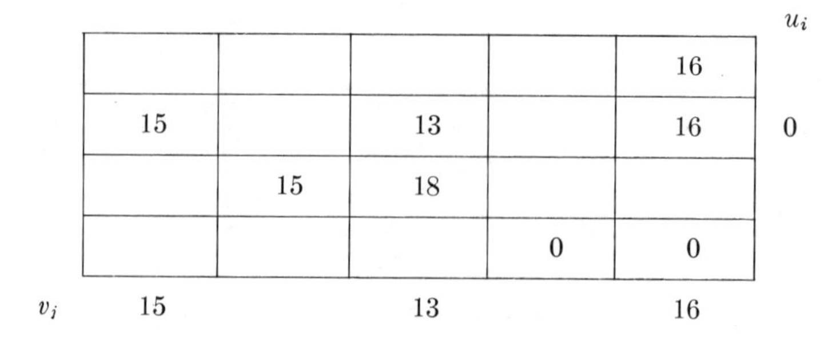

						u_i
					16	
	15		13		16	0
		15	18			
				0	0	
v_j	15		13		16	

In this case, these v_j immediately yield the rest of the u_i since $18 = u_3 + 13$, $16 = u_1 + 16$, and $0 = u_4 + 16$, so that $u_3 = 5$, $u_1 = 0$, and $u_4 = -16$. These values in turn give $15 = 5 + u_2$ and $0 = -16 + v_4$, so that $v_2 = 10$ and $v_4 = -16$. This completes the set of u_i and v_j.

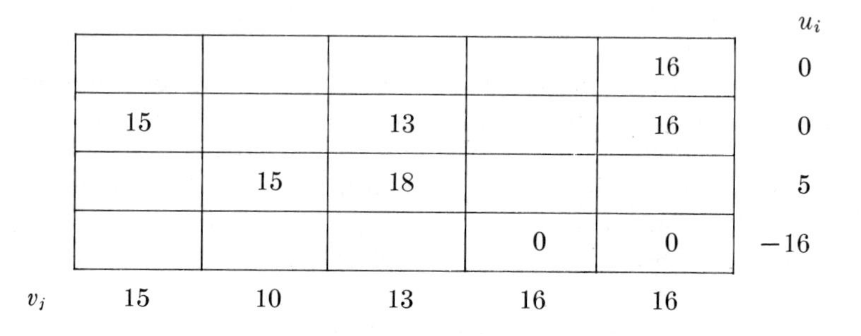

						u_i
					16	0
	15		13		16	0
		15	18			5
				0	0	-16
v_j	15	10	13	16	16	

Calculating $c_{ij} - (u_i + v_j)$ for the vacant cells yields the following matrix.

5	9	1	5	·
·	10	·	3	·
-2	·	·	-1	M$-$
1	6	3	·	·

Since two cells have negative evaluation numbers, the solution being considered is not optimal. Cell (3, 1) has a larger negative number than cell (3, 4), so x_{31} is chosen as the entering basic variable.

The leaving basic variable is chosen according to the same criterion as for the general linear programming problem, namely, the one that reaches zero first as the entering basic variable is increased. It was indicated earlier that introducing a new allocation would create a unique closed loop, and that one must alternately subtract and add the amount of this allocation to the other corners of the loop in order to restore feasibility. This is illustrated in the following transportation array.

		Destination					
		1	2	3	4	5	*Supply*
Source	1					40	40
	2	30−		20+		10	60
	3	+	40	50−			90
	4				40	10	50
Demand		30	40	70	40	60	

Since adding an allocation to cell (3, 1) requires subtracting that amount from cells (2, 1) and (3, 3), the one which begins with the smallest allocation must reach zero first as the new allocation is increased. Therefore, x_{21} is the leaving basic variable, and $x_{31} = 30$ in the next basic feasible solution. This solution is given below.

		Destination					
		1	2	3	4	5	*Supply*
Source	1					40	40
	2			50		10	60
	3	30	40	20			90
	4				40	10	50
Demand		30	40	70	40	60	

To test whether this solution is optimal, another set of u_i and v_j is derived.

						u_i
					16	−5
			13		16	−5
	18	15	18			0
				0	0	−21
v_j	18	15	18	21	21	

The resulting matrix of $[c_{ij} - (u_i + v_j)]$ values is shown below.

7	9	1	5	·
2	10	·	3	·
·	·	·	−1	M−
3	6	3	·	·

Since cell (3, 4) has a negative evaluation number, the solution is not optimal, and x_{34} is the new entering basic variable. The corresponding leaving basic variable is identified below as x_{25}.

		Destination 1	2	3	4	5	*Supply*
Source	1					40	40
	2			50+		10−	60
	3	30	40	20−	+		90
	4				40 −	10+	50
Demand		30	40	70	40	60	

Therefore, the next basic feasible solution is as follows.

		Destination 1	2	3	4	5	*Supply*
Source	1					40	40
	2			60			60
	3	30	40	10	10		90
	4				30	20	50
Demand		30	40	70	40	60	

The corresponding set of u_i and v_j values, and the matrix of $[c_{ij} - (u_i + v_j)]$ values are given below.

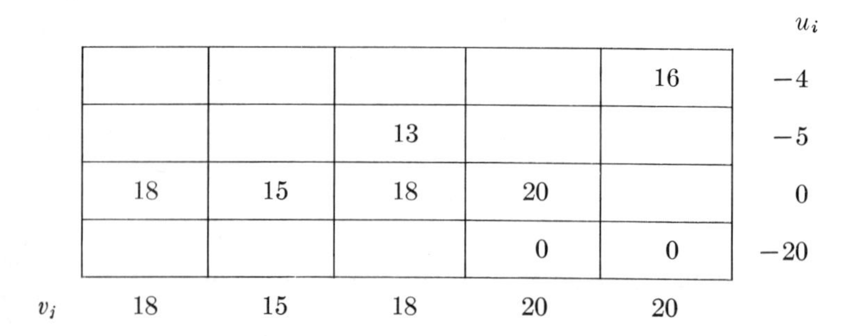

						u_i
					16	−4
			13			−5
	18	15	18	20		0
				0	0	−20
v_j	18	15	18	20	20	

6	8	0	5	·
2	10	·	4	1
·	·	·	·	M−
2	5	2	·	·

Since none of the evaluation numbers are negative, this last basic feasible solution is optimal. The evaluation number of zero for cell (1, 3) indicates that a tie exists for the optimal solution since x_{13} could enter the basis without changing the cost. If this is done, the following solution would be obtained as the second optimal basic feasible solution.

		Destination 1	2	3	4	5	*Supply*
Source	1			10		30	40
	2			60			60
	3	30	40		20		90
	4				20	30	50
Demand		30	40	70	40	60	

6.2.6 DEGENERACY

In the above example, the solution procedure encountered only nondegenerate basic feasible solutions—those with exactly $(m + n - 1)$ strictly positive allocations in independent positions. However, one is not always this fortunate. The basic feasible solutions may be degenerate from the initial iteration onward, or they may suddenly become degenerate at any intermediate iteration.

To illustrate how degeneracy can arise and what corrective action is required, consider a slightly revised version of the illustrative example. Suppose that the supply from source 3 is changed from 90 to 70, and that the demand at destination 3 is changed from 70 to 50. Vogel's approximation method would still derive the same set of cells having positive allocations, but x_{33} would be changed from 50 to 30. This initial basic feasible solution is presented below.

		Destination 1	2	3	4	5	*Supply*
Source	1					40	40
	2	30		20		10	60
	3		40	30			70
	4				40	10	50
Demand		30	40	50	40	60	

The $[c_{ij} - (u_i + v_j)]$ values must be exactly what they were before, so x_{31} is again chosen as the entering basic variable. But which should be the leaving basic variable?

		Destination 1	2	3	4	5	*Supply*
Source	1					40	40
	2	30−		20+		10	60
	3	+	40	30−			70
	4				40	10	50
Demand		30	40	70	40	60	

Cells (2, 1) and (3, 3) reach zero simultaneously, so there is no longer any obvious rationale for choosing between them. Either may be chosen. However, the one crucial consideration whenever there is a tie for the leaving basic variable is that the one(s) not chosen should be clearly identified as still being basic variables. It is necessary to identify all $(m + n - 1)$ cells corresponding to basic variables before it is possible to correctly calculate the u_i and v_j values and conduct the subsequent optimality test.

Since the cells corresponding to basic variables are normally identified by their positive allocations, the usual device for identifying a degenerate basic variable is to assign a fictional, infinitesimally small allocation. The amount of this "allocation" is conventionally denoted by ϵ. As long as it is needed, this ϵ is carried through subsequent manipulations as though it were a real allocation.

When one obtains a degenerate initial basic feasible solution, the additional (degenerate) basic variables may be selected arbitrarily, provided that the resulting $(m + n - 1)$ strictly positive and ϵ allocations are in independent positions.

To illustrate this ϵ technique, suppose that x_{21} is chosen arbitrarily as the leaving basic variable in the above case. This yields the following feasible solution.

		Destination 1	2	3	4	5	*Supply*
Source	1					40	40
	2			50		10	60
	3	30	40	ϵ			70
	4				40	10	50
Demand		30	40	50	40	60	

Since the basic variables are the same as before, it would again be found that this solution is not optimal, and that x_{34} should be the new entering basic variable. Attempting to introduce a positive allocation in the (3, 4) cell has the following result.

		Destination					
		1	2	3	4	5	Supply
Source	1					40	40
	2			50+		10−	60
	3	30	40	ϵ−	+		70
	4				40−	10+	50
Demand		30	40	50	40	60	

Since the degenerate basic variable happens to be one of the candidates for the leaving basic variable in this case, it is chosen because it "reaches" zero first. Therefore, the amount of the new "allocation" is ϵ, which yields the following basic feasible solution (after dropping the ϵ where it is not needed to identify a degenerate basic variable).

		Destination					
		1	2	3	4	5	Supply
Source	1					40	40
	2			50		10	60
	3	30	40		ϵ		70
	4				40	10	50
Demand		30	40	50	40	60	

Since the basic variables are again the same as those obtained in the preceding section, this solution would again be identified as optimal (with a tie involved). Thus, the ϵ is no longer needed and should be dropped, giving the following "real" optimal solution.

		Destination					
		1	2	3	4	5	Supply
Source	1					40	40
	2			50		10	60
	3	30	40				70
	4				40	10	50
Demand		30	40	50	40	60	

The real total cost of the subsequent solutions did not happen to change in this example after the ϵ was introduced. However, this frequently will not be the case.

6.3 THE TRANSHIPMENT PROBLEM

The transhipment problem is a direct extension of the transportation problem that includes the possibility of transhipment, i.e., each source or destination is also permitted to act as an intermediate point for shipments from other sources to other destinations. This is a valuable extension since transhipments commonly occur in actual practice. For example, rather than shipping a special cargo directly from port 1 to port 3, it may be cheaper to include it with regular cargoes from port 1 to port 2 and then from port 2 to port 3. Fortunately, considering these transhipment possibilities need not substantially increase the computational effort. A procedure has been developed[27] whereby, after making some minor adjustments, the transhipment problem can be solved as if it were a transportation problem.

To motivate the solution procedure for the transhipment problem, begin by considering the transportation problem where no transhipments are allowed. The cost and requirements table was given in Section 6.2.1 as follows.

		Destination				
		1	2	$\cdots$	n	*Supply*
Source	1	c_{11}	c_{12}	$\cdots$	c_{1n}	a_1
	2	c_{21}	c_{22}	$\cdots$	c_{2n}	a_2
	$\cdot$	$\cdot$	$\cdot$		$\cdot$	$\cdot$
	$\cdot$	$\cdot$	$\cdot$		$\cdot$	$\cdot$
	$\cdot$	$\cdot$	$\cdot$		$\cdot$	$\cdot$
	m	c_{m1}	c_{m2}	$\cdots$	c_{mn}	a_m
Demand		b_1	b_2	$\cdots$	b_n	

Now label sources $1, 2, \cdots, m$ as points $1, 2, \cdots, m$, and destinations $1, 2, \cdots, n$ as points $(m + 1), (m + 2), \cdots, (m + n)$. Let c'_{ij} denote the unit cost of a shipment from point i to point j if any such shipments were to be made. (Thus, $c'_{ij} = c_{i(j-m)}$ if $i \leq m$ and $j \geq m + 1$.) Assume that $c'_{ij} > 0$ $(i \neq j)$, and let $c'_{ii} = 0$. The corresponding cost and requirements table is shown in Table 6.1. Notice that the supply from each of the destinations (points $m + 1$ through $m + n$) is zero, and the demand at each source (points 1 through m) is zero, so that shipments are still possible only from sources to destinations. Thus, the relabeling has changed nothing, so that

[27] Alex Orden, "The Transhipment Problem," *Management Science*, **2**, 276–285 (1956). This article also contains an example and a rigorous proof of the validity of the procedure.

TABLE 6.1. Initial Cost and Requirements Table for Transhipment Problem

		Point							Supply
		1	2	$\cdots$	m	$m+1$	$\cdots$	$m+n$	
Point	1	c'_{11}	c'_{12}	$\cdots$	c'_{1m}	c_{11}	$\cdots$	c_{1n}	a_1
	2	c'_{21}	c'_{22}	$\cdots$	c'_{2m}	c_{21}	$\cdots$	c_{2n}	a_2
	$\vdots$	$\vdots$	$\vdots$		$\vdots$	$\vdots$		$\vdots$	$\vdots$
	m	c'_{m1}	c'_{m2}	$\cdots$	c'_{mm}	c_{m1}	$\cdots$	c_{mn}	a_m
	$m+1$	$c'_{(m+1)1}$	$c'_{(m+1)2}$	$\cdots$	$c'_{(m+1)m}$	$c'_{(m+1)(m+1)}$	$\cdots$	$c'_{(m+1)(m+n)}$	0
	$\vdots$	$\vdots$	$\vdots$		$\vdots$	$\vdots$		$\vdots$	$\vdots$
	$m+n$	$c'_{(m+n)1}$	$c'_{(m+n)2}$	$\cdots$	$c'_{(m+n)m}$	$c'_{(m+n)(m+1)}$	$\cdots$	$c'_{(m+n)(m+n)}$	0
Demand		0	0	$\cdots$	0	b_1	$\cdots$	b_n	

this transportation problem is equivalent to the original one. Now suppose that transhipments are to be allowed, so that shipments from any source to any destination may go via any one or more of the other points. How can this transportation problem formulation be modified to permit transhipments while still being solvable by a transportation problem solution procedure?

This problem would be easy if it were known just what amount was to be transhipped through each point. It would only be necessary to add this amount to both the supply and the demand for the point. This would give the total amounts leaving and entering each point, which are the relevant "supply" and "demand" figures for transportation problem solution procedures. Unfortunately, the transhipment amounts are part of the solution and so are not initially known. However, it is possible to obtain an upper bound on the transhipment amounts. Let

$$s = \sum_{i=1}^{m} a_i = \sum_{j=1}^{n} b_j$$

(the second equality must hold in order for feasible solutions to exist), which is just the total net amount to be shipped from sources to destinations. Then, since it would not be worthwhile for any shipments to go through any points more than once (since $c'_{ij} > 0$ for $i \neq j$), s must be an upper bound on the amount transhipped through any given point. Suppose that s were added to each of the supply amounts and to each of the demand amounts. This would permit all desirable transhipments, but how can the undesirable ones be prevented? This is done automatically! Recall that the problem is formulated so that each point plays the role of both a source and a destination. Hence, given a positive supply and a positive demand, it is mathematically possible for a point to send shipments to itself, thereby reducing the real supply and demand by that amount. Furthermore, since $c'_{ii} = 0$, the solution procedure would always find it worthwhile to have a point send fictional shipments to itself at zero cost rather than make those transhipments that would increase total cost. Therefore, the only real shipments involving point i would be the a_i generated there or the b_{i-m} absorbed there, plus any shipments such that total cost is decreased by transhipping them through point i. Consequently, the optimal solution may be obtained by solving that transportation problem which has the cost and requirements table shown in Table 6.2. After obtaining the optimal solution yielded by a transportation problem solution procedure, x_{ii} (the amount shipped from point i to itself) should be reset to zero ($i = 1, 2, \cdots, m + n$) in order to eliminate the fictional shipments. The resulting solution will be the optimal solution for the transhipment problem.

TABLE 6.2. Final Cost and Requirements Table for Transhipment Problem

		Point							
		1	2	$\cdots$	m	$m+1$	$\cdots$	$m+n$	*Supply*
	1	c'_{11}	c'_{12}	$\cdots$	c'_{1m}	c_{11}	$\cdots$	c_{1n}	$a_1 + s$
	2	c'_{21}	c'_{22}	$\cdots$	c'_{2m}	c_{21}	$\cdots$	c_{2n}	$a_2 + s$
	$\vdots$	$\vdots$	$\vdots$		$\vdots$	$\vdots$		$\vdots$	$\vdots$
Point	m	c'_{m1}	c'_{m2}	$\cdots$	c'_{mm}	c_{m1}	$\cdots$	c_{mn}	$a_m + s$
	$m+1$	$c'_{(m+1)1}$	$c'_{(m+1)2}$	$\cdots$	$c'_{(m+1)m}$	$c'_{(m+1)(m+1)}$	$\cdots$	$c'_{(m+1)(m+n)}$	s
	$\vdots$	$\vdots$	$\vdots$		$\vdots$	$\vdots$		$\vdots$	$\vdots$
	$m+n$	$c'_{(m+n)1}$	$c'_{(m+n)2}$	$\cdots$	$c'_{(m+n)m}$	$c'_{(m+n)(m+1)}$	$\cdots$	$c'_{(m+n)(m+n)}$	s
Demand		s	s	$\cdots$	s	$b_1 + s$	$\cdots$	$b_n + s$	

When discussing the transportation problem, it was observed that many problems having nothing to do with transportation fit the mathematical model for the transportation problem. It is not surprising, then, that it has been found that the transhipment problem model also fits certain problems arising in some entirely different context. For this reason, it will be useful to formally write down the mathematical model and note its structure.

Let x_{ij} $(i \neq j)$ be the amount shipped from point i to point j, where the x_{ij} are the decision variables. Since x_{ii}, c'_{ii}, and s were introduced earlier only as artificial computational devices, they will not appear in the model. Using notation introduced earlier in this section, the mathematical model becomes the following. Minimize

$$\sum_{i=1}^{m+n} \sum_{\substack{j=1 \\ i \neq j}}^{m+n} c'_{ij} x_{ij},$$

subject to

$$\sum_{\substack{j=1 \\ j \neq i}}^{m+n} (x_{ij} - x_{ji}) = \begin{cases} a_i, & \text{for } i = 1, 2, \cdots, m \\ -b_{i-m}, & \text{for } i = m+1, \cdots, m+n, \end{cases}$$

and

$$x_{ij} \geq 0, \text{ for } i, j = 1, 2, \cdots, m+n \; (i \neq j).$$

Notice that this model has the special structure that each decision variable appears in exactly two constraint equations, once with a coefficient of $+1$ and once with a coefficient of -1. Any problem whose mathematical model has this structure can be solved by the efficient procedure described in this section.

6.4 THE ASSIGNMENT PROBLEM

The assignment problem is to the transportation problem as the transportation problem is to the general linear programming problem. In other words, the assignment problem is just a special case of the transportation problem, but it is one with such a simple structure that it can be solved more efficiently by its own solution procedure.

The mathematical formulation of the transportation problem reduces to the assignment problem when $m = n$, $a_i = 1$ for all i, and $b_j = 1$ for all j. In other words, the number of sources must equal the number of destinations, and each supply and each demand must equal one. (It also is always required that $x_{ij} = 0$ or 1, although this would be satisfied by all basic feasible solutions.) Thus, the following transportation array illustrates one sample solution for an assignment problem.

		Destination 1	2	3	4	*Supply*
Source	1	0	1	0	0	1
	2	0	0	0	1	1
	3	1	0	0	0	1
	4	0	0	1	0	1
Demand		1	1	1	1	

Each "source" (assignee) is assigned to its unique "destination" (assignment). The problem is to determine how the assignments should be made in order to minimize total cost. The procedure for doing this is developed in the following examples.

Example 1

A job shop has purchased three new machines of different types. There are four available locations in the shop where a machine could be installed. Some of these locations are more desirable than others for particular machines because of their proximity to work centers which would have a heavy work flow to and from these machines. Therefore, the objective is to assign the new machines to the available locations in order to minimize total cost of materials handling. The estimated cost per unit time of materials handling involving each of the machines is given below for the respective locations.

		Location 1	2	3	4
Machine	*A*	13	10	12	11
	B	15	x	13	20
	C	5	7	10	6

Location 2 is not considered suitable for machine *B*. There would be no work flow between the new machines.

In order to formulate this problem as an assignment problem, a dummy machine must be introduced for the extra location. Also, an extremely large cost M should be attached to the assignment of machine B to location 2 in order to prevent this assignment in the optimal solution. The resulting assignment problem cost matrix is shown below.

	1	2	3	4
A	13	10	12	11
B	15	M	13	20
C	5	7	10	6
D	0	0	0	0

The solution procedure for the assignment problem amounts to nothing more than converting the original cost matrix into an equivalent cost matrix for which the optimal solution is obvious. This latter cost matrix is one consisting of only positive or zero elements where all the assignments can be made to the zero element positions. Since the total cost cannot be negative, this set of assignments with a zero total cost is clearly optimal. The question remaining is how to convert the original cost matrix into this form.

The key to the solution procedure is the fact that one can add or subtract any constant from every element of a row or column of the cost matrix without really changing the problem. That is, the optimal solution for the new cost matrix must also be optimal for the old one, and conversely. To illustrate this, subtract 10 from every element in row *A*, which yields:

	1	2	3	4
A	3	0	2	1
B	15	M	13	20
C	5	7	10	6
D	0	0	0	0

Since any feasible solution must have exactly one assignment in row *A*, the total cost for the new matrix must always be exactly 10 less than for the old matrix. Hence, the solution which minimizes total cost for one matrix must also minimize total cost for the other.

Notice that, whereas, the original matrix had only strictly positive elements in the first three rows, the new matrix has a zero element in row *A*. Since the objective is to obtain enough strategically located zero elements to yield a complete set of assignments, this process should be continued on the other rows and columns. Negative elements are to be avoided, so the constant to be subtracted should be the minimum element in the row or column. Doing this for rows *B* and *C* yields the following.

	1	2	3	4
A	3	0	2	1
B	2	M−	0	7
C	0	2	5	1
D	0	0	0	0

This cost matrix has all the zero elements required for a complete assignment, so $A - 2$, $B - 3$, $C - 1$, $D - 4$ is the optimal solution.

Unfortunately, the optimal solution is not always obtained quite so easily, as illustrated in the next example.

Example 2

Consider how to find the optimal solution for the assignment problem with the following cost matrix.

	1	2	3	4	5
A	11	17	8	16	20
B	9	7	12	6	15
C	13	16	15	12	16
D	21	24	17	28	26
E	14	10	12	11	15

As in the preceding example, the minimum element in each row is subtracted from every entry in that row. The result is shown below.

	1	2	3	4	5
A	3	9	0	8	12
B	3	1	6	0	9
C	1	4	3	0	4
D	4	7	0	11	9
E	4	0	2	1	5

A complete set of assignments with zero elements is not possible this time. To obtain more zero elements, subtract the minimum element in each column from all its entries. This gives the following matrix.

	1	2	3	4	5
A	2	9	0	8	8
B	2	1	6	0	5
C	0	4	3	0	0
D	3	7	0	11	5
E	3	0	2	1	1

The next step is to determine if a complete set of assignments can be made in positions with zero elements. Since any row or column with only a single zero element must have its assignment there, begin by successively going through the rows and columns reserving such assignments. Thus, $A - 3$ must be reserved for row A, which eliminates $D - 3$ from further consideration for an assignment.

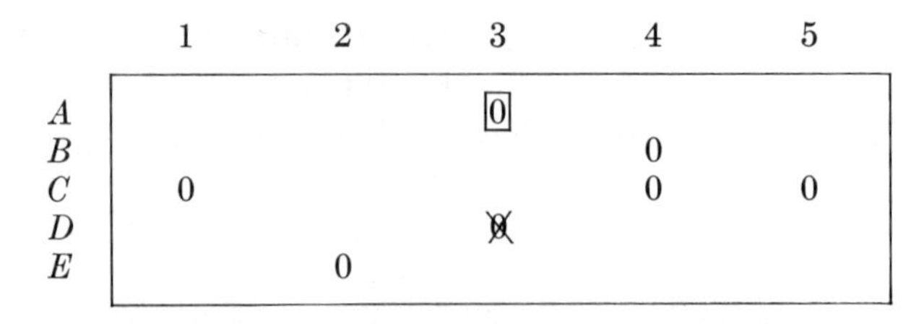

Similarly, $B - 4$ is reserved for row B, which eliminates $C - 4$, and $E - 2$ is reserved for row E.

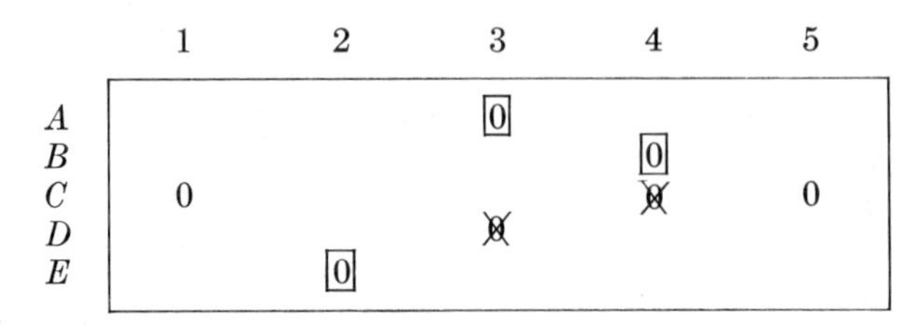

Starting on the columns, $C - 1$ must be reserved for column 1, which eliminates the last zero element, namely, the one at $C - 5$.

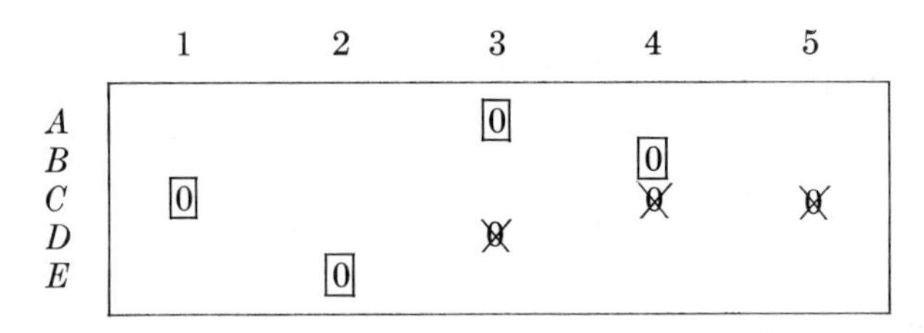

Therefore, it is possible to make only four of the five assignments in zero element positions, so more zero elements need to be created.

It is no longer obvious how to obtain even more zero elements without eliminating the present ones or creating negative elements. This can be done, but it requires a rather ingenious procedure involving adding and subtracting a constant from a combination of rows and columns. This procedure begins by drawing a set of lines through some of the rows and columns in such a way as to cover all the zeros. This is preferably done with a minimum number of lines; one such example is shown below.

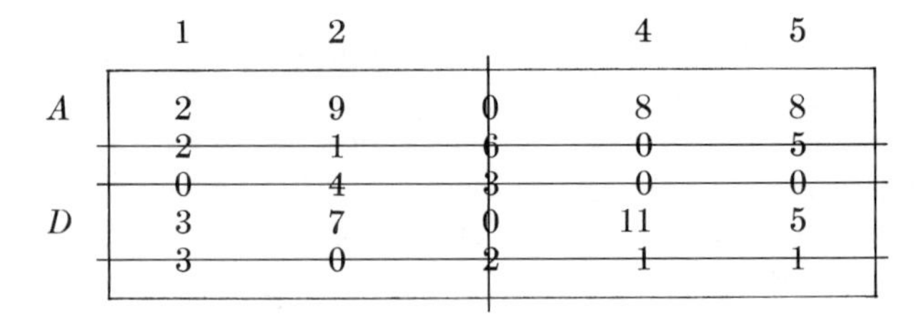

A procedure for finding such a minimum set of lines is included in the summary at the end of this section. The minimum number of lines must equal the number of assignments that can be made in positions with zero elements—four in this case.

The reader may now be able to deduce what remains to be done. Notice that the minimum element not crossed out is 2 in position $A - 1$. Therefore, subtracting 2 from every element in the entire table, i.e., from every row or from every column, will create a new zero element in this position. Then, in order to restore the previous zero elements and eliminate negative elements, add 2 to each row or column with a line covering it—rows B, C, and E, and column 3. The result is given below.

	1	2	3	4	5
A	0	7	0	6	6
B	2	1	8	0	5
C	0	4	5	0	0
D	1	5	0	9	3
E	3	0	4	1	1

A shortcut for obtaining this matrix from the preceding one is to subtract 2 from just the elements without a line through them and then add 2 to every element that lies at the intersection of two lines.

Another attempt can now be made to make a complete set of assignments in zero element positions. Proceeding as before, assignments $B - 4$, $D - 3$, $E - 2$, $C - 5$, and $A - 1$ are made, as summarized below.

	1	2	3	4	5
A	[0]	7	~~0~~	6	6
B	2	1	8	[0]	5
C	~~0~~	4	5	~~0~~	[0]
D	1	5	[0]	9	3
E	3	[0]	4	1	1

Since this is indeed a complete set of assignments, it is an optimal solution and the procedure is completed. If a complete set had not been obtained, the above procedure would be repeated until an optimal solution were found.

When making assignments to zero element positions, it is possible to arrive at a point where each remaining row or column would contain either no or at least two unmarked zeros. Although a very complex procedure is available for making the maximum number of additional assignments in zero element positions, this can usually be done more easily by trial and error for problems small enough to be done manually.

A summary of the solution procedure for the assignment problem follows:

(1) Subtract the minimum element of each row in the cost matrix from every element of that row. Then do the same for each column.
(2) Examine the rows and columns successively. For each row/column with exactly one remaining zero element, reserve that position for an assignment and eliminate other zero element positions in that column/row from further consideration. Repeat as required for rows and columns without reserved positions until all zero element positions are reserved or eliminated. (If this is not possible, see the preceding paragraph.) If the reserved positions comprise a complete set of assignments, it is an optimal solution. Otherwise, go to step (3).
(3) Draw a minimum number of lines to cover all zero elements as follows:

(a) Mark all rows that do not have assignments.
(b) Mark all columns which have zeros in marked rows.
(c) Mark all rows that have assignments in marked columns.
(d) Repeat steps (b) and (c) until no more rows or columns can be marked.
(e) Draw a line through each unmarked row and through each marked column.

(4) Examine all elements uncovered by a line. Select the minimum of these and subtract it from the uncovered elements. Then add it to each element that lies at the intersection of two lines. Go to step 2.

SELECTED REFERENCES

1. Dantzig, George B., *Linear Programming and Extensions,* Princeton University Press, Princeton, N.J., 1963, chaps. 14–21.
2. Garvin, Walter W., *Introduction to Linear Programming,* McGraw-Hill, New York, 1960, Part II.
3. Reinfeld, N. V., and Vogel, W. R., *Mathematical Programming,* Prentice-Hall, Englewood Cliffs, N.J., 1958.

PROBLEMS

1. Tom would like exactly six pints of home brew today and at least eight pints of home brew tomorrow. Dick is willing to sell a maximum of eight pints total at a price of 50 cents per pint today and 45 cents per pint tomorrow. Harry is willing to sell a maximum of seven pints total at a price of 48 cents per pint today and 47 cents per pint tomorrow.

Tom wishes to know what his purchases should be in order to minimize his cost while satisfying his minimum thirst requirements.

(a) Formulate the linear programming model for this problem, and construct the initial simplex tableau (see Chapter 5).
(b) Formulate this problem as a transportation problem by constructing the appropriate cost and requirements table.
(c) Solve the problem as formulated in (b).

2. A corporation has decided to produce three new products. Five branch plants now have excess production capacity. The unit manufacturing cost of the first product would be $26, $28, $24, $30, and $27 in plants 1, 2, 3, 4, and 5, respectively. The unit manufacturing cost of the second product would be $29, $33, $28, $32, and $31 in plants 1, 2, 3, 4, and 5, respectively. The unit manufacturing cost of the third product would be $40, $43, and $39 in plants 1, 2, and 3, respectively, whereas, plants 4 and 5 do not have the capability for producing this product. Sales forecasts indicate that 300, 200, and 400 units of products 1, 2, and 3, respectively, should be produced per day. Plants 1, 2, 3, 4, and 5 have the capacity to produce 200, 400, 200, 500, and 300 units daily, respectively, regardless of the product or combination of products involved. Assume that any plant having the capability and capacity can produce any combination of the products in any quantity.

Management wishes to know how to allocate the new products to the plants in order to minimize total manufacturing cost.

(a) Formulate this problem as a transportation problem by constructing the appropriate cost and requirements table.
(b) Solve the problem as formulated in (a).

3. Consider the transportation problem having the following cost and requirements table.

		Destination				
		1	2	3	4	*Supply*
Source	1	5	8	3	6	30
	2	4	5	7	4	50
	3	6	2	4	5	40
Demand		30	20	40	30	

(a) Use the northwest corner rule to obtain an initial basic feasible solution for this problem.

(b) Use Vogel's approximation method to obtain an initial basic feasible solution.
(c) Obtain an optimal solution.

4. Consider the transportation problem having the following cost and requirements table.

		Destination 1	2	3	4	5	6	*Supply*
Source	1	21	12	28	17	9	0	50
	2	15	13	20	M	12	0	60
	3	18	17	22	10	8	0	40
	4	M	2	10	5	0	0	70
	5	33	29	35	27	23	0	30
Demand		40	30	50	60	50	20	

(a) Use the northwest corner rule to obtain an initial basic feasible solution for this problem.
(b) Use Vogel's approximation method to obtain an initial basic feasible solution.
(c) Obtain an optimal solution.

5. A firm producing a single product has two plants and three customers. The two plants will produce 60 and 40 units, respectively, during the next time period. The firm has made a commitment to sell 50 units to customer 1 and at least 20 units to customer 3. Both customers 2 and 3 also want to buy as many of the remaining units as possible. The net profit associated with shipping a unit from plant i for sale to customer j is given by the following table.

		Customer 1	2	3
Plant	1	5	7	6
	2	2	3	5

Management wishes to know how many units to sell to customers 2 and 3 and how many units to ship from each of the plants to each of the customers in order to maximize profit.

(a) Formulate this problem as a transportation problem by constructing the appropriate cost and requirements table.
(b) Solve the problem as formulated in (a).

6. Suppose that the air freight charge per ton between seven particular locations is given by the following table (except where no direct air freight service is available).

Location	1	2	3	4	5	6	7
1	—	12	27	—	45	36	15
2	12	—	10	25	32	—	22
3	27	10	—	28	50	28	10
4	—	25	28	—	16	20	32
5	45	32	50	16	—	26	35
6	36	—	28	20	26	—	20
7	15	22	10	32	35	20	—

A certain corporation must ship a certain perishable commodity from locations 1, 2, and 3 to locations 4, 5, 6, and 7. A total of 30, 50, and 20 tons of this commodity are to be sent from locations 1, 2, and 3, respectively. A total of 15, 30, 25, and 30 tons are to be sent to locations 4, 5, 6, and 7, respectively. Shipments can be sent through intermediate locations at a cost equal to the sum of the costs for each of the legs of the journey. The problem is to determine the shipping plan which minimizes the total freight cost.

(a) Formulate this problem as a transhipment problem by constructing the appropriate cost and requirements table to be solved by a transportation problem solution procedure.
(b) Use Vogel's approximation method to obtain an approximate solution to the problem formulated in (a).
(c) Obtain an optimal solution to the problem formulated in (a).

7. Reconsider problem 2. Suppose that the sales forecasts have been revised downward, so that each plant has the capacity to produce all that is required of any one product. Therefore, management has decided that each new product should be assigned to only one plant and that no plant should be assigned more than one product (so that three plants are each to be assigned one product, and two plants are to be assigned none).

(a) Formulate this problem as an assignment problem by constructing the appropriate cost matrix.
(b) Solve the problem as formulated in (a).

8. Solve the assignment problems having the following cost matrices.

(a)

	1	2	3	4
A	10	12	9	11
B	5	10	7	8
C	12	14	13	11
D	8	15	11	9

(b)

	1	2	3	4	5	6	7
A	35	22	60	41	27	52	44
B	51	39	42	33	65	47	58
C	25	32	53	41	50	36	43
D	32	28	40	46	34	55	49
E	43	36	45	63	57	49	42
F	27	18	31	46	35	42	34
G	48	50	72	59	43	64	58

CHAPTER 7

Network Analysis, Including PERT

7.1 INTRODUCTION

Network analysis has long played an important role in electrical engineering. However, there has been a growing awareness in recent years that certain concepts and tools of network theory are also very useful in many other contexts as well. For example, important applications of network analysis have been made in information theory, cybernetics, the study of transportation systems, and the planning and control of research and development projects. As a result, certain aspects of network analysis (commonly called "network flow theory") are becoming an increasingly useful tool of operations research.

A fundamental problem of network theory involves allocating flows in order to maximize the flow through a network connecting a source and a destination. Another problem, which commonly arises in the study of transportation systems, is finding the shortest route through a network. A similar problem is to choose a set of connections that provide a route between any two points of a network in such a way as to minimize the total length of these connections. The planning and control of research and development projects are a fourth problem which has been attacked by techniques involving network analysis; the technique in this case is a recently developed one known as PERT (Program Evaluation and Review Technique). After briefly presenting necessary background material on the theory of graphs (networks), the remainder of the chapter is devoted to these four problems.

7.2 INTRODUCTION TO THE THEORY OF GRAPHS

According to the terminology of the theory of graphs, a "graph" consists of a set of junction points called "*nodes*" with certain pairs of the nodes being joined by lines called "*branches*" (or "arcs," "links," or "edges"). Thus, Figure 7.1 is an example of a graph, where the circles are the nodes and the lines connecting them are the branches.

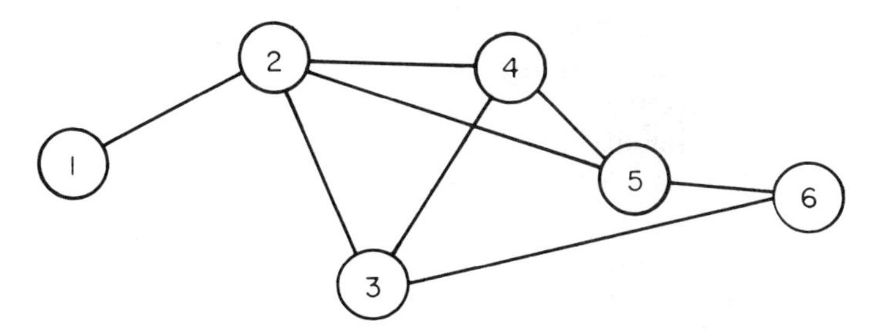

FIGURE 7.1. Example of a graph.

A "*network*" is considered to be a graph with a flow of some type in its branches. Numerous examples of systems satisfying this definition of network are to be found in the physical world, as indicated by Table 7.1.

TABLE 7.1. Components of Typical Networks

Nodes	*Branches*	*Flow*
Intersections	Roads	Vehicles
Airports	Air lanes	Aircraft
Switching points	Wires, channels	Messages
Pumping stations	Pipes	Fluid
Work centers	Materials handling routes	Jobs

Additional terminology has been developed to describe graphs. A "*chain*" between nodes i and j is a sequence of branches connecting these two nodes. For example, one of the chains connecting nodes 1 and 6 in Figure 7.1 is the sequence of branches, (1, 2), (2, 5), (5, 6), or vice versa. When the direction of travel along the chain is also specified, it will be called a "path." A "cycle" is a chain connecting a node to itself.

Thus, (2, 4), (4, 3), and (3, 2) form a cycle in Figure 7.1. A graph is said to be a "*connected graph*" if there is a chain connecting every pair of nodes. Thus, the graph of Figure 7.1 is a connected graph, but it would not be if branches (2, 3), (3, 4), and (5, 6) were removed. A "*tree*" is a connected graph containing no cycles. For example, Figure 7.1 would be a tree if branches (3, 6), (3, 4), and (4, 5) were removed. One of the theorems of graph theory states that a graph having n nodes is connected if it has $(n - 1)$ branches and no cycles (so that such a graph is a tree).

A branch of a graph is said to be "*oriented*" (or "*directed*") if there is a sense of direction attributed to the branch so that one node is considered the point of origin and the other node the point of destination. An "*oriented graph*" is one in which all the branches are oriented. If an oriented graph is a network, the orientation of a branch is assumed to be the feasible direction of flow along the branch. However, a network need not be oriented since it may be feasible to have flow in either direction along a branch. The flow "*capacity*" of a branch in a specified direction is the upper limit to the feasible magnitude of the rate of flow (or total quantity of flow) in the branch in that direction. The flow capacity may be any non-negative quantity, including infinity. A branch is oriented if the flow capacity is zero in one direction. A node may also have a limited flow capacity—although that possibility will be ignored here.

A node in a network is sometimes referred to as a "*source*" if every one of its branches has an orientation such that the flow moves away from that node. Similarly, it is sometimes called a "*sink*" if each of its branches is oriented toward that node. Thus, sources may be thought of as the generators of the flow and sinks as the absorbers of that flow.

7.3 THE MAXIMAL FLOW PROBLEM

Consider a connected network having a single source and a single sink. Assume conservation of flow (i.e., flow into the node equals flow out of the node) at each node other than the source and the sink. Suppose that the rate of flow along branch (i, j) from node i to node j can be any non-negative quantity not exceeding the specified flow capacity c_{ij}. The "maximal flow problem" is to determine the feasible steady-state pattern of flows through the network which maximizes the total flow from the source to the sink.

Figure 7.2 gives an example of a maximal flow problem. The source and the sink are nodes 1 and 7, respectively. The flow capacity c_{ij} is shown by the number along branch (i, j) nearest node i. For example, the flow capacity from node 1 to node 2 is 7 and from node 2 to node 1 is 0. The problem is to determine the feasible flow in each branch which will maximize F, the total flow out of the source. (Because of the conservation of flow assumption, F is also the total flow into the sink.) A quick examination reveals that one feasible flow pattern is a flow of 4 along the path $1 \to 2 \to 4 \to 7$ and a flow of 3 along the path $1 \to 3 \to 6 \to 7$, yielding $F = 7$. However, there may be other feasible flow patterns yielding a larger value of F. A general procedure for finding the optimal solution is developed shortly.

Actually, the maximal flow problem can be formulated as a linear programming problem. Although this will now be done in order to give a mathematical description of the problem, it should be emphasized that the solution procedure to be developed shortly is much more efficient for solving this problem than the simplex method. Suppose there are N nodes, where nodes 1 and N are the source and sink, respectively. For each branch

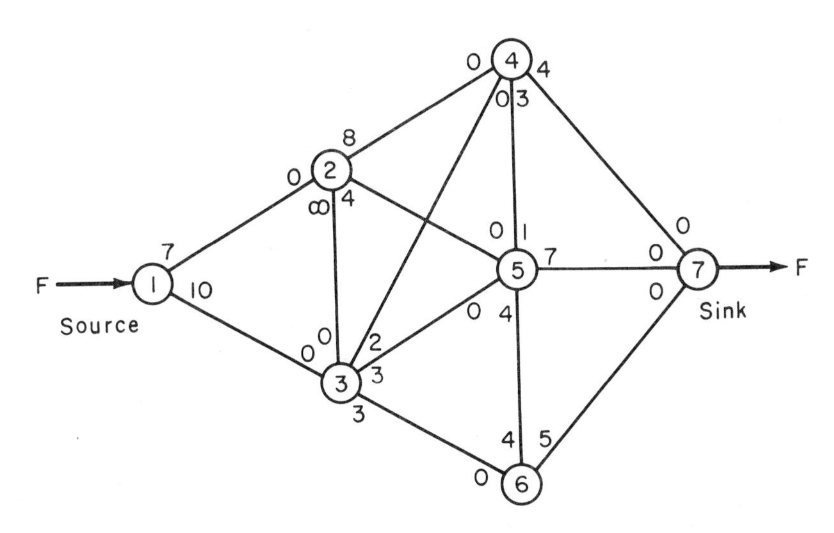

FIGURE 7.2. Example of a maximal flow problem.

(i, j), let x_{ij} denote the rate of flow from node i to node j. The flow capacity constraints are

$$0 \leq x_{ij} \leq c_{ij}, \qquad \text{for each branch } (i, j)\,. \tag{1}$$

The conservation of flow constraint is

$$\sum_i x_{ik} - \sum_j x_{kj} = 0, \qquad \text{for } k = 2, 3, \cdots, N-1\,, \tag{2}$$

where these summations are taken over those i and j corresponding to branches leading into and out of node k, respectively. Since

$$F = \sum_k x_{1k} = \sum_k x_{kN}\,,$$ [28]

either summation may be used as the objective function. Selecting the first one arbitrarily, the linear programming model for this problem is to maximize

$$F = \sum_k x_{1k}\,,$$

subject to constraints (1) and (2).

Rather than using the simplex method, a more efficient solution procedure for this problem is essentially to follow one's intuition! This process had already been started for the example of Figure 7.2 when it was observed that flows of 4 and 3 could be assigned to paths $1 \to 2 \to 4 \to 7$ and $1 \to 3 \to 6 \to 7$, respectively. One effect of these assignments would be to decrease the remaining flow capacity in each branch along the path (in the

[28] The second equality may be shown by summing all of the conservation of flow constraints. The reader is asked to do this in problem 2 at the end of the chapter.

direction of the path) by the amount of the flow assigned. After making these changes in the remaining flow capacity, one would search for new paths with positive flow capacity from the source to the sink. Continue assigning the maximum flows along these paths until no more such paths can be found. This procedure is illustrated below.

Original network: See Figure 7.2.
Assign flow of 4 to $1 \rightarrow 2 \rightarrow 4 \rightarrow 7$.

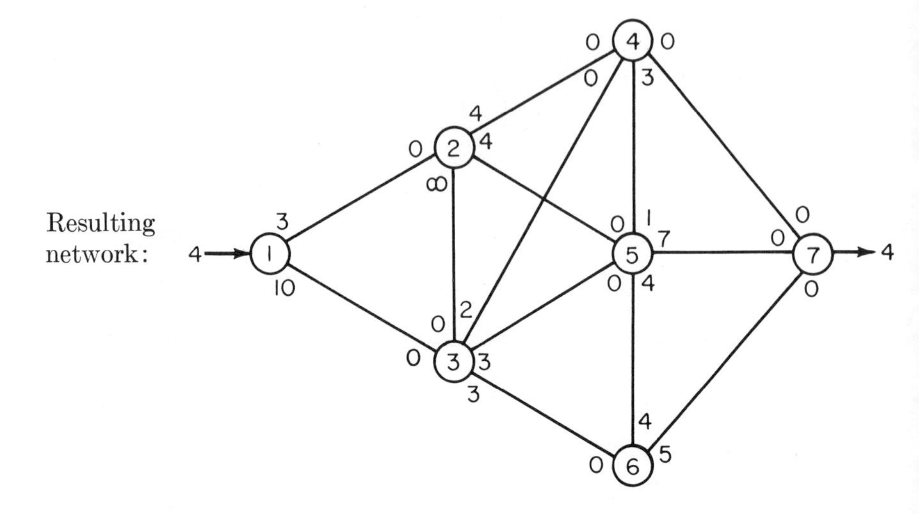

Assign flow of 3 to $1 \rightarrow 3 \rightarrow 6 \rightarrow 7$.

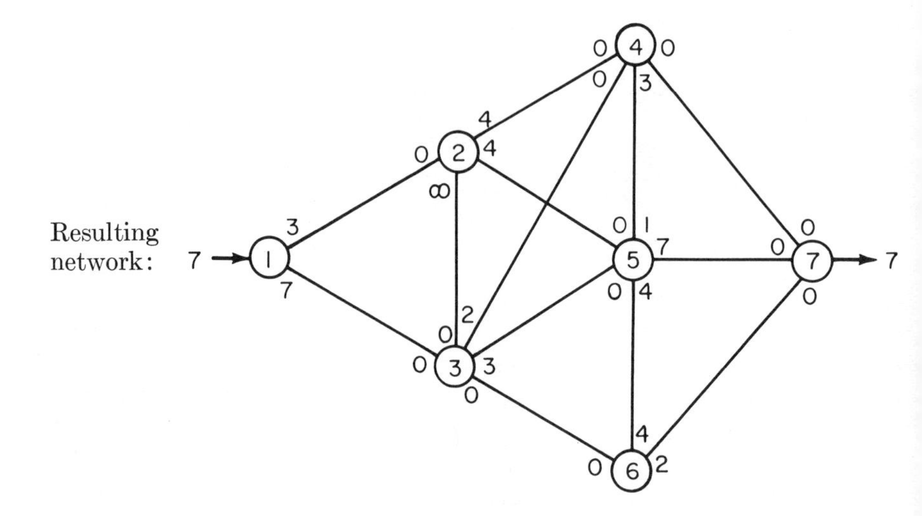

Assign flow of 3 to $1 \rightarrow 2 \rightarrow 4 \rightarrow 5 \rightarrow 7$.

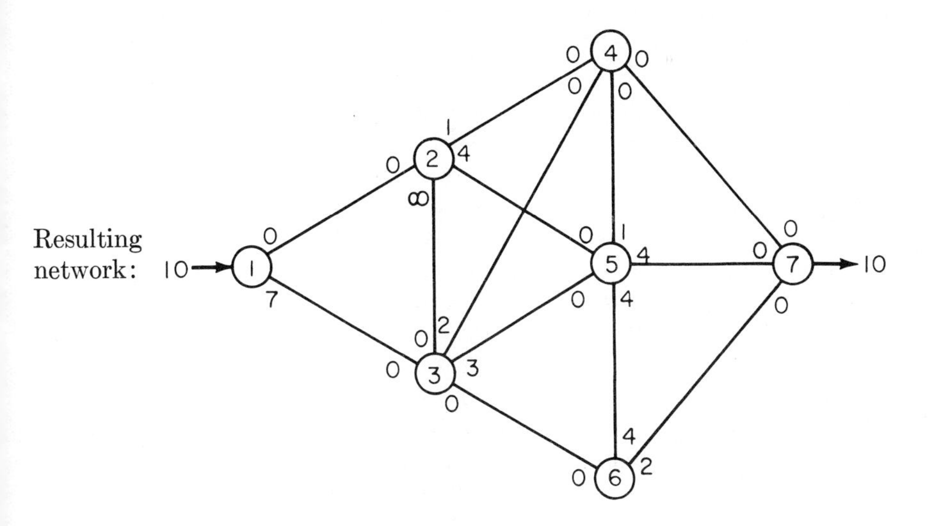

Assign flow of 3 to $1 \rightarrow 3 \rightarrow 5 \rightarrow 7$.

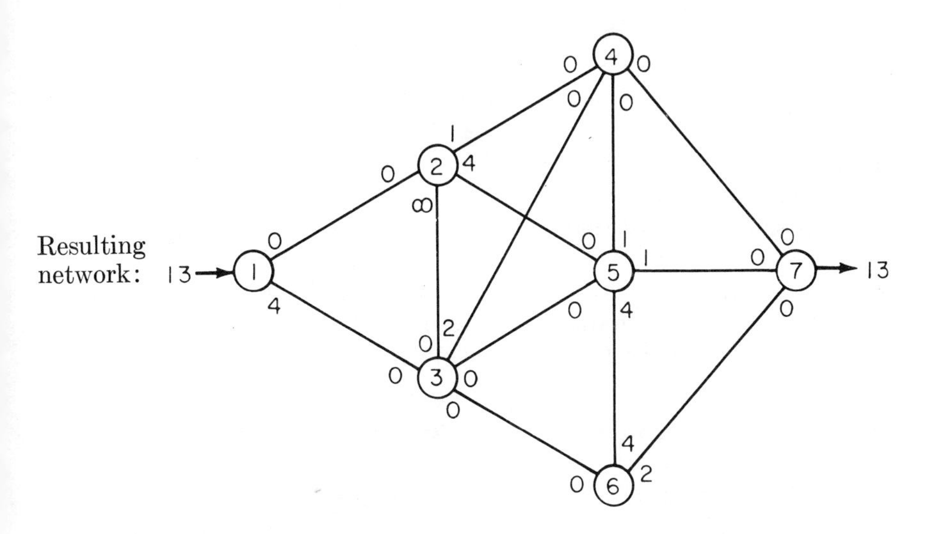

No paths with positive flow capacity remain.

Should not the flow pattern developed above be optimal? The answer is no, it need not be, and, in fact, it is not in this case. However, the procedure is almost flawless; it requires only one refinement before it will guarantee an optimal solution. The effect of this refinement is to permit previously assigned flow to take an alternate route in order to open up new paths from the source to the sink with positive flow capacity. To illustrate, recall that the procedure began by assigning a flow of 4 to the path $1 \rightarrow 2 \rightarrow 4 \rightarrow 7$. However, this flow could have been sent from node 2 to the sink along various alternate routes. Notice what would have happened if half of this flow (2) had been assigned instead to the path $1 \rightarrow 2 \rightarrow 5 \rightarrow 6 \rightarrow 7$. All flow assignments subsequently made would still have been feasible. However, after making these flow assignments, it would now be possible to assign an additional flow of 2 to the path $1 \rightarrow 3 \rightarrow 4 \rightarrow 7$, thereby increasing the total flow from $F = 13$ to $F = 15$.

How does one refine the procedure in order to identify improvements such as the one discovered above? The trick involved is to permit assigning fictional flows in the "wrong" direction (one with zero flow capacity) along a branch when the real effect of this assignment is only to cancel out part or all of the previously assigned flow in the "right" direction. To illustrate, consider the network with $F = 13$ developed above. In order to achieve the discovered improvement to $F = 15$, one desires to increase the flow by 2 along paths $1 \rightarrow 3 \rightarrow 4$ and $2 \rightarrow 5 \rightarrow 6 \rightarrow 7$ and decrease the flow by 2 from node 2 to node 4. However, this is also accomplished by assigning instead a flow of 2 along the path $1 \rightarrow 3 \rightarrow 4 \rightarrow 2 \rightarrow 5 \rightarrow 6 \rightarrow 7$, where the real effect of assigning a "flow" of 2 from node 4 to node 2 is to decrease the previously assigned flow from node 2 to node 4 by 2. In order to permit this, the procedure should have increased the flow capacity from node 4 to node 2 by 4 and then by 3 when flows of these amounts were assigned to paths passing through node 2 to node 4. Thus, the needed refinement in the procedure is that whenever a quantity of flow is assigned to a branch, the capacity in the opposite direction in that branch should be increased by the same quantity.

It should be noted that, when the procedure is completed, it is only the net flow in a branch that is relevant. Therefore, when flow has been assigned to a branch in both directions, the smaller of the two flows should be subtracted from both directions, leaving only the net flow.

The proper solution procedure may now be summarized as follows.

SUMMARY OF SOLUTION PROCEDURE[29]

(1) Find a path from source to sink with positive flow capacity. (If none exists, the net flows already assigned constitute an optimal flow pattern.)
(2) Search this path for the branch with the smallest flow capacity (denote this capacity as c^*) and increase the flow in this path by c^*.
(3) Decrease by c^* the flow capacity of each branch in the path. Increase by c^* the flow capacity in the opposite direction for each branch in the path. Return to step (1).

[29] It is assumed that the flow capacities are either integers or rational numbers.

Applying this corrected solution procedure to the example of Figure 7.2 yields the results summarized below.

Original network: See Figure 7.2.
Assign flow of 4 to $1 \to 2 \to 4 \to 7$.

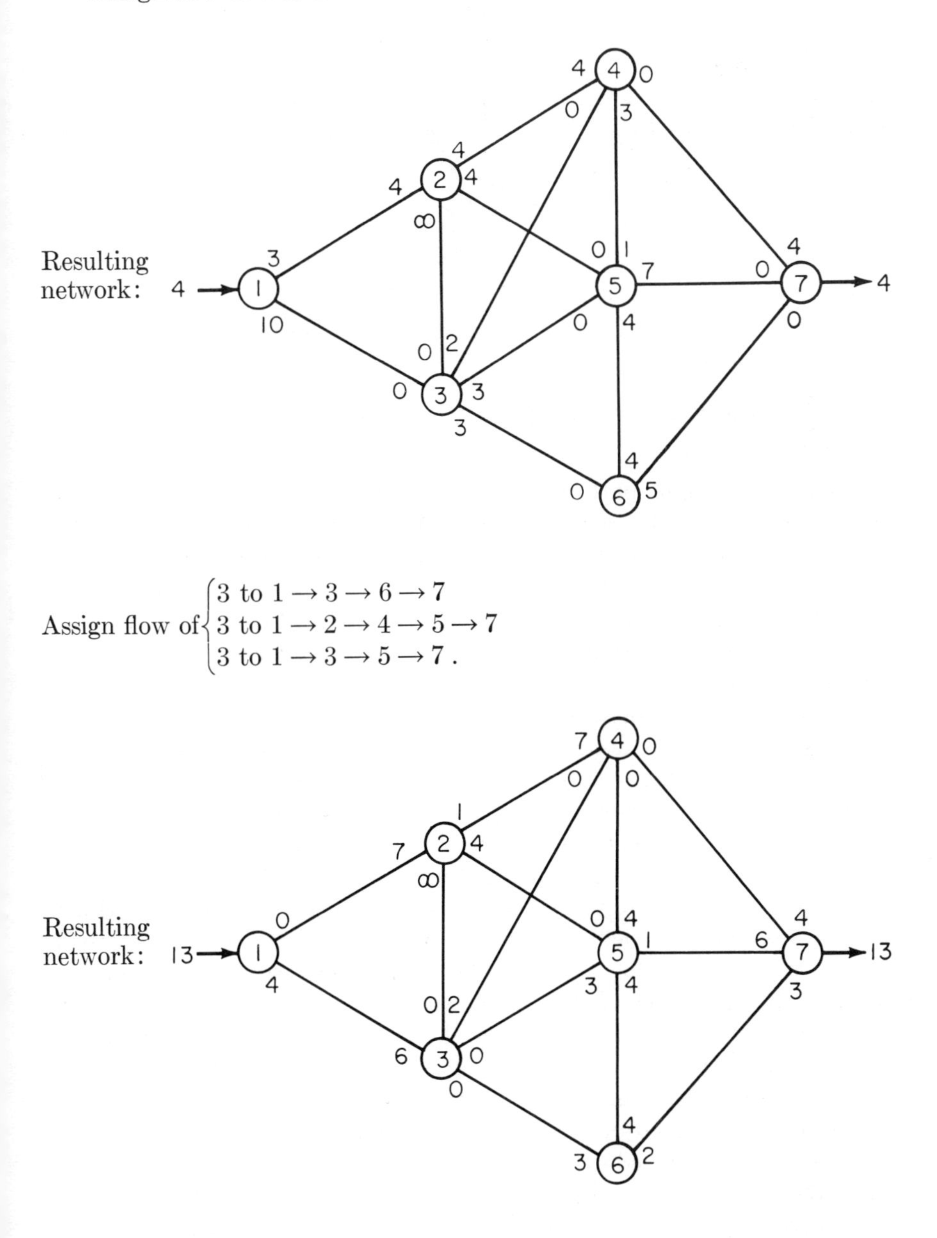

Assign flow of $\begin{cases} 3 \text{ to } 1 \to 3 \to 6 \to 7 \\ 3 \text{ to } 1 \to 2 \to 4 \to 5 \to 7 \\ 3 \text{ to } 1 \to 3 \to 5 \to 7. \end{cases}$

Assign flow of 2 to $1 \to 3 \to 4 \to 2 \to 5 \to 6 \to 7$.

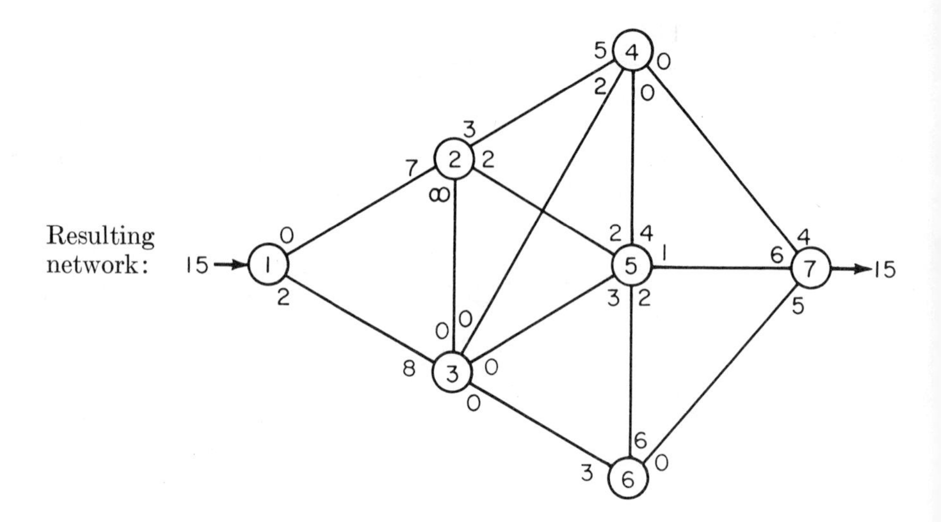

No paths with positive capacity remain. Hence, the current flow pattern is optimal.

The current flow pattern may be identified either by cumulating the flow assignments or by comparing the remaining flow capacities with the original flow capacities. Using the latter method, the direction of net flow in a branch would be in the direction whose remaining flow capacity is less than the original capacity. The magnitude of this flow would equal the amount by which this original flow capacity has been decreased. The reader can verify this fact by reviewing the way in which the flow capacities are modified by the solution procedure.

Perhaps the most disagreeable aspect of this solution procedure when large networks are involved is the necessity of finding a path from source to sink with positive flow capacity. This task may be simplified by the following systematic procedure. Begin by determining all nodes that can be reached from the source along a (single) branch with positive flow capacity. Then, for each of these nodes that were reached, determine all *new* nodes (those not yet reached) that can be reached from this node along a branch with positive flow capacity. Repeat this successively with the new nodes as they are reached. The result will be the identification of a tree of all the nodes that can be reached from the source along a path with positive flow capacity. Hence, this fanning-out procedure will always identify a path from source to sink with positive flow capacity, if one exists. The procedure is illustrated in Figure 7.3 for the network of Figure 7.2.

Although the procedure illustrated in Figure 7.3 is a relatively straightforward one, it would be helpful if one could recognize when optimality has been reached without an exhaustive search for a non-existent path. This is sometimes possible, due to an important theorem of network theory known as the max-flow min-cut theorem. A "*cut*" may be defined as any set of oriented branches containing at least one branch from every path from source to sink. The "*cut value*" is the sum of the flow capacities of the branches (in the direction of the orientation designated by the cut) of the cut. The *max-flow min-cut theorem* states that, for any network with a

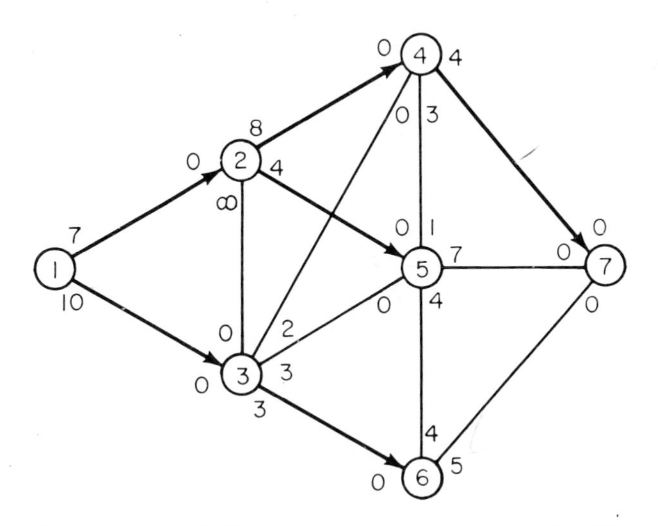

FIGURE 7.3. Procedure for finding a path from source to sink with positive flow capacity.

single source and sink, the maximum feasible flow from source to sink equals the minimum cut value for any of the cuts of the network. Thus, the value of any cut provides an upper bound to F, and the smallest of the cut values is equal to the maximum value of F. Therefore, if one happens to notice a cut in the original network whose value equals the value of F currently attained by the solution procedure, the current flow pattern must be optimal. Equivalently, optimality has been attained whenever there exists a cut in the current network whose value is zero with respect to the remaining flow capacities. To illustrate, consider the cut in the network of Figure 7.2 indicated in Figure 7.4.

Notice that the value of the cut in Figure 7.4 is $(7 + 0 + 2 + 3 + 3) = 15$, which was found to be the maximum value of F, so this cut is a minimal cut. Notice also that, in the network given earlier where $F = 15$, the corresponding cut has a value of zero with respect to the remaining flow capacities. If this had been noticed, it would not have been necessary to search for additional paths from source to sink with positive flow capacity.

It is possible to systemize the over-all solution procedure described above so that it can be solved on a computer. This can be done either by proceeding in a straightforward way or by reducing the problem to tableau form. The latter method is detailed and not particularly instructive, so the interested reader is referred elsewhere for a description, as well as for a

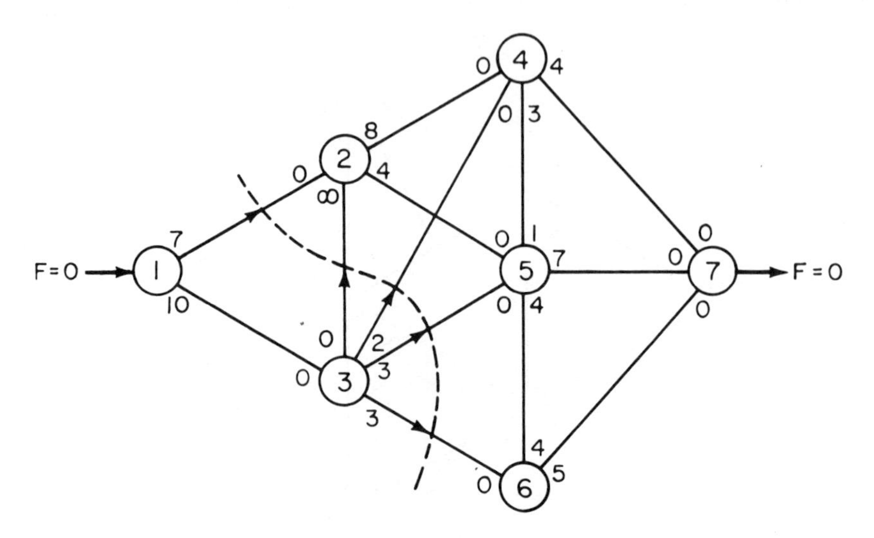

FIGURE 7.4. An example of a minimal cut.

proof of the results quoted above and a proof that the over-all procedure must yield an optimal solution.[30]

7.4 THE SHORTEST ROUTE PROBLEM

The shortest route problem is concerned with finding the shortest route from an origin to a destination through a connecting network, given the non-negative distance associated with the respective branches of the network. Although various similar solution procedures have been proposed, the version to be described here is perhaps the shortest and simplest. The essence of this procedure is that it fans out from the origin successively identifying the shortest route to each of the nodes of the network in the ascending order of their (shortest) distances from the origin, thereby solving the problem when the destination node is reached. A method for doing this is now developed, followed by an example.

Suppose that, for a certain value of $n (n = 1, 2, \cdots)$, it is known which

[30] See reference 3 at the end of the chapter for a description of the tableau form. See references 1, 2, and 3 for the indicated proofs.

$(n - 1)$ nodes (excluding the origin) are nearest the origin along the shortest connecting chain, as well as the corresponding (shortest) routes and distances. [These $(n - 1)$ nodes plus the origin node will be referred to as the "original" nodes. All other nodes will be referred to as "new" nodes.] Given this information, how does one identify the node that has the nth smallest distance to the origin along its shortest route, i.e., which of the new nodes is closest to the origin? To qualify as a candidate, a new node must be connected by a branch to one of the original nodes. (Otherwise, the intervening new node would be closer to the origin.) Furthermore, it must be the closest new node to one of the original nodes to which it is connected by a single branch. (Otherwise, whichever route were taken to the origin, there would always be another new node which would have a head start.) Thus, since there are n original nodes, there are, at most, n candidates for the new node that is closest to the origin. To select the winning candidate, proceed as follows. For each of the original nodes connected by a branch to a new node, compute the sum of (1) the known (shortest) distance from the origin to that node, and (2) the distance from that node to the nearest new node along a single branch. Each sum must be the distance along the corresponding route from the origin to this new node. Therefore, the new node corresponding to the smallest sum must be the new node which is closest to the origin. Furthermore, its shortest route must be the route whose distance yielded this smallest sum.

Therefore, in order to find the shortest route from origin to destination, one should repeat the above process of finding the nth nearest node to the origin successively for $n = 1, 2, 3$, etc., until the destination node is reached. This procedure is now illustrated by the example given in Figure 7.5.

For later computational convenience, construct a list for each node of the branches leading out of that node in the order of the ascending branch distances. It is not necessary to include branches into the origin or out of the destination.

(O)	(A)	(B)	(C)	(D)	(E)	(F)	(G)	(H)	(T)
OA–7	AD–6	BE–4	CD–2	DC–2	EB–4	FD–2	GC–3	HE–6	
OB–8	AB–7	BD–6	CF–3	DF–2	EH–6	FC–3	GF–5	HG–8	
	AC–8	BA–7	CG–3	DA–6	ED–7	FG–5	GD–6	HT–8	
			CA–8	DB–6	EG–9	FT–9	GH–8		
				DG–6			GT–8		
				DE–7			GE–9		

$n = 1$: Since the origin is the only "original" node initially, only the (O) column need be considered at this point. Hence, node A is immediately identified as the nearest node to the origin. To indicate this, circle the OA–7 entry. To prepare for the next iteration, write the distance to node A above

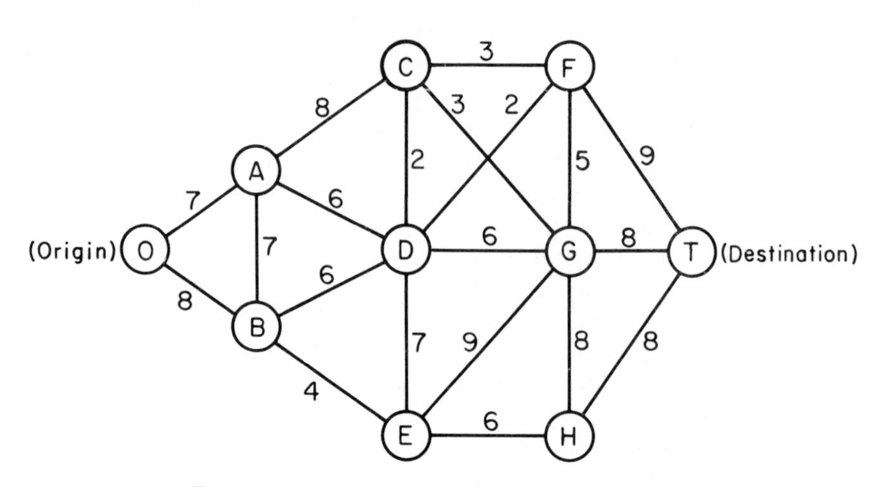

FIGURE 7.5. Example for shortest route problem.
Numbers represent actual distances.

the (A) column, and cross out branches leading into A in all columns in which they appear. The lists should now look as follows.

(O)	7 (A)	(B)	(C)	(D)	(E)	(F)	(G)	(H)	(T)
(OA-7)	AD-6	BE-4	CD-2	DC-2	EB-4	FD-2	GC-3	HE-6	
OB-8	AB-7	BD-6	CF-3	DF-2	EH-6	FC-3	GF-5	HG-8	
	AC-8	~~BA-7~~	CG-3	~~DA-6~~	ED-7	FG-5	GD-6	HT-8	
			~~CA-8~~	DB-6	EG-9	FT-9	GH-8		
				DG-6			GT-8		
				DE-7			GE-9		

$n = 2$: The candidates for the second nearest node to the origin are those new nodes nearest nodes O and A, namely, nodes B and D, respectively. Comparing their distances yields $(0 + 8) = 8$ for node B and $(7 + 6) = 13$ for node D, so select B. Circle OB–8, write 8 above the (B) column, and cross out all branches leading into B. Since this exhausts the (O) column of new nodes, place an X above the branches to indicate that this column can be ignored henceforth. The resulting lists are given below.

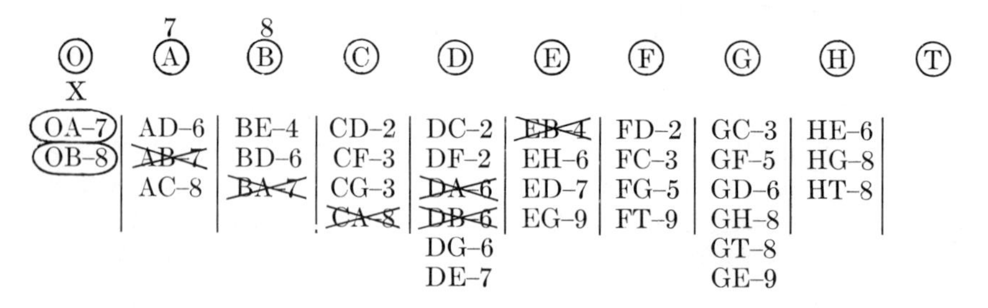

(O) X	7 (A)	8 (B)	(C)	(D)	(E)	(F)	(G)	(H)	(T)
(OA-7)	AD-6	BE-4	CD-2	DC-2	~~EB-4~~	FD-2	GC-3	HE-6	
(OB-8)	~~AB-7~~	BD-6	CF-3	DF-2	EH-6	FC-3	GF-5	HG-8	
	AC-8	~~BA-7~~	CG-3	~~DA-6~~	ED-7	FG-5	GD-6	HT-8	
			~~CA-8~~	~~DB-6~~	EG-9	FT-9	GH-8		
				DG-6			GT-8		
				DE-7			GE-9		

$n = 3$: Compare the distance for node D, $(7 + 6) = 13$, and the distance for node E, $(8 + 4) = 12$. Select node E and make the corresponding changes in the lists.

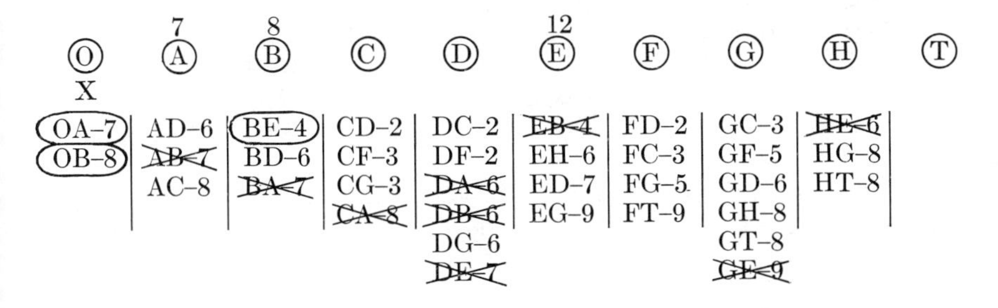

$n = 4$: Compare the distances for node D, $(7 + 6) = 13$ via node A and $(8 + 6) = 14$ via node B, and the distance for node H, $(12 + 6) = 18$. Select node D via node A and modify the lists.

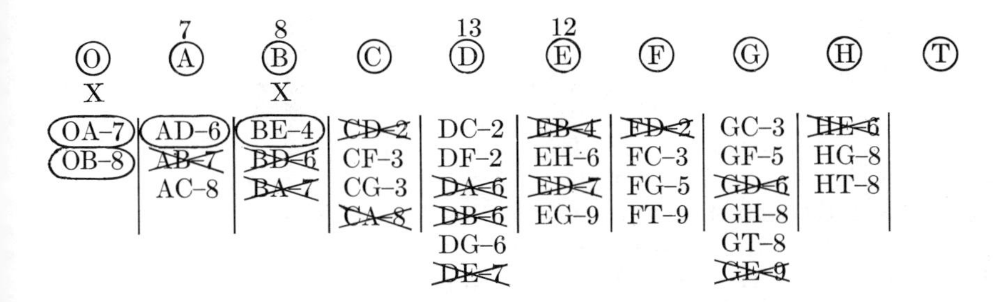

$n = 5$: Compare AC$(7 + 8)$, DC$(13 + 2)$, DF$(13 + 2)$, and EH$(12 + 6)$. The first three tie, so select both node C (via A or D) and node F. Modify the lists.

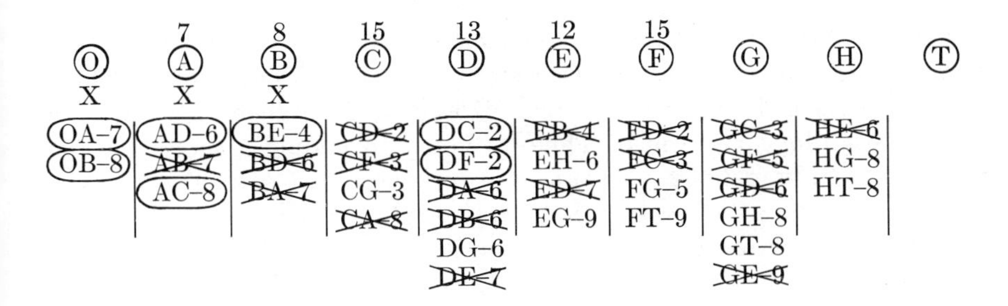

$n = 7$: Compare CG$(15 + 3)$, DG$(13 + 6)$, EH$(12 + 6)$, and FG$(15 + 5)$. Because of the tie, select both node G (via C) and node H. Modify the lists.

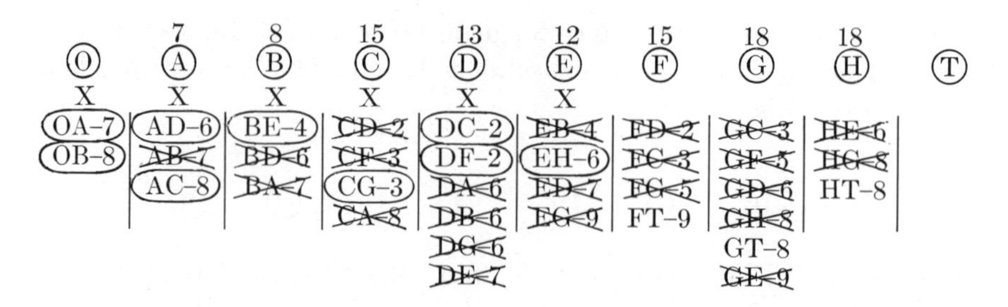

$n = 9$: Compare FT(15 + 9), GT(18 + 8), and HT(18 + 8). Thus, the shortest route to node T is via node F. The final version of the lists follows.

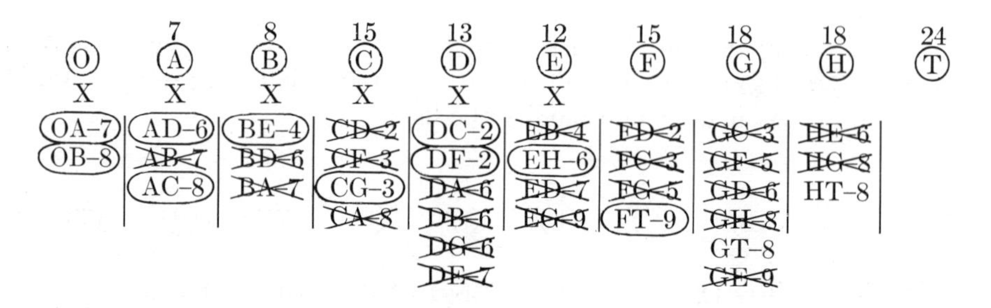

The shortest route from the destination to the origin can now be traced back through the circled branches as T → F → D → A → O. Therefore, the shortest route from the origin to the destination has been identified as O → A → D → F → T, with a total distance of 24. As an added bonus, the procedure has also identified the shortest route from the origin to each of the other nodes.

7.5 THE MINIMAL SPANNING TREE PROBLEM

Now consider a variation of the shortest route problem known as the minimal spanning tree problem. As before, a set of nodes and the distances between pairs of these nodes are given. However, the branches between the nodes are no longer specified. Thus, rather than finding a shortest route through a fully defined network, the problem involves choosing the branches for the network that have the shortest total length while providing a route between each pair of nodes. To achieve this, the branches would be chosen in such a way that the resulting network comprises a tree (as defined in Section 7.2) that "spans" (i.e., connects to) all of the given nodes. In short, the problem is to find the "spanning tree" with a minimum total branch length.

This problem has a number of important practical applications. For example, it can sometimes be helpful in the planning of transportation networks. The nodes would be terminals and the branches would be transportation lanes (highways, railroad tracks, air lanes, etc.). In this context, the minimal spanning tree problem is to determine which transportation lanes would service all of the terminals in a minimum total distance. Other examples where a comparable decision arises include the planning of large-scale communication networks and of distribution networks.

The minimal spanning tree problem can be solved in a very straightforward way, since it happens to be one of the few operations research problems where being greedy at each stage of the solution procedure will still lead to an over-all optimal solution at the end! Thus, beginning with any node, the first stage involves choosing the shortest possible branch to another node, without worrying about the effect this would have on subsequent decisions. At the second stage, one would identify the unconnected node that is closest to either of these connected nodes, and then add the corresponding branch to the network. This process would be repeated, as summarized below, until all of the nodes have been connected. The resulting network is guaranteed to be a "minimal spanning tree."

SUMMARY OF SOLUTION PROCEDURE

(1) Select any node arbitrarily and then connect it to the nearest distinct node.
(2) Identify the unconnected node that is closest to a connected node, and then connect these two nodes. Repeat this until all nodes have been connected.

This procedure can be executed in a way very much like that for the shortest route problem. To illustrate, consider again the example summarized in Figure 7.5. Suppose that the nodes and distances are as given there, but that the branches are yet to be specified for this network. (Also assume that the unspecified distances in Figure 7.5 are all larger than the ones given.) It is once again convenient to construct a list for each node of the potential branches leading out of that node in the order of their ascending distances. As shown below, these lists are identical to those given for the shortest route problem except that there is no longer an "origin" or "destination," so that potential branches into node O or out of node T also are included.

Ⓞ	Ⓐ	Ⓑ	Ⓒ	Ⓓ	Ⓔ	Ⓕ	Ⓖ	Ⓗ	Ⓣ
OA–7	AD–6	BE–4	CD–2	DC–2	EB–4	FD–2	GC–3	HE–6	TG–8
OB–8	AO–7	BD–6	CF–3	DF–2	EH–6	FC–3	GF–5	HG–8	TH–8
	AB–7	BA–7	CG–3	DA–6	ED–7	FG–5	GD–6	HT–8	TF–9
	AC–8	BO–8	CA–8	DB–6	EG–9	FT–9	GH–8		
				DG–6			GT–8		
				DE–7			GE–9		

$n = 1$: The first stage begins by selecting any node arbitrarily. To facilitate comparison with the shortest route problem, let this be node O. Node A is then immediately identified as the nearest node by looking at the top of the list for node O, so branch OA is added to the network. To indicate this, circle the OA–7 and AO–7 entries, and place an X above the list for these two connected nodes. The lists should now look as follows.

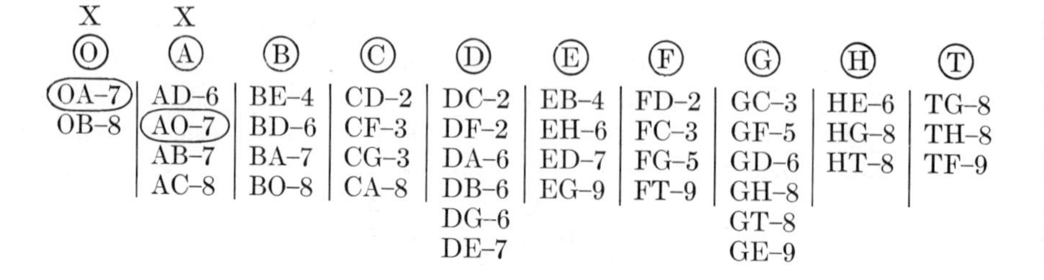

X	X								
(O)	(A)	(B)	(C)	(D)	(E)	(F)	(G)	(H)	(T)
(OA–7)	AD–6	BE–4	CD–2	DC–2	EB–4	FD–2	GC–3	HE–6	TG–8
OB–8	(AO–7)	BD–6	CF–3	DF–2	EH–6	FC–3	GF–5	HG–8	TH–8
	AB–7	BA–7	CG–3	DA–6	ED–7	FG–5	GD–6	HT–8	TF–9
	AC–8	BO–8	CA–8	DB–6	EG–9	FT–9	GH–8		
				DG–6			GT–8		
				DE–7			GE–9		

$n = 2,3$: To identify the unconnected node that is closest to any one of the connected nodes (O and A), merely compare the top remaining entry in the list for these nodes (OB–8 and AD–6). Since $6 < 8$, AD becomes the next branch to be added to the network. To indicate this, circle AD–6 and DA–6, and place an X above the list for node D. The next branch would then be selected by comparing OB–8, AB–7, and DC–2, which indicates that DC is to be added to the network. Thus, circle DC–2 and CD–2,

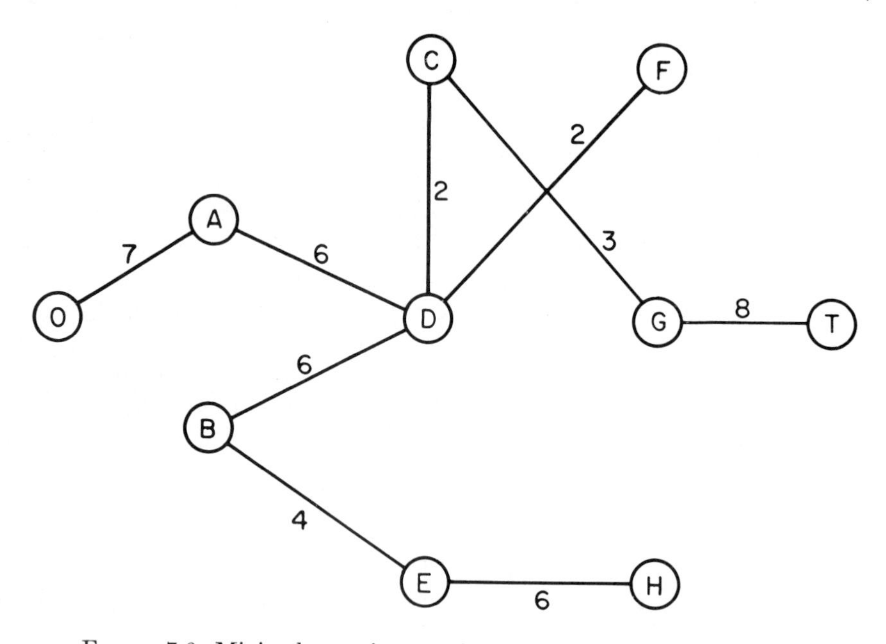

Figure 7.6. Minimal spanning tree for example shown in Figure 7.5.

and indicate that node C is now a connected node by placing an X above its list. Since one should not place a branch between two nodes that are already connected, any potential branches from the newest connected node to any of the others should be eliminated from future consideration by crossing them off the lists. Therefore, cross out CA–8 and AC–8. At this point, the lists should appear as shown below.

X	X		X	X					
Ⓞ	Ⓐ	Ⓑ	Ⓒ	Ⓓ	Ⓔ	Ⓕ	Ⓖ	Ⓗ	Ⓣ
OA–7	AD–6	BE–4	CD–2	DC–2	EB–4	FD–2	GC–3	HE–6	TG–8
OB–8	AO–7	BD–6	CF–3	DF–2	EH–6	FC–3	GF–5	HG–8	TH–8
	AB–7	BA–7	CG–3	DA–6	ED–7	FG–5	GD–6	HT–8	TF–9
	~~AC–8~~	BO–8	~~CA–8~~	DB–6	EG–9	FT–9	GH–8		
				DG–6			GT–8		
				DE–7			GE–9		

$n = 4$: By proceeding in the same way, one would now choose the branches, DF, CG, DB, BE, EH, and GT (or HT), in that order. After modifying the lists accordingly, they would look as follows.

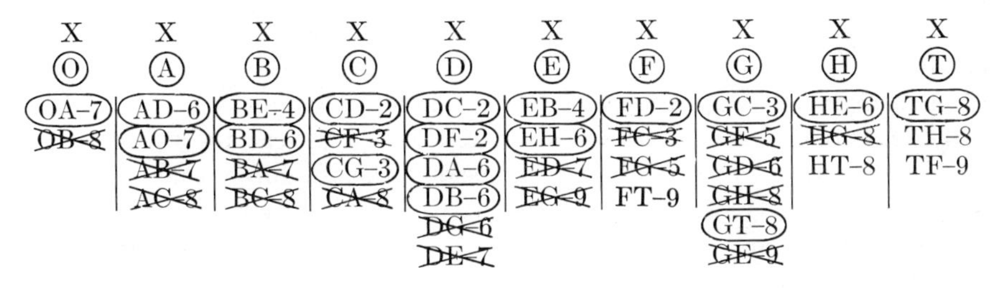

X	X	X	X	X	X	X	X	X	X
Ⓞ	Ⓐ	Ⓑ	Ⓒ	Ⓓ	Ⓔ	Ⓕ	Ⓖ	Ⓗ	Ⓣ
OA–7	AD–6	BE–4	CD–2	DC–2	EB–4	FD–2	GC–3	HE–6	TG–8
~~OB–8~~	AO–7	BD–6	~~CF–3~~	DF–2	EH–6	~~FC–3~~	~~GF–5~~	~~HG–8~~	TH–8
	~~AB–7~~	~~BA–7~~	CG–3	DA–6	~~ED–7~~	~~FG–5~~	~~GD–6~~	HT–8	TF–9
	~~AC–8~~	~~BO–8~~	~~CA–8~~	DB–6	~~EG–9~~	FT–9	~~GH–8~~		
				~~DG–6~~			GT–8		
				~~DE–7~~			~~GE–9~~		

Since all of the nodes have been connected at this point, the solution procedure is now completed. The resulting network, shown in Figure 7.6, has a total branch length of 44.

Although it may appear at first glance that the choice of the initial node would affect the resulting final solution and its total branch length, this actually is not the case. To illustrate, suppose that node D had been chosen for the initial node (since it has the shortest potential branches) instead of node O in the above example. The procedure then would have successively chosen the following branches: DC, DF, CG, DA, DB, BE, EH, AO, and GT (or HT). Notice that this network is identical to the one obtained by starting with node O. As the reader can quickly verify, the same result would have been obtained with any other initial node.

7.6 PERT

PERT (Program Evaluation and Review Technique) was originally developed in 1958 and 1959 for measuring and controlling development progress for the Polaris Fleet Ballistic Missile program. The use of PERT was largely credited with the successful coordination of the several thousand contractors and agencies participating in the Polaris program, advancing the completion date by more than two years. As a result, subsequent applications of the PERT technique have been made to other government programs, such as the Air Force's Minuteman, Skybolt, Dyna-Soar, and B–70, the Army's Nike-Zeus, Pershing, and Hawk, and the Navy's Eagle and Missileer. American private industry has also increasingly adopted PERT to assist in the management of projects which involve many interrelated activities.

Although the original application of PERT was for evaluating the schedule for a research and development program, it is also being used to measure and control progress on numerous other types of special projects. Examples of these project types include construction programs, programming of computers, preparation of bids and proposals, maintenance planning, and the installation of computer systems.

One of the primary objectives of PERT is to determine the probability of meeting specified deadlines. PERT also identifies the activities which are most likely to be bottlenecks, and, therefore, where the greatest effort should be made to stay on schedule. A third objective is to evaluate the effect of changes in the program. For example, it will evaluate the effect of a contemplated shift of resources from the less critical activities to the activities identified as probable bottlenecks. Other resources and performance trade-offs may also be evaluated. It will also evaluate the effect of a deviation of the actual time requirement for an activity from what had been predicted.

The first step in the application of PERT is to develop a network representation of the project plan. An example of such a representation, normally called the system flow plan, is given in Figure 7.7.

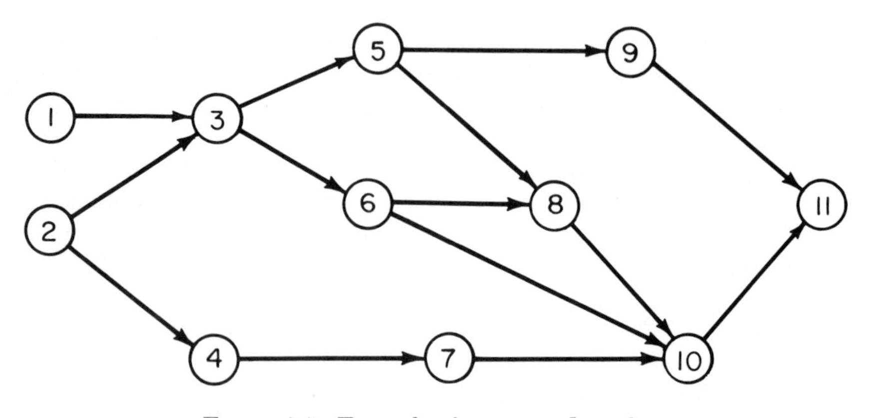

FIGURE 7.7. Example of a system flow plan.

Each node represents an "event," which is a specific, definable accomplishment recognizable at a particular instant in time. Each branch represents an "activity," which is one of the tasks required by the project. The arrowheads indicate the sequences in which the events must be achieved. Thus, an event is the completion of all the activities leading into that node, and this event must precede the initiation of the activities leading out of that node. (In reality, it is often possible to overlap successive phases of a project, so the flow plan may represent an approximate idealization of the project plan.) The node toward which all activities lead (the sink of the network) is the event corresponding to the completion of the currently planned project; it is event 11 in Figure 7.7. The flow plan may either represent the plan for the project from its inception or, if the project has already begun, the plan for the completion of the project. In the latter case, each source of the network (nodes 1 and 2 in Figure 7.7) represents either the event of continuing a current activity or the event of initiating a new activity which may begin at any time.

The original version of PERT made the realistic assumption that the time required to perform each activity in the system flow plan is actually a random variable having some probability distribution. However, since this complicates the procedure somewhat, a simplified version that takes these times to be predictable constants instead is often used in practice. It is useful to consider briefly this simplified version first in order to introduce some of the basic concepts of PERT. To do this, consider the following very simple system flow plan, where the numbers indicate the time (in months) required to perform these respective activities.

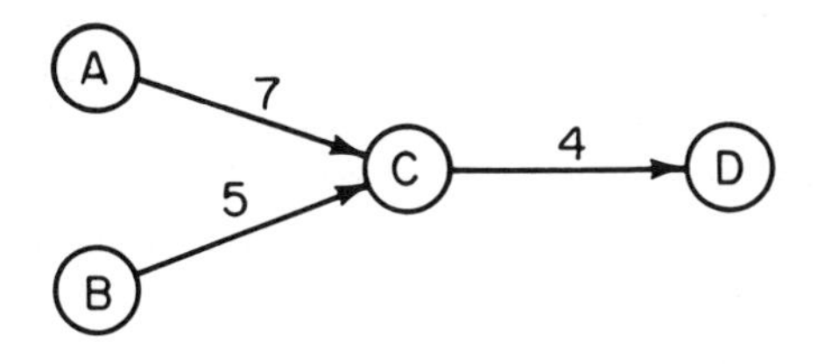

Assuming these time estimates are correct, it is evident that events C and D cannot occur any earlier than 7 and 11 months hence, respectively, but that the BC activity can be delayed two months without delaying events C and D. These two comments are directly related to two basic concepts of PERT, namely, "earliest time" and "latest time." For any particular event, its earliest time may be defined as the time at which the event will occur if the preceding activities are started as early as possible. Thus, the earliest times for events C and D are 7 and 11, respectively. Similarly, the latest time for an event may be defined as the latest time at which the event can occur without delaying the completion of the project beyond its earliest time. Thus, the latest times for events A, B, C, and D are 0, 2, 7, and 11, respectively. "Slack" and "critical path" are two other basic concepts of PERT. The slack for an event is the difference between its latest time and earliest time, so it is 0, 2, 0, and 0 for events A, B, C, and D, respectively. Thus, the slack indicates how much delay in reaching the event can be tolerated without delaying project completion. A critical path for the project may be defined as a path through the network such that the events on this path have zero slack. Thus, $A \rightarrow C \rightarrow D$ is the critical path in this example.

Now consider the original version of PERT, where the activity times are random variables. After developing the system flow plan, the next step is to obtain and organize the basic data required to derive the output information exhibited in Table 7.2. Referring to Table 7.2, it is seen that earliest time, latest time, and slack are still the basic concepts. However, the earliest time for an event is now taken to be a random variable, although it is still defined exactly as before. The two sub-columns are for the expected value and variance of this random variable. Similarly, the latest time is now a random variable defined as the latest time at which the event can occur without delaying the completion of the project beyond its *expected* earliest time. The expected value and variance of latest time are to be obtained. Slack is the difference between the expected latest time and the expected earliest time. Original schedule refers to the schedule for event occurrences established at the beginning of the project. The last column gives the probability that earliest time will not exceed the time given by the original schedule for the event. The derivation of values for Table 7.2 is illustrated subsequently.

TABLE 7.2. Output Information for PERT

Event number	*Earliest time*		*Latest time*		*Slack*	*Original schedule*	*Probability of meeting schedule*
	Expected value	*Variance*	*Expected value*	*Variance*			

It is now evident that, in order to derive the desired output, it is necessary to estimate the expected value and variance of the time required for each of the activities. Because of certain simplifying assumptions and approximations that will be made, no additional input information is required. Nevertheless, the concepts of expected value and variance may be quite complex for the individuals qualified to estimate the time requirements for the activities. Therefore, it may be unrealistic to require that these quantities be estimated directly for each of perhaps hundreds of activities. With this in mind, PERT uses a simplified estimating procedure, whereby estimates of intuitively meaningful quantities are obtained and then converted into estimates of the expected value and variance. This procedure involves obtaining three estimates of the elapsed time required for each activity, namely, a "most likely" estimate, an "optimistic" estimate, and a "pessimistic" estimate. The most likely estimate, denoted by m, is intended to be the most realistic estimate of the time the activity might consume. The optimistic estimate, denoted by a, estimates the time in which the activity can be completed if everything goes exceptionally well. The pessimistic estimate, denoted by b, is an estimate of the longest time the activity would require under the most adverse conditions, barring acts of God.

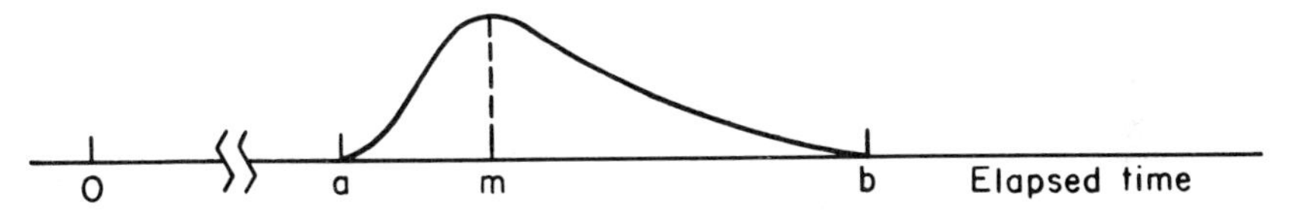

FIGURE 7.8. Model of probability distribution for estimating expected elapsed time for activity.

Two assumptions are made in order to convert m, a, and b into estimates of the expected value and variance of the elapsed time required by the activity. One of these assumptions is that σ, the standard deviation (square root of the variance), equals $\frac{1}{6}$ of the range of reasonably possible time requirements; i.e.,

$$\sigma^2 = \left[\frac{1}{6}(b - a)\right]^2$$

is the desired estimate of the variance. The rationale for this assumption is that the tails of many probability distributions (such as the normal distribution) are considered to lie at about three standard deviations from the mean, so that there would be a spread of about six standard deviations between the tails. For example, the control charts commonly used for statistical quality control are constructed so that the spread between the control limits is estimated to be six standard deviations.

In order to obtain the estimated expected value, an assumption about the probability distribution of the time required for the activity is also required. This assumption is that the distribution is approximately beta, where the mode is m, the lower bound is a, the upper bound is b, and $\sigma = (b - a)/6$. Such a distribution is shown in Figure 7.8.

Using the model illustrated in Figure 7.8, it can be derived that the expected value of the distribution (denoted by t_e in the PERT literature) is approximately

$$t_e = \frac{1}{3}\left[2m + \frac{1}{2}(a + b)\right].$$

This equation is, therefore, used to compute the estimated expected value of elapsed time required for an activity. Notice that the "midrange," $(a + b)/2$, lies midway between a and b, so that t_e is the weighted arithmetic mean of the mode and the midrange, the mode carrying two-thirds of the entire weight. It should be noted that the assumption of a beta distribution is an arbitrary one, but that it has served its purpose of locating the expected value with respect to m, a, and b in what seems to be a reasonable way.

TABLE 7.3. Input Data for Example of Figure 7.7

Event number	*Immediately preceding events*			*Immediately following events*		
	Event number	*Elapsed time estimates*		*Event number*	*Elapsed time estimates*	
		Expected value	*Variance*		*Expected value*	*Variance*
11	10 9	4 5	5 3			
10	8 7 6	8 6 1	10 5 2	11	4	5
9	5	7	5	11	5	3
8	6 5	3 5	4 7	10	8	10
7	4	2	4	10	6	5
6	3	5	5	8 10	3 1	4 2
5	3	6	5	8 9	5 7	7 5
4	2	5	10	7	2	4
3	2 1	6 10	7 6	5 6	6 5	5 5
2				3 4	6 5	7 10
1				3	10	6

In order to illustrate the derivation of the output information, assume that the procedure outlined above has been used for each of the activities of the example of Figure 7.7 and has yielded the data given in Table 7.3.

To permit readily finding the variance of earliest time and latest time, it is assumed that the elapsed times for the individual activities are statistically independent. It is evident from the definition of earliest time that if there is only one path leading to a particular event, the earliest time for that event is the sum of the elapsed times of the activities leading to the event. Therefore, for this case, the expected value and variance of earliest time are the sum of the expected values and of the variances, respectively, of these activity times. For example, there is only one path leading to event 7, namely, $2 \rightarrow 4 \rightarrow 7$. Hence, the expected value and variance of earliest time for event 7 are $(5 + 2) = 7$ and $(10 + 4) = 14$, respectively. Similarly, the definition of latest time implies that if there is only one path leading from a particular event to the terminal event, then the latest time for that event is the expected earliest time for the terminal event minus the sum of the elapsed times of the activities on that path. When this is true, the expected value of latest time would be the expected earliest time for the terminal event minus the sum of the expected values of these activity times; the variance of latest time would be the sum of the variances of these times. For example, the variance of latest time for event 7 is $(5 + 5) = 10$.

Unfortunately, difficulties arise when there is more than one path leading to or from an event. For example, there are several paths leading to event 8.

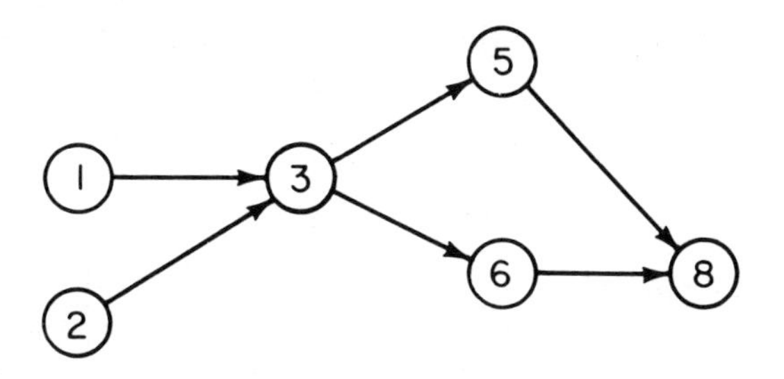

These paths are $1 \rightarrow 3 \rightarrow 5 \rightarrow 8$, $1 \rightarrow 3 \rightarrow 6 \rightarrow 8$, $2 \rightarrow 3 \rightarrow 5 \rightarrow 8$, and $2 \rightarrow 3 \rightarrow 6 \rightarrow 8$. The earliest time for event 8 is the maximum of the total elapsed times along these four paths. It would be very difficult to find the exact expected value and variance for such a maximum. Therefore, a simplifying approximation is used. This approximation supposes that the largest total elapsed time *always* occurs on the path with the largest *expected* total elapsed time. Thus, since the expected total elapsed times on the paths leading to event 8 are $(10 + 6 + 5) = 21$, $(10 + 5 + 3) = 18$, $(6 + 6 + 5) = 17$, and $(6 + 5 + 3) = 14$, respectively, so that path $1 \rightarrow 3 \rightarrow 5 \rightarrow 8$

has the largest value (21), it is supposed that the *actual* total elapsed time is always largest on this path. It would then follow that the expected value and variance of earliest time for event 8 are the expected value and variance of total elapsed time along this path, 21 and $(6 + 5 + 7) = 18$, respectively. Notice that this simplification of considering only the path with the largest expected total elapsed time leading to (or from) the event has reduced the problem of finding the expected value and variance of earliest time (or latest time) to the one path problem considered earlier. The price paid for using this simplification is that the approximate expected value of earliest time (or latest time) is always in error on the small (large) side since the possibility that another path will turn out to have the largest total elapsed time is ignored.

Slack for an event is simply calculated as the expected latest time minus the expected earliest time.

Before the probability of meeting the schedule for an event can be determined, it is necessary to know the probability distribution of earliest time. PERT assumes that this distribution is normal. The rationale for this assumption is that earliest time is the sum of many random variables, and the general version of the Central Limit Theorem (see Section 3.15) implies that such a sum is approximately normal under a wide range of conditions. Given the mean and variance, it is then a straightforward procedure (see Section 3.7.4) to find the probability that a normal random variable (earliest time) will be less than a specified quantity (scheduled time for the occurrence of the event).

Given the input data of Table 7.3, all of the desired output information can now be computed for the example of Figure 7.7. This information is exhibited in Table 7.4.

Recall that one of the objectives of PERT is to identify the activities

TABLE 7.4. Output Information for Example

Event number	*Earliest time*		*Latest time*		*Slack*	*Original schedule*	*Probability of meeting schedule*
	Expected value	*Variance*	*Expected value*	*Variance*			
11	33	33	33	0	0	30	0.30
10	29	28	29	5	0	26	0.29
9	23	16	28	3	5	21	0.31
8	21	18	21	15	0	20	0.41
7	7	14	23	10	16	10	0.79
6	15	11	18	19	3	13	0.27
5	16	11	16	22	0	15	0.38
4	5	10	21	14	16	6	0.62
3	10	6	10	27	0	8	0.21
2	0	0	4	34	4	—	—
1	0	0	0	33	0	—	—

which are most likely to be bottlenecks. This can now be done by examining the slack column of Table 7.4. Notice that some of the events have positive slack, while others have zero slack. If the events with zero slack are joined together, they will form a path from the present to the terminal event, as shown in Figure 7.9. As indicated earlier, this path is referred to as the "critical path."

There always exists a critical path through the system flow plan, and it can always be identified by tracing through the events with zero slack. If the expected elapsed times of the activities are interpreted as distances, the critical path would be interpreted as the longest route through the network.

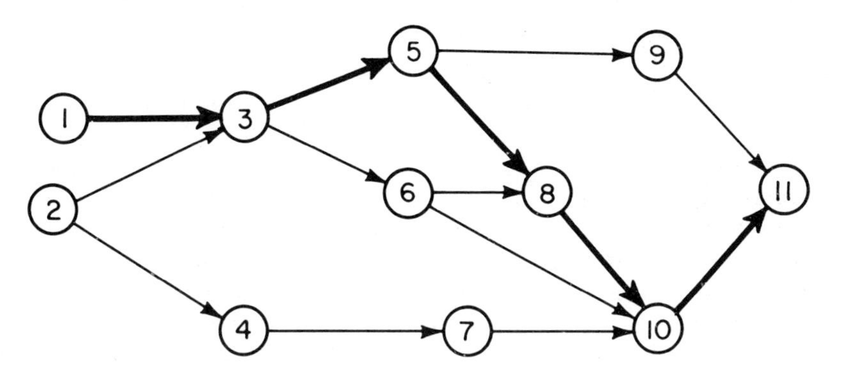

FIGURE 7.9. The critical path.

The critical path is obviously significant since, should any event on this path slip beyond its expected date of accomplishment, the terminal event can be expected to slip by the same amount. Therefore, top priority should be placed on the activities on this path. If the expected earliest time of the terminal event is not satisfactory, then improvements should be concentrated on these activities. On the other hand, events not on the critical path all have positive slack, so minor deviations from the expected date for accomplishing these events probably will not affect the project completion date. However, it should be noted that this critical path analysis is based only on expected values, so that there is at least a small probability that some path other than the indicated critical one will actually turn out to be the longest.

Elaborate computer programs have been developed to implement PERT.[31] Hence, one can quickly determine the effect of a proposed change or the effect of a slip in schedule. This ability to measure and evaluate the current status of the project, thereby improving management control, has been one of the most frequently cited values of PERT.

[31] See C. Phillips, *Journal of Industrial Engineering*, **XV**, 14–20 (1964) for information on PERT computer programs available at that time.

PERT has been the center of considerable controversy, both on the theoretical level and on the practical working level, since its introduction. There has been much notable success and much notable wreckage ascribed to the application of PERT. This was probably to be expected, considering how new and sometimes poorly understood it was when used to assist in the vital planning and control function for extremely costly projects. However, it seems clear that PERT-like techniques are here to stay, although improvements in the original PERT have been and will continue to be made.

It might be well to summarize a bit of the analytical work relating to PERT. Healy[32] has shown that, with the current estimating procedure, the mechanics of subdividing or grouping activities in a PERT flow plan can influence the computed probabilities of events meeting schedule. Thus, showing too much planning and scheduling detail on the flow plan might actually bias these probabilities. Fulkerson[33] develops a method for obtaining an approximation of expected earliest time (or latest time) for the multi-path case which is always better than (or at least as good as) the approximation provided by the "longest path" method described earlier. Eisner[34] has developed a generalized network approach, especially applicable for a research project, which allows for initial uncertainty as to which chains of activities will be required and which will not. Van Slyke[35] has used Monte Carlo simulation to study PERT networks.

Numerous techniques similar to PERT have been proposed in recent years under dozens of different names. Some of these emphasize the cost and/or the level of technical performance of the activities in addition to their elapsed times (although it should be noted that the current government version of PERT also emphasizes cost aspects). The most noteworthy of these (partially because it was a parallel effort rather than a derivative of PERT) is the Critical Path Method (CPM), which is concerned with the planning, scheduling, and cost–control aspects of project work. The interested reader is referred to excellent technical articles by Kelly[36] and by Fulkerson.[37]

SELECTED REFERENCES

1. Dantzig, George B., *Linear Programming and Extensions,* Princeton University Press, Princeton, N.J., 1963, chaps. 17 and 19.

[32] See T. Healy, *Operations Research,* **9**, 341–348 (1961); also see Comments on pp. 348–350.
[33] See D. Fulkerson, *Operations Research,* **10**, 808–817 (1962).
[34] See H. Eisner, *Operations Research,* **10**, 115–125 (1962).
[35] See R. Van Slyke, *Operations Research,* **11**, 839–860 (1963).
[36] See J. Kelly, *Operations Research,* **9**, 296–320 (1961).
[37] See D. Fulkerson, *Management Science,* **7**, 167–178 (1961).

2. Ford, Lester R., Jr., and Fulkerson, Delbert R., *Flows in Networks,* Princeton University Press, Princeton, N.J., 1962.
3. Hadley, G., *Linear Programming,* Addison-Wesley, Reading, Mass., 1962, chap. 10.
4. MacCrimmon, Kenneth R., and Ryavec, Charles A., "An Analytical Study of the PERT Assumptions," *Operations Research,* **12,** No. 1, 16–37 (1964).
5. Malcolm, Donald G., Roseboom, John H., Clark, Charles E., and Fazar, Willard, "Application of a Technique for Research and Development Program Evaluation," *Operations Research,* **7,** No. 5, 646–669 (1959).
6. Pocock, J. W., "PERT As an Analytical Aid for Programming—Its Payoff and Problems," *Operations Research,* **10,** No. 6, 893–903 (1962).

PROBLEMS

1. For each of the following networks, find the maximal flow from the source to the sink, given that the flow capacity from node i to node j is the number along branch (i, j) nearest node i.

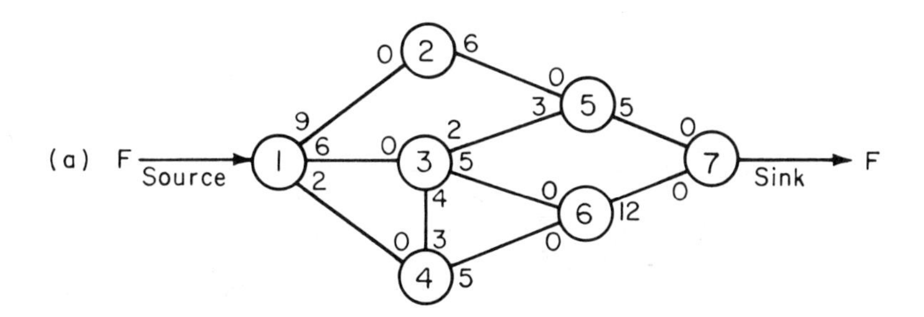

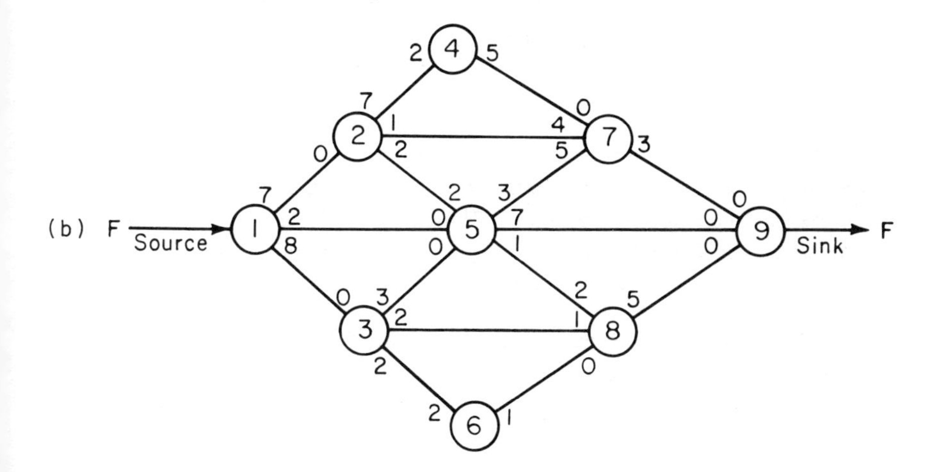

2. Referring to the linear programming formulation of the maximal flow problem in Section 7.3, show that

$$\sum_k x_{1k} = \sum_k x_{kN} .$$

(*Hint:* Sum the conservation of flow constraints.)

3. Find the shortest route through each of the following networks, where the numbers represent actual distances between the corresponding nodes.

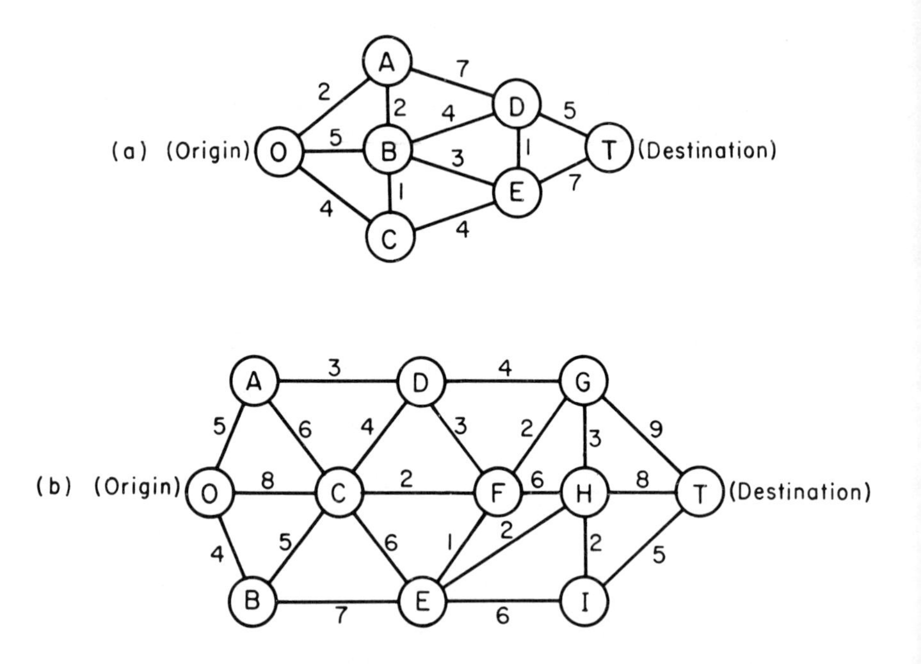

4. Reconsider the networks shown in problem 3. Assume that the nodes and actual distances between nodes are as shown there (where unspecified distances between nodes are greater than any of the given distances), but assume that the branches have not yet been specified. Find the minimal spanning tree for each of these networks.

5. Both the shortest route problem and the minimal spanning tree problem have been described in terms of distances being associated with the branches of the network. What are some meaningful quantities other than distance for which these problems can be formulated and solved in an analogous way?

6. Consider the following PERT system flow plan. Assume that the time required (in weeks) for each activity is a predictable constant, and that it is given by the number along the corresponding branch. Find the earliest time, latest time, and slack for each event. Also identify the critical path.

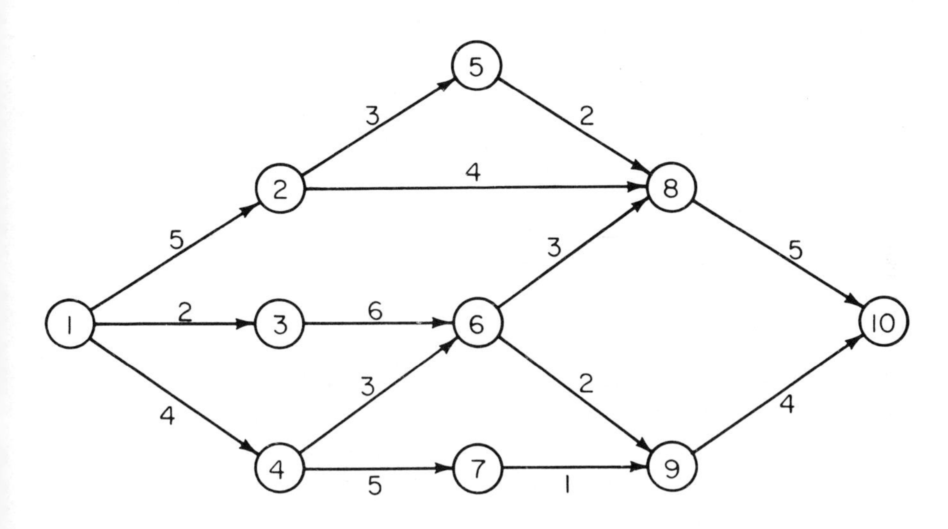

7. Consider the following PERT system flow plan.

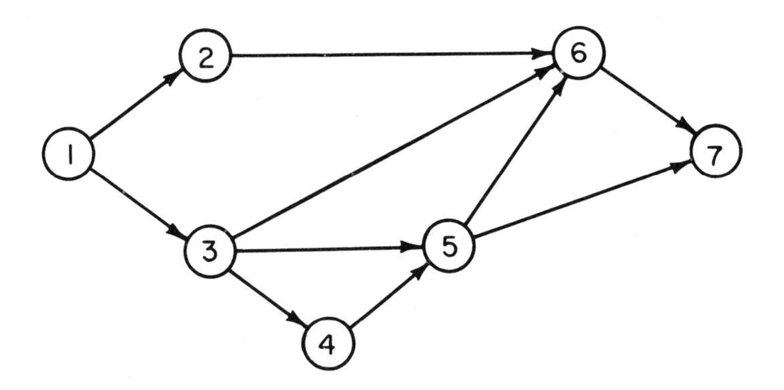

Suppose that the usual three estimates for the time required (in months) for each of these activities are the following.

Activity	*Optimistic estimate*	*Most likely estimate*	*Pessimistic estimate*
$1 \to 2$	8	9	10
$1 \to 3$	6	7	9
$2 \to 6$	9	12	15
$3 \to 4$	5	5	5
$3 \to 5$	8	10	11
$3 \to 6$	11	15	20
$4 \to 5$	3	4	6
$5 \to 6$	5	6	8
$5 \to 7$	8	10	12
$6 \to 7$	4	5	10

The original schedule for the respective events had been set on the basis of the most likely estimates, and so is the following (letting the present be time 0).

Event number	1	2	3	4	5	6	7
Original schedule	0	9	7	12	17	23	28

Derive the output information exhibited in Table 7.2 for each of the events, and identify the critical path.

CHAPTER 8

Dynamic Programming

8.1 INTRODUCTION

Dynamic programming is a mathematical technique often useful for making a sequence of interrelated decisions. It provides a systematic procedure for determining the combination of decisions which maximizes overall effectiveness.

In contrast to linear programming, there does not exist a standard mathematical formulation of "the" dynamic programming problem. Rather, dynamic programming is a general type of approach to problem solving, and the particular equations used must be developed to fit each individual situation. Therefore, a certain degree of ingenuity and insight into the general structure of dynamic programming problems is required to recognize when a problem can be solved by dynamic programming procedures, and how it would be done. These abilities can probably best be developed by an exposure to a wide variety of dynamic programming applications and a study of the characteristics which are common to all of these situations. A large number of illustrative examples is presented for this purpose.

8.2 EXAMPLE 1

A problem specially constructed[38] to illustrate the features of dynamic programming is the "stagecoach problem." This problem concerns a mythical salesman who had to travel west by stagecoach through unfriendly Indian country about a hundred years ago. Although his starting point and destination were fixed, he had considerable choice as to which

[38] This problem was developed by Professor Harvey M. Wagner of Stanford University.

states (or territories which subsequently became states) to travel through en route, as indicated by the following diagram.

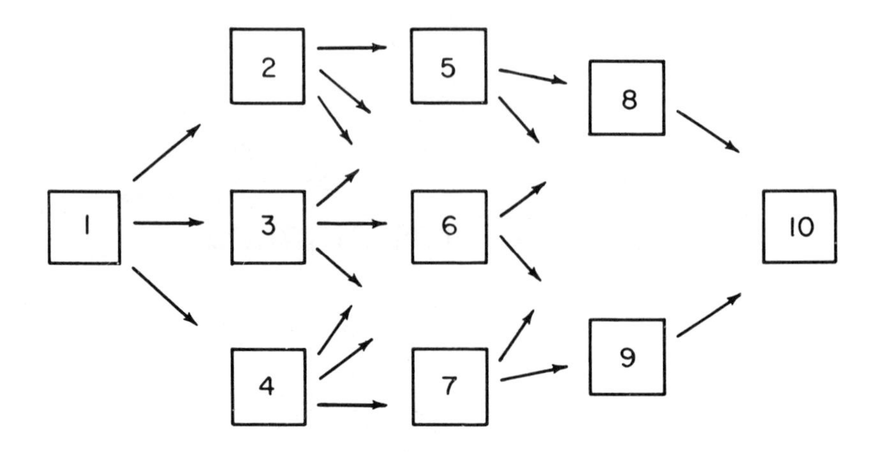

Thus, four stages were required to travel from his point of embarkation in state 1 to his destination in state 10.

This salesman was a prudent man who was quite concerned for his safety on this trip. After some thought, a rather clever way of determining his safest route occurred to him. Life insurance policies were offered to stagecoach passengers. Since the cost of each policy was based on a careful evaluation of the safety of that run, the safest route should be the one with the cheapest life insurance policy.

The cost for the standard policy on the stagecoach run from state i to state j, which will be denoted by c_{ij}, is given below.

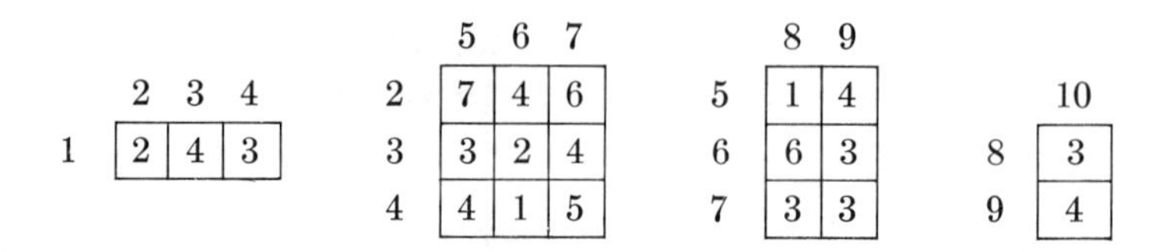

	2	3	4
1	2	4	3

	5	6	7
2	7	4	6
3	3	2	4
4	4	1	5

	8	9
5	1	4
6	6	3
7	3	3

	10
8	3
9	4

Which route minimizes the total cost of the policy?

SOLUTION

It should first be noted that making the decision which is best for each successive stage need not yield the over-all optimal decision. Following this strategy of selecting the cheapest run offered by each successive stage would give the route, $1 \rightarrow 2 \rightarrow 6 \rightarrow 9 \rightarrow 10$, at a total cost of 13. However, it should be evident that sacrificing a little on one stage may permit greater savings thereafter. For example, $1 \rightarrow 4 \rightarrow 6$ is cheaper over-all than $1 \rightarrow 2 \rightarrow 6$.

One possible approach to solving this problem is to use trial and error. However, the number of possible routes is large (18), and having to calculate the total cost for each one of them is not an appealing task.

Fortunately, dynamic programming provides a solution with much less effort than exhaustive enumeration. Dynamic programming starts with a small portion of the problem and finds the optimal solution for this smaller problem. It then gradually enlarges the problem, finding the current optimal solution from the previous one, until the original problem is solved in its entirety. The details involved in implementing this general philosophy are given below.

Let the decision variables, $x_n (n = 1, 2, 3, 4)$, be the immediate destination when there are n more stages to go. Thus, the route selected would be $1 \rightarrow x_4 \rightarrow x_3 \rightarrow x_2 \rightarrow x_1$, where $x_1 = 10$. Let $f_n(s, x_n)$ be the total cost of the best over-all policy for the last n stages, given that the salesman is in state s and selects x_n as the immediate destination. Given s and n, let x_n^* denote the value of x_n which minimizes $f_n(s, x_n)$, and let $f_n^*(s)$ be the corresponding minimum value of $f_n(s, x_n)$. Thus, $f_n^*(s) = f_n(s, x_n^*)$. The objective is to find $f_4^*(1)$ and the corresponding policy. Dynamic programming does this by successively finding $f_1^*(s)$, $f_2^*(s)$, $f_3^*(s)$, and then $f_4^*(1)$.

When the salesman has only one more stage to go, his route is entirely determined by his final destination. Therefore, the immediate solution to the one-stage problem is as follows.

s	$f_1^*(s)$	x_1^*
8	3	10
9	4	10

When the salesman has two more stages to go, the solution requires a few calculations. For example, assume that the salesman is in state 5. He must next go to either state 8 or 9 at a cost of 1 or 4, respectively. If he chooses state 8, the minimum additional cost after reaching there is given in the above table as 3, so that the total cost for this decision would be $1 + 3 = 4$. Similarly, the total cost if he chooses state 9 is $4 + 4 = 8$. Therefore, he would choose state 8, $x_2^* = 8$, since it gives the minimum total cost, $f_2^*(5) = 4$. Proceeding similarly for $s = 6$ and $s = 7$ yields the following results for the two-stage problem.

s \ x_2	$f_2(s, x_2) = c_{sx_2} + f_1^*(x_2)$ 8	9	$f_2^*(s)$	x_2^*
5	4	8	4	8
6	9	7	7	9
7	6	7	6	8

The solution for the three-stage problem is obtained in a similar fashion. In this case, $f_3(s, x_3) = c_{sx_3} + f_2^*(x_3)$. For example, if the salesman is in state 2 and chooses to go to state 5 next, the minimum total cost, $f_3(2, 5)$, would be the cost of the first stage, $c_{25} = 7$, plus the minimum cost from state 5 onward, $f_2^*(5) = 4$, so that $f_3(2, 5) = 7 + 4 = 11$. Similarly, $f_3(2, 6) = 4 + 7 = 11$ and $f_3(2, 7) = 6 + 6 = 12$, so that the minimum total cost from state 2 onward is $f_3^*(2) = 11$, and the immediate destination should be $x_3^* = 5$ or 6. The complete results for the three-stage problem are given below.

s \ x_3	$f_3(s, x_3) = c_{sx_3} + f_2^*(x_3)$ 5	6	7	$f_3^*(s)$	x_3^*
2	11	11	12	11	5 or 6
3	7	9	10	7	5
4	8	8	11	8	5 or 6

Moving to the four-stage problem, the cost of the optimal policy, given the immediate destination, is again the sum of the cost of the first stage plus the minimum cost thereafter. The consequent results are given below.

s \ x_4	$f_4(s, x_4) = c_{sx_4} + f_3^*(x_4)$ 2	3	4	$f_4^*(s)$	x_4^*
1	13	11	11	11	3 or 4

The optimal solution can now be written down. The results for the four-stage problem indicate that the salesman should go initially to either state 3 or state 4. Suppose that he chooses $x_4^* = 3$. The three-stage problem result for $s = 3$ is $x_3^* = 5$. This leads to the two-stage problem which gives $x_2^* = 8$ for $s = 5$, and the one-stage problem yields $x_1^* = 10$ for $s = 8$. Hence, one optimal route is $1 \rightarrow 3 \rightarrow 5 \rightarrow 8 \rightarrow 10$. Choosing $x_4^* = 4$ leads to the other two optimal routes, $1 \rightarrow 4 \rightarrow 5 \rightarrow 8 \rightarrow 10$ and $1 \rightarrow 4 \rightarrow 6 \rightarrow 9 \rightarrow 10$. They all yield a total cost of $f_4^*(1) = 11$.

8.3 CHARACTERISTICS OF DYNAMIC PROGRAMMING PROBLEMS

It will be found that the stagecoach problem discussed previously is a literal prototype of dynamic programming problems. In fact, this problem was purposely designed to provide a literal physical interpretation of the rather abstract structure of dynamic programming problems. Therefore, one way to recognize a situation which can be formulated as a dynamic programming problem is to notice that its basic structure is analogous to that of the stagecoach problem.

These basic features which characterize dynamic programming problems are presented and discussed below.

(1) The problem can be divided up into stages, with a policy decision required at each stage.

The stagecoach problem was literally divided up into its four "stages" (stagecoaches) on the four legs of the journey. The policy decision at each stage was the destination for that particular stagecoach. Other dynamic programming problems similarly require making a sequence of decisions.

(2) Each stage has a number of states associated with it.

The states associated with each stage in the stagecoach problem were the states or territories in which the salesman could be located when embarking on that particular leg of the journey. In general, the states are the various possible conditions in which the system might find itself at that stage of the problem. The number of states may be either finite, as in the stagecoach problem, or infinite, as in examples 6 and 7.

(3) The effect of the policy decision at each stage is to transform the current state into a state associated with the next stage (possibly according to a probability distribution).

The salesman's decision as to his next destination led him from his current state to the next state on his journey. This suggests that dynamic programming problems can be interpreted in terms of the networks described in Chapter 7. Each node would correspond to a state. The network would consist of columns of nodes, with each column corresponding to a stage, so that flow from a node can go only to a node in the next column to the right. The number assigned as the "distance" between connected nodes can sometimes be interpreted as the contribution to the objective function made by going from one state to the other. If this is the case, the objective would be to find either the shortest or the longest route through the network.

(4) Given the current state, an optimal policy for the remaining stages is independent of the policy adopted in previous stages.

Given the state in which the salesman is currently located, the optimal life insurance policy (and its associated route) from this point onward is independent of how he got there. For dynamic programming problems in general, knowledge of the current state of the system conveys all of the information about its previous behavior necessary for determining the optimal policy henceforth. This is the Markovian property discussed in Chapter 13.

(5) The solution procedure begins by finding the optimal policy for each state of the last stage.

The solution of this one-stage problem is usually trivial, as it was for example 1.

(6) A recursive relationship is available which identifies the optimal policy for each state with n stages remaining, given the optimal policy for each state with $(n - 1)$ stages remaining.

In example 1, this recursive relationship was

$$f_n^*(s) = \min_{x_n} \{c_{sx_n} + f_{n-1}^*(x_n)\} .$$

Therefore, finding the optimal policy when starting in state s with n stages to go required finding the minimizing value of x_n. This policy would consist of using this value of x_n and thereafter following the optimal policy when starting in state x_n with $(n - 1)$ stages to go.

The precise form of the recursive relationship differs somewhat among dynamic programming problems. However, notation analogous to that introduced in the preceding section will continue to be used here. Thus, let the variable (or vector), x_n, be the decision variable when there are n more stages to go $(n = 1, 2, \cdots, N)$. Let $f_n(s, x_n)$ be the maximizing/minimizing value of the objective function, given that the system starts in state s with n stages to go and x_n is selected. [Thus, $f_n(x_n, s) = c_{sx_n} + f_{n-1}^*(x_n)$ in example 1.] Let $f_n^*(s)$ be the maximum/minimum value of $f_n(s, x_n)$ over all possible values of x_n. The recursive relationship will always be of the form

$$f_n^*(s) = \max_{x_n}/\min_{x_n} \{f_n(s, x_n)\} ,$$

where $f_n(s, x_n)$ would be written in terms of s, x_n, $f_{n-1}^*(\cdot)$, and probably some measure of the first-stage effectiveness/ineffectiveness of x_n.

(7) Using this recursive relationship, the solution procedure moves backward stage by stage—each time finding the optimal policy for each state of that stage—until it finds the optimal policy when starting at the initial stage.

This was demonstrated by the stagecoach problem, where the optimal policy was successively found when beginning in each state with 1, 2, 3, and 4 stages to go, respectively. For all dynamic programming problems, a table such as the following would be obtained for each stage ($n = 1, 2, \cdots, N$).

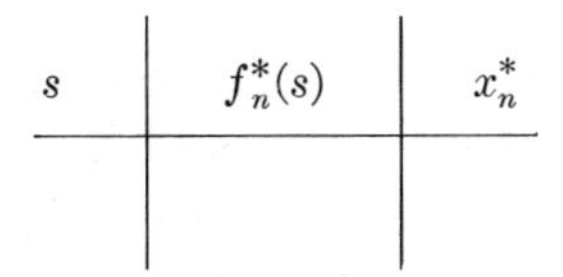

When this table is finally obtained for the initial stage ($n = N$), the problem of interest is solved. Since the initial state would be known, the initial decision is specified by x_N^* in this table. The optimal value of the other decision variables would then be specified by the other tables according to the state of the system at those stages.

8.4 EXAMPLE 2

The owner of a chain of four grocery stores has purchased six crates of fresh strawberries. The estimated probability distribution of potential sales of the strawberries before spoilage differs among the four stores. Therefore, the owner wishes to know how he should allocate the six crates to the four stores in order to maximize expected profit.

For administrative reasons, the owner does not wish to split crates between stores. However, he is willing to distribute zero crates to any of his stores.

The following table gives the estimated total expected profit at each store when it is allocated various numbers of crates.

		Store			
		1	2	3	4
	0	0	0	0	0
	1	4	2	6	2
	2	6	4	8	3
Number	3	7	6	8	4
of crates	4	7	8	8	4
	5	7	9	8	4
	6	7	10	8	4

SOLUTION

This problem requires making four interrelated decisions, namely, how many cartons to allocate to each of the four stores. Therefore, even though there is no fixed sequence, these four stores can be considered as the four stages in a dynamic programming formulation. The decision variables, x_n $(n = 1, 2, 3, 4)$, would be the number of cartons allocated at the nth stage from the end. Arbitrarily order the stages so that stage n corresponds to store n. Thus, x_n $(n = 1, 2, 3, 4)$ is the number of crates allocated to store $(5 - n)$.

The identification of the states may not be quite as obvious. However, the analyst should ask himself questions such as the following. What is it that changes from one stage to the next? Given that the decisions were made at the previous stages, how could one describe the status of the situation at the current stage? What information about the current state of affairs is necessary to determine the optimal policy hereafter? Based upon these considerations, it should become evident that the "state of the system" is the number of crates still available (not already allocated at previous stages).

Let $p_i(x)$ be the expected profit from allocating x crates to store i, as given earlier in a table. Thus, the objective is to maximize $[p_1(x_4) + p_2(x_3) + p_3(x_2) + p_4(x_1)]$, subject to the restrictions that $x_1 + x_2 + x_3 + x_4 = 6$ and that x_1, x_2, x_3, x_4 are non-negative integers. The notation presented in the preceding section will be used here. Thus, $f_n(s, x_n)$ is the profit associated with the optimal policy, given that there are s crates available for n remaining stores and x_n is the initial allocation;

$$f_n^*(s) = \max_{x_n=0,1,\cdots,s} f_n(s, x_n) .$$

Therefore,

$$f_n(s, x_n) = p_{5-n}(x_n) + f_{n-1}^*(s - x_n) ,$$

so that the recursive relationship is

$$f_n^*(s) = \max_{x_n=0,1,\cdots,s} \{p_{5-n}(x_n) + f_{n-1}^*(s - x_n)\}, \qquad \text{for } n = 2, 3, 4 .$$

When $n = 1$,

$$f_1^*(s) = \max_{x_1=0,1,\cdots,s} p_4(x_1) .$$

The resulting calculations are given below, beginning, of course, with the last stage $(n = 1)$ and proceeding backward to the first stage $(n = 4)$.

s	$f_1^*(s)$	x_1^*
0	0	0
1	2	1
2	3	2
3	4	3
4	4	3, 4
5	4	3, 4, 5
6	4	3, 4, 5, 6

s \ x_2	$f_2(s, x_2) = p_3(x_2) + f_1^*(s - x_2)$: 0	1	2	3	4	5	6	$f_2^*(s)$	x_2^*
0	0							0	0
1	2	6						6	1
2	3	8	8					8	1, 2
3	4	9	10	8				10	2
4	4	10	11	10	8			11	2
5	4	10	12	11	10	8		12	2
6	4	10	12	12	11	10	8	12	2, 3

s \ x_3	$f_3(s, x_3) = p_2(x_3) + f_2^*(s - x_3)$: 0	1	2	3	4	5	6	$f_3^*(s)$	x_3^*
0	0							0	0
1	6	2						6	0
2	8	8	4					8	0, 1
3	10	10	10	6				10	0, 1, 2
4	11	12	12	12	8			12	1, 2, 3
5	12	13	14	14	14	9		14	2, 3, 4
6	12	14	15	16	16	15	10	16	3, 4

s \ x_4	$f_4(s, x_4) = p_1(x_4) + f_3^*(s - x_4)$: 0	1	2	3	4	5	6	$f_4^*(s)$	x_4^*
6	16	18	18	17	15	13	7	18	1, 2

The state at a particular stage is equal to the state at the preceding stage minus the allocation at the preceding stage. Therefore, it is easy to successively select the x_4^*, x_3^*, x_2^*, x_1^* giving an optimal solution. In this case, there are eight alternative optimal solutions. They are summarized below.

Store 1 x_4^*	*Store 2* x_3^*	*Store 3* x_2^*	*Store 4* x_1^*
1	2	2	1
1	3	1	1
1	3	2	0
1	4	1	0
2	1	2	1
2	2	1	1
2	2	2	0
2	3	1	0

8.5 EXAMPLE 3

A government space project is conducting research on a certain engineering problem that must be solved before man can fly to the moon safely.

Three research teams are currently trying three different approaches for solving this problem. The estimate has been made that, under present circumstances, the probability that the respective teams—call them A, B, and C—will not succeed is 0.40, 0.60, and 0.80, respectively. Thus, the current probability that all three teams will fail is $(0.40)\ (0.60)\ (0.80) = 0.192$. Since the objective is to minimize this probability, the decision has been made to assign two more top scientists among the three teams in order to lower it as much as possible.

The following table gives the estimated probability that the respective teams will fail when 0, 1, or 2 additional scientists are added to that team.

		Team		
		A	*B*	*C*
Number of new scientists	0	0.40	0.60	0.80
	1	0.20	0.40	0.50
	2	0.15	0.20	0.30

How should the two additional scientists be allocated to the teams?

SOLUTION

Although the physical situations are vastly different, the underlying structure of this problem is actually very similar to that of example 2. In this case, scientists replace strawberry crates and research teams replace grocery stores. Therefore, instead of allocating crates to stores, scientists are to be allocated to teams. The only basic difference between the two problems is in their objective functions.

With so few scientists and teams involved, this problem could be solved very easily by a process of exhaustive enumeration. However, the dynamic programming solution is also very brief, and it is presented for illustrative purposes.

It is evident that the stages correspond to the team, and the state s is the number of new scientists still available for assignation at that stage. Arbitrarily order the stages so that stages 1, 2, and 3 correspond to teams A, B, and C, respectively. The decision variables, $x_n (n = 1, 2, 3)$, are the number of scientists allocated at the nth stage from the end. Let $p_n(x_n)$ denote the probability at the nth stage from the end, given x_n. Since the objective is to minimize the probability of failure at all stages, $f_n(s, x_n)$ would be the minimum probability of failure at all of the last n stages, given s and x_n;

$$f_n^*(s) = \min_{x_n=0,1,\cdots,s} f_n(s, x_n) .$$

Since this definition of $f_n(s, x_n)$ assumes that the optimal policy would be followed after the allocation of x_n, it follows that

$$f_n(s, x_n) = p_n(x_n) \cdot f^*_{n-1}(s - x_n) .$$

Therefore the recursive relationship is

$$f^*_n(s) = \min_{x_n=0,1,\cdots,s} \{p_n(x_n) \cdot f^*_{n-1}(s - x_n)\}, \qquad \text{for } n = 2, 3,$$

and, when $n = 1$,

$$f^*_1(s) = \min_{x_1=0,1,\cdots,s} p_1(x_1) .$$

The resulting calculations are shown below.

s	$f^*_1(s)$	x_1
0	0.80	0
1	0.50	1
2	0.30	2

s \ x_2	$f_2(s, x_2) = p_2(x_2)\, f^*_1(s - x_2)$: 0	1	2	$f^*_2(s)$	x^*_2
0	0.48			0.48	0
1	0.30	0.32		0.30	0
2	0.18	0.20	0.16	0.16	2

s \ x_3	$f_3(s, x_3) = p_3(x_3) \cdot f^*_2(s - x_3)$: 0	1	2	$f^*_3(s)$	x^*_3
2	0.064	0.060	0.072	0.060	1

Therefore, the optimal solution must have $x^*_3 = 1$, which makes $s = 1$ at stage 2, so that $x^*_2 = 0$, which makes $s = 1$ at stage 3, so that $x^*_1 = 1$. Thus, teams A and C should each receive one additional scientist. The new probability that all three teams will fail would then be 0.060.

8.6 EXAMPLE 4

An enterprising young statistician believes that he has developed a system for winning a popular Las Vegas game. His colleagues do not believe that this is possible, so they have made a large bet with him. They bet that, starting with three chips, he will not have five chips after three plays of the game. Each play of the game involves betting any desired number of available chips and then either winning or losing this number of chips. The statistician believes that his system will give him a probability of 2/3 of winning a given play of the game.

Assuming he is correct, determine his optimal policy regarding how many chips to bet (if any) at each of the three plays of the game. The decision at each play should take into account the results of earlier plays. The objective is to maximize the probability of winning his bet with his colleagues.

SOLUTION

The plays of the game clearly constitute the stages in the dynamic programming formulation. The decision variables, x_n ($n = 1, 2, 3$), are the number of chips to bet at the nth stage from the end. The state of the system at any stage is the number of chips available for betting at that stage, since this is the information required for making an optimal decision on how many chips to bet.

Since the objective is to maximize the probability that the statistician will win his bet, the objective function to be maximized at each stage must be the probability of finishing the three plays with at least five chips. Expressing this probability mathematically requires a little care. The usual notation will be used. Thus, let $f_n(s, x_n)$ be the probability corresponding to the optimal policy when one starts with s chips available and n stages to go and makes the initial decision x_n. Let

$$f_n^*(s) = \max_{x_n=0,1,\cdots,s} f_n(s, x_n),$$

and let x_n^* be a maximizing value of x_n. The objective function with n stages to go, $f_n(s, x_n)$, must reflect the fact that it may still be possible to eventually accumulate five chips even if the statistician should lose the next play. If he should lose, the state at the next stage would be $(s - x_n)$, and the probability of finishing with at least five chips would then be $f_{n-1}^*(s - x_n)$. If he should win the next play instead, the state would become $(s + x_n)$, and the corresponding probability would be $f_{n-1}^*(s + x_n)$. Since the alleged probability of winning a given play is 2/3, it now follows that

$$f_n(s, x_n) = \frac{2}{3} f_{n-1}^*(s + x_n) + \frac{1}{3} f_{n-1}^*(s - x_n).$$

Therefore, the recursive relationship is

$$f_n^*(s) = \max_{x_n=0,1,\cdots,s} \left\{\frac{2}{3} f_{n-1}^*(s + x_n) + \frac{1}{3} f_{n-1}^*(s - x_n)\right\}, \qquad \text{for } n = 2, 3.$$

When $n = 1$, x_1^* and $f_1^*(s)$ are obvious. Computational results are given below.

s	$f_1^*(s)$	x_1^*
0	0	—
1	0	—
2	0	—
3	2/3	2 (or more)
4	2/3	1 (or more)
≥ 5	1	0 (or $\leq s - 5$)

s \ x_2	$f_2(s, x_2) = \frac{2}{3}f_1^*(s + x_2) + \frac{1}{3}f_1^*(s - x_2)$					$f_2^*(s)$	x_2^*
	0	1	2	3	4		
0	0					0	—
1	0	0				0	—
2	0	4/9	4/9			4/9	1, 2
3	2/3	4/9	2/3	2/3		2/3	0, 2, 3
4	2/3	8/9	2/3	2/3	2/3	8/9	1
≥ 5	1					1	0 (or $\leq s - 5$)

s \ x_3	$f_3(s, x_3) = \frac{2}{3}f_2^*(s + x_3) + \frac{1}{3}f_2^*(s - x_3)$				$f_3^*(s)$	x_3^*
	0	1	2	3		
3	2/3	20/27	2/3	2/3	20/27	1

Therefore, the optimal policy is the following.

$$x_3^* = 1\begin{cases} \text{if win, } x_2^* = 1 & \begin{cases} \text{if win, } x_1^* = 0 \\ \text{if lose, } x_1^* = 2,\ 3 \end{cases} \\ \text{if lose, } x_2^* = 1 \text{ or } 2 & \begin{cases} \text{if win, } x_1^* = 2,\ 3, \text{ or } 1,\ 2,\ 3,\ 4 \\ \text{if lose, bet is lost.} \end{cases} \end{cases}$$

8.7 EXAMPLE 5

A manufacturer has received an order to supply three items of a particular type. However, the customer has specified such stringent quality requirements that the manufacturer will probably have to produce more than three items in order to obtain three acceptable items. The manufacturer estimates that each item of this type that he produces will be acceptable with probability 1/2 and defective (without possibility for rework) with probability 1/2. Thus, the number of acceptable items produced in a lot of size L will have a binomial distribution, i.e., the probability of producing m acceptable items in L tries is

$$\frac{L!}{m!(L-m)!}\left(\frac{1}{2}\right)^L .$$

Marginal production costs for this product are estimated to be \$100 per item (even if defective), and excess items are worthless. In addition, a setup cost of \$300 must be incurred whenever the production process is set up for this product. If inspection reveals that a completed lot has not yielded enough acceptable items, the production process must be set up again at an additional cost of \$300. The manufacturer has time to make no more than three production runs. If three acceptable items have not been obtained by the end of the third production run, the cost to the manufacturer in lost sales income and in penalty costs would be \$500 for each undelivered item.

The objective is to determine the policy regarding the lot size for the required production run(s) which minimizes total expected cost for the manufacturer.

SOLUTION

The dynamic programming stages are obviously the production runs. The decision variables, $x_n (n = 1, 2, 3)$, are the production lot size at the nth stage from the end. The number of acceptable items still to be obtained (three minus the number previously obtained) will serve to describe the state of the system at any stage.

The objective function with n stages to go, $f_n(s, x_n)$, is the minimum total expected cost over the remaining stages, given that the state is s and the immediate decision is x_n. This objective function is to be minimized with respect to x_n, so that

$$f_n^*(s) = \min_{x_n=0,1,\cdots} f_n(s, x_n) ,$$

and x_n^* is the minimizing value of x_n. Use one hundred dollars as the unit of money. The total expected cost has three components, namely, the current setup cost, the current unit production cost, and the expected additional cost caused by not obtaining the required number of acceptable items at the current stage. The first two components are obviously $(3 + x_n)$ if $x_n > 0$ and zero if $x_n = 0$. Writing the expression for the expected additional cost requires a careful application of the definition of expected value (for discrete random variables) as given in Chapter 3. If the lot size for the current production run is x_n, then the number of acceptable items obtained can be any integer from 0 to x_n. Therefore, if s acceptable items are still required, the number short at the end of the production run can be any integer from s on down to 0 or $s - x_n$, whichever is larger. There are a definite probability and a definite cost associated with each of these shortage amounts. By definition, the expected additional cost is obtained by multiplying each of these costs by its corresponding probability and then adding all these products. Therefore, the desired total expected cost in hundreds of dollars is

$$f_1(s, x_1) = \begin{cases} 5s, & \text{if } x_1 = 0 \\ 3 + x_1 + \sum_{m=0}^{x_1} \left[\dfrac{x_1!}{m!(x_1 - m)!} \left(\dfrac{1}{2}\right)^{x_1} \right] [5(s - m)], & \text{if } 0 < x_1 \leq s \\ 3 + x_1 + \sum_{m=0}^{s} \left[\dfrac{x_1!}{m!(x_1 - m)!} \left(\dfrac{1}{2}\right)^{x_1} \right] [5(s - m)], & \text{if } x_1 \geq s \end{cases}$$

and

$$f_n(s, x_n) = \begin{cases} f^*_{n-1}(s), & \text{if } x_n = 0 \\ 3 + x_n + \sum_{m=0}^{x_n} \left[\dfrac{x_n!}{m!(x_n - m)!} \left(\dfrac{1}{2}\right)^{x_n} \right] [f^*_{n-1}(s - m)], & \text{if } 0 < x_n \leq s \\ 3 + x_n + \sum_{m=0}^{s} \left[\dfrac{x_n!}{m!(x_n - m)!} \left(\dfrac{1}{2}\right)^{x_n} \right] [f^*_{n-1}(s - m)], & \text{if } x_n \geq s \end{cases}$$

for $n = 2, 3$. The consequent computational results are the following.

$s \backslash x_1$	$f_1(s, x_1)$: 0	1	2	3	4	5	6	7	≥ 8	$f_1^*(s)$	x_1^*
0	0									0	0
1	5	$6\frac{1}{2}$	$6\frac{1}{4}$	> 6	> 6	> 6	> 6	> 6	> 6	5	0
2	10	$11\frac{1}{2}$	10	$9\frac{1}{8}$	$8\frac{14}{16}$	$9\frac{3}{32}$	> 9	> 9	> 9	$8\frac{7}{8}$	4
3	15	$16\frac{1}{2}$	15	$13\frac{1}{2}$	$12\frac{5}{16}$	$11\frac{19}{32}$	$11\frac{22}{64}$	$11\frac{62}{128}$	> 12	$11\frac{11}{32}$	6

$s \backslash x_2$	$f_2(s, x_2)$: 0	1	2	3	4	5	6	7	≥ 8	$f_2^*(s)$	x_2^*
0	0									0	0
1	5	$6\frac{1}{2}$	$6\frac{1}{4}$	>6	>6	>6	>6	>6	>6	5	0
2	$8\frac{14}{16}$	$10\frac{30}{32}$	$9\frac{46}{64}$	$8\frac{126}{128}$	$8\frac{206}{256}$	$9\frac{40}{512}$	$>9\frac{1}{2}$	$>9\frac{1}{2}$	$>9\frac{1}{2}$	$8\frac{103}{128}$	4
3	$11\frac{22}{64}$	$14\frac{7}{64}$	$13\frac{67}{128}$	$12\frac{318}{512}$	$11\frac{822}{1024}$	$11\frac{622}{2048}$	$11\frac{742}{4096}$	$11\frac{3230}{8192}$	$>11\frac{1}{2}$	$11\frac{371}{2048}$	6

$s \backslash x_3$	$f_3(s, x_3)$: 0	1	2	3	4	5	6	7	≥ 8	$f_3^*(s)$	x_3^*
3	$11\frac{742}{4096}$	$13\frac{8134}{8192}$	$13\frac{7334}{16384}$	$12\frac{18822}{32768}$	$11\frac{50790}{65536}$	$11\frac{37702}{131072}$	$11\frac{45094}{262144}$	$11\frac{213772}{524288}$	$>11\frac{1}{2}$	$11\frac{22547}{131072}$	6

Therefore, the optimal policy is to produce six items on the first production run; if less than three of these are acceptable, then produce six, four, or no more items if three, two, or one more acceptable items are required, respectively; repeat this strategy on a third production run if still short.

8.8 EXAMPLE 6

The workload for a certain job shop is subject to considerable seasonal fluctuation. However, machine operators are difficult to hire and costly to train, so the manager is reluctant to lay off workers during the slack seasons. He is likewise reluctant to maintain his peak season payroll when it is not required. Furthermore, he is definitely opposed to overtime work on a regular basis. Since all work is done to custom orders, it is not possible to build up inventories during slack seasons. Therefore, the manager is in a dilemma as to what his policy should be regarding employment levels.

The following estimates are given for the manpower requirements during the four seasons of the year for the forseeable future.

Season	*Spring*	*Summer*	*Autumn*	*Winter*	*Spring*	...
Requirements	255	220	240	200	255	...

Employment will not be permitted to fall below these levels. Any employment above these levels is wasted at an approximate cost of $2000 per man per season. It is also estimated that the hiring and firing costs are such that the total cost of changing the level of employment from one season to the next is $200 times the square of the difference in employment levels. Fractional levels of employment are possible because of a few part-time employees; assume that the above cost data also apply on a fractional basis.

What should be the employment in each season in order to minimize total cost?

SOLUTION

On the basis of the data available, it is clear that it would not be worthwhile for the employment level to go above the peak season requirements of 255. Therefore, spring employment should be at 255, and the problem reduces to finding the employment level for the other three seasons.

It is evident that the seasons should be the dynamic programming stages. There is actually an indefinite number of stages since the problem extends into the indefinite future. However, each year begins an identical cycle, and since spring employment is known, it is possible to consider only one cycle of four seasons ending with the spring season.

The decision variables, x_n ($n = 1, 2, 3, 4$), are the employment levels at the nth stage from the end. It is necessary that the spring season be the last stage since the optimal value of the decision variable for each state at the last stage must either be known or obtainable without considering other stages. For every other season, the solution for the optimal employment level must consider the effect on costs in the following season. Therefore, x_1, x_2, x_3, and x_4 are the employment levels for spring, winter, autumn, and summer, respectively.

The cost at the current stage depends only on the current decision x_n and the employment in the previous season. The preceding employment level is all the information about the current state of affairs that is required to determine the optimal policy henceforth. Therefore, it is evident that the state of the system is described by the employment level at the previous stage.

The objective function with n stages to go, $f_n(s, x_n)$, must be the minimum total cost over the remaining stages, given that the state is s and the initial decision is x_n. Thus, $f_n^*(s)$ is the minimum value of $f_n(s, x_n)$ over all permissible values of x_n, and x_n^* is the minimizing value of x_n.

The primary difference between this example and the preceding ones is that the number of possible states and the number of possible values of the decision variables are now infinite instead of finite. However, this does not create any new fundamental difficulty. The former procedure was to use exhaustive enumeration to select the optimal value of a decision variable for each possible state. The procedure in the present situation is to use calculus instead to find the optimal value of the decision variable as a function of the state of the system.

Since the value of the decision variable x_n at a given stage becomes the state at the following stage,

$$f_n(s, x_n) = 200(x_n - s)^2 + 2000(x_n - r_n) + f_{n-1}^*(x_n),$$

where r_n is the minimum manpower requirement at the nth stage from the end. It is already known that $x_1^* = 255 = r_1$, so the necessary results for the last stage are available.

s	$f_1^*(s)$	x_1^*
≤ 255	$200(255 - s)^2$	255

(The cost of the optimal policy after the last stage of the current cycle is a fixed constant and can, therefore, be omitted from consideration.)

The two-stage problem involves finding the minimizing value of x_2 in the relationship,

$$
\begin{aligned}
f_2^*(s) &= \min_{x_2 \geq r_2} f_2(s, x_2) \\
&= \min_{x_2 \geq r_2} \{200(x_2 - s)^2 + 2000(x_2 - r_2) + f_1^*(x_2)\} \\
&= \min_{x_2 \geq 200} \{200(x_2 - s)^2 + 2000(x_2 - 200) + 200(255 - x_2)^2\} .
\end{aligned}
$$

For any fixed value of s, the partial derivative of $f_2(s, x_2)$ with respect to x_2 is

$$
\frac{\partial}{\partial x_2} f_2(s, x_2) = 400(x_2 - s) + 2000 - 400(255 - x_2) .
$$

Notice that the second derivative is

$$
\frac{\partial^2}{\partial x_2^2} f_2(s, x_2) = 800 ,
$$

and is, therefore, positive for all values of x_2. Hence, the value of x_2 which minimizes $f_2(s, x_2)$ over *all* values of x_2 is found (if it exists) by solving the equation,

$$
\begin{aligned}
\frac{\partial}{\partial x_2} f_2(s, x_2) &= 0 \\
&= 800x_2 - 400s - 100{,}000 \\
&= 400(2x_2 - s - 250) .
\end{aligned}
$$

Thus,

$$
x_2 = \frac{s + 250}{2}
$$

is this minimizing value. However, the problem of concern here is to minimize $f_2(s, x_2)$ only over values of $x_2 \geq 200$. If the above value of x_2 happened to lie in this range (which would occur when $s \geq 150$), it must be the desired value. However, if $s < 150$, further analysis is required. Notice that if $s < 150$, then

$$
\frac{\partial}{\partial x_2} f_2(s, x_2)
$$

is positive for all values of $x_2 \geq 200$. Under these circumstances, $x_2 = 200$ must be the minimizing value over the feasible region. Therefore, the optimal value of x_2 is

$$
x_2^* = \begin{cases} \dfrac{s + 250}{2}, & \text{if } s \geq 150 \\ 200, & \text{if } s \leq 150 . \end{cases}
$$

$f_2^*(s)$ is found, of course, by setting $x_2 = x_2^*$ in the $f_2(s, x_2)$ function. Thus, if $s \geq 150$,

$$f_2^*(s) = 200\left(\frac{s + 250}{2} - s\right)^2 + 2000\left(\frac{s + 250}{2} - 200\right) + 200\left(255 - \frac{s + 250}{2}\right)^2$$

$$= 50(250 - s)^2 + 1000(s - 150) + 50(260 - s)^2 .$$

Similarly, if $s < 150$,

$$f_2^*(s) = 200(200 - s)^2 + 0 + 200(55)^2 .$$

Therefore, the required results for the two-stage problem are the following.

s	$f_2^*(s)$	x_2^*
≤ 150	$200(200 - s)^2 + 605{,}000$	200
150–255	$50(250 - s)^2 + 50(260 - s)^2 + 1000(s - 150)$	$\frac{s + 250}{2}$

The three-stage and four-stage problems are solved in a similar fashion. Thus,

$$\begin{aligned} f_3(s, x_3) &= 200(x_3 - s)^2 + 2000(x_3 - r_3) + f_2^*(x_3) \\ &= 200(x_3 - s)^2 + 2000(x_3 - 240) \\ &\quad + 50(250 - x_3)^2 + 50(260 - x_3)^2 + 1000(x_3 - 150) \end{aligned}$$

in the region of interest, $240 \leq x_3 \leq 255$. The problem is to find the minimizing value of x_3 in this region, so that

$$f_3^*(s) = \min_{x_3 \geq 240} f_3(s, x_3) .$$

Setting

$$\begin{aligned} \frac{\partial}{\partial x_3} f_3(s, x_3) &= 0 \\ &= 400(x_3 - s) + 2000 - 100(250 - x_3) - 100(260 - x_3) + 1000 \\ &= 200(3x_3 - 2s - 240) \end{aligned}$$

yields

$$x_3 = \frac{2s + 240}{3} .$$

Since

$$\frac{\partial^2}{\partial x_3^2} f_3(s, x_3) = 600 > 0 ,$$

this is the desired minimizing value if $s \geq 240$. If $s < 240$, then

$$\frac{\partial}{\partial x_3} f_3(s, x_3) > 0 \qquad \text{for } x_3 = 240 ,$$

so that $x_3 = 240$ would be the minimizing value. The next step is to plug these values of x_3 into $f_3(s, x_3)$ in order to obtain $f_3^*(s)$ for $s \geq 240$ and $s < 240$. After some algebraic manipulation, the following results are obtained.

s	$f_3^*(s)$	x_3^*
≤ 240	$200(240 - s)^2 + 115{,}000$	240
240–255	$\frac{200}{9}[2(250 - s)^2 + (265 - s)^2 + 30(3s - 575)]$	$\frac{2s + 240}{3}$

For the four-stage problem,

$$f_4(s, x_4) = 200(x_4 - s)^2 + 2000(x_4 - r_4) + f_3^*(x_4) .$$

Since $r_4 = 220$, the region of interest is $220 \leq x_4 \leq 255$. The expression for $f_3^*(x_4)$ will differ in the two portions, $220 \leq x_4 \leq 240$ and $240 \leq x_4 \leq 255$, of this region. Therefore,

$$f_4(s, x_4) = \begin{cases} 200(x_4 - s)^2 + 2000(x_4 - 220) + 200(240 - x_4)^2 + 115{,}000 , \\ \qquad\qquad \text{if } x_4 \leq 240 \\ 200(x_4 - s)^2 + 2000(x_4 - 220) + \frac{200}{9}[2(250 - x_4)^2 \\ \qquad + (265 - x_4)^2 + 30(3x_4 - 575)], \\ \qquad\qquad \text{if } 240 \leq x_4 \leq 255 . \end{cases}$$

Considering first the case where $x_4 \leq 240$,

$$\begin{aligned} \frac{\partial}{\partial x_4} f_4(s, x_4) &= 400(x_4 - s) + 2000 - 400(240 - x_4) \\ &= 400(2x_4 - s - 235) . \end{aligned}$$

It is known that $s = 255$ (spring employment), so that

$$\begin{aligned} \frac{\partial}{\partial x_4} f_4(s, x_4) &= 800(x_4 - 245) \\ &< 0 \end{aligned}$$

for all $x_4 \leq 240$. Therefore, $x_4 = 240$ is the minimizing value of $f_4(s, x_4)$ over the region, $x_4 \leq 240$.

When $240 \leq x_4 \leq 255$,

$$\begin{aligned} \frac{\partial}{\partial x_4} f_4(s, x_4) &= 400(x_4 - s) + 2000 - \frac{200}{9}[4(250 - x_4) + 2(265 - x_4) - 90] \\ &= \frac{400}{3}(4x_4 - 3s - 225) . \end{aligned}$$

Since

$$\frac{\partial^2}{\partial x_4^2} f_4(s, x_4) > 0 \qquad \text{for all } x_4 ,$$

set

$$\frac{\partial}{\partial x_4} f_4(s, x_4) = 0 ,$$

which yields

$$x_4 = \frac{3s + 225}{4} .$$

Since $s = 255$, $x_4 = 247.5$ therefore minimizes $f_4(s, x_4)$ over the region, $240 \leq x_4 \leq 255$. Since this region includes $x_4 = 240$, which minimizes $f_4(s, x_4)$ over the region where $x_4 \leq 240$, it is clear that $x_4 = 247.5$ also minimizes $f_4(s, x_4)$ over the entire region of interest, $220 \leq x_4 \leq 255$. Hence,

$$\begin{aligned} f_4^*(255) &= 200(247.5 - 255)^2 + 2000(247.5 - 220) \\ &\quad + \frac{200}{9} [2(250 - 247.5)^2 + (265 - 247.5)^2 + 30(742.5 - 575)] \\ &= 185{,}000 . \end{aligned}$$

These results are summarized below.

s	$f_4^*(s)$	x_4^*
255	185,000	247.5

Therefore, the optimal policy is $x_4 = 247.5$, $x_3 = 245$, $x_2 = 247.5$, $x_1 = 255$, with a total estimated cost per cycle of $185,000.

8.9 EXAMPLE 7

Consider the linear programming problem, maximize

$$Z = 3x_1 + 5x_2 ,$$

subject to

$$\begin{aligned} x_1 \quad\quad &\leq 4 \\ x_2 &\leq 6 \\ 3x_1 + 2x_2 &\leq 18 \\ x_1 \geq 0, \; x_2 &\geq 0 , \end{aligned}$$

that was solved in Section 5.5 by the simplex method. It so happens that small linear programming problems like this one can also be solved (although much less efficiently) by dynamic programming. Consider how this would be done.

SOLUTION

This problem requires making two interrelated decisions, namely, the level of activity 1, x_1, and the level of activity 2, x_2. Therefore, these two activities can be interpreted as the two stages in a dynamic programming formulation. Although they can be taken in either order, let stage $n =$ activity n $(n = 1, 2)$. Thus, x_n is the decision variable at the nth stage (rather than the nth stage from the end, as previously).

What are the states? In other words, given that the decision had been made at stage 1, what information is needed about the current state of affairs before making the decision at stage 2? A little thought should suggest that the required information is the amount of slack left in the constraints (other than the non-negativity restrictions). To amplify, interpret the right-hand side of these constraints, 4, 6, and 18, as the total available amount of resources 1, 2, and 3, respectively. Then the state s is the amount of the respective resources remaining to be allocated. Thus,

$$s = (R_1, R_2, R_3) ,$$

where R_i is the amount of resource i remaining to be allocated $(i = 1, 2, 3)$.

Therefore, in contrast to the preceding examples, this problem has three state variables (i.e., a state vector with three components) rather than one. From a theoretical standpoint, this is not particularly serious. It only means that, instead of considering all possible values of the one state variable, it is necessary to consider all possible *combinations* of values of the several state variables. However, from the standpoint of computational efficiency, this tends to be a very serious complication. Since the number of combinations, in general, can be as large as the *product* of the number of possible values of the respective variables, the number of required calculations tends to "blow up" rapidly when additional decision variables are introduced. (This phenomenon has been given the apt name of "the curse of dimensionality.")

A second complication is that, like example 6, each decision variable is continuous rather than discrete, so it possesses an infinite number of possible values. Therefore, rather than consider each possible value separately, it is necessary to use the approach introduced in example 6 of solving for the optimal value of each decision variable as a function of the state of the system.

Despite these complications, this problem is small enough so that it can still be solved without great difficulty. To do so, the usual notation needs to be introduced. Thus, interpreting Z as profit, the objective function with n stages to go, $f_n(R_1, R_2, R_3, x_{3-n})$, must be the maximum total profit over the remaining stages, given that the state is (R_1, R_2, R_3) and the initial decision is x_{3-n}. Given (R_1, R_2, R_3), then $f_n^*(R_1, R_2, R_3)$ is the maximum value of $f(R_1, R_2, R_3, x_{3-n})$ over all feasible values of x_{3-n}, and x_{3-n}^* is the maximizing value of x_{3-n}.

To solve at the last stage, note that

$$f_1(R_1, R_2, R_3, x_2) = 5x_2 ,$$

where the feasible values of x_2 are those satisfying the set of restrictions, $x_2 \le R_2$, $2x_2 \le R_3$, $x_2 \ge 0$. Therefore,

$$f_1^*(R_1, R_2, R_3) = \max_{\substack{x_2 \le R_2 \\ 2x_2 \le R_3 \\ x_2 \ge 0}} \{5x_2\} .$$

Thus, the solution is immediately apparent, as given below.

R_1, R_2, R_3	$f_1^*(R_1, R_2, R_3)$	x_2^*
$R_i \ge 0$	$5 \min\left\{R_2, \frac{R_3}{2}\right\}$	$\min\left\{R_2, \frac{R_3}{2}\right\}$

For the two-stage problem, it is evident that

$$f_2(R_1, R_2, R_3, x_1) = 3x_1 + f_1^*(R_1 - x_1, R_2, R_3 - 3x_1) ,$$

where the feasible values of x_1 are those satisfying the set of restrictions, $x_1 \le R_1$, $3x_1 \le R_3$, $x_1 \ge 0$. Therefore, since it is known that $R_1 = 4$, $R_2 = 6$, $R_3 = 18$ at the first stage, the desired recursive relationship is

$$\begin{aligned} f_2^*(4, 6, 18) &= \max_{\substack{x_1 \le 4 \\ 3x_1 \le 18 \\ x_1 \ge 0}} \{3x_1 + f_1^*(4 - x_1, 6, 18 - 3x_1)\} \\ &= \max_{0 \le x_1 \le 4} \left\{3x_1 + 5 \min\left\{6, \frac{18 - 3x_1}{2}\right\}\right\} . \end{aligned}$$

Notice that

$$\min\left\{6, \frac{18 - 3x_1}{2}\right\} = \begin{cases} 6, & \text{if } 0 \le x_1 \le 2 \\ 9 - \frac{3}{2} x_1, & \text{if } 2 \le x_1 \le 4 , \end{cases}$$

so that

$$3x_1 + 5 \min\left\{6, \frac{18 - 3x_1}{2}\right\} = \begin{cases} 3x_1 + 30, & \text{if } 0 \le x_1 \le 2 \\ 45 - \frac{9}{2} x_1, & \text{if } 2 \le x_1 \le 4 . \end{cases}$$

Since both

$$\max_{0 \le x_1 \le 2} \{3x_1 + 30\} \quad \text{and} \quad \max_{2 \le x_1 \le 4} \left\{45 - \frac{9}{2} x_1\right\}$$

achieve their maximum at $x_1 = 2$, it follows that $x_1^* = 2$, as shown below.

R_1, R_2, R_3	$f_2^*(R_1, R_2, R_3)$	x_1^*
4, 6, 18	36	2

Therefore, the optimal solution for this problem is

$$x_1 = 2 \quad \text{and} \quad x_2 = \min\left\{6, \frac{18 - 3(2)}{2}\right\} = 6\,,$$

with a total profit of 36.

SELECTED REFERENCES

1. Bellman, Richard, and Dreyfus, Stuart, *Applied Dynamic Programming*, Princeton University Press, Princeton, N.J., 1962.
2. Howard, Ronald A., *Dynamic Programming and Markov Processes*, MIT Press, Cambridge, Mass., 1960.

PROBLEMS

1. A county chairman of a certain political party is making plans for an upcoming presidential election. He has received the services of six volunteer workers for precinct work, and he wishes to assign them to four precincts in such a way as to maximize their effectiveness. He feels that it would be inefficient to assign a worker to more than one precinct, but he is willing to assign no workers to any one of the precincts if they can accomplish more in other precincts.

The following table gives the estimated increase in the plurality (positive or negative) of the party's candidate in each precinct if it were allocated various numbers of workers.

Number	*Precinct*			
of workers	1	2	3	4
0	0	0	0	0
1	25	20	33	13
2	42	38	43	24
3	55	54	47	32
4	63	65	50	39
5	69	73	52	45
6	74	80	53	50

Use dynamic programming to determine how many of the six workers should be assigned to each of the four precincts in order to maximize the total estimated increase in the plurality of the party's candidate.

2. Use dynamic programming to solve example 1 of Section 6.2.2. Assume that production quantities must be integer multiples of ten.

3. Consider an electronic system consisting of four components, each of which must function in order for the system to function. The reliability of the system can be improved by installing several parallel units in one or more of the components. The following table gives the probability that the respective components will function if they consist of 1, 2, or 3 parallel units.

Number of parallel units	*Probability of functioning*			
	Component 1	*Component 2*	*Component 3*	*Component 4*
1	0.60	0.40	0.70	0.50
2	0.75	0.65	0.90	0.60
3	0.85	0.80	0.95	0.80

The probability that the system will function is the product of the probabilities that the respective components will function.

The cost of installing 1, 2, or 3 parallel units in the respective components is given by the following table.

Number of parallel units	*Cost*			
	Component 1	*Component 2*	*Component 3*	*Component 4*
1	$ 6	$10	$ 5	$ 8
2	$11	$16	$10	$13
3	$15	$22	$14	$17

Due to budget limitations, a maximum of $45 can be expended.

Use dynamic programming to determine how many parallel units should be installed in each of the four components in order to maximize the probability that the system will function.

4. Reconsider example 4. Suppose that the bet is changed to: "starting with *two* chips, he will not have five chips after *four* plays of the game." By referring to the previous computational results, make a few more calculations to determine what the new optimal policy is for the enterprising young statistician.

5. Suppose that the situation described in example 5 has changed somewhat. After a more careful analysis, the manufacturer now estimates that each item produced will be acceptable with probability 2/3, rather than 1/2, so that the probability of producing m acceptable items in L tries is

$$\frac{L!}{m!(L-m)!}\left(\frac{2}{3}\right)^m\left(\frac{1}{3}\right)^{L-m}.$$

Furthermore, he now feels that he will only have time to make two production runs at the most. Use dynamic programming to determine the new optimal policy for the manufacturer.

6. Resolve example 6 when the total cost of changing the level of employment from one season to the next is changed to \$50 times the square of the difference in employment levels.

7. Consider the following non-linear programming problem. Maximize

$$Z = 10x_1 - 2x_1^2 - x_1^3 + 8x_2 - x_2^2\,,$$

subject to

$$x_1 + x_2 \leq 2$$

and

$$x_1 \geq 0,\ x_2 \geq 0\,.$$

Use dynamic programming to solve this problem.

8. Consider the following "fixed-charge" problem. Maximize

$$Z = g_1(x_1) + g_2(x_2) + 3x_3\,,$$

subject to

$$\begin{aligned} x_1 + x_2 \qquad\quad &\leq 10 \\ 2x_1 + x_2 + 3x_3 &\leq 30 \end{aligned}$$

and

$$x_1 \geq 0,\ x_2 \geq 0,\ x_3 \geq 0\,,$$

where

$$g_1(x_1) = \begin{cases} 0, & \text{if } x_1 = 0 \\ -4 + 5x_1, & \text{if } x_1 > 0\,, \end{cases}$$

$$g_2(x_2) = \begin{cases} 0, & \text{if } x_2 = 0 \\ -10 + 7x_2, & \text{if } x_2 > 0\,. \end{cases}$$

Use dynamic programming to solve this problem.

CHAPTER 9

Game Theory

9.1 INTRODUCTION

Life is full of conflict and competition. Numerous examples involving adversaries in conflict include parlor games, military battles, political campaigns, advertising and marketing compaigns by competing business firms, etc. A basic feature in many of these situations is that the final outcome depends primarily on the combination of strategies selected by the adversaries. *Game theory* is a mathematical theory that deals with the general features of competitive situations like these in a formal, abstract way. It places particular emphasis on the decision-making process of the adversaries.

The bulk of the research on game theory has been on *2-person zero-sum games.* As the name implies, these games involve only two adversaries or *players* (who may be armies, teams, firms, etc.). They are called *zero-sum* because one player wins whatever the other one loses, so that the sum of their net winnings is zero. The discussion hereafter concentrates on this kind of game, although other types are also mentioned at the end of the chapter.

To illustrate the basic characteristics of a game theory model, consider a simplified version of the game called "Two-Finger Morra." In this version, each player simultaneously shows either one or two fingers. If the number of fingers match, then player I wins, say, \$1 from player II. If they don't match, player I would pay \$1 to player II. Thus, each player has two *strategies,* to show either one finger or two fingers. The resulting payoff to player I in dollars is shown in the following *payoff table.*

Payoff table

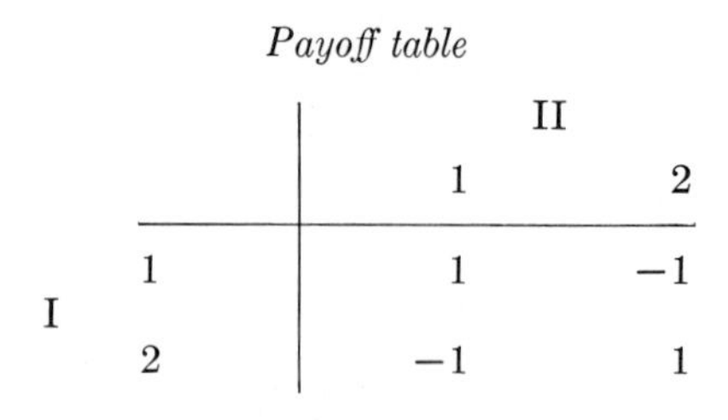

		II: 1	II: 2
I	1	1	−1
I	2	−1	1

In general, a game is characterized by

(1) the strategies of player I
(2) the strategies of player II
(3) the payoff table.

A strategy may involve only a simple action, as in this example. On the other hand, in more complicated games involving a series of moves, a strategy is a predetermined rule that specifies completely how one intends to respond to each possible circumstance at each stage of the game. Before the game begins, each player knows the strategies available to himself, the ones available to his opponent, and the payoff table. The actual play of the game consists of the players simultaneously choosing a strategy without knowing their opponent's choice.

The payoff table usually is given only for player I, since the table for player II is just the negative of this one, due to the zero-sum nature of the game. The entries in the payoff may be in any units desired, such as dollars, provided that they accurately represent the "utility" to player I of the corresponding outcome. It should be noted that utility is not necessarily proportional to the amount of money (or of many other commodities) when large quantities are involved. For example, \$2,000,000 (after taxes) is probably worth much less than twice as much as \$1,000,000 to a poor man. In other words, given the choice between (1) a 50% chance of receiving \$2,000,000 rather than nothing, and (2) being sure of getting \$1,000,000, he probably would much prefer the latter. On the other hand, the outcome corresponding to an entry of 2 in a payoff table should be "worth twice as much" to player I as the outcome corresponding to an entry of 1. Thus, given the choice, he should be indifferent between a 50% chance of receiving the former outcome (rather than nothing) and definitely receiving the latter outcome instead.

A primary objective of game theory is to develop rational criteria for selecting a strategy. This is done under the assumption that both players are rational, and that each will uncompromisingly attempt to do as well as possible, relative to his opponent. This is in contrast to statistical decision theory (see Chapter 4), which essentially assumes that the decision-maker is playing a game with a passive opponent, nature, which chooses its "strategies" in some random fashion. Instead, game theory assumes that both players are actively trying to promote their own welfare in opposition to that of the opponent.

It is quite apparent that the general problem of how to make decisions in a competitive environment is a very important one. Therefore, it would appear that game theory should have great practical import. Unfortunately, this has not been the case. It has received modest application in military problems, but there have been very few industrial applications. The reason seems to be that game theory has only been capable of analyzing very simple competitive situations. Thus, there has been a great gap between what the theory can handle and most actual competitive situations in industry and elsewhere. However, this is not to say that game theory is not an important tool of operations research. Indeed, its formulation, logic, and criteria are important conceptual tools. Thus, the primary contribution of game theory has been its concepts rather than its formal application to solving real problems.

The following sections develop, by means of illustrative examples, the standard game theory criteria for choosing strategies. They also describe systematic procedures for identifying the line of play that is optimal according to these criteria.

9.2 SOLVING SIMPLE GAMES

Example 1

Consider a game having the following payoff table.

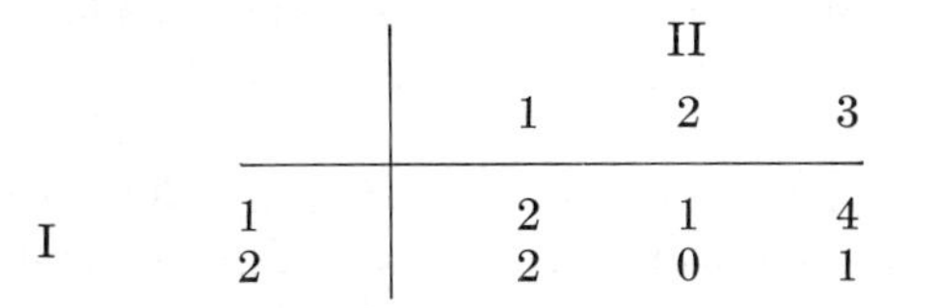

		II		
		1	2	3
I	1	2	1	4
	2	2	0	1

Which strategy should player I play? The answer is obviously strategy 1, since it "dominates" strategy 2, i.e., it is at least as good as strategy 2, regardless of what the opponent does. Similarly, player II would automatically discard his strategy 3 from consideration since it is dominated by another strategy (strategy 2) which has uniformly lower payoffs to player I. Since both players are assumed to be rational, player II would further deduce that player I will play strategy 1 and that he should therefore play strategy 2 to minimize his losses. As a result, player I will always receive a payoff of 1 from player II, so that the *value* of this game is said to be 1. If the payoff is in dollars, player I should pay \$1 to player II to make it a *fair game.*

Thus, the concept of a dominated strategy is a very useful one for reducing the size of the payoff table that needs to be considered and, in cases like this one, actually identifying the optimal solution to the game.

Example 2

Now consider a game whose payoff table is the following:

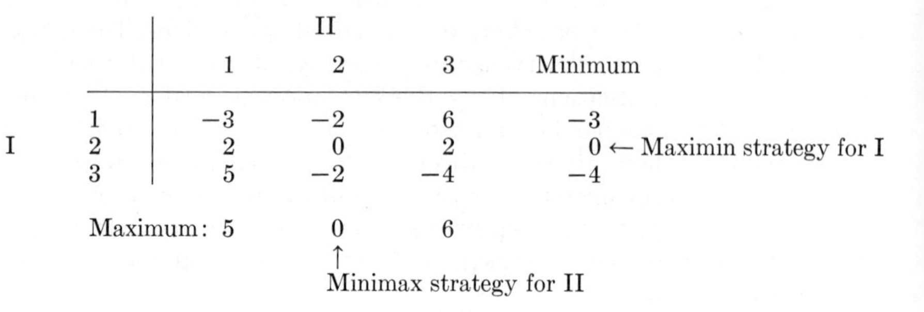

		II			
		1	2	3	Minimum
I	1	-3	-2	6	-3
	2	2	0	2	0 ← Maximin strategy for I
	3	5	-2	-4	-4
	Maximum:	5	0 ↑ Minimax strategy for II	6	

This game does not have dominated strategies, so it is not obvious what the players should do. What line of reasoning does game theory say they should use? Consider player I. By selecting strategy 1, he could win 6 or he could lose as much as 3. However, since player II is rational, and so will protect himself from large payoffs to I, it seems probable that playing strategy 1 would result in a loss to I. Similarly, by selecting strategy 3, player I could win 5, but more probably his intelligent opponent would avoid this and administer him a loss, which could be as large as 4. On the other hand, if player I selects strategy 2, he is guaranteed not to lose anything, and he could even win something. Therefore, since it provides a better guarantee than the others, strategy 2 seems to be a "rational" choice for player I against his rational opponent. By arguing in a similar manner, player II would see that he could lose as much as 5, 0, and 6 by using strategies 1, 2, and 3, respectively, so the apparent "rational" choice is strategy 2. Furthermore, even when either player learns the other's strategy, he cannot improve by changing his own, so this strategy can be used safely and, if necessary, repeatedly.

The end product of the line of reasoning described above is that each player should play in such a way as to minimize his maximum losses whenever this would not give an advantage to the opponent. This so-called *minimax criterion* is a standard criterion proposed by game theory for selecting a strategy. In terms of the payoff table, it implies that player I should select the strategy whose minimum payoff is largest, whereas player II should choose the one whose maximum payoff to I is the smallest. This is illustrated in the payoff table above, where strategy 2 is identified as the "maximin" strategy for player I, and strategy 2 is the minimax strategy for player II. The maximin and minimax values, which are both zero here, are referred to as the *lower value* and the *upper value* of the game, respectively. When they are equal, the common quantity is called the *value* of the game. It is zero here, so the game is fair.

Notice the interesting fact that the same entry in this payoff table yields both the lower value and the upper value. The reason is that this entry is both the minimum in its row and the maximum in its column. The position of any such entry is called a *saddle point.*

The fact that this game possesses a saddle point was actually crucial in determining how it should be played. Because of the saddle point, neither player can take advantage of the opponent's strategy to improve his own position. In particular, when player II predicts or learns that player I is using strategy 2, player II would only increase his losses if he were to change from his original plan of using his strategy 2. Similarly, player I would only worsen his position if he were to change his plan. Thus, neither player has any motive to consider changing strategies, either to take advantage of his opponent or to prevent the opponent from taking advantage of him. Therefore, since this solution is a *stable* one, players I and II should exclusively use their maximin and minimax strategies, respectively.

As the next example illustrates, some games do not possess a saddle point, in which case a more complicated analysis is required.

Example 3

Finally, consider a game which has the following payoff table.

		II			
		1	2	3	Minimum
I	1	0	-2	2	$-2 \leftarrow$ Lower value of the game
	2	5	4	-3	-3
	3	2	3	-4	-4
	Maximum:	5	4	2 $\uparrow$ Upper value of the game	

How should this game be played? Suppose that both players attempt to apply the minimax criterion in the same way as was done in the preceding example. Player I would notice that the lower value of the game is -2, so he can guarantee that he will lose no more than 2 by playing strategy 1. Similarly, since the upper value of the game is 2, player II can guarantee that he will not lose more than 2 by playing strategy 3.

However, notice that there is no value of the game, and therefore no saddle point. What are the resulting consequences if both players should plan to use the strategies derived above? If they actually were to use them, player I would win 2 from player II, which would make player II unhappy. Since he is rational and can therefore foresee this outcome, player II would then conclude that he can do much better, actually winning 2 rather than losing 2, by playing strategy 2 instead. Since player I is also rational, he would anticipate this switch and conclude that he can improve considerably, from -2 to 4, by changing to strategy 2. Realizing this, player II would then consider switching back to strategy 3 to convert a loss of 4 to a gain of 3. This would cause player I to again consider using strategy 1, and then the whole cycle would start over again. In short, the originally suggested solution (player I to play strategy 1 and player II to play strategy 3) is *unstable*, so it is necessary to develop a more satisfactory solution. But what kind of solution should it be?

The key fact seems to be that whenever one player's strategy is predictable, the opponent here can take great advantage of this information to improve his position. Therefore, an essential feature of a "rational" plan for playing the game is that neither player should be able to deduce which strategy the other will use. Hence, rather than applying some known criterion for determining a single strategy that will definitely be used, it is necessary to choose among several acceptable strategies on some kind of random basis. By doing this, neither player knows in advance which of his own strategies will be used, let alone what his opponent will do.

This suggests, in very general terms, the kind of approach that is required for games lacking a saddle point. The next section discusses this approach more fully. Given this foundation, attention is then turned to procedures for finding an optimal way of playing such games. This particular example will continue to be used to illustrate these ideas as they are developed.

9.3 GAMES WITH MIXED STRATEGIES

Whenever a game does not possess a saddle point, game theory advises each player to assign a probability distribution over his set of strategies. To express this mathematically, let

$$x_i = \text{probability that player I will use strategy } i \ (i = 1, 2, \cdots, m),$$
$$y_j = \text{probability that player II will use strategy } j \ (j = 1, 2, \cdots, n),$$

where m and n are the respective numbers of available strategies. Thus, player I would specify his plan for playing the game by assigning values to $x_1, x_2, \cdots, x_m$. Since these values are probabilities, they would need to be nonnegative and add up to one. Similarly, the plan for player II would be described by the values he assigned to his decision variables, $y_1, y_2, \cdots, y_n$. These plans, $(x_1, x_2, \cdots, x_m)$ and $(y_1, y_2, \cdots, y_n)$, are usually referred to as *mixed strategies*, and the original strategies would then be called *pure strategies*. When actually playing the game, it is necessary for each player to use one of his pure strategies. However, this one would be chosen by using some random device to obtain a random observation from the probability distribution specified by the mixed strategy, where this observation would indicate which particular pure strategy to use.

To illustrate, suppose that players I and II in Example 3 select the mixed strategies, $(x_1, x_2, x_3) = (1/2, 1/2, 0)$ and $(y_1, y_2, y_3) = (0, 1/2, 1/2)$, respectively. This would say that player I is giving an equal chance (probability of 1/2) to choosing either (pure) strategy 1 or 2, but he is discarding strategy 3 entirely. Similarly, player II is randomly choosing between his last two pure strategies. To play the game, each player could then flip a coin to determine which of his two acceptable pure strategies he will actually use.

Although no completely satisfactory quantity is available for evaluating mixed strategies, a very useful one is the *expected payoff* (in the statistical sense described in Section 3.8). Applying the definition of expected value, this quantity would be

$$\text{expected payoff} = \sum_{i=1}^{m} \sum_{j=1}^{n} p_{ij} x_i y_j ,$$

where p_{ij} is the payoff if player I uses pure strategy i and player II uses pure strategy j. It does not disclose anything about the "risks" involved in playing the game, but it does indicate what the average payoff will tend to be if the game is played many times. Thus, in the above example, there are four possible payoffs (-2, 2, 4, and -3), each occurring with a probability of 1/4, so the expected payoff is $1/4(-2 + 2 + 4 - 3) = 1/4$.

The time has now come to extend the concept of the minimax criterion to games having mixed strategies. In this context, the *minimax criterion* says that a given player should select the strategy that maximizes the minimum expected payoff (i.e., that minimizes the maximum expected loss) to himself. By minimum expected payoff is meant the smallest possible expected payoff that can result from any mixed strategy with which the opponent can counter. Thus, the mixed strategy for player I that is optimal according to this criterion is the one that guarantees him the largest possible expected payoff, regardless of which mixed strategy player II might use. The value of this "maximin" expected payoff is called the *lower value* of the game and is denoted by $\underline{v}$. Similarly, the optimal strategy for player II is the one which guarantees him the smallest possible expected loss, regardless of what player I does. The corresponding value of the expected payoff to player I is the *upper value* of the game, $\bar{v}$.

Recall that when only pure strategies were being used, games not having a saddle point turned out to be unstable. The reason essentially was that $\underline{v} < \bar{v}$, so that the players would want to change their strategy to improve their position. Similarly, for games with mixed strategies, it is necessary that $\underline{v} = \bar{v}$ in order for the optimal solution to be stable. Fortunately, according to the *Minimax Theorem* of game theory, this condition always holds for such games, as indicated below.

Minimax Theorem: If mixed strategies are allowed, there always exists a value of the game, i.e., $\underline{v} = \bar{v} = v$.

Thus, if both players use their mixed strategy that is optimal according to the minimax criterion, the expected payoff would be v, and neither player can do better by unilaterally changing his strategy. One proof of this theorem is included in Section 9.5.

Having noted that a stable optimal solution does exist, it now remains to be shown how to find this solution. There are several methods of doing this. One is a graphical procedure that may be used whenever one of the players only has two (undominated) pure strategies; this approach is described in the next section. When larger games are involved, the usual method is to transform the problem into a linear programming problem, which would then be solved by the simplex method on an electronic computer. Section 9.5 discusses this approach.

9.4 A GRAPHICAL SOLUTION PROCEDURE

Consider any game with mixed strategies such that, after eliminating dominated strategies, one of the players has only two pure strategies. To be specific, let this player be player I. Since his mixed strategies are (x_1, x_2) and $x_2 = 1 - x_1$, it is only necessary for him to solve for the optimal value of x_1. However, it is straightforward to plot the expected payoff as a function of x_1 for each of his opponent's pure strategies. It is then simple to identify the point that maximizes the minimum expected payoff. The opponent's minimax mixed strategy can also be identified quite easily from the graph.

To illustrate this procedure, consider Example 3 given in Section 9.2. Notice that the third pure strategy for player I is dominated by his second, so the payoff table can be reduced to the following:

				II	
		Probability	y_1	y_2	y_3
	Probability	*Pure strategy*	1	2	3
I	x_1	1	0	−2	2
	$1 - x_1$	2	5	4	−3

Therefore, for each of the pure strategies available to player II, the expected payoff for player I would be:

(y_1, y_2, y_3)	*Expected payoff*
(1, 0, 0)	$0x_1 + 5(1 - x_1) = 5 - 5x_1$
(0, 1, 0)	$-2x_1 + 4(1 - x_1) = 4 - 6x_1$
(0, 0, 1)	$2x_1 - 3(1 - x_1) = -3 + 5x_1$

Now plot these expected payoff lines on a graph.

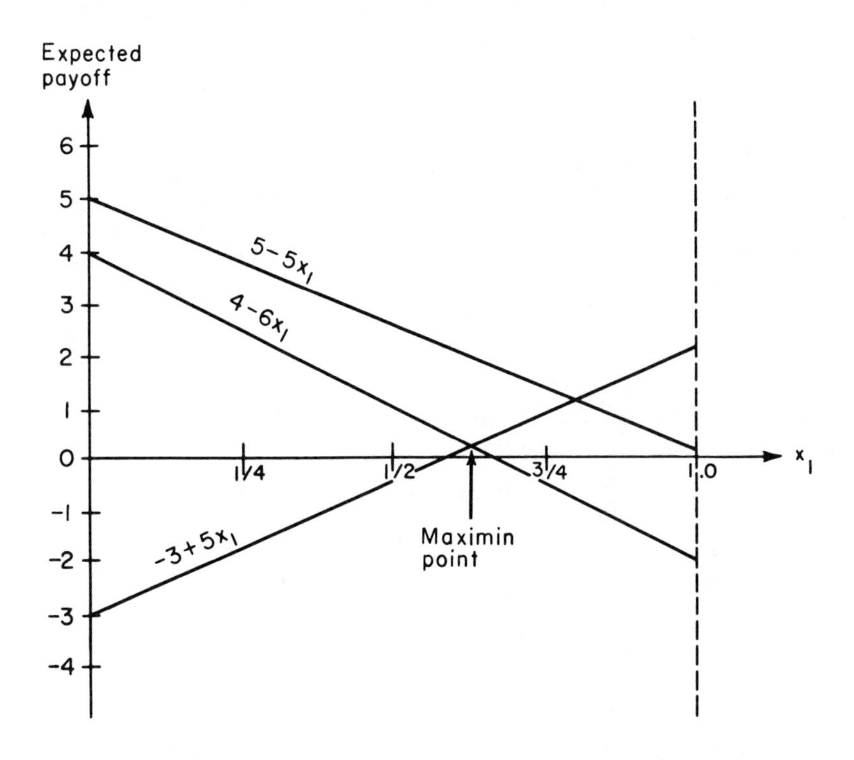

FIGURE 9.1. Graphical procedure for solving games.

For any given value of x_1 and of (y_1, y_2, y_3), the expected payoff will be the appropriate weighted average of the corresponding points on these three lines. In particular,

$$\text{expected payoff} = y_1(5 - 5x_1) + y_2(4 - 6x_1) + y_3(-3 + 5x_1) .$$

Thus, given x_1, the minimum expected payoff is given by the corresponding point on the "bottom" line. According to the minimax (or maximin) criterion, player I should select the value of x_1 giving the largest minimum expected payoff, so that

$$\underline{v} = v = \max_{0 \leq x_1 \leq 1} \left\{ \min \left(-3 + 5x_1,\ 4 - 6x_1 \right) \right\},$$

Therefore, it is evident that the optimal value of x_1 is the one at the intersection of the two lines, $(-3 + 5x_1)$ and $(4 - 6x_1)$. Solving algebraically,

$$-3 + 5x_1 = 4 - 6x_1 ,$$

so that $x_1 = 7/11$; thus, $(x_1, x_2) = (7/11, 4/11)$ is the optimal mixed strategy for player I, and

$$\underline{v} = v = -3 + 5\left(\frac{7}{11}\right) = \frac{2}{11}$$

is the value of the game.

In order to find the corresponding optimal mixed strategy for player II, one would now reason as follows. According to the definition of upper value and the Minimax Theorem, the expected payoff resulting from this strategy, $(y_1, y_2, y_3) = (y_1^*, y_2^*, y_3^*)$, will satisfy the condition,

$$y_1^* (5 - 5x_1) + y_2^* (4 - 6x_1) + y_3^* (-3 + 5x_1) \leq \bar{v} = v = \frac{2}{11}$$

for all values of $x_1 (0 \leq x_1 \leq 1)$; furthermore, when player I is playing optimally (i.e., $x_1 = 7/11$), this inequality will be an equality, so that

$$\frac{20}{11} y_1^* + \frac{2}{11} y_2^* + \frac{2}{11} y_3^* = v = \frac{2}{11} .$$

Since (y_1, y_2, y_3) is a probability distribution, it is also known that

$$y_1^* + y_2^* + y_3^* = 1 .$$

Therefore, it is evident that $y_1^* = 0$, since $y_1^* > 0$ would violate the next to last equation, i.e., the expected payoff on the graph at $x_1 = 7/11$ would be above the maximin point. (In general, any line that does not pass through the maximin point must be given a zero weight to avoid increasing the expected payoff above this point.) Hence,

$$y_2^*(4 - 6x_1) + y_3^*(-3 + 5x_1) \begin{cases} \leq \dfrac{2}{11}, & \text{for } 0 \leq x_1 \leq 1 \\ = \dfrac{2}{11}, & \text{for } x_1 = \dfrac{7}{11} . \end{cases}$$

But y_2^* and y_3^* are numbers, so the left-hand side is merely the equation of a straight line, which is a fixed weighted average of the two "bottom" lines on the graph. Since the ordinate of this line must equal $2/11$ at $x_1 = 7/11$, and it must never exceed 2/11, the line necessarily is horizontal. (This conclusion is always true, unless the optimal value of x_1 is either zero or one, in which case player II also should use a single pure strategy.) Therefore,

$$y_2^* (4 - 6x_1) + y_3^* (-3 + 5x_1) = \frac{2}{11}, \qquad \text{for } 0 \leq x_1 \leq 1 .$$

Hence, to solve for y_2^* and y_3^*, merely select two values of x_1, say zero and one, and solve the resulting two simultaneous equations. Thus,

$$4y_2^* - 3y_3^* = \frac{2}{11},$$

$$-2y_2^* + 2y_3^* = \frac{2}{11},$$

so that $y_3^* = 6/11$ and $y_2^* = 5/11$. Therefore, the optimal mixed strategy for player II is $(y_1, y_2, y_3) = (0, 5/11, 6/11)$.

If, in another problem, there should happen to be more than two lines passing through the maximin point, so that more than two of the y_j^* can be greater than zero, this would imply that there are many ties for the optimal mixed strategy for player II. One such strategy can then be identified by arbitrarily setting all but two of these y_j^* equal to zero and solving for the remaining two in the manner described above.

Although this graphical procedure has only been illustrated on one particular problem, essentially the same reasoning can be used to solve any game with mixed strategies that has only two undominated pure strategies for one of the players.

9.5 SOLVING BY LINEAR PROGRAMMING

Any game with mixed strategies can be solved rather easily by transforming the problem into a linear programming problem. As will be seen, this requires nothing more than applying the definitions of lower value and upper value, and the Minimax Theorem.

First consider how to find the optimal mixed strategy for player I. As indicated in Section 9.3,

$$\text{expected payoff} = \sum_{i=1}^{m} \sum_{j=1}^{n} p_{ij} x_i y_j ,$$

and the strategy $(x_1, x_2, \cdots, x_m)$ is optimal if

$$\sum_{i=1}^{m} \sum_{j=1}^{n} p_{ij} x_i y_j \geq \underline{v} = v$$

for all opposing strategies $(y_1, y_2, \cdots, y_n)$. Thus, this inequality will need to hold, for example, for each of the pure strategies of player II, so that

$$\begin{aligned}
p_{11}x_1 + p_{21}x_2 + \cdots + p_{m1}x_m &\geq v \\
p_{12}x_1 + p_{22}x_2 + \cdots + p_{m2}x_m &\geq v \\
&\vdots \\
p_{1n}x_1 + p_{2n}x_2 + \cdots + p_{mn}x_m &\geq v\,.
\end{aligned}$$

However, notice that these inequalities imply that

$$\sum_{j=1}^{n} y_j \left(\sum_{i=1}^{m} p_{ij}x_i \right) \geq \sum_{j=1}^{n} y_j v = v$$

since

$$\sum_{j=1}^{n} y_j = 1\,,$$

so that imposing this set of m linear inequalities is equivalent to requiring the original inequality to hold for all strategies $(y_1, y_2, \cdots, y_n)$. But these are legitimate linear programming constraints, as are the additional constraints,

$$\begin{aligned}
x_1 + x_2 + \cdots + x_m &= 1 \\
x_i &\geq 0, \qquad \text{for } i = 1, 2, \cdots, m\,,
\end{aligned}$$

that are required to insure that the x_i are probabilities. Therefore, any solution $(x_1, x_2, \cdots, x_m)$ that satisfies this entire set of linear programming constraints is the desired optimal mixed strategy. The two remaining problems are (1) v is unknown, and (2) the linear programming problem has no objective function. Fortunately, both of these problems can be solved at one stroke by the clever trick of replacing the unknown constant v by the variable x_{m+1}, and then maximizing x_{m+1}, so that x_{m+1} automatically will equal v (by definition) at the optimal solution to the linear programming problem!

To summarize, player I would find his optimal mixed strategy by solving the linear programming problem. Minimize

$$-x_{m+1},$$

subject to

$$\begin{aligned}
p_{11}x_1 + p_{21}x_2 + \cdots + p_{m1}x_m - x_{m+1} &\geq 0 \\
p_{12}x_1 + p_{22}x_2 + \cdots + p_{m2}x_m - x_{m+1} &\geq 0 \\
&\vdots \\
p_{1n}x_1 + p_{2n}x_2 + \cdots + p_{mn}x_m - x_{m+1} &\geq 0 \\
-(x_1 + x_2 + \cdots + x_m) &= -1
\end{aligned}$$

and

$$x_i \geq 0, \qquad \text{for } i = 1, 2, \cdots, m\,.$$

(The objective function and equality constraint have been rewritten here in an equivalent way for later convenience.) A close examination of this formulation reveals one flaw, namely, that x_{m+1} is not restricted to be nonnegative, but this is easily rectified, as will be discussed shortly.

Now consider player II. He obviously could find his optimal mixed strategy by rewriting the payoff table as the payoff to himself rather than player I, and then proceeding exactly as described above. However, it is enlightening to summarize his formulation in terms of the original payoff table. By proceeding in a way that is completely analogous to that described above, player II would conclude that his optimal mixed strategy is given by the optimal solution to the linear programming problem. Maximize

$$-y_{n+1},$$

subject to

$$\begin{aligned}
p_{11}y_1 + p_{12}y_2 + \cdots + p_{1n}y_n - y_{n+1} &\leq 0 \\
p_{21}y_1 + p_{22}y_2 + \cdots + p_{2n}y_n - y_{n+1} &\leq 0 \\
&\cdot \\
&\cdot \\
&\cdot \\
p_{m1}y_1 + p_{m2}y_2 + \cdots + p_{mn}y_n - y_{n+1} &\leq 0 \\
-(y_1 + y_2 + \cdots + y_n) &= -1
\end{aligned}$$

and

$$y_j \geq 0, \qquad \text{for } j = 1, 2, \cdots, n\,.$$

Now notice the key fact that this linear programming problem and the one given for player I are *dual* to each other in the sense described in Section 5.7. (In particular, this problem is in the form given for the "primal" problem, and the one for player I is the corresponding dual problem.) This has several important implications. One is that the optimal mixed strategies for both players can be found by solving only one of the linear programming problems, since the optimal dual solution is an automatic by-product of the simplex method calculations to find the optimal primal solution. A second is that this brings all of duality theory (described in Section 5.7 and in Chapter 15) to bear upon the interpretation and analysis of games. A related implication is that this provides a very simple proof of the Minimax Theorem. Let x_{m+1}^* and y_{n+1}^* denote the value of x_{m+1} and y_{n+1} in the optimal solution of the respective linear programming problems. It is known from the Dual Theorem given in Section 5.7 (and proven in Chapter 15) that $-x_{m+1}^* = -y_{n+1}^*$, so that $x_{m+1}^* = y_{n+1}^*$. However, it is evident from the definition of lower value and upper value that $\underline{v} = x_{m+1}^*$ and $\bar{v} = y_{n+1}^*$, so it follows that $\underline{v} = \bar{v}$ as claimed by the Minimax Theorem.

One remaining loose end needs to be tied up, namely, what to do about x_{m+1} and y_{n+1} being unrestricted in sign in the linear programming formulations. In order to apply the simplex method to solve such a problem, all of the variables involved need to be non-negative. If it is clear that $v \geq 0$, so that the optimal value of x_{m+1} and y_{n+1} is non-negative, then it is safe to restrict these variables to non-negative values for purposes of solving the problem. However, if $v < 0$, then an adjustment needs to be made. One possibility is to use the trick described in Section 5.6.5 for applying the simplex method when a variable is unconstrained in sign. Another is to reverse players I and II so that the payoff table would be rewritten as the payoff to the original player II, which would make the corresponding value of v positive. A third, and the most commonly used, procedure is to add a sufficiently large fixed constant to all of the entries in the payoff table so that the new value of the game will be positive. (For example, setting this constant equal to minus the largest negative entry will suffice.) Since this same constant is added to every entry, this adjustment cannot alter the optimal mixed strategies in any way, so they would now be obtained in the usual manner. The indicated value of the game would be increased by the amount of the constant, but this can be readjusted after the solution has been obtained.

9.6 EXTENSIONS

Although this chapter has only considered 2-person zero-sum games with a finite number of pure strategies, it would be incorrect to conclude that game theory is limited solely to this kind of game. In fact, some research has been done on several more complicated types of games. These are summarized below.

One such type is the "n-person game," where more than two players may participate in the game. This is a particularly important generalization since, in many kinds of competitive situations, there frequently are more than two competitors involved. This is often the case, for example, in competition among business firms, in international diplomacy, etc. Unfortunately, the existing theory for such games is less satisfactory than for 2-person games.

Another generalization is the "non-zero-sum game," where the sum of the payoffs to the players need not be zero (or any other fixed constant). This reflects the fact that many competitive situations include non-competitive aspects that contribute to the mutual advantage or mutual disadvantage of the players. For example, the advertising strategies of competing companies can affect not only how they will split the market, but also the total size of the market for their competing products. Since mutual gain is possible, non-zero-sum games are further classified in terms of the degree to which the players are permitted to cooperate. At one extreme is the "non-cooperative game," where there is no preplay communication between the players. At the other extreme is the "cooperative game," where preplay discussions and binding agreements are permitted. For example, competitive situations involving trade regulations between countries, or collective bargaining between labor and management, might be formulated as cooperative games. When there are more than two players, cooperative games also allow some or all of the players to form coalitions.

Still another extension is to the class of "infinite games," where the players have an infinite number of pure strategies available to them. These games are designed for the kind of situation where the strategy to be selected can be represented by a *continuous* decision variable. For example, this decision variable might be the time at which to take a certain action, or the proportion of one's resources to allocate to a certain activity, in a competitive situation. Much research has been concentrated on such games in recent years.

However, the analysis required in these extensions beyond the 2-person zero-sum finite game is relatively complex, and will not be pursued further here.

SELECTED REFERENCES

1. Dresher, Melvin, *Games of Strategy: Theory and Applications,* Prentice-Hall, Englewood Cliffs, N.J., 1961.
2. Luce, R. Duncan, and Raiffa, Howard, *Games and Decisions,* Wiley, New York, 1957.
3. Stoller, David S., *Operations Research: Process and Strategy,* University of California Press, Berkeley, Calif., 1964, Part III.
4. Vajda, S., *An Introduction to Linear Programming and the Theory of Games,* Methuen, London, and Wiley, New York, 1960, Part II.

PROBLEMS

1. Consider the games having the following payoff tables. For each game, determine whether it has a saddle point. If it does, determine the optimal strategy for each player according to the minimax criterion, and the value of the game.

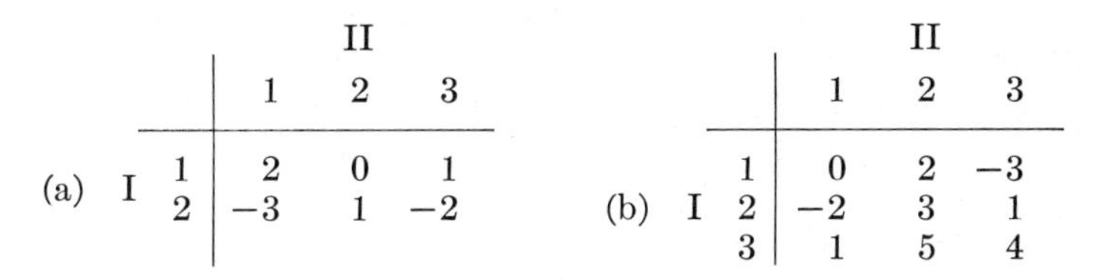

(a)

		II		
		1	2	3
I	1	2	0	1
	2	−3	1	−2

(b)

		II		
		1	2	3
I	1	0	2	−3
	2	−2	3	1
	3	1	5	4

(c)

		II		
		1	2	3
I	1	0	4	−2
	2	3	−5	1
	3	−2	1	6
	4	1	0	4

(d)

		II			
		1	2	3	4
I	1	−2	5	0	−3
	2	1	0	3	−1
	3	−3	2	−1	−5
	4	0	4	1	−2

2. Two manufacturers currently are competing for sales in two different but equally profitable product lines. In both cases, the sales volume for manufacturer II is three times as large as that for manufacturer I. Due to a recent technological breakthrough, both manufacturers will be making a major improvement in both products. However, they are uncertain as to what development and marketing strategy they should follow.

If both product improvements are developed simultaneously, either manufacturer can have them ready for sale in 12 months. Another alternative is to have a "crash program" to develop only one product first in order to try to get it marketed ahead of the competition. By doing this, manufacturer II could have one product ready for sale in 9 months, whereas manufacturer I would require 10 months (due to previous commitments for its production facilities). For either manufacturer, the second product could then be ready for sale in an additional 9 months.

For either product line, if both manufacturers market their improved models simultaneously, it is estimated that manufacturer I would increase its share of the total future sales of this product by 5% of the total (from 25% to 30%). Similarly, manufacturer I would increase its share by 15%, 35%, and 45% of the total if it markets the product sooner than manufacturer II by 2 months, 6 months, and 8 months, respectively. On the other hand, manufacturer I would lose 5%, 11%, 13%, and 15% of the total if manufacturer II markets it sooner by 1 month, 3 months, 7 months, and 10 months, respectively.

Formulate this problem as a 2-person zero-sum game, and then determine which strategy the respective manufacturers should use according to the minimax criterion.

3. Two politicians are running against each other for a particular political office. Campaign plans must now be made for the final three days before the election. Polls indicate that the anticipated election result currently is a toss-up. Both politicians plan to campaign in two key areas having 10,000 and 5,000 votes, respectively. In order to avoid wasting campaigning time, they plan to travel at night and spend an integer number of days (0, 1, 2, or 3) in the respective areas. However, they are uncertain how they should divide the three available days among these areas.

For either area, it is estimated that both politicians would get 50% of the vote if they spend the same number of days there. However, if one politician spends no time in the area, the other would get 55%, 58%, and 60% of the vote if he spends one, two, and three days there, respectively. If either spends one day there, the other would get 53% and 55% of the vote in the area by being there two days and three days, respectively. If one spends two days there, his opponent would get 52% of the vote by campaigning in the area all three days. However, since the necessary arrangements must be made in advance, neither politician will learn his opponent's campaign schedule until after he has finalized his own.

Formulate and solve this problem according to the minimax criterion.

4. For each of the following payoff tables, use the graphical procedure described in Section 9.4 to determine the value of the game and the optimal mixed strategy for each player according to the minimax criterion.

(a)

		II 1	2	3
I	1	2	0	1
	2	1	4	3

(b)

		II 1	2	3
I	1	−2	3	0
	2	3	1	−1
	3	−3	4	2
	4	5	−2	−4

5. Consider the following military situation. Side I is interested in bombing two areas, each containing a vast factory complex of side II. However, side I has only one bomber squadron to devote to this, and the entire squadron must be sent to only one target area in order to be effective. Side II can defend effectively against such an attack if it can send all of its available fighters to meet the bomber squadron. However, the two areas are so far apart that these fighters can be available for defending only one of the areas at any particular time.

If they are not defended by the fighters, the military value of bombing target area 2 is considered to be twice that of bombing target area 1. However, if they are defended, the bombers must turn back with heavy losses without reaching the target. The military value of this loss is considered to be equal in magnitude to the gain if target area 1 were to be bombed undefended.

Use game theory to formulate this problem and to determine the optimal mixed strategy of the respective sides according to the minimax criterion.

6. Consider the following parlor game between two players. It begins when a referee flips a coin, notes whether it comes up heads or tails, and then shows this result to only player I. Player I may then either (1) pass and thereby pay $1 to player II, or (2) he may bet. If player I passes, the game is terminated. However, if he bets, the game continues, in which case player II may then either (1) pass and thereby pay \$1 to player I, or (2) he may call. If player II calls, the referee then shows him the coin; if it came up heads, player II pays \$2 to player I; if it came up tails, player II receives \$2 from player I.

(a) Give the pure strategies for each player. (Hint: Player I will have four pure strategies, each one specifying how he would respond to each of the two results the referee can show him; player II will have two pure strategies, each one specifying how he will respond if player I bets.)

(b) Develop the payoff table for this game, using expected values for the entries when necessary. Determine whether it has a saddle point or not.

(c) Determine the optimal mixed strategy for each player according to the minimax criterion. Also give the corresponding value of the game.

7. For each of the following payoff tables, transform the problem of finding the minimax mixed strategies into an equivalent linear programming problem.

(a)

		II		
		1	2	3
I	1	9	1	4
	2	0	6	3
	3	5	2	8

(b)

		II				
		1	2	3	4	5
I	1	−6	4	−1	−4	5
	2	1	−5	−9	−3	−1
	3	−4	0	−7	4	−1
	4	2	−3	5	−9	−5

8. Consider the problem of finding the minimax mixed strategies for the game described in Example 3, Section 9.2.

(a) Formulate this problem as a linear programming problem.

(b) Solve by the simplex method.

9. Briefly describe what you feel are the advantages and disadvantages of the minimax criterion.

Part IV

TECHNIQUES: PROBABILISTIC MODELS

CHAPTER 10

Queueing Theory

10.1 INTRODUCTION

Queueing theory involves the mathematical study of "queues" or waiting lines. The formation of waiting lines is, of course, a common phenomenon which occurs whenever the current demand for a service exceeds the current capacity to provide that service. Decisions regarding the amount of capacity to provide must be made frequently in industry and elsewhere. However, since it is frequently impossible to accurately predict when units will arrive to seek service and/or how much time will be required to provide that service, these decisions often are difficult ones. Providing too much service would involve excessive costs. On the other hand, not providing enough service capacity would cause the waiting line to become excessively long at times. Excessive waiting also is costly in some sense, whether it be a social cost, or the cost of lost customers, or the cost of idle employees, etc. Therefore, the ultimate goal is to achieve an economic balance between the cost of service and the cost associated with waiting for that service. Queueing theory itself does not directly solve this problem. However, it does contribute vital information required for such a decision by predicting various characteristics of the waiting line such as the average waiting time.

Queueing theory provides a large number of alternative mathematical models for describing a waiting line situation. Mathematical results predicting some of the characteristics of the waiting line often are available for these models. After some general discussion, this chapter presents most of the more elementary models and their basic results. The next chapter discusses how the information provided by queueing theory might be used for making decisions.

10.2 ILLUSTRATIVE EXAMPLE

A classic study[38] conducted at Boeing Aircraft serves to illustrate the nature of a waiting line problem and its analysis. The study was made to determine the number of clerks that should be assigned to tool crib counters in use throughout the Boeing factory area. These cribs store tools required by mechanics in the shops and assembly lines. The tools are handed out by clerks as the mechanics arrive and request them; they are returned to the clerks when no longer needed. The problem arose because of two conflicting pressures; one, the complaints of foremen when they felt that their mechanics were waiting too long in line, which would have led to more clerks; the other, the pressure of management to reduce overhead, which would have led to fewer clerks.

Consider a tool crib such that the average time between arrivals is 50 seconds and the average time required by a clerk to serve a mechanic is 60 seconds. It may appear quite definite at first glance that two clerks should be assigned to this crib. However, service times vary and arrivals occur at random. Hence, a long line of waiting mechanics would form at certain times, while the clerks would be idle at other times. It is therefore necessary to use queueing theory to predict the *average* length of time an arriving mechanic would have to wait before being served. Using the queueing model selected in the study (see Sec. 10.6.1), this average waiting time would be 33.8 seconds with two clerks, 4.7 seconds with three clerks, and 0.8 seconds with four clerks. Since the crib has an average of 540 callers during a $7\frac{1}{2}$-hour working day, this indicates that having three clerks rather than two reduces the expected total idle time of mechanics by approximately $4\frac{1}{2}$ hours. However, increasing the number of clerks increases the expected total idle time of clerks by $7\frac{1}{2}$ hours per day for each additional clerk. If the cost of idle time were $3 per hour for clerks and $7 per hour for mechanics, it is easily calculated (as illustrated in Section 11.6.2) that the average total daily cost of idle time at this crib would be the following.

Number of clerks	*Total cost of idle time*
2	$53.50
3	$45.40
4	$63.80

These results imply that three clerks should be assigned to this tool crib.

[38] Reported by Georges Brigham in "On a Congestion Problem in an Aircraft Factory," *Operations Research*, **3**, No. 4, 412–428 (1955).

10.3 BASIC STRUCTURE OF QUEUEING MODELS

10.3.1 The Basic Queueing Process

The basic process assumed by most queueing models is the following. Units requiring service are generated over time by an "input source." These units enter the queueing system and join a "queue." At certain points in time, a member of the queue is selected for service by some rule known as the "service discipline." The required service is then performed for the unit by the "service mechanism," after which the unit leaves the queueing system. This process is depicted below.

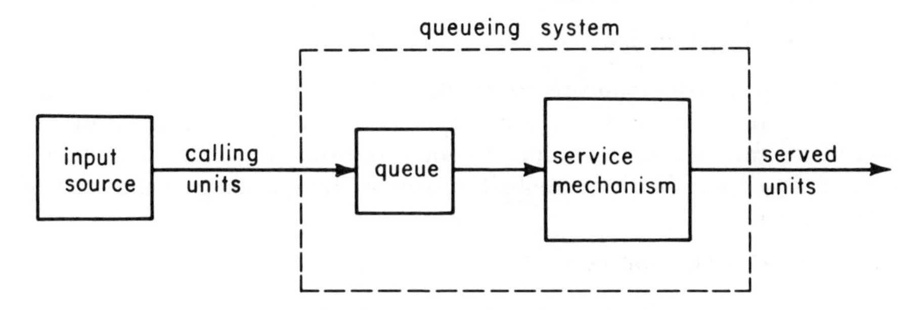

FIGURE 10.1. The basic queueing process.

There are many alternative assumptions that can be made about the various elements of the queueing process. These are discussed below.

10.3.2 Input Source (Calling Population)

One characteristic of the input source or calling population is its "size." The size is the total number of units that might require service from time to time, i.e., the total number of distinct potential customers. It may be assumed to be either infinite or finite. Since the calculations are far easier for the infinite case, this assumption often is made even when the actual size is some relatively large finite number. The finite case is more difficult analytically because the number of units in the queueing system affects the number of potential calling units outside the system at any point in time. However, the finite assumption must be made if the rate at which the input source generates calling units is significantly affected by the number of units in the queueing system.

The statistical pattern by which calling units are generated over time must also be specified. The common assumption is that they are generated according to a Poisson process, i.e., the number of calling units generated until any specific time has a Poisson distribution (see Chapter 3). This is the case where arrivals to the queueing system occur at random, but at a certain average rate. An equivalent assumption is that the probability distribution of the time between consecutive arrivals ("inter-arrival time") is an exponential distribution (see Chapter 3).

Any unusual assumptions about the behavior of the calling units must also be specified. One example is balking, where the calling unit refuses to enter the system and is lost if the queue is too long.

10.3.3 Queue

A queue is characterized by the maximum permissible number of units that it can contain. Queues are called infinite or finite according to whether this number is infinite or finite.

10.3.4 Service Discipline

The service discipline refers to the order in which members of the queue are selected for service. For example, it may be first-come-first-served, or random, or according to some priority procedure, etc. First-come-first-served usually is implicitly assumed by queueing models unless stated otherwise.

10.3.5 Service Mechanism

The service mechanism consists of one or more service facilities, each of which contains one or more "parallel service channels" (servers). If there is more than one service facility, the calling unit may receive service from a sequence of these ("service channels in series"). At a given facility, the unit enters one of the parallel service channels and is completely serviced by that server. A queueing model must specify the arrangement of the facilities and the number of servers (parallel channels) at each one. Most elementary models assume one service facility with either one or a finite number of servers.

The time elapsed from the commencement of service to its completion for a unit at a service facility is referred to as the service time or holding time. A queueing model must specify the probability distribution of service times for each server (and possibly for various types of calling units), although it is common to assume the same distribution for all servers. The Erlang (gamma) distribution or one of its special cases, the exponential distribution and the degenerate distribution (constant service time), is frequently selected.

10.3.6 An Elementary Queueing Process

As suggested in the previous sections, queueing theory has studied many different types of waiting line situations. However, it has concentrated primarily on the following situation. A single waiting line (which may be empty at times) forms in front of a single service facility, within which are stationed one or more servers. Each calling unit generated by an input source is serviced by one of the servers, perhaps after some waiting in the queue (waiting line). The queueing system involved is depicted below.

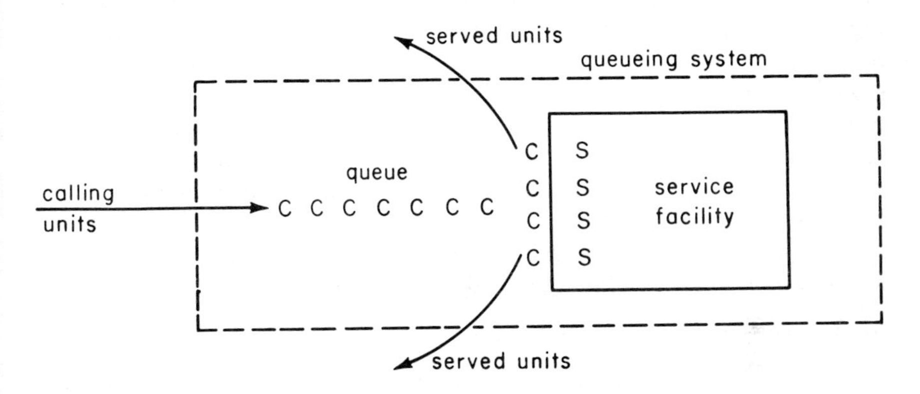

FIGURE 10.2. An elementary queueing system (each calling unit is indicated by a C and each server by an S).

It is readily recognized that the queueing process in the illustrative example of Sec. 10.2 is of this type. The input source generates calling units in the form of mechanics requiring service at the tool crib in their section of the factory. The tool crib is the service facility and the tool crib clerks are the servers.

A server need not be a single individual. It may be a group of persons, e.g., a repair crew, who combine forces to perform simultaneously the required service for a calling unit. Furthermore, servers need not even be people. In many cases, a server may be a machine or a piece of equipment, e.g., a fork lift truck, which performs a given service on call (although probably with human guidance). By the same token, the calling units in the waiting line need not be people. For example, they may be items waiting for a certain operation by a given type of machine, or they may be cars waiting in front of a toll booth.

It is not necessary that there actually be a physical waiting line forming in front of a physical structure which constitutes the service facility. That is to say, the members of the "queue" may be scattered throughout an area waiting for a server to come to them, e.g., machines waiting to be repaired. The server or group of servers assigned to a given area would comprise the service facility for that area. Queueing theory would still give the average number waiting, the average waiting time, etc., since it is irrelevant whether the calling units wait together in a group or not. The only essential requirement for queueing theory to be applicable is that changes in the number of units waiting for a given service should occur just as though the physical situation described in Fig. 10.2 (or a legitimate counterpart) prevailed.

In this connection, the following analogy to the queueing process may be a useful one. Consider an urn (queueing system) containing balls (calling units). Suppose that a little gremlin (input source) outside the urn occasionally tosses a ball (calling unit) into the urn, and one or more little gremlins (servers) inside the urn occasionally toss a ball (served unit) out of the urn. Queueing theory will answer probabilistic questions concerning the number of callers in the urn and the elapsed time they spend in the urn. Therefore, any situation which can be simulated in this way can also be formulated as a problem in queueing theory.

All of the queueing models discussed in Sections 10.4, 10.5, and 10.6 are of the elementary type described in this section.

10.3.7 Terminology and Notation

Unless otherwise noted, the following standard terminology and notation will be used henceforth.

Line length = number of calling units in the queueing system.
Queue length = number of calling units waiting for service
= line length minus number of units being served.
E_n = the state in which there are n calling units in the queueing system.
$P_n(t)$ = probability that exactly n calling units are in the queueing system at time t.
s = number of servers (parallel service channels) in the queueing system.
λ_n = mean arrival rate (expected number of arrivals per unit time) of new calling units when n units are in the system.
μ_n = mean service rate (expected number of units completing service per unit time) when n units are in the system.

When λ_n is a constant for all n, this constant is denoted by λ. When the mean service rate per busy server is a constant for all $n \geq 1$, this constant is denoted by μ. Under these circumstances, $1/\lambda$ and $1/\mu$ are the expected time between arrivals and the expected service time, respectively. Also, $\rho = \lambda/s\mu$ is the utilization factor for the service facility, i.e., the expected fraction of time the servers are busy.

Certain notation also is required to describe "steady-state" results. When a queueing system has recently begun operation, the state of the system (number of units in the system) will be greatly affected by the initial state and the time that has since elapsed. The system is now said to be in a "transient" condition. However, after sufficient time has elapsed, the state of the system becomes essentially independent of the initial state and of the elapsed time (except under unusual circumstances). The system has now reached a "steady-state" condition. Queueing theory has tended to focus largely on the steady-state condition, partially because the transient case is more difficult analytically. (Some transient results exist, but they generally are beyond the technical scope of this book.) The following notation assumes that the system is in a steady-state condition.

P_n = probability that exactly n calling units are in the queueing system.
L = expected line length.
L_q = expected queue length.
W = expected waiting time in the system (includes service time).
W_q = expected waiting time in the queue (excludes service time).

Finally, the standard mathematical "little o" notation will be used. Thus, $o(\Delta t)$ represents any function of Δt which is negligible compared to Δt when Δt itself is sufficiently small. More precisely, $o(\Delta t)$ represents any function of Δt such that

$$\lim_{\Delta t \to 0} \frac{o(\Delta t)}{\Delta t} = 0 .$$

For example, $(\Delta t)^2$ can be replaced by $o(\Delta t)$ since

$$\lim_{\Delta t \to 0} \frac{(\Delta t)^2}{\Delta t} = \lim_{\Delta t \to 0} (\Delta t) = 0 .$$

This notation will be very useful for summarizing negligible terms which do not enter into the final results.

10.3.8 Relationship between L and W

Assume that λ_n is a constant, λ, for all n. It has then been proven that, in a steady-state queueing process,

$$L = \lambda W$$

under essentially general conditions.[39] Furthermore, the same proof also shows that

$$L_q = \lambda W_q .$$

[39] John D. C. Little, "A Proof for the Queueing Formula: $L = \lambda W$," *Operations Research*, **9**, No. 3, 383–387 (1961).

Now assume that the mean service time is a constant, $1/\mu$, for all $n \geq 1$. It is then obvious that

$$W = W_q + \frac{1}{\mu}.$$

These relationships are extremely important since they enable all four of the fundamental quantities, L, W, L_q, and W_q, to be immediately determined as soon as one of these is found analytically. This is fortunate since some of these quantities often are much easier to find than others when solving a queueing model from basic principles.

10.4 THE BIRTH–DEATH PROCESS

10.4.1 Formulation

Most elementary queueing models assume that the inputs (arriving units) and outputs (leaving units) of the queueing system occur according to a birth–death process. The term "birth" refers to the arrival of a new calling unit into the queueing system, and "death" refers to the departure of a served unit. Broadly speaking, the *birth–death process* considered here is one where births and deaths occur completely at random, and their mean occurrence rates depend only on the current state of the system (number of calling units in the queueing system). More precisely, the assumptions of the birth–death process are the following.

I. Birth Postulate: Given that the system is in state $E_n (n = 0, 1, 2, \cdots)$ at time t, the probability that exactly one birth will occur during the time interval from t to $(t + \Delta t)$ is $[\lambda_n \, \Delta t + o(\Delta t)]$, where λ_n is a positive constant.
II. Death Postulate: Given that the system is in state $E_n (n = 0, 1, 2, \cdots)$ at time t, the probability that exactly one death will occur during the time interval from t to $(t + \Delta t)$ is $[\mu_n \, \Delta t + o(\Delta t)]$, where $\mu_0 = 0$, and μ_n is a positive constant if $n > 0$.
III. Multiple Jump Postulate: Given that the system is in state E_n $(n = 0, 1, 2, \cdots)$ at time t, the probability that the number of births and deaths combined will exceed one during the time interval from t to $(t + \Delta t)$ is $o(\Delta t)$.

Since adding or subtracting negligible terms must still yield a negligible term, the sum or difference of $o(\Delta t)$ terms can be written as a single $o(\Delta t)$ term. Therefore, because of Postulate III, Postulate I will still hold if "exactly one birth" is replaced by "exactly one birth and no deaths." Similarly, Postulate II will still hold if "exactly one death" is replaced by "exactly one death and no births."

One of the following four mutually exclusive events must occur during the time interval from t to $(t + \Delta t)$: (1) exactly one birth and no deaths, (2) exactly one death and no births, (3) number of births and deaths combined exceeds one, (4) no births or deaths. Thus, the sum of the probabilities of these events must equal one. Therefore, the probability of the event (4) is one minus the probabilities for the first three events, as given by the postulates. This yields the following corollary to the three postulates.

Corollary: Given that the system is in state $E_n (n = 0, 1, 2, \cdots)$ at time t, the probability that neither a birth nor a death occurs during the time interval from t to $(t + \Delta t)$ is $[1 - \lambda_n \Delta t - \mu_n \Delta t + o(\Delta t)]$.

10.4.2 Analysis

Most of the information of usual interest in queueing models would be available if one knew both the probability distribution of line length and the probability distribution of waiting time in the system. In the present general context of the birth–death process, it is not possible to solve the second problem directly. However, certain limited results regarding $P_n(t)$ can be obtained. This is done below.

For $n > 0$, the system could reach the state E_n at time $(t + \Delta t)$ from its state at time t in one of the four mutually exclusive ways described in the following table.

State at t	Events from t to $(t + \Delta t)$	Probability
E_{n-1}	One birth	$P_{n-1}(t)[\lambda_{n-1} \Delta t + o(\Delta t)]$
E_{n+1}	One death	$P_{n+1}(t)[\mu_{n+1} \Delta t + o(\Delta t)]$
?	Multiple events	$o(\Delta t)$
E_n	None	$P_n(t)[1 - \lambda_n \Delta t - \mu_n \Delta t + o(\Delta t)]$

Using these probabilities obtained from the postulates, it follows that

$$P_n(t + \Delta t) = P_{n-1}(t)[\lambda_{n-1} \Delta t + o(\Delta t)] + P_{n+1}(t)[\mu_{n+1} \Delta t + o(\Delta t)] + o(\Delta t) + P_n(t)[1 - \lambda_n \Delta t - \mu_n \Delta t + o(\Delta t)] .$$

Combining $o(\Delta t)$ terms,

$$P_n(t + \Delta t) = P_{n-1}(t)\lambda_{n-1} \Delta t + P_{n+1}(t)\mu_{n+1} \Delta t + P_n(t)[1 - \lambda_n \Delta t - \mu_n \Delta t] + o(\Delta t) .$$

Subtracting $P_n(t)$ from both sides and dividing through by Δt yields

$$\frac{P_n(t + \Delta t) - P_n(t)}{\Delta t} = \lambda_{n-1}P_{n-1}(t) + \mu_{n+1}P_{n+1}(t) - (\lambda_n + \mu_n)P_n(t) + \frac{o(\Delta t)}{\Delta t} .$$

Since the equation holds for all positive values of Δt,

$$\lim_{\Delta t \to 0} \left\{ \frac{P_n(t + \Delta t) - P_n(t)}{\Delta t} \right\} = \lim_{\Delta t \to 0} \left\{ \lambda_{n-1}P_{n-1}(t) + \mu_{n+1}P_{n+1}(t) - (\lambda_n + \mu_n)P_n(t) + \frac{o(\Delta t)}{\Delta t} \right\} .$$

By definition, the left side is the derivative and the last term on the right side equals zero. Therefore,

$$\frac{d\,P_n(t)}{dt} = \lambda_{n-1}P_{n-1}(t) + \mu_{n+1}P_{n+1}(t) - (\lambda_n + \mu_n)P_n(t), \qquad \text{for } n > 0\,.$$

When $n = 0$, set $\lambda_{-1} = 0$ and $\mu_0 = 0$, so that

$$\frac{d\,P_0(t)}{dt} = \mu_1 P_1(t) - \lambda_0 P_0(t)\,.$$

This provides a set ($n = 0, 1, 2, \cdots$) of differential equations which, if they could be solved, would provide the value of $P_n(t)$. Unfortunately, a convenient general solution is not available. The next two sections obtain the solution for certain interesting special cases, after which the steady-state solution is obtained.

10.4.3 A Pure Birth Process

Assume that $\lambda_n = \lambda$ and $\mu_n = 0$ for all $n (n = 0, 1, 2, \cdots)$. Since this implies that deaths never occur, the process becomes a pure birth process with a constant mean arrival rate. The resulting differential equations are

$$\frac{d\,P_0(t)}{dt} = -\lambda P_0(t),$$

$$\frac{d\,P_n(t)}{dt} = \lambda P_{n-1}(t) - \lambda P_n(t), \qquad \text{for } n = 1, 2, \cdots.$$

Assume that the system is in state E_0 at time $t = 0$. It is fairly easy to see (or to derive) that the solution to the $n = 0$ differential equation is

$$P_0(t) = e^{-\lambda t}\,.$$

The general solution is

$$P_n(t) = \frac{(\lambda t)^n e^{-\lambda t}}{n!}, \qquad \text{for } n = 0, 1, 2, \cdots,$$

which is easily verified by substitution. Carefully note that this probability distribution for n is the Poisson distribution with parameter λt. Therefore, both the mean and variance of line length at time t are λt, and the mean arrival rate is λ.

Although this pure birth process is not particularly interesting in its own right, it does provide very valuable information about many other queueing models. It is one component of the over-all queueing process assumed by a very large proportion of queueing models, and it therefore describes the input from the input source for such models. The important conclusion is that, for these cases, births occur according to a Poisson process with parameter λ for all $n (n = 1, 2, \cdots)$. These models are said to assume a "Poisson input."

This Poisson result also leads to an interesting result regarding the probability distribution of elapsed time between consecutive births. This result will now be derived. $P_0(t) = e^{-\lambda t}$ implies that the probability that no births will occur during the time interval from 0 to t is $e^{-\lambda t}$. Thus, the probability that the first birth will occur in this time interval is $[1 - e^{-\lambda t}]$. Let the random variable T be the time of the first birth. It has just been seen that the cumulative distribution function of T is

$$F(t) = P\{T \leq t\} = 1 - e^{-\lambda t}, \qquad \text{for } t \geq 0.$$

Therefore, the probability density function of T is

$$f(t) = \frac{dF(t)}{dt} = \lambda e^{-\lambda t}, \qquad \text{for } t \geq 0.$$

Thus, T has an exponential distribution. A Poisson process has the Markov property of "lack of memory" (described in Chapter 13), so that the process starts "from scratch" again after each birth. Therefore, the result for T also verifies that the probability distribution of time between consecutive births is exponential with parameter λ. Queueing models which use this birth process are therefore said to assume "exponential inter-arrival times." This assumption (including the independence of the inter-arrival times) is completely equivalent to assuming a Poisson input, and these models are frequently described in both ways.

It is worthwhile to point out that the exponential result verifies that the expected time between arrivals (births) is

$$\begin{aligned} E(T) &= \int_0^\infty t\lambda e^{-\lambda t}\, dt \\ &= 1/\lambda. \end{aligned}$$

10.4.4 A Pure Death Process

Assume that $\lambda_n = 0$ for $n = 0, 1, 2, \cdots$, and that $\mu_n = \mu$ for $n = 1, 2, 3, \cdots$. Also assume that the system is in state E_M at time $t = 0$. The first assumption implies that births never occur, so this is a pure death process with a constant mean service rate until the process terminates at state E_0. Thus, this process is equivalent to the pure birth process of the preceding section except that it moves in the opposite direction (line length decreases rather than increases), and it is terminated after M events. It is not surprising, therefore, that the results are very analogous.

In this case, the differential equations reduce to

$$\begin{aligned} \frac{dP_n(t)}{dt} &= \mu P_{n+1}(t) - \mu P_n(t), \qquad \text{for } n = 0, 1, 2, \cdots, M - 1, \\ \frac{dP_M(t)}{dt} &= -\mu P_M(t). \end{aligned}$$

Note that $(M - n)$, and not n, is the number of events (deaths) that have occurred in this process. Proceeding just as in the previous section, the probability that no events have occurred by time t is

$$P_M(t) = e^{-\mu t} .$$

Furthermore, the probability that $(M - n)$ events have occurred, where $(M - n) < M$, is

$$P_n(t) = \frac{(\mu t)^{M-n} e^{-\mu t}}{(M - n)!}, \qquad \text{for } n = 1, 2, \cdots, M .$$

The only remaining possibility is that M events have occurred, so that

$$P_0(t) = 1 - \sum_{n=1}^{M} P_n(t) .$$

Thus, the probability distribution of the number of deaths is a truncated Poisson distribution with parameter μt. Therefore, the mean service (death) rate is μ until the process terminates.

The argument employed in the previous section would now verify that the probability distribution of elapsed time between consecutive deaths is an exponential distribution with parameter μ, given that the system is not empty. Queueing models which use this death process as the output of each server are said to assume "exponential service times" or "exponential holding times."

It is now possible to derive a result useful in finding waiting times. Let the random variable T be the time remaining before the pure death process terminates. The objective is to find $f(t|E_n)$, the probability density function of T given that the system is in state E_n. If the service discipline is first-come-first-served, $f(t|E_n)$ gives the probability distribution of waiting time (including service) for the nth unit in line. This is easily obtained. Since each unit has an exponential service time, T is the sum of n independent and identically distributed random variables, which is known to yield a gamma distribution (see Chapter 3). Thus,

$$f(t|E_n) = \frac{\mu^n t^{n-1} e^{-\mu t}}{(n - 1)!}, \qquad \text{for } t \geq 0 .$$

This distribution is also commonly referred to in queueing theory as the *Erlang distribution*. To determine the probability of excessive delays, one would find

$$P\{T > t|E_n\} = \int_t^\infty f(x|E_n)dx .$$

10.4.5 **Steady-State Solution**

When the queueing system has reached a steady-state condition (assuming that this is possible for the particular queueing model), the state probabilities $\{P_n(t)\}$ become constants independent of time. Thus, the steady-state solution for P_n may be obtained either by solving for $P_n(t)$ in the transient case (which yields a unique solution in this case) and letting $t \to \infty$, or by setting $dP_n(t)/dt = 0$ in the differential equations and solving the resulting equations. Since an elementary general transient solution is not available for the birth–death process, the second approach will be used in this case.

Assume that the parameters of the birth–death process are such that a steady-state solution exists, i.e.,

$$\lim_{t \to \infty} P_n(t) = P_n$$

exists, so that

$$\lim_{t \to \infty} \left\{ \frac{dP_n(t)}{dt} \right\} = 0 .$$

Hence, let $t \to \infty$ in the differential equations of Sec. 10.4.2, which yields

$$\begin{aligned} 0 &= \lambda_{n-1}P_{n-1} + \mu_{n+1}P_{n+1} - (\lambda_n + \mu_n)P_n, && \text{if } n > 0 , \\ 0 &= \mu_1 P_1 - \lambda_0 P_0 \qquad , && \text{if } n = 0 . \end{aligned}$$

The $n = 0$ equation immediately yields

$$P_1 = \frac{\lambda_0}{\mu_1} P_0 .$$

When $n > 0$, each equation yields

$$P_{n+1} = \frac{\lambda_n}{\mu_{n+1}} P_n + \frac{\mu_n P_n - \lambda_{n-1} P_{n-1}}{\mu_{n+1}} .$$

For the moment, consider just the numerator of the second term. When $n > 1$,

$$\begin{aligned} u_n P_n - \lambda_{n-1} P_{n-1} &= \mu_n \left[\frac{\lambda_{n-1}}{\mu_n} P_{n-1} + \frac{\mu_{n-1} P_{n-1} - \lambda_{n-2} P_{n-2}}{\mu_n} \right] - \lambda_{n-1} P_{n-1} \\ &= \mu_{n-1} P_{n-1} - \lambda_{n-2} P_{n-2} . \end{aligned}$$

Repeating this result on successively smaller values of n must finally yield

$$\mu_n P_n - \lambda_{n-1} P_{n-1} = \mu_1 P_1 - \lambda_0 P_0 .$$

From the solution to the $n = 0$ equation,

$$\mu_1 P_1 = \lambda_0 P_0 ,$$

so that

$$\mu_n P_n - \lambda_{n-1} P_{n-1} = 0 .$$

Hence,

$$\begin{aligned} P_n &= \frac{\lambda_{n-1}}{\mu_n} P_{n-1} \\ &= \frac{\lambda_{n-1}}{\mu_n}\left[\frac{\lambda_{n-2}}{\mu_{n-1}} P_{n-2}\right] \\ &= \cdots \\ &= \frac{\lambda_{n-1}\lambda_{n-2}\cdots\lambda_0}{\mu_n\mu_{n-1}\cdots\mu_1} P_0 . \end{aligned}$$

This result may be written more concisely as

$$P_n = \frac{\prod_{i=0}^{n-1} \lambda_i}{\prod_{i=1}^{n} \mu_i} P_0, \qquad \text{for } n = 1, 2, \cdots .$$

The only step remaining is to derive the expression for P_0. This is easily done since

$$\sum_{n=0}^{\infty} P_n = 1 ,$$

so that

$$P_0 = \frac{1}{1 + \sum_{n=1}^{\infty} \frac{\prod_{i=0}^{n-1} \lambda_i}{\prod_{i=1}^{n} \mu_i}} .$$

Given this information,

$$L = \sum_{n=0}^{\infty} nP_n$$

and

$$L_q = \sum_{n=s}^{\infty} (n - s)P_n .$$

These summations have analytic solutions for a number of interesting special cases, as seen in subsequent sections. Otherwise, they can be approximated by summing a finite number of terms on an electronic computer.

10.5 SINGLE-SERVER MODELS (s = 1)

10.5.1 Poisson Input and Exponential Service Times

This model is just a special case of the birth–death process which combines the pure birth process of Sec. 10.4.3 and the pure death process of

Sec. 10.4.4. Thus, $\lambda_n = \lambda$ for $n = 0, 1, 2, \cdots$, and $\mu_n = \mu$ for $n = 1, 2, \cdots$.

Although a transient solution for $P_n(t)$ has been obtained for this case, it is a very complicated one that cannot be computed readily. However, a simple steady-state solution is easily obtained, by directly applying the results given in Sec. 10.4.5. Thus, if $\lambda < \mu$, then

$$P_0 = \frac{1}{1 + \sum_{n=1}^{\infty} \frac{\prod_{i=0}^{n-1} \lambda_i}{\prod_{i=1}^{n} \mu_i}}$$

$$= 1 \Big/ \sum_{n=0}^{\infty} \left(\frac{\lambda}{\mu}\right)^n$$

$$= 1 \Big/ \left[\frac{1}{1 - \lambda/\mu}\right]$$

$$= 1 - \frac{\lambda}{\mu},$$

and, for $n > 0$,

$$P_n = P_0 \frac{\prod_{i=0}^{n-1} \lambda_i}{\prod_{i=1}^{n} \mu_i}$$

$$= P_0 \left(\frac{\lambda}{\mu}\right)^n.$$

Using the utilization factor introduced in Sec. 10.3.7, $\rho = \lambda/\mu$, it follows that

$$P_n = (1 - \rho)\rho^n, \qquad \text{for } n = 0, 1, 2, \cdots.$$

Therefore,

$$L = \sum_{n=0}^{\infty} n(1 - \rho)\rho^n$$

$$= (1 - \rho)\rho \sum_{n=0}^{\infty} \frac{d}{d\rho}(\rho^n)$$

$$= (1 - \rho)\rho \frac{d}{d\rho}\left(\sum_{n=0}^{\infty} \rho^n\right)$$

$$= (1 - \rho)\rho \frac{d}{d\rho}\left(\frac{1}{1 - \rho}\right)$$

$$= \frac{\rho}{1 - \rho} = \frac{\lambda}{\mu - \lambda}.$$

Similarly,

$$L_q = \sum_{n=1}^{\infty} (n - 1)P_n$$
$$= L - 1(1 - P_0)$$
$$= \frac{\lambda^2}{\mu(\mu - \lambda)} .$$

When $\lambda \geq \mu$, so that the arrival rate exceeds the service rate, the above solution "blows up" (since the summation for computing P_0 diverges). For this case, the queue would "explode" and grow without bound.

Assuming again that $\lambda < \mu$, it is now possible to derive the probability distribution of waiting time. Assuming a first-come-first-served service discipline, let the random variable T be the waiting time (including service) of a random arrival. If this random arrival finds that the state of the system had just been E_{n-1}, he would become the nth unit in line, and his waiting time distribution would be as given in Sec. 10.4.4. Since

$$P\{T > t\} = \sum_{n=1}^{\infty} P_n P\{T > t | E_n\} ,$$

and both terms on the right-hand side are known, it is possible to find

$$P\{T > t\} = e^{-\mu(1-\rho)t} .$$

Thus, the probability density function of T is

$$f(t) = \mu(1 - \rho)e^{-\mu(1-\rho)t}, \qquad \text{for } t \geq 0 .$$

Note that this is an exponential distribution with parameter $\mu(1 - \rho)$. Therefore,

$$W = E(T) = \frac{1}{\mu(1 - \rho)} = \frac{1}{\mu - \lambda} ;$$
$$W_q = W - \frac{1}{\mu} = \frac{\lambda}{\mu(\mu - \lambda)} .$$

To illustrate the above results, consider a box office ticket window being manned by a single individual. Customers arrive to purchase tickets according to a Poisson input process with a mean rate of 30 per hour. The time required to serve a customer has an exponential distribution with a mean of 90 seconds. Therefore, using a minute as the unit of time,

$$\lambda = \frac{1}{2} \text{ customers/minute}$$
$$\frac{1}{\mu} = \frac{3}{2} \text{ minutes/customer} ,$$

so the utilization factor (the expected fraction of time the server is busy) is

$$\rho = \frac{\lambda}{\mu} = \frac{3}{4}.$$

Hence,

$$P_n = \frac{1}{4}\left(\frac{3}{4}\right)^n, \qquad \text{for } n = 0, 1, 2, \cdots,$$
$$L = 3, \; L_q = 2\tfrac{1}{4},$$
$$W = 6 \text{ minutes/customer}, \; W_q = 4\tfrac{1}{2} \text{ minutes/customer},$$
$$P\{T > t\} = e^{-\frac{1}{6}t}.$$

10.5.2 **Poisson Input and Arbitrary Service Times**

Assume that arrivals occur according to a Poisson process with parameter λ, as described in Sec. 10.4.3. The service times for the calling units may have any probability distribution. Assume only that the service times for the respective units are independent with some common probability distribution whose mean $1/\mu$ and variance σ^2 are known. Since the "Death Postulate" does not hold for this general case, the analysis presented in Sec. 10.4 cannot be applied here. However, by using more advanced techniques (such as the imbedded Markov chain technique mentioned in Chapter 13), it is still possible to derive certain results for this model. The basic steady-state results when $\rho = \lambda/\mu < 1$ are the following.

$$P_0 = 1 - \rho,$$
$$L_q = \frac{\lambda^2\sigma^2 + \rho^2}{2(1-\rho)},$$
$$L = \rho + L_q,$$
$$W_q = \frac{L_q}{\lambda},$$
$$W = W_q + \frac{1}{\mu}.$$

For any fixed expected service time $1/\mu$, notice that L_q, L, W_q, and W all increase as σ^2 is increased. This is an important result since it indicates that, in addition to his average speed, the consistency of the server also has an important bearing on the performance of the service facility.

When the service–time distribution is exponential, $\sigma^2 = 1/\mu^2$, and the above results will, of course, reduce to the corresponding results in the preceding section.

10.5.3 **Poisson Input and Constant Service Times**

This model is just that special case of the preceding model such that the service time for every calling unit is some fixed constant, so that $\sigma^2 = 0$. Therefore,

$$L_q = \frac{\rho^2}{2(1-\rho)},$$

and so forth for L, W_q, and W.

Notice that L_q and W_q are exactly half as large as for the exponential service time case of Sec. 10.5.1.

10.5.4 **Poisson Input and Erlang Service Times**

Assume that the input is Poisson and that the probability distribution of service times is the Erlang (gamma) distribution. Thus, this is another special case of the model of Sec. 10.5.2.

The probability density function for the Erlang distribution is

$$f(t) = \frac{(\mu k)^k}{(k-1)!} t^{k-1} e^{-k\mu t}, \qquad \text{for } t \geq 0,$$

where μ and k are positive[40] parameters of the distribution. The mean and variance are $1/\mu$ and $1/k\mu^2$, respectively. Thus, k is the parameter which determines the dispersion of the distribution.

The Erlang distribution is a very important distribution in queueing theory for two reasons. One of these was suggested in Sec. 10.4. In particular, suppose that $T_1, T_2, \cdots, T_k$ are k independent random variables with an identical exponential distribution whose mean is $1/k\mu$. Then their sum,

$$T = T_1 + T_2 + \cdots + T_k,$$

has an Erlang distribution with parameters μ and k. The discussion of the pure death process in Sec. 10.4.4 revealed that certain natural assumptions about the time required to perform a particular service lead to an exponential distribution. However, the total service required by a calling unit may involve the server performing not just one specific task but a sequence of k tasks. If the respective tasks have an identical exponential distribution for their duration, the total service time would have an Erlang distribution. This would be the case, for example, if the server must perform the same exponential task k times for each calling unit.

The Erlang distribution is very useful also because it is a large (two-parameter) family of distributions permitting only non-negative values. Hence, empirical service–time distributions can usually be reasonably approximated by an Erlang distribution. In fact, both the exponential distribution and the degenerate (constant) distribution are special cases of the Erlang distribution with $k = 1$ and $k = \infty$, respectively. Intermediate values of k provide intermediate distributions with mean $= 1/\mu$, mode $= (k-1)/\mu k$, and variance $= 1/k\mu^2$, as suggested by Fig. 10.3.

Results for this model may be derived by using a modified birth–death

[40] An integer is usually selected for the value of k. However, this is not necessary; merely replace $(k-1)!$ by the special gamma function, $\Gamma(k)$.

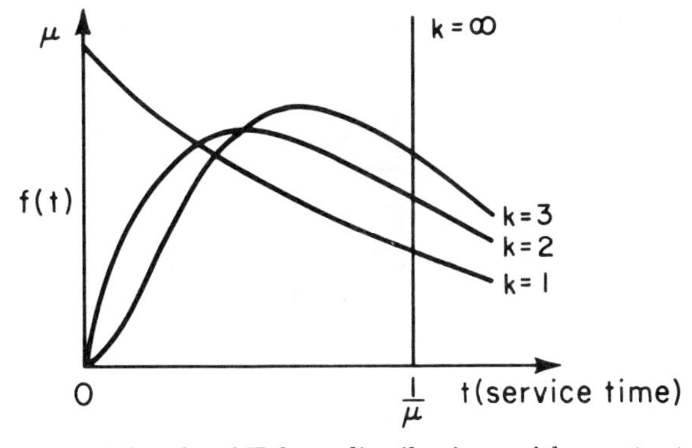

FIGURE 10.3. A family of Erlang distributions with constant mean $1/\mu$.

process where the state of the system is the number of remaining service phases (k per unit) to finish the units presently in the system. However, some of the basic steady-state results may be obtained immediately by using the fact that this model is a special case of the model of Sec. 10.5.2, where $\sigma^2 = 1/k\mu^2$. Hence,

$$L_q = \frac{\lambda^2 \dfrac{1}{k\mu^2} + \rho^2}{2(1-\rho)} = \frac{1+k}{2k} \frac{\lambda^2}{\mu(\mu-\lambda)};$$

$$W_q = \frac{1+k}{2k} \frac{\lambda}{\mu(\mu-\lambda)};$$

$$W = W_q + \frac{1}{\mu};$$

$$L = \lambda W.$$

10.5.5 Poisson Input and Exponential Service Times with a Finite Queue

This is just the model of Sec. 10.5.1, except that the line length is not permitted to exceed some specified number (denoted by M). Any calling units that arrive while the queue is "full" must leave the system permanently without being served. Thus, this model may be treated as a special case of the birth–death process where

$$\lambda_n = \begin{cases} \lambda, & \text{if } n = 0, 1, 2, \cdots, M-1 \\ 0, & \text{if } n \geq M, \end{cases}$$

and $\mu_n = \mu$ for $n = 1, 2, \cdots$.

The physical interpretation for this model may be either that there is only room for M units in the system (as in a parking lot), or that the arriving customers will "take their business elsewhere" if the waiting line is too long ($\geq M$).

By referring to Sec. 10.4.5, the steady-state results are obtained as follows.

$$P_0 = 1 \Big/ \sum_{n=0}^{M} \left(\frac{\lambda}{\mu}\right)^n$$

$$= 1 \Big/ \left[\frac{1 - \left(\frac{\lambda}{\mu}\right)^{M+1}}{1 - \frac{\lambda}{\mu}}\right]$$

$$= \frac{1 - \rho}{1 - \rho^{M+1}},$$

so that

$$P_n = \left(\frac{1 - \rho}{1 - \rho^{M+1}}\right) \rho^n, \qquad \text{for } n = 0, 1, 2, \cdots M .$$

Hence,

$$L = \sum_{n=0}^{M} nP_n$$

$$= \left(\frac{1 - \rho}{1 - \rho^{M+1}}\right) \rho \sum_{n=0}^{M} \frac{d}{d\rho} (\rho^n)$$

$$= \left(\frac{1 - \rho}{1 - \rho^{M+1}}\right) \rho \frac{d}{d\rho} \left(\sum_{n=0}^{M} \rho^n\right)$$

$$= \left(\frac{1 - \rho}{1 - \rho^{M+1}}\right) \rho \frac{d}{d\rho} \left(\frac{1 - \rho^{M+1}}{1 - \rho}\right)$$

$$= \rho \frac{-(M + 1)\rho^M + M\rho^{M+1} + 1}{(1 - \rho^{M+1})(1 - \rho)}$$

$$= \frac{\rho}{1 - \rho} - \frac{(M + 1)\rho^{M+1}}{1 - \rho^{M+1}} .$$

As usual (when $s = 1$),

$$L_q = L - (1 - P_0) .$$

Notice that the above results do not require that $\lambda < \mu$.

The reader may verify that the second term in the final expression for L converges to zero as $M \to \infty$, so that the above results converge to the results of Sec. 10.5.1.

10.5.6 **A Limited Source Model**

Assume that the input source is limited, i.e., the size of the calling population is finite. Let M denote the number of units in the population.

One common physical interpretation for this model is that of machine servicing, where one repairman (or operator) is assigned the responsibility of maintaining (or operating) a certain group of M machines. They are in the "waiting line" when they are down waiting for service, whereas they are outside the queueing system while they are running.

Assume that each calling unit has the following properties. If the unit is outside the queueing system at time t, the probability that it will have entered the system by time $(t + \Delta t)$ is $[\lambda \Delta t + o(\Delta t)]$. If the unit is being serviced by the server at time t, the probability that it will have completed service by time $(t + \Delta t)$ is $[\mu \Delta t + o(\Delta t)]$.

As Secs. 10.4.3 and 10.4.4 indicate, the above assumptions imply that both the time spent outside the system between services and the service times have an exponential distribution with means $(1/\lambda)$ and $(1/\mu)$, respectively. Furthermore, when all of the units are considered simultaneously, the Multiple Jump Postulate is satisfied since the probability of more than one event during the time interval from t to $(t + \Delta t)$ is of the order of magnitude of $(\Delta t)^2$, which is a $o(\Delta t)$ term. Hence, if the system is in state E_n at time t, so that $(M - n)$ units are outside the system, the probability that exactly one new unit will enter the system during the time interval from t to $(t + \Delta t)$ is $[(M - n)\lambda \Delta t + o(\Delta t)]$. Therefore, this model is actually a special case of the birth–death process where

$$\lambda_n = \begin{cases} (M - n)\lambda, & \text{if } n = 0, 1, 2, \cdots, M \\ 0, & \text{if } n \geq M, \end{cases}$$

and $\mu_n = \mu$ for $n = 1, 2, \cdots$. The consequent steady-state results are given below.

$$P_0 = 1 \bigg/ \sum_{n=0}^{M} \left[\frac{M!}{(M - n)!} \left(\frac{\lambda}{\mu}\right)^n \right];$$

$$P_n = \frac{M!}{(M - n)!} \left(\frac{\lambda}{\mu}\right)^n P_0, \qquad \text{if } n = 1, 2, \cdots M;$$

$$L_q = \sum_{n=1}^{M} (n - 1)P_n,$$

which can be made to reduce to

$$L_q = M - \frac{\lambda + \mu}{\lambda}(1 - P_0);$$

$$L = \sum_{n=0}^{M} nP_n = L_q + (1 - P_0)$$

$$= M - \frac{\mu}{\lambda}(1 - P_0).$$

10.5.7 A Model with State-Dependent Service Rate and/or Arrival Rate

All of the models thus far have assumed that the mean service rate is always a constant, regardless of how many units are in the queue. Unfortunately, this often is not the case in real world situations. When there is a large backlog of work (i.e., a long queue), it is quite likely that the server will tend to work faster than when the backlog is small or non-existent. This increase in the service rate may result merely because the server increases his effort when he is under the pressure of a long queue. However, it may also result in part because the quality of the service is compromised or because assistance is obtained on certain service phases.

Given that the mean service rate does increase as the queue size is increased, one would want to develop a theoretical model which seems to describe the pattern by which it increases. This model not only should be a reasonable approximation of the actual pattern, but it also should be simple enough to be practical for implementation. Such a model has recently been proposed.[41] It is summarized below.

Let

$$\mu_n = n^c \mu_1, \qquad \text{for } n = 0, 1, 2, \cdots,$$

where:

n = the number of units in the system.

μ_n = the mean service rate when there are n units in the system.

$1/\mu_1$ = the expected "normal" service time—the expected time to service a unit when that unit is the only one in the system.

c = the "pressure coefficient"—a constant that indicates the degree to which the service rate of the system is affected by the system state.

Thus, for example, selecting $c = 1$ hypothesizes that the mean service rate is directly proportional to the line length n; $c = 1/2$ implies that the mean service rate is proportional to the square root of n, etc. The preceding queueing models in Sec. 10.5 have implicitly assumed that $c = 0$.

Now assume additionally that the queueing system has a Poisson input with $\lambda_n = \lambda$ (for $n = 0, 1, 2, \cdots$) and exponential service times with μ_n as given above. This is now a special case of the birth–death process, so that the steady-state results are easily obtained.

$$P_n = \frac{\left(\frac{\lambda}{\mu_1}\right)^n}{(n!)^c} P_0, \qquad \text{for } n = 0, 1, 2, \cdots,$$ [42]

[41] Richard W. Conway and William L. Maxwell, "A Queueing Model with State Dependent Service Rate," *Journal of Industrial Engineering*, **12,** 132–136 (1961).

[42] When $n = 0$, the usual convention that $0! = 1$ is being used.

where

$$P_0 = 1 \Bigg/ \sum_{n=0}^{\infty} \frac{\left(\frac{\lambda}{\mu_1}\right)^n}{(n!)^c}.$$

$$L = \sum_{n=0}^{\infty} nP_n; \qquad L_q = L - (1 - P_0);$$

$$W = \frac{L}{\lambda}; \qquad W_q = \frac{L_q}{\lambda}.$$

Analytical expressions for the summations involving P_0 and L are not available in general. However, P_0 and L have been closely approximated[43] for various values of c and λ/μ_1 by summing a finite number of terms on an electronic computer.

Rather than increasing the service rate, a queueing system may react to a long queue by decreasing the arrival rate instead. This may be done, for example, by diverting some of the units requiring service to another service facility. A model, similar to the preceding one, for describing mean arrival rates for this case is the following. Let

$$\lambda_n = (n + 1)^{-b}\lambda_0, \qquad \text{for } n = 0, 1, 2, \cdots,$$

where b is a constant whose interpretation is analogous to that for c. The steady-state results (P_n, L_q, and L) for the birth–death process with this λ_n, and with $\mu_n = \mu$ for $n = 1, 2, \cdots$, are identical to those obtained for the preceding model when $c = b$.

A more general model which combines the two preceding ones can also be used when both the mean arrival rate and the mean service rate are state-dependent. Thus, let

$$\mu_n = n^a\mu_1, \qquad \text{for } n = 0, 1, 2, \cdots,$$
$$\lambda_n = (n + 1)^{-b}\lambda_0, \qquad \text{for } n = 0, 1, 2, \cdots.$$

The steady-state results (P_n, L_q, and L) for the birth–death process with these parameters are identical to those given earlier (where $\lambda_n = \lambda$) when $c = a + b$.

10.6 MULTIPLE-SERVER MODELS (s > 1)

10.6.1 Poisson Input and Exponential Service Times

This model assumes that arrivals occur according to a Poisson input with parameter λ and that the service time for each unit has an exponential distribution with mean $(1/\mu)$. Thus, this service time distribution is the

[43] Conway and Maxwell, *op. cit.*

same, regardless of which one of the s servers performs the service for the unit. Hence, the model is the direct multiple-server extension of the model of Sec. 10.5.1.

The mean service rate for the over-all queueing system (μ_n), i.e., the mean rate at which served units leave the system, depends on the state of the system E_n. The mean service rate per busy server is μ. Therefore, the over-all service rate must be $\mu_n = n\mu$, provided that $n \leq s$. However, if $n \geq s$, so that all of the servers are busy, then $\mu_n = s\mu$. Hence, this model is a special case of the birth–death process with $\lambda_n = \lambda$ (for $n = 0, 1, 2, \cdots$) and

$$\mu_n = \begin{cases} n\mu, & \text{if } 0 \leq n \leq s \\ s\mu, & \text{if } n \geq s\,. \end{cases}$$

The consequent steady-state results follow.

If $\lambda < s\mu$, so that the mean arrival rate is less than the maximum mean service rate, then

$$P_0 = 1 \Bigg/ \left[\sum_{n=0}^{s-1} \frac{\left(\frac{\lambda}{\mu}\right)^n}{n!} + \frac{\left(\frac{\lambda}{\mu}\right)^s}{s!} \sum_{n=s}^{\infty} \left(\frac{\lambda}{s\mu}\right)^{n-s} \right]$$

$$= 1 \Bigg/ \left[\sum_{n=0}^{s-1} \frac{\left(\frac{\lambda}{\mu}\right)^n}{n!} + \frac{\left(\frac{\lambda}{\mu}\right)^s}{s!} \frac{1}{1 - \frac{\lambda}{s\mu}} \right],$$

and

$$P_n = \begin{cases} \dfrac{\left(\frac{\lambda}{\mu}\right)^n}{n!} P_0, & \text{if } 0 \leq n \leq s \\[2ex] \dfrac{\left(\frac{\lambda}{\mu}\right)^n}{s!s^{n-s}} P_0, & \text{if } n \geq s\,. \end{cases}$$

Using the notation, $\rho = \lambda/\mu s$,

$$L_q = \sum_{n=s}^{\infty} (n - s)\, P_n$$

$$= \sum_{j=0}^{\infty} jP_{s+j}$$

$$= \sum_{j=0}^{\infty} j \frac{\left(\frac{\lambda}{\mu}\right)^s}{s!} \rho^j P_0$$

$$= P_0 \frac{\left(\frac{\lambda}{\mu}\right)^s}{s!} \rho \sum_{j=0}^{\infty} \frac{d}{d\rho} (\rho^j)$$

$$= P_0 \frac{\left(\frac{\lambda}{\mu}\right)^s}{s!} \rho \frac{d}{d\rho} \left(\sum_{j=0}^{\infty} \rho^j \right)$$

$$= P_0 \frac{\left(\frac{\lambda}{\mu}\right)^s}{s!} \rho \frac{d}{d\rho} \left(\frac{1}{1 - \rho} \right)$$

$$= \frac{P_0 \left(\frac{\lambda}{\mu}\right)^s \rho}{s!(1 - \rho)^2}.$$

$$W_q = \frac{L_q}{\lambda};$$

$$W = W_q + \frac{1}{\mu};$$

$$L = \lambda \left(W_q + \frac{1}{\mu} \right) = L_q + \frac{\lambda}{\mu}.$$

Since the computations required above are somewhat uninviting, it is well to know that graphs of μW_q versus (λ/μ) are available[44] for various values of s.

It is also possible to obtain the probability distribution of waiting times, assuming a first-come-first-served service discipline. The standard notation, $P(> t)$, will be used to denote the probability that the elapsed time a random arrival has to wait in the queue (before being served) is longer than t. It is evident that, since the arrival must wait in the queue if there are s or more units in the system,

$$P(> 0) = \sum_{n=s}^{\infty} P_n$$

$$= P_0 \frac{\left(\frac{\lambda}{\mu}\right)^s}{s!} \sum_{j=0}^{\infty} \rho^j$$

$$= \frac{P_0 \left(\frac{\lambda}{\mu}\right)^s}{s!(1 - \rho)}.$$

[44] T. M. Manglesdorf, "Waiting Line Theory Applied to Manufacturing Problems," S. M. Thesis, M. I. T., 1955. Reprinted in *Analyses of Industrial Operations*, edited by E. H. Bowman and R. B. Fetter, Richard D. Irwin, Homewood, Ill., 1959.

By using a method similar to that outlined in Sec. 10.5.1, it is possible to obtain

$$P(>t) = e^{-s\mu t(1-\rho)}\,P(>0)\,.$$

To include the effect of service time, let the random variable T be the waiting time including service of a random arrival.

$$P\{T > t\} = e^{-\mu t}\left[1 + \frac{P_0\left(\frac{\lambda}{\mu}\right)^s}{s!(1-\rho)}\left(\frac{1 - e^{-\mu t(s-1-\lambda/\mu)}}{s - 1 - \lambda/\mu}\right)\right].$$

If $\lambda \geq s\mu$, so that the mean arrival rate exceeds the mean service rate, the queue grows without bound.

10.6.2 Poisson Input and Non-Exponential Service Times

Multiple-server models are inherently more difficult to analyze than single-server models. Therefore, when $s > 1$, it is almost impossible to obtain usable results, except when the service-time distribution is exponential so that the birth–death process is applicable. Certain limited results have been obtained for the case of constant service times, but the equations involved are too complicated for routine computation. However, some graphs giving computational results are available[45] for this case.

10.6.3 Poisson Input and Exponential Service Times with a Finite Queue

This model is the direct multiple-server extension of the model of Sec. 10.5.5. Thus, it is equivalent to the model of Sec. 10.6.1, except that the line length is not permitted to exceed some specified number M. It is therefore a special case of the birth–death process, where

$$\lambda_n = \begin{cases} \lambda, & \text{if } 0 \leq n < M \\ 0, & \text{if } n \geq M\,, \end{cases}$$

$$\mu_n = \begin{cases} n\mu, & \text{if } 0 \leq n \leq s \\ s\mu, & \text{if } n \geq s\,. \end{cases}$$

Hence,

$$P_n = \begin{cases} \dfrac{\left(\frac{\lambda}{\mu}\right)^n}{n!}\,P_0, & \text{if } n \leq \min\{s, M\} \\[2ex] \dfrac{\left(\frac{\lambda}{\mu}\right)^n}{s!s^{n-s}}\,P_0, & \text{if } s \leq n \leq M \\[2ex] 0, & \text{if } n > M\,, \end{cases}$$

[45] John R. Shelton, "Solution Methods for Waiting Line Problems," *Journal of Industrial Engineering*, **11**, 293–303 (1960).

where

$$P_0 = 1 \Bigg/ \left[\sum_{n=0}^{\min\{s,M\}} \frac{\left(\frac{\lambda}{\mu}\right)^n}{n!} + \frac{\left(\frac{\lambda}{\mu}\right)^s}{s!} \sum_{n=s+1}^{M} \left(\frac{\lambda}{s\mu}\right)^{n-s} \right].$$

If $M \le s$, it trivially follows that $L_q = 0$ and

$$L = \sum_{n=0}^{M} nP_n .$$

If $M > s$, the method used in Sec. 10.6.1 yields

$$L_q = \frac{P_0 \left(\frac{\lambda}{\mu}\right)^s \rho}{s!(1-\rho)^2} \left[1 - \rho^{M-s} - (M-s)\rho^{M-s}(1-\rho)\right],$$

and it is then easy to show (see Problem 14) that

$$L = \sum_{n=0}^{s-1} nP_n + L_q + s\left(1 - \sum_{n=0}^{s-1} P_n\right).$$

10.6.4 A Limited Source Model

Consider the direct multiple-server extension ($1 < s \le M$) of the model of Sec. 10.5.6. The resulting model is the special case of the birth–death process such that

$$\lambda_n = \begin{cases} (M-n)\lambda, & \text{if } n \le M \\ 0, & \text{if } n \ge M \end{cases}$$

and

$$\mu_n = \begin{cases} n\mu, & \text{if } 0 \le n \le s \\ s\mu, & \text{if } n \ge s . \end{cases}$$

Hence,

$$P_n = \begin{cases} P_0 \dfrac{M!}{(M-n)!n!} \left(\dfrac{\lambda}{\mu}\right)^n, & \text{if } 0 \le n \le s \\ P_0 \dfrac{M!}{(M-n)!s!s^{n-s}} \left(\dfrac{\lambda}{\mu}\right)^n, & \text{if } s \le n \le M \\ 0, & \text{if } n > M , \end{cases}$$

where

$$P_0 = 1 \Bigg/ \left[\sum_{n=0}^{s-1} \frac{M!}{(M-n)!n!} \left(\frac{\lambda}{\mu}\right)^n + \sum_{n=s}^{M} \frac{M!}{(M-n)!s!s^{n-s}} \left(\frac{\lambda}{\mu}\right)^n \right].$$

Finally,

$$L_q = \sum_{n=s}^{M} (n-s)P_n ;$$

$$L = \sum_{n=0}^{s-1} nP_n + L_q + s\left(1 - \sum_{n=0}^{s-1} P_n\right).$$

Extensive tables of computational results are now available[46] for this model (including the special case, $s = 1$, which was discussed in Sec. 10.5.6).

10.6.5 A Model with State-Dependent Service Rate and/or Arrival Rate

As discussed in Sec. 10.5.7, it is not always realistic to make the usual assumption that the mean service rate per busy server is a constant independent of the queue size. Therefore, it would be very desirable to have a model which seems to provide a reasonable representation of how this service rate might actually vary with queue size. Such a model was recently proposed[47] as a direct multiple-server generalization of the single-server model of Sec. 10.5.7. Recall that the mean service rate in the single-server model was obtained by multiplying the "normal" (unpressured) mean service rate by n^c, where n is the number of calling units in the system and c is the "pressure coefficient." When all of the s servers are busy and therefore under pressure, the multiple-server generalization will multiply the normal mean service rate by $(n/s)^c$, since n/s is the number of calling units in the system per server. In other words, the model hypothesizes that

$$\mu_n = \begin{cases} n\mu_1, & \text{if } n \leq s\,. \\ \left(\dfrac{n}{s}\right)^c s\mu_1, & \text{if } n \geq s\,. \end{cases}$$

When it is additionally assumed that the queueing system has a Poisson input with $\lambda_n = \lambda$ (for $n = 0, 1, 2, \cdots$) and exponential service times with μ_n as given above, the model becomes another special case of the birth–death process. The resulting steady-state results are shown below.

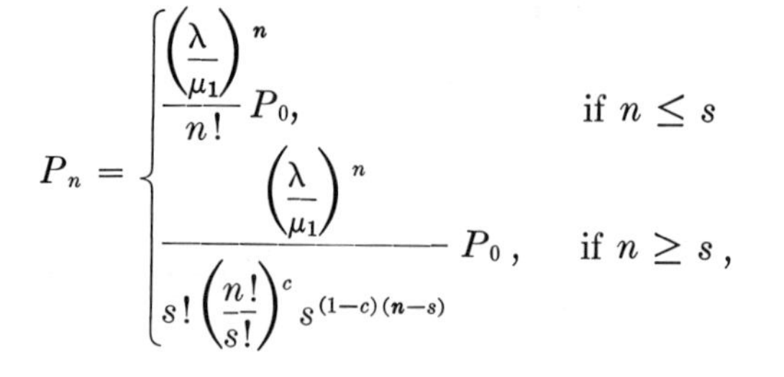

$$P_n = \begin{cases} \dfrac{\left(\dfrac{\lambda}{\mu_1}\right)^n}{n!} P_0, & \text{if } n \leq s \\ \dfrac{\left(\dfrac{\lambda}{\mu_1}\right)^n}{s!\left(\dfrac{n!}{s!}\right)^c s^{(1-c)(n-s)}} P_0\,, & \text{if } n \geq s\,, \end{cases}$$

[46] L. G. Peck and R. N. Hazelwood, *Finite Queueing Tables*, Wiley, New York, 1958.

[47] F. S. Hillier, R. W. Conway, and W. L. Maxwell, "A Multiple Server Queueing Model with State Dependent Service Rate," *Journal of Industrial Engineering*, **15,** 153–157 (1964).

where

$$P_0 = 1 \Bigg/ \left[\sum_{n=0}^{s-1} \frac{\left(\frac{\lambda}{\mu_1}\right)^n}{n!} + \left(\frac{s^s}{s!}\right)^{1-c} \sum_{n=s}^{\infty} \frac{\left(\frac{\lambda}{\mu_1 s^{1-c}}\right)^n}{(n!)^c} \right].$$

Therefore,

$$L_q = \sum_{n=s}^{\infty} (n - s)P_n = P_0 \left(\frac{s^s}{s!}\right)^{1-c} \sum_{n=s}^{\infty} \frac{\left(\frac{\lambda}{\mu_1 s^{1-c}}\right)^n}{(n!)^c};$$

$$L = \sum_{n=0}^{s-1} n\mathrm{P}_n + L_q + s\left(1 - \sum_{n=0}^{s-1} P_n\right);$$

$$W_q = \frac{L_q}{\lambda}; \qquad W = \frac{L}{\lambda}.$$

Computational results for P_0, L_q, and L have been tabulated[48] for various values of c, (λ/μ_1), and s.

One can also generalize this model to permit the mean arrival rate to react to the line length in a similar fashion.
Thus, let

$$\mu_n = \begin{cases} n\mu_1, & \text{if } n \leq s \\ \left(\frac{n}{s}\right)^a s\mu_1, & \text{if } n \geq s\,, \end{cases}$$

$$\lambda_n = \begin{cases} \lambda_1, & \text{if } n \leq s - 1 \\ \left(\frac{s}{n+1}\right)^b \lambda_1, & \text{if } n \geq s - 1\,. \end{cases}$$

The birth–death process with these parameters yields the same P_n, L_q, and L as given above when $c = a + b$.

10.7 PRIORITY-DISCIPLINE MODELS

Priority-discipline models are those where the service discipline is based on a priority system. Thus, the order in which members of the queue are selected for service is on the basis of their assigned priorities.

Many "real world" situations fit these priority-discipline models much more closely than other available models. Rush jobs are taken ahead of other jobs, and important customers may be given precedence over others.

[48] *Ibid.*

Therefore, the use of priority-discipline models would often provide a very welcome refinement over the more usual queueing models, since they would distinguish between waiting times, etc., for the different types of calling units.

Unfortunately, the inclusion of priorities has made the mathematical analysis sufficiently complicated that only limited results are available. Almost all of these results are for the single-server case. However, usable results are available for one multiple-server model. This model assumes that there are N priority classes (class 1 has the highest priority and class N the lowest), and that the members of the highest priority class represented in the queue would be selected on a first-come-first-served basis. Service is nonpreemptive, i.e., units being served cannot be ejected back into the queue if a higher priority unit enters the queueing system. A Poisson input process and exponential service times are assumed for each priority class. The model also makes the somewhat restrictive assumption that the mean service time is the same for all priority classes. However, it does permit the mean arrival rate to differ among the priority classes.

Under these assumptions, it has been determined that W_k, the steady-state expected waiting time (including service) for a member of priority class k, is

$$W_k = \frac{1}{A \cdot B_{k-1} \cdot B_k} + \frac{1}{\mu}, \qquad \text{for } k = 1, 2, \cdots, N,$$

where

$$A = s!\left(\frac{s\mu - \lambda}{\rho^s}\right) \sum_{j=0}^{s-1} \frac{\rho^j}{j!} + s\mu,$$

$$B_0 = 1,$$

$$B_k = 1 - \frac{\sum_{i=1}^{k} \lambda_i}{s\mu}, \qquad \text{for } k = 1, 2, \cdots, N,$$

and where

s = number of servers,

μ = mean service rate per busy server,

λ_i = mean arrival rate for priority class i, for $i = 1, 2, \cdots, N$,

$$\lambda = \sum_{i=1}^{N} \lambda_i,$$

$$\rho = \frac{\lambda}{\mu},$$

when

$$\sum_{i=1}^{k} \lambda_i < \mu .$$

It is also known that L_k, the steady-state expected number of members of priority class k in the queueing system (including those being served), is

$$L_k = \lambda_k W_k, \qquad \text{for } k = 1, 2, \cdots, N .$$

To determine the expected waiting time *excluding* service for priority class k, merely subtract $1/\mu$ from W_k; the corresponding expected queue length would again be obtained by multiplying by λ_k. For the special case where $s = 1$, the expression for A reduces to $A = \mu^2/\lambda$.

Now consider the case where service is preemptive, so that the lowest priority unit being served is ejected back into the queue whenever a higher priority unit enters the queueing system. A server is thereby freed to begin servicing the new arrival immediately. If the other assumptions of the above model are retained, it has been found that, when $s = 1$,

$$W_k = \frac{1/\mu}{B_{k-1} \cdot B_k}, \qquad \text{for } k = 1, 2, \cdots, N ,$$

for the preemptive service case. Because of the Markov property of the exponential distribution, this result holds whether service for the preempted item can resume at the point of interruption or must start at the beginning again. As usual,

$$L_k = \lambda_k W_k, \qquad \text{for } k = 1, 2, \cdots, N .$$

The corresponding results excluding service time are obtained just as for the preceding model.

Some results are also available for a few other single-server priority-discipline models involving other service-time distributions and/or unequal expected service times.

Work has recently begun on queueing models with a service discipline based on "dynamic" priorities, where the priority of a member of the queue depends in part upon how long this member has already waited.[49]

10.8 NETWORK MODELS

It would sometimes be of practical interest to have information available about networks of service facilities, where calling units must receive service at some or all of these facilities. For example, orders being processed through a job shop must be routed through a sequence of machine groups

[49] For example, see J. R. Jackson, "Waiting Time Distributions for Queues with Dynamic Priorities," *Naval Research Logistics Quarterly*, **9**, No. 1, 31–36 (1962).

(service facilities). It is therefore necessary to study the entire network in order to obtain such information as expected total waiting time, expected number of units in the entire system, etc.

Analytical results on queueing networks have been quite limited, due to the difficulty of the problem. Essentially all of the work has been confined to the case of a Poisson input process and exponential service times. Most of the results that have been obtained have necessarily been quite involved and unsuitable for general routine use. A summary of these results is available elsewhere[50] for the interested reader.

However, one simple basic result has been obtained that is of such fundamental importance that it warrants special attention here. This result may be stated as follows.

Theorem 10.1: Assume that a service facility with s servers has a Poisson input with parameter λ and the same exponential service-time distribution for each server, where $s\mu > \lambda$. Then the steady-state *output* of this service facility is also a Poisson process with parameter λ.[51]

Notice that Theorem 10.1 makes no assumption about the type of service discipline used. Therefore, if the model for the service facilities corresponds to any of the basic models discussed in Secs. 10.5.1, 10.6.1, and 10.7, the served units will leave the service facility according to a Poisson distribution. Hence, if these units must then go to another service facility for further service, this second facility will have a Poisson input. Thus, suppose that calling units must all receive service at a series of service facilities in a fixed sequence. Assume further that the units arrive at the first facility according to a Poisson process with parameter λ, and that each facility has the same exponential service-time distribution for its servers. It then follows from Theorem 10.1 that (under steady-state conditions) each service facility has a Poisson input with parameter λ. Therefore, the elementary models of Secs. 10.5.1, 10.6.1, or 10.7 can be used to analyze each service facility independently of the others. (Theorem 10.1 can even be used to draw essentially the same conclusion when the calling units pass through a network of service facilities in different sequences according to transition probabilities.[52]) The expected total waiting time and the expected number of units in the entire system can then be obtained by summing the corresponding quantities obtained at the respective facilities.

Unfortunately, Theorem 10.1 and its implications do not hold for the case of finite queues discussed in Secs. 10.5.5 and 10.6.3. This case is actually quite important in practice, since there is often a definite limitation on the

[50] Thomas L. Saaty, *Elements of Queueing Theory with Applications*, McGraw-Hill, New York, 1961, Chapter 12.

[51] For a proof see Saaty, *op. cit.*

[52] See James R. Jackson, "Jobshop-Like Queueing Systems," *Management Science*, **10,** No. 1, 131–142 (1963).

line length in front of service facilities in networks. The facilities must be analyzed jointly in this case, and only limited results have been obtained.

10.9 SIMULATION

Although considerable progress has been made in developing analytical queueing results, there still remain many potentially useful queueing models which are extremely difficult or impossible to analyze mathematically. It appears that simulation, which is discussed in Chapter 14, offers the best hope of eventually obtaining usable results for such models. Simulation has already been used many times to analyze unique queueing-type problems as they have arisen in practice.

SELECTED REFERENCES

1. Cox, D. R., and Smith, Walter L., *Queues*, Wiley, New York, 1961.
2. Morse, Philip M., *Queues, Inventories, and Maintenance*, Wiley, New York, 1958.
3. Saaty, Thomas L., *Elements of Queueing Theory*, McGraw-Hill, New York, 1961.
4. Saaty, Thomas L., *Mathematical Methods of Operations Research*, McGraw-Hill, New York, 1959, chap. 11.
5. Syski, R., *Introduction to Congestion Theory in Telephone Systems*, Oliver and Boyd, Edinburgh and London, 1960, chaps. 1, 3, 4, 6, and 9.

PROBLEMS[53]

1. Consider a typical barber shop. Demonstrate that it is a queueing system by describing its components.

2. Identify the calling units in the queue, and the servers in the queueing system representation of each of the following situations:

(a) the check-out stand in a grocery store
(b) a hospital emergency room
(c) the toll booth for a bridge
(d) an electronic computer center
(e) a shipping dock
(f) a group of semi-automatic machines assigned to one operator
(g) the materials handling equipment in a factory area
(h) a plumbing shop
(i) a job shop producing to custom orders
(j) a secretarial typing pool.

[53] Also see the end of Chapter 11 for problems involving the application of queueing theory.

3. The jobs to be performed on a particular machine arrive according to a Poisson input process with a mean rate of one per hour. Suppose that the machine breaks down and will require two hours to be repaired. What is the probability that the number of new jobs that will arrive during this time is (a) zero, (b) two, (c) five or more?

4. Consider a single-server queueing system with a Poisson input and exponential service times. Suppose that the expected service time is exactly one minute. Compare the expected line length L for the cases where the mean arrival rate is 0.50, 0.90, and 0.99 units per minute, respectively. Do the same for L_q, W, W_q, and $P\{T > 5\}$.

5. It is necessary to determine how much in-process storage space to allocate to a particular work center in a new factory. Jobs would arrive at this work center according to a Poisson process with a mean rate of two per hour, and the time required to perform the necessary work has an exponential distribution with a mean of 0.4 hours. If each job would require one square foot of floor space while in in-process storage at the work center, how much space must be provided in order to accommodate all waiting jobs (a) 50%, (b) 90%, (c) 99% of the time? (Hint: The sum of a geometric series is

$$\sum_{i=0}^{n} x^i = \frac{1 - x^{n+1}}{1 - x},$$

if $0 < x < 1$.)

6. Consider a single-server queueing system with a Poisson input with known mean arrival rate λ. Suppose that the service-time distribution is unknown, but that the expected service time $1/\mu$ is known.

(a) Compare the expected waiting time in the queue if the service-time distribution were (i) exponential, (ii) constant, (iii) Erlang with the amount of variation (i.e., the standard deviation) halfway between the constant and exponential cases.

(b) What is the effect on the expected waiting time in the queue, and expected queue length, if both λ and μ are doubled and the scale of the service-time distribution is changed accordingly.

7. Consider a general single-server queueing system such that both the service-time distribution and the distribution of time between consecutive arrivals are arbitrary (although the same for all calling units). Use only basic definitions and the relationships given in Sec. 10.3.8 in order to verify the following general relationships.

(a) $L = L_q + (1 - P_0)$.
(b) $L = L_q + \rho$.
(c) $P_0 = 1 - \rho$.

8. Plans are being made for opening a small car wash operation, and the decision must be made as to how much space to provide for waiting cars. It is estimated that customers would arrive randomly (i.e., a Poisson input process) with a mean rate of one every five minutes, unless the waiting area is full, in which case the customer would take his car elsewhere. The time that can be attributed to washing one car has an exponential distribution with a mean of four minutes. Compare the expected fraction of potential customers that would be lost because of inadequate waiting space if (a) zero, (b) two, or (c) four spaces (not including the car being washed) were to be provided.

9. Suppose that one repairman has been assigned the responsibility of maintaining three machines. For each machine, the probability distribution of the running time before a breakdown is exponential with a mean of eight hours. The repair time also has an exponential distribution with a mean of two hours.

(a) Calculate the expected number of machines that are not running.
(b) As a crude approximation, it could be assumed that the calling population is infinite, so that the input process is Poisson with a mean arrival rate of three every eight hours. Compare the result from Part (a) with that obtained by making this approximation using (i) the corresponding infinite queue model, (ii) the corresponding finite queue model.

10. Consider a two-server queueing system with a Poisson input and exponential service times. Suppose that the expected service time is exactly two minutes.

(a) Compare the expected line length L for the cases where the mean arrival rate is 0.50, 0.90, and 0.99 units per minute, respectively. Do the same for L_q, W, W_q, and $P\{T > 5\}$.
(b) Compare the results obtained in Part (a) with those obtained in Problem 4.

11. A company currently has two tool cribs, each with a single clerk, in its manufacturing area. One tool crib handles only the tools for the heavy machinery, while the second one handles all other tools. However, for each crib, the arrival process is Poisson with a mean rate of 20 per hour, and the service-time distribution is exponential with a mean of two minutes.

Because of complaints that the mechanics coming to the tool cribs have to wait too long, the proposal has been made to combine the two tool cribs so that either clerk can handle either kind of tool as the demand arises. It is believed that the mean arrival rate to the combined two-clerk tool crib would double to forty per hour, while the expected service time would continue to be two minutes.

Compare the status quo and the proposal with respect to the total expected number of mechanics at the tool crib(s), the expected waiting time (including service) for each mechanic, and the probability that he has to wait more than five minutes.

12. Consider a queueing system with a Poisson input with a mean arrival rate of 15 calling units per hour. When there is only one unit in the system, it is processed by a single clerk, with an expected service time of three minutes. However, whenever there is more than one unit in the system, this clerk is joined by a helper, who helps him process the *same* unit. This reduces the expected service time to two minutes. In both cases, the service-time distribution is exponential.

(a) What is the steady-state probability distribution of the number of calling units in the system?
(b) What is the expected number of units in the system?

13. Consider a single-server queueing system. It has been observed that this server seems to speed up as the number of calling units in the system increases, and that the pattern of acceleration seems to fit the model presented in Sec. 10.5.7. Furthermore, it is estimated that the expected service time is three minutes when there is only one unit in the system, whereas it is only two minutes when there are five units in the system. Determine the pressure coefficient c for the model of Sec. 10.5.7.

14. Consider the model for a multiple-server queueing system with a finite queue that was presented in Sec. 10.6.3. Derive the expressions for L_q and L that are given there for the case where $M > s$.

15. A particular work center in a job shop can be represented as a single-server queueing system where jobs arrive according to a Poisson process with a mean rate of 4.5 per day. Although the arriving jobs are of three distinct types, the time required to perform any of these jobs has the same exponential distribution with a mean of 0.2 working days. The practice has been to work on arriving jobs on a first-come-first-served basis. However, it is important that jobs of "type 1" do not have to wait very long, whereas this is only moderately important for jobs of "type 2," and relatively unimportant for jobs of "type 3." These three types arrive with a mean rate of 1.5, 2.0, and 1.0 per day, respectively. Since all three types have been experiencing rather long delays on the average, it has been proposed that the jobs be selected according to an appropriate priority discipline instead.

Compare the expected waiting time (including service) for each of the three types of jobs if the service discipline were (a) first-come-first-served, (b) nonpreemptive priority, or (c) preemptive priority.

16. Consider the queueing theory model with a nonpreemptive priority service discipline that was presented at the beginning of Sec. 10.7. Suppose that $s = 1$, $N = 2$, and $(\lambda_1 + \lambda_2) < \mu$, and let P_{ij} be the steady-state probability that there are i members of the higher priority class and j members of the lower priority class in the queueing system ($i = 0, 1, 2, \cdots$; $j = 0, 1, 2, \cdots$). Use a method analogous to that presented in Sec. 10.4 to derive a system of linear equations whose simultaneous solution is the P_{ij}. Do not actually obtain this solution.

17. Consider a single-server queueing system with a Poisson input, Erlang service times, and a finite queue. In particular, suppose that $k = 2$; the mean arrival rate is 3 calling units per hour, the expected service time is 0.25 hours, and the maximum permissible number of calling units in the system is two. Derive the steady-state probability distribution of the number of calling units in the system, and then calculate the expected number. Compare this with the corresponding results when the service-time distribution is exponential instead.

CHAPTER 11

The Application of Queueing Theory

11.1 INTRODUCTION

Queueing theory has enjoyed a prominent place among the modern analytical techniques of operations research. However, the emphasis thus far has been on developing a mathematical descriptive theory. Little attention has yet been given to the practical application of this theory to achieving the goal of operations research, optimal decision-making. Therefore, research regarding proper procedures for using queueing theory is needed.

This chapter is devoted to elaborating on the limited information available about the proper use of queueing theory for decision-making.

11.2 CHOOSING THE MODEL

One of the difficult aspects of choosing the proper queueing model involves selecting the appropriate probability distribution for the pattern of arrivals and for the service times. If the queueing system is already in operation in some form, statistical theory may be used to help make these decisions. One would need to collect statistical data over time regarding the number of arrivals within time intervals of fixed size (or the time between arrivals) and the service times. One efficient method for collecting such data is reported in the study cited in Sec. 10.2. Assuming that the mean arrival rate and the mean service time do not change while the data are collected (which may be tested statistically), a frequency histogram would be constructed (see Sec. 4.8.1) for both the arrival distribution and the service-time distribution. The general shape and the amount of spread in these frequency histograms should suggest certain standard probability distributions. Since the Poisson input and exponential service-time queueing models provide the most information, one would be especially interested in verifying that these are the true underlying distributions. (It is equivalent to verify that the number of arrivals over a time interval of fixed length has a Poisson distribution or that the time between arrivals has an exponential distribution.) Since the mean and standard deviation of an exponential distribution are equal, a quick check on whether this is a plausible distribution is provided by comparing the sample mean and standard deviation. After selecting an hypothesized distribution for arrivals and for service times, the chi-square goodness of fit test (described in Sec. 4.8.2) may then be used to test the hypothesis that the observed data were generated by the hypothesized distribution. Acceptance of the hypothesis would verify the choice of this distribution for the queueing model (although it does not guarantee an exact match with the true underlying distribution). If the hypothesis is rejected, one must either seek another distribution which gives a more acceptable statistical fit or use an approximate model.

It is not always feasible to verify model distributions statistically. This is the case, for example, if one is designing a new queueing system rather than redesigning an existing one. Nevertheless, it may be possible to draw some conclusions about the appropriate model distributions by analyzing the nature of the input source and of the service mechanism. If the input source generates individual calling units completely at random (at some fixed mean rate), where future arrivals are independent of the pattern of past arrivals, then the input is a Poisson process. It is probably reasonable to assert that actual queueing systems usually have a Poisson input or an acceptable facsimile. Even when an attempt is made to schedule the arrivals so as to maintain a more uniform workload on the queueing system, it is frequently observed that unavoidable deviations from the schedule result in the input still being approximately Poisson.

On the other hand, actual queueing systems often would have a service-time distribution other than exponential. In fact, the exponential distribution has two (related) properties which make it inappropriate for many types of service situations. One of these properties is the fact that the exponential distribution has a strictly decreasing probability density function, as illustrated in Fig. 11.1.

Thus, if the random variable T has an exponential distribution, then

$$P\{0 \leq T \leq \Delta t\} > P\{t \leq T \leq t + \Delta t\}$$

for any non-zero value of t and any strictly positive quantity Δt. Since the maximum value of $f(t)$ is at $t = 0$, it is not only possible but relatively likely that T will take on a small value near zero. In fact,

$$P\left\{0 \leq T \leq \frac{1}{2}\frac{1}{\mu}\right\} > P\left\{\frac{1}{2}\frac{1}{\mu} \leq T \leq \frac{3}{2}\frac{1}{\mu}\right\},$$

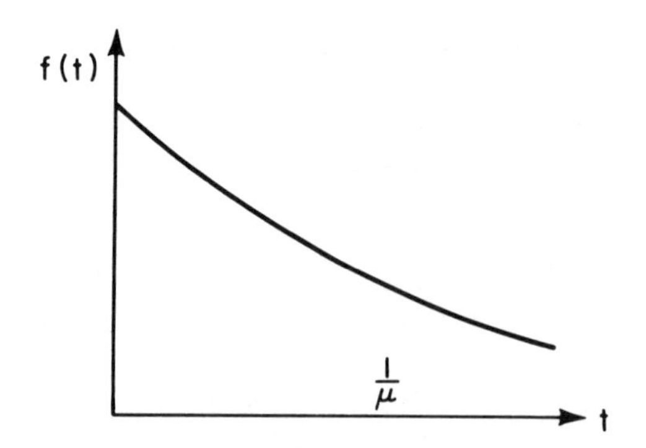

FIGURE 11.1. Probability density function, $f(t) = \mu e^{-\mu t}$, for the exponential distribution.

where $1/\mu$ is the mean, so that the value T takes on is more likely to be "small" (i.e., less than half of the mean) than "near" the mean (i.e., no further away than an amount equal to half of the mean). Is this really a reasonable assumption for the service-time distribution? It depends entirely on the nature of the service involved.

If the service required is essentially identical for each calling unit, with the server always performing the same sequence of service operations, then the actual service times would tend to be near the expected service time. Small deviations from the mean may occur, but usually only because of minor variations in the efficiency of the server. A small service time far below the mean would be essentially impossible because a certain minimum amount of time is needed to perform the required service operations even when the server is working at top speed. The exponential distribution clearly would not provide a close approximation to the service-time distribution for this type of situation. The Erlang distribution with a relatively large value of the shape parameter k (possibly $k = \infty$, which yields constant service times) may be more appropriate.

On the other hand, consider the type of situation where the specific tasks required of the server differ among the calling units. The broad nature of the service may be the same, but the specific type and amount of service differ. For example, this might be the case in the tool crib situation discussed in Sec. 10.2. It is likely that an occasional mechanic would need several non-standard tools that would require the tool crib clerk to spend several minutes for the search and paper work involved. Many other mechanics would require only a single standard tool that can be checked out in a few seconds. Similarly, bank tellers and grocery store check-out clerks are other servers of this general type where the required service is often brief but must occasionally be extensive. An exponential service-time distribution would seem quite plausible for this type of service situation.

The second property of the exponential distribution that deserves special attention is its "lack of memory." In particular, if the random variable T is the length of time a process continues before an event occurs (e.g., a service completion), and it has an exponential distribution, then

$$P\{T > t + \Delta t | T > \Delta t\} = P\{T > t\}$$

for any non-negative quantity Δt. Thus, the process "forgets," in effect, how long it has been going. (This surprising phenomenon occurs because

$$P\{T > t\} = e^{-\mu t}$$

and

$$\begin{aligned} P\{T > t + \Delta t | T > \Delta t\} &= \frac{P\{T > \Delta t, T > t + \Delta t\}}{P\{T > \Delta t\}} \\ &= \frac{P\{T > t + \Delta t\}}{P\{T > \Delta t\}} \\ &= \frac{e^{-\mu(t+\Delta t)}}{e^{-\mu \Delta t}} \\ &= e^{-\mu t}.) \end{aligned}$$

Therefore, an exponential service-time distribution implies that the probability distribution of the time remaining until service is completed is always the same, regardless of how long the calling unit has already been in service. For example, suppose that a calling unit is still being serviced after the expected service time, $1/\mu$, has elapsed; given this fact, the expected time remaining until service is completed is still $1/\mu$, just as though service were beginning now. This would not be realistic in a situation where the server must perform the same fixed sequence of service operations (whose total expected time is $1/\mu$) for each calling unit. In this case, if considerable service time has already elapsed, it is likely that the initial service operations are already completed so that the conditional expected service time for the remaining service operations is less than $1/\mu$. On the other hand, in the type of situation where the required service operations differ among the calling units, the "lack of memory" property may be quite realistic. For this case, if considerable service time has already elapsed for a particular calling unit, the only implication is that the unit requires more extensive service than most.

11.3 ESTIMATING MODEL PARAMETERS

Little research has been done on deriving optimal statistical estimators of the parameters of various queueing models.[54] However, this section sug-

[54] For one of the few research papers on this topic, see reference 6 at the end of this chapter.

gests a few convenient estimating procedures. The assumption is made throughout that statistical data regarding arrivals and service times can be obtained (as discussed in the previous section), so that objective estimates of the model parameters can be obtained.

Consider a queueing system where the mean arrival rate and the mean service rate per busy server are both fixed constants (λ and μ, respectively). To estimate λ, one may count the number of calling units, N, that enter the queueing system over a time interval of specified length t[55]; an unbiased estimator[56] of λ would then be

$$\hat{\lambda} = \frac{N}{t}.$$

An alternative approach is to instead fix the number of calling units observed rather than the length of the time interval. Thus, let T be the total elapsed time that the system is observed until the last of the specified number of arrivals, n, has entered the system. An estimator of $1/\lambda$ is then given by T/n, so that

$$\hat{\hat{\lambda}} = \frac{n}{T}$$

is an estimator of λ. If the system has a Poisson input, then either $\hat{\lambda}$ or $\hat{\hat{\lambda}}$ is a maximum likelihood estimator[57] of λ, depending upon how the data are recorded. To estimate μ, one may tabulate both the total number of units served, M, and the sum of the busy times (time spent servicing a calling unit) of the servers, B, over a time interval of specified length; an estimator of μ would then be

$$\hat{\mu} = \frac{M}{B}.$$

However, it is unclear how to count units that are in the process of being served at the beginning or end of the time interval, and it would create a bias to consider only the number and service times of the units that are completely served during the time interval. Therefore, it is usually preferable to use the alternative approach of fixing the number of calling units observed rather than the length of the time interval. Thus, let B be the sum of the service times of the first m calling units that begin service after initiating the observation of the system, where m is a prespecified number. (In a multiple-server system, it may be more convenient to record the sum of m service times for only *one* of the servers, which is also permissible.) An estimator of $1/\mu$ is then given by B/m, so that

$$\hat{\hat{\mu}} = \frac{m}{B}$$

[55] Fixed constants are being denoted by a lower-case letter, whereas random variables are being denoted by upper-case letters.

[56] See Sec. 4.5.1.

[57] See Sec. 4.5.5.

is an estimator of μ. If the service-time distribution is exponential, then $\hat{\mu}$ is a maximum likelihood estimator of μ.

When the service-time distribution is assumed to be Erlang, it is also necessary to estimate the shape parameter k. One convenient but rather crude method used in practice is to estimate the variance of service times by the sample variance, and then select the integer value of k such that the corresponding distribution comes closest to having this variance.

Now suppose that the mean service rate per busy server varies with queue size as described in Secs. 10.5.7 and 10.6.5, so that $\mu_n = (n/s)^c s\mu_1$ if $n \geq s$. Hence, $\log \mu_n = c \log (n/s) + \log (s\mu_1)$, if $n \geq s$. Assuming an exponential service-time distribution, a maximum likelihood estimator of μ_n is the observed number of units that completed service while n units were in the system divided by the total observed time n units were in the system. After obtaining these estimates, $\hat{\mu}_n(n - s = 0, 1, 2, \cdots)$, plot $\log \hat{\mu}_n$ versus $\log (n/s)$. The slope c and the intercept, $\log (s\mu_1)$, of the $\log \mu_n$ line can then be estimated by the method of least squares (see Sec. 4.7.1). Confidence intervals for $\log \mu_n$ can also be obtained from linear regression theory (see Sec. 4.7.3).

11.4 DECISION-MAKING

Queueing-type situations requiring decision-making arise in a wide variety of contexts. For this reason, it is not possible to present a meaningful decision-making procedure applicable to all of these situations. Instead, this section attempts to give a broad conceptual picture of the general approach to a predominant group of waiting line problems.

A large proportion of waiting line problems that arise in practice involve making one or a combination of the following decisions:

1. Number of servers at a service facility.
2. Efficiency of the servers.
3. Number of service facilities.

When such problems are formulated in terms of a queueing model, the corresponding decision variables usually would be s (number of servers at each facility), μ (mean service rate per busy server), and λ (mean arrival rate at each facility). The number of service facilities is directly related to λ since, assuming a uniform work load among the facilities, λ equals the total mean arrival rate to all facilities divided by the number of facilities.

The tool crib example of Sec. 10.2 illustrates a problem requiring a decision on the number of servers. One example illustrating a decision on the efficiency of the servers is the selection of the type of materials handling equipment (the servers) to purchase in order to transport certain kinds of loads (the calling units). Another such example arises when selecting the

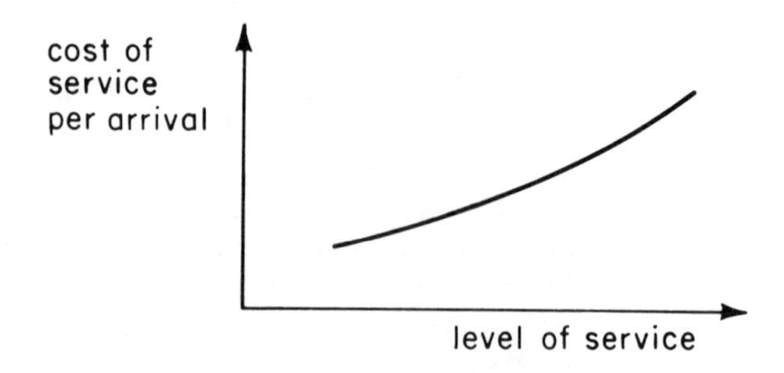

Figure 11.2. Service cost as a function of service level.

size of a maintenance crew (where the entire crew is one server). A decision as to the number of service facilities to distribute throughout an area may be required for such facilities as restrooms, first-aid centers, drinking fountains, tool cribs, etc.

All of the specific decisions discussed above involve the general question of the appropriate level of service to provide in a queueing system. As discussed in Sec. 10.1, decisions regarding the amount of service capacity to provide usually are based primarily on two considerations. One is the cost incurred by providing the service, as shown in Fig. 11.2. The other consideration is the amount of waiting for that service, as suggested in Fig. 11.3. Figure 11.3 would be obtained, of course, by using the appropriate waiting time equation from queueing theory.

It is readily apparent that these two considerations create conflicting pressures on the decision-maker. The objective of reducing service costs recommends a minimal level of service. On the other hand, long waiting times are undesirable, which recommends a high level of service. Therefore, it is necessary to strive for some type of compromise. To assist in this endeavor, Figs. 11.2 and 11.3 may be combined, as shown in Fig. 11.4. The problem is thereby reduced to selecting the point on the curve of Fig. 11.4

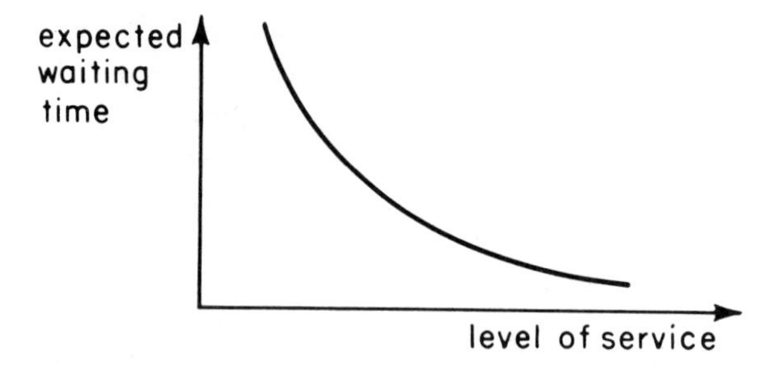

Figure 11.3. Expected waiting time as a function of service level.

which gives the best balance between the average delay in being serviced and the cost of providing that service. Reference back to Figs. 11.2 or 11.3 would indicate the corresponding level of service.

Unfortunately, it is all too easy to terminate further analysis and make a quick subjective judgment on the basis of Fig. 11.4 (or less). Actually, the most crucial portion of the analysis still lies ahead. An intelligent decision on the proper balance between delays and service costs can be made only after the relative seriousness of delays and service costs has been estab-

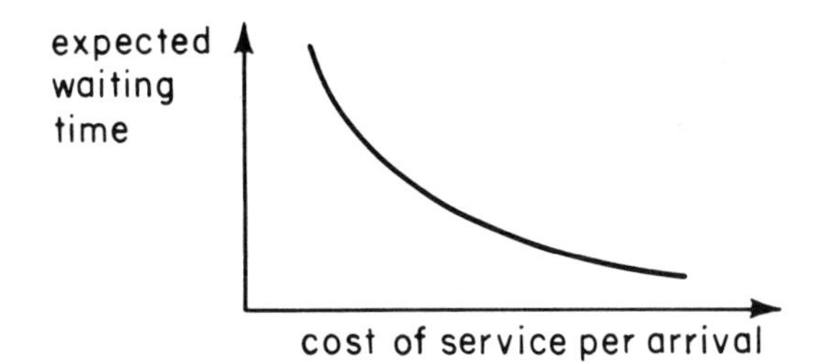

FIGURE 11.4. Relationship between average delay and service cost.

lished. This requires obtaining answers to such questions as, how much expenditure on service is equivalent (in its detrimental impact) to a calling unit being delayed one unit of time? Thus, in order to compare service costs and waiting times, it is necessary to adopt (explicitly or implicitly) a common measure of their impact. The natural choice for this common measure is cost, so that it becomes necessary to estimate the "cost" of waiting. This cost probably cannot be identified entirely with expenditures on the accounting books. Nevertheless, a given amount of waiting can be considered as equivalent in its long-run impact (from the viewpoint of the decision-maker) to an expenditure of a certain amount. If one assumes that this cost of waiting is proportional to the total amount of waiting, it is sufficient to estimate the cost of waiting per unit time per arrival.

A common viewpoint in practice is that the cost of waiting is often too intangible to be amenable to estimation; hence, the decision must instead be based on more tangible, even if less fundamental, criteria such as the desired expected waiting time in Fig. 11.4. The fallacy in this viewpoint is that it is impossible to avoid doing the equivalent of estimating waiting costs when analyzing the problem rationally. Whether it is done explicitly or implicitly, any comparison of waiting times and service costs must inevitably reduce to estimating the cost that is equivalent to the waiting. The only question is whether the estimation should be done explicitly or implicitly. This depends, in part, upon the time and cost required to develop a reasonable explicit estimate as opposed to the potential savings. However, it seems evident that performing the penetrating analysis required to obtain this explicit estimate should provide a sounder basis for the required decision than superficial criteria that are ultimately based on these same cost considerations in a very imprecise and intuitive way. In addition to using a better estimate, this explicit procedure permits using rigorous mathematical analysis to accurately identify the decision which minimizes total estimated expected cost.

Granted that an explicit estimate of the cost of waiting would be desirable, the next question is how one would develop this estimate. Because of the diversity of waiting line situations, no single estimating process is generally applicable. One type of situation is where the calling unit is a customer. From the viewpoint of the decision-maker, the cost of waiting probably would consist primarily of the cost of lost business. This lost business may occur immediately (because the customer grew impatient and left) and/or in the future (because the customer was sufficiently irritated that he did not come again). The cost is very difficult to estimate in this situation, and it may be necessary to revert to other criteria, such as a tolerable probability distribution of waiting times. A second type of situation is where the calling unit is a job to be performed for a customer. As for the preceding situation, part of the cost of waiting that is relevant to the decision-maker is the cost attributable to a deterioration in customer relations. However, there may also be more readily identifiable costs, such as those due to idle in-process inventories or increased expediting and administrative effort.

A situation which may be more amenable to estimating waiting costs is one in which the calling units are internal to the organization providing the service. For example, the calling units may be machines or, as in the tool crib illustration of Sec. 10.2, employees of a firm. Therefore, it may be possible to directly identify some or all of the costs associated with the idleness of these calling units. A detailed discussion of the estimating process for this situation is available elsewhere.[58] However, in order to illustrate the underlying rationale (and to warn against a common pitfall), consider the case where the calling units are machine operators. At first glance, it is easy to jump to the conclusion that the relevant cost to the firm if such an employee waits in a queue is his wage during the waiting time. However, this would imply that the net reduction in the earnings of the firm because an operator has to wait is equal to his wage. There is no reason why this particular relationship should hold in general. Perhaps one reason this approach is sometimes used in practice is the misconception that what is being

[58] Frederick S. Hillier, "Cost Models for the Application of Priority Waiting Line Theory to Industrial Problems," *Journal of Industrial Engineering*, **16**, No. 3, 178–185 (1965).

"wasted" by the waiting is the operator's wage. But he will receive the same wage regardless of the waiting, and what is instead being lost is the contribution to the firm's earnings that the operator would have made otherwise. Furthermore, the worker does not work in a vacuum. Rather, he is the catalyst that causes the efforts of all the economic resources involved (machinery and equipment, materials, managerial skill, capital, etc.) to result in one of the changes in the product necessary to make it salable. Thus, while the output of the machine operator and his colleagues

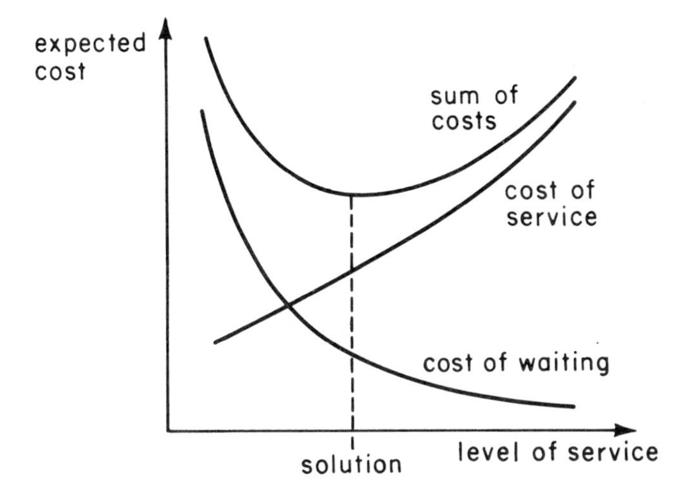

FIGURE 11.5. Conceptual solution procedure for many waiting line problems.

is essential if a salable product is to be produced, the sale of that product must not only pay their wages but must also pay for the other necessary economic resources as well. Therefore, when the operator is idle waiting in a queue, what is being wasted is productive output that would have helped pay the fixed expenses of the firm in addition to the operator's wage. In short, rather than focusing solely on the value of the one economic resource that physically waits in the queue, the emphasis should instead be on finding the value of all the economic resources that would be idled as a consequence of this waiting.

Given that the cost of waiting has been evaluated explicitly, the remainder of the analysis is conceptually straightforward. The objective would be to determine the level of service which minimizes the total of the expected cost of service and the expected cost of waiting for that service. This concept is depicted in Fig. 11.5. The expected cost of waiting curve in Fig. 11.5 is obtained by combining the estimated cost of waiting (as a function of waiting time) and the waiting time (as a function of level of service) indicated by queueing theory. If the cost of waiting is considered to be proportional to the total amount of waiting, this curve would just be a multiple of the curve shown in Fig. 11.3.

Despite the simplicity of the conceptual solution procedure of Fig. 11.5, certain practical difficulties can arise during the detailed analysis. For example, when a combination of the three previously discussed decisions concerning level of service is involved, the level of service axis of Fig. 11.5 actually requires more than one dimension. The next section develops cost models and efficient solution procedures for cases such as these. It also introduces and implements the concept that when a decision on the number of service facilities is required, time spent in traveling to and from a facility should be included in the analysis (as part of the total time waiting for service).

11.5 COST MODELS[59]

11.5.1 General Assumptions

All of the following cost models assume that the total cost of waiting (from the viewpoint of the decision-maker) is directly proportional to the total time that all calling units spend in the system, both waiting and in service. Hence, their applicability is limited primarily to the type of situation where the calling units are internal to the organization providing the service. The waiting cost functions assume that the queueing system is in a steady-state condition. The models also assume that the cost of service at each service facility is the sum of a fixed cost and a cost proportional to the number of servers at the facility. This fixed cost will be ignored except where it is relevant to the analysis.

It should be recognized that non-linear cost functions might occasionally be more appropriate. The substitution of such functions in the models and solution procedures should be straightforward in most cases.

The models per se make no assumptions about the input distribution, the service-time distribution, or the service discipline (although the absence of priorities is implied until Sec. 11.5.7). However, all of the accompanying results given here assume that each service facility involved has a Poisson input and a service discipline which is first-come-first-served or its equivalent in terms of giving the same expected number and expected waiting time in the queueing system. The service-time distribution is specified in each case.

For simplicity of presentation, it is assumed that the mean arrival rate and the mean service rate per busy server are both constants independent of the state of the queueing system. However, each of these assumptions

[59] The material in this section is drawn from Frederick S. Hillier, "Economic Models for Industrial Waiting Line Problems," *Management Science*, **10**, No. 1, 119–130 (1963).

is actually required only when that mean rate is a decision variable. The decision variables for all of the models are some combination of the following three quantities: (1) number of servers, (2) mean service rate per busy server, and (3) mean arrival rate at each service facility (i.e., number of service facilities).

11.5.2 **Notation**

The general queueing theory notation introduced in Sec. 10.3.7 will be used as needed. Thus, s, μ, and λ are the three decision variables mentioned above. It should be noted that even when the number of service facilities is being determined, the general queueing notation used still refers to the parameters or properties of each single service facility. The parameters (s, μ, λ) are assumed to be the same for each of the service facilities considered.

The general cost parameters are denoted as follows:

C_w = cost of waiting per unit time for one calling unit.
C_{si} = marginal cost of providing service capacity as defined for model i.
$E(C_i)$ = expected total variable cost per unit time as defined for model i.

11.5.3 **Model 1—Unknown** s

Model 1 is designed for the simple case where μ and λ are known, and it is desired to determine the proper number of servers to have on duty at the service facility. The tool crib example of Sec. 10.2 illustrated a problem of this type.

FORMULATION OF MODEL 1

Definition: C_{s1} = marginal cost of a server per unit time.
$E(C_1)$ = expected total variable cost per unit time.
Given: $\mu, \lambda, C_w, C_{s1}$.
To find: s.
Objective: Minimize $E(C_1) = sC_{s1} + C_wL$.

The usual method of solution for this model is trial and error, as illustrated in Example 2 of Sec. 11.6 for the tool crib example. However, for the case of a Poisson input and exponential service times (the model of Sec. 10.6.1), the solutions have already been computed and graphically summarized.[60]

It should be noted that the objective function for model 1 can be de-

[60] T. M. Mangelsdorf, "Waiting Line Theory Applied to Manufacturing Problems," S. M. Thesis, M.I.T., 1955. Reprinted in reference 1 (see the end of this chapter); see Fig. 4.2 on p. 280. Also see Fig. 4.1 for a graph of μW_q versus λ/μ.

fined in alternative ways by deleting certain "fixed" costs. Since λ and μ are constants, the time that calling units spend waiting while being served is unavoidable. Hence, L may be replaced by L_q. Furthermore, the service costs incurred while the servers are busy cannot be reduced, so sC_{s1} can be replaced by $(s - \lambda/\mu)C_{s1}$. Thus, $[(s - \lambda/\mu)C_{s1} + C_w L_q]$ is the expected total variable cost of "idleness" (idle servers or calling units waiting to be served) per unit time. This was actually the objective function used in the study cited in Sec. 10.2. The $E(C_1)$ function was chosen here instead because it is still applicable when μ and/or λ also become decision variables in subsequent models.

11.5.4 Model 2—Unknown μ and s

Model 2 is designed for the case where both the efficiency of service, measured by μ, and the number of servers, s, at a service facility need to be selected. One example is where both the type and quantity of materials handling equipment to transport certain kinds of loads must be selected for purchase. Another type of example is the selection of the number of crews, and the size of each crew for jointly performing a certain task, e.g., maintenance work, loading and unloading operations, inspection work, setup of machines, etc. In many cases, only a few alternative values of μ are available, e.g., the efficiency of the alternative types of materials handling equipment or the efficiency of the alternative crew sizes.

Formulation of Model 2

Definitions: $f(\mu)$ = marginal cost of a server per unit time when the mean service rate is μ.
A = set of feasible values of μ.
$E(C_2)$ = expected total variable cost per unit time.
Given: λ, C_w, $f(\mu)$, A.
To find: μ, s.
Objective: Minimize $E(C_2) = sf(\mu) + C_w L$, subject to $\mu \epsilon A$.

Notice that $E(C_2) = E(C_1)$ when $f(\mu) = C_{s1}$. Hence, for a fixed value of μ, one can find the minimum value of $E(C_2)$ and the corresponding value of s by using model 1. Assuming that the number of feasible values of μ is finite, the problem may therefore be solved by repeating this for all feasible values of μ. The desired solution would be the value of μ, and the corresponding value of s, which gives the over-all minimum value of $E(C_2)$. For the case of a Poisson input and exponential service times, this is easily done since μW_q and minimizing values of s have been computed[61] and $L = (\lambda/\mu)(\mu W_q + 1)$.

When the number of feasible values of μ is infinite, an exact solution

[61] *Ibid.*

must be obtained analytically if this is possible. One such case for which an explicit solution has been found is the following.

FORMULATION OF MODEL 2a

Special case of model 2 with the following restrictions:

(1) Poisson input.
(2) Exponential service times.
(3) $A = \{\mu: \lambda/s < \mu < \infty\}$.
(4) $f(\mu) = C_{s2}\mu$, where C_{s2} is the expected marginal cost of serving one customer when the mean service rate is one, so

$$E(C_{2a}) = sC_{s2}\,\mu + C_w L\,.$$

To find the solution for model 2a, first consider what the value of s should be. For any fixed value of the product $s\mu$ such that $s\mu > \lambda$, the only variable term of $E(C_{2a})$ is $C_w L$. However, it can be demonstrated[62] that, for fixed values of λ and $s\mu$, L increases as s is increased. Therefore, regardless of what the best value of $s\mu$ is, $s = 1$ must yield a smaller value of $E(C_{2a})$ than any other positive value, i.e., $s = 1$ is the optimal value of s.

Given that $s = 1$, Sec. 10.5.1 indicates that $L = \lambda/(\mu - \lambda)$, so $E(C_{2a})$ reduces to

$$E(C_{2a}) = C_{s2}\,\mu + C_w \frac{\lambda}{\mu - \lambda}\,.$$

Since μ is the only remaining decision variable (λ is a given constant), $E(C_{2a})$ would be minimized with respect to μ by setting the derivative equal to zero and solving:

$$\frac{dE(C_{2a})}{d\mu} = C_{s2} - \frac{\lambda C_w}{(\mu - \lambda)^2} = 0\,,$$

so

$$\mu = \lambda + \sqrt{\frac{\lambda C_w}{C_{s2}}}$$

is the minimizing value of μ (since $d^2E(C_{2a})/d\mu^2 > 0$ for all $\mu > \lambda$). Therefore, $s = 1$ and this value of μ provide the desired solution for model 2a.

One possible application of model 2a is to the problem of selecting the number of crews and their size. Assume that the mean service rate for a crew is proportional to the size of the crew, so that $f(\mu) = C_{s2}\,\mu$. The solution to model 2a implies that one large crew, whose size[63] corresponds to the indicated μ, is better than several small crews. This is an enlightening and

[62] For example, see reference 4 (at the end of this chapter), p. 103.

[63] Since the indicated size might not be an integer, it may be necessary to round off. However, because $E(C_{2a})$ is a convex function of μ, either rounding down or rounding up must yield the optimal crew size.

useful result, but it should be recognized that the assumed $f(\mu)$ function often would be only a rough approximation.

An important special case of model 2 is where the number of servers is restricted to one. For example, the problem may be to determine the type of machinery or equipment to use for a certain job, or the skill (speed) requirements for a certain manual operation, or the proper size of a crew, etc. If the number of feasible values of μ is finite, the problem may be solved by trial and error. Otherwise, it may be difficult to identify a solution which is optimal or almost optimal. However, a satisfactory solution procedure can be derived for many reasonable service-cost functions and service-time distributions. An example is the following model 2b.

FORMULATION OF MODEL 2b

Special case of model 2 with the following restrictions:

(1) $s = 1$.
(2) Poisson input.
(3) Erlang service times, with known positive shape parameter k.
(4) $A = \{\mu: \lambda < \mu < \infty\}$.
(5) $f(\mu) = C_{s2}\mu^{1+\Delta}$, where Δ is a known non-negative constant and C_{s2} is defined as for model 2a.

$$E(C_{2b}) = C_{s2}\,\mu^{1+\Delta} + C_w L$$
$$= C_{s2}\,\mu^{1+\Delta} + C_w\left[\frac{k+1}{2k}\,\frac{\lambda^2}{\mu(\mu-\lambda)} + \frac{\lambda}{\mu}\right].$$

It can be shown that $d^2E(C_{2b})/d\mu^2 > 0$ for $\mu > \lambda$ and that the minimizing value of $\mu > \lambda$ occurs at the unique solution of

$$\frac{dE(C_{2b})}{d\mu} = C_{s2}(1+\Delta)\mu^{\Delta} - \frac{\lambda C_w}{(\mu-\lambda)^2}\left[1 + \left(\frac{1-k}{k}\right)\frac{\lambda}{\mu}\left(2 - \frac{\lambda}{\mu}\right)\right] = 0\,.$$

(The reader is asked to verify this in problem 8.) Therefore, one can quickly converge to the solution for model 2b by trial and error or by more systematic numerical methods.

Model 2b is a rather useful one because it encompasses the usual situation where the (variable) cost of service is either proportional or more than proportional to the mean service rate. Thus, $\Delta = 0$ corresponds to the proportional case (as in model 2a), whereas $\Delta > 0$ corresponds to the more-than-proportional case. For example, $\Delta = 1$ implies that the (variable) cost of service must be quadrupled in order to double the mean service rate. This kind of assumption should be quite realistic for such problems as determining the optimal crew size, since the size (i.e., cost) of a crew does tend to be proportional or more than proportional to its efficiency (i.e., mean service rate).

11.5.5 Model 3—Unknown λ and s

Model 3 is designed especially for the case where it is necessary to select both the number of service facilities and the number of servers at each one. The typical situation would be where a population (such as the employees in an industrial building) must be provided with a certain service, and one needs to determine what proportion of the population, and therefore what value of λ, should be assigned to each service facility. Examples of such service facilities are restrooms, medical centers, tool cribs, and storage facilities. In many of these situations, there is also the question of how many servers to provide at each facility, e.g., how many stalls in the restrooms, how many doctors at the medical center, etc.

The analysis is simplified by requiring that λ and s must be the same for all service facilities. It should therefore be recognized that a slight improvement in the indicated solution might be achieved by permitting minor deviations in these parameters at individual facilities.

FORMULATION OF MODEL 3

Definitions: C_{s3} = marginal cost of a server per unit time.
C_f = fixed cost of service per service facility per unit time.
λ_p = mean arrival rate for entire population.
$E(C_3)$ = expected total variable cost per unit serviced.
n = number of service facilities $= \lambda_p/\lambda$.

Given: $\mu, C_w, C_{s3}, C_f, \lambda_p$.

To find: λ, s.

Objective: Minimize $E(C_3)$, subject to $\lambda = \dfrac{\lambda_p}{n}$, where $n = 1, 2, \cdots$.

Before giving the expression for $E(C_3)$, a special case is considered which, at first glance, appears to be the proper general case. However, a result is obtained for this special case which will motivate a more satisfactory general formulation.

FORMULATION OF MODEL 3a

Definition: Same as model 3, where $E(C_{3a})$ replaces $E(C_3)$.

Given: $\mu, C_w, C_{s3}, C_f, \lambda_p$.

To find: λ, s.

Objective: Minimize $E(C_{3a}) = (C_f + sC_{s3})/\lambda + C_w W$, subject to $\lambda = \lambda_p/n$, where $n = 1, 2, \cdots$.

This expression for $E(C_{3a})$ can be obtained in the following way. The expected total variable cost per unit time for all n service facilities is

$$\lambda_p E(C_{3a}) = n(C_f + sC_{s3}) + nC_w L$$
$$= n\lambda\left[\frac{C_f + sC_{s3}}{\lambda} + C_w W\right]$$
$$= \lambda_p\left[\frac{C_f + sC_{s3}}{\lambda} + C_w W\right],$$

so that $E(C_{3a})$ is as given above.

Solution[64] *for Model 3a:* The optimal value of λ is $\lambda^* = \lambda_p$, i.e., provide only one service facility for the entire population.

Proof: Suppose, to the contrary, that $\lambda^* = \lambda_p/n$, where n is a positive integer other than one; let s^* denote the corresponding optimal solution for s. Compare $E(C_{3a})$ for this solution with $E(C_{3a})$ for $\lambda = \lambda_p$ and $s = ns^*$. Notice that the cost of service, $(C_f + sC_{s3})/\lambda$, is less by $(n - 1)C_f/\lambda_p$ for the latter solution. Therefore, in order to contradict the possibility that λ_p/n can indeed be the optimal value of λ, it is sufficient to show that the cost of waiting, $C_w W$, is also less for the latter solution.

Define the queueing system to consist of all n service facilities, although the calling units still go to their individual facilities for service as before, and no transfers between facilities are possible. Consider all possible states of the system. For some states, there will be units waiting for service at some facilities, while there will be idle servers at other facilities. For such states, the total number in the system queue (i.e., the total number of calling units in the system that are waiting for service) could be reduced if the barriers between the facilities were removed and those in the queue could be serviced by the otherwise idle servers. Thus, by removing the barriers, i.e., by leaving one facility ($\lambda = \lambda_p$, $s = ns^*$), the expected system queue length, L_q, is reduced. Therefore, since $L_q = \lambda_p(W - 1/\mu)$, $C_w W$ is also reduced.

Hence, $(\lambda, s) = (\lambda_p/n, s^*)$ cannot be the optimal solution since a better one, namely, $(\lambda, s) = (\lambda_p, ns^*)$, can always be found. This contradiction verifies the indicated solution that $\lambda^* = \lambda_p$.

This solution is an interesting result which, if it were carried to an extreme, would be ridiculous. It says, for example, that there should be only one restroom, albeit a large one, in the entire Pentagon! So what is wrong with model 3a? The primary deficiency is that it considered only the cost of service and the cost of waiting at the service facility, and totally ignored the cost of the time wasted in traveling to and from the facility. Since travel time would be prohibitive with only one service facility for a large population, enough separate facilities must be distributed throughout the population to hold travel time down to a reasonable level.

[64] The solution only assumes conditions that generally hold, namely, $C_f \geq 0$, $C_{s3} \geq 0$, and a queueing system such that $L = \lambda W$ (see Sec. 10.3.8).

It will be assumed that the cost of waiting per unit time for one calling unit, C_w, is equal to the cost of having the unit spend one unit of time traveling to and from the service facility. Therefore, in order to introduce this cost into the analysis, it becomes necessary to estimate expected travel time, both ways, per arrival. To accomplish this, several alternative travel-time models are introduced. Each of these models assumes that the portion of the population assigned to the service facility is distributed uniformly throughout the assigned area, that each arrival returns to its original location, that all arrivals travel at the same average velocity, and that the service facility is centrally located within the allocated area.

TRAVEL-TIME MODELS

Definitions: T = travel time, both ways, for an arrival.
v = average velocity of calling units in traveling to and from the facility.
A = total amount of area under study.

$$a = \frac{A}{\lambda_p}$$

= area allocated to each portion of the population requiring service at a mean rate of once per unit time.

Given: v, a.
To find: Expected value of T, $E(T)$.

TRAVEL-TIME MODEL 1

Description: Square area, rectangular travel (as along a system of orthogonal aisles).

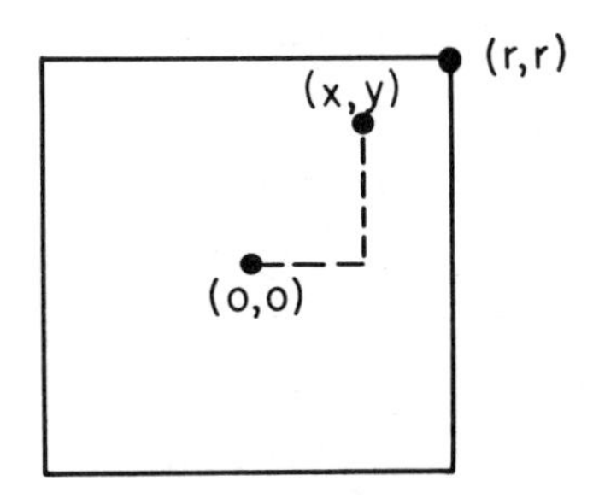

FIGURE 11.6. Graphical representation of travel-time model 1.

To find $E(T)$ for travel-time model 1, note that

$$E(T) = \frac{2}{v} E(D) ,$$

where the random variable D is the distance along a path of rectangular travel from the original location of the arrival to the facility. Thus,

$$D = |X| + |Y| ,$$

where the bivariate random variable, (X, Y), is the original location of the arrival in an orthogonal (x, y) coordinate system, and the location of the facility (at the center of the square area) is taken to be the origin (see Fig. 11.6). The amount of area assigned to the facility is $a\lambda$, so $r = \sqrt{a\lambda}/2$ is the maximum value that can be taken on by either $|X|$ or $|Y|$. Since the calling units are assumed to be distributed uniformly throughout the square area, it is evident that both X and Y have a uniform distribution (see Sec. 3.7.3) over the interval from $-r$ to $+r$, so the probability density function for each one equals $1/2r$ over this interval. Therefore, both $|X|$ and $|Y|$ have a uniform distribution, with the probability density function equal to $1/r$, over the interval from 0 to r. Since X and Y are independent random variables, it now follows that

$$\begin{aligned} E(D) &= \int_0^r \int_0^r (x + y) \left(\frac{1}{r^2}\right) dx\, dy \\ &= \int_0^r \left(\frac{1}{r}\right) x\, dx + \int_0^r \left(\frac{1}{r}\right) y\, dy \\ &= r . \end{aligned}$$

Hence,

$$\begin{aligned} E(T) &= \frac{2}{v} r = \frac{2}{v} \frac{\sqrt{a\lambda}}{2} \\ &= \frac{\sqrt{a\lambda}}{v} \end{aligned}$$

is the desired solution for travel-time model 1.

TRAVEL-TIME MODEL 2

Description: Square area, direct travel.

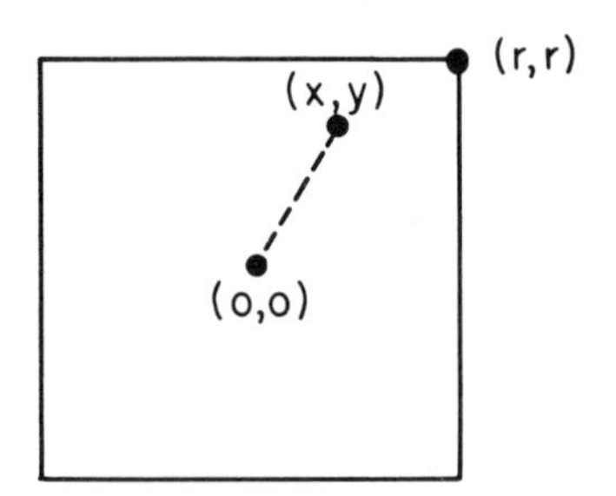

FIGURE 11.7. Graphical representation of travel-time model 2.

By proceeding in a manner that is directly analogous to that for travel-time model 1, it follows that

$$E(T) = \frac{2}{v} \cdot 8 \int_0^{\pi/4} \int_0^{r \sec \theta} \rho \left(\frac{1}{4r^2}\right) \rho \, d\rho \, d\theta$$

$$= \frac{4}{3v}\left[\frac{\sqrt{2}}{2} + \frac{1}{2}\log_e \tan\left(\frac{3\pi}{8}\right)\right] r$$

$$\doteq 0.7652 \frac{\sqrt{a\lambda}}{v}$$

is the desired solution for travel-time model 2.

Travel-Time Model 3

Description: Circular area, direct travel.

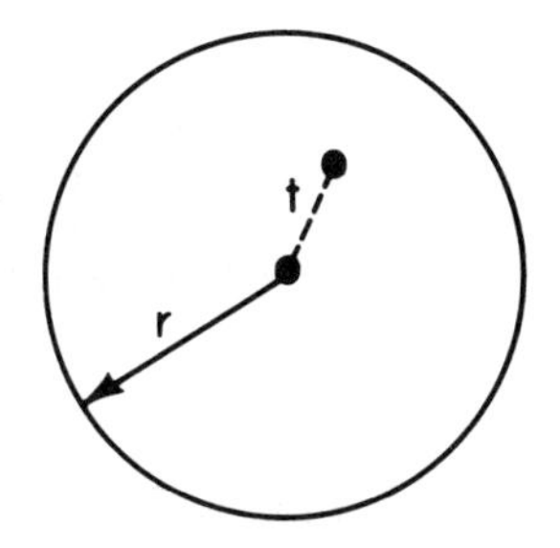

Figure 11.8. Graphical representation of travel-time model 3.

Proceeding essentially as before, the solution for travel-time model 3 is

$$E(T) = \frac{2}{v} \int_0^r t \left(\frac{2\pi t}{\pi r^2}\right) dt$$

$$= \frac{2}{v}\frac{2r}{3} = \frac{4}{3v}\sqrt{\frac{a\lambda}{\pi}}$$

$$\doteq 0.7523 \frac{\sqrt{a\lambda}}{v}.$$

Of these three models, it appears that travel-time model 1 often would be the most appropriate one for industrial situations since it simulates the common mode of travel along a system of orthogonal aisles. However, because the area assigned to a service facility depends on the physical layout involved, the shape of the area will sometimes be an odd one that does not correspond precisely to any of these models. Fortunately, the close correspondence between the values of T for travel-time models 2 and 3 gives some indication that T is not very sensitive to the shape of the area assigned to the service facility.

The completed formulation of cost for model 3 will incorporate the travel-time models and their assumptions. The additional assumption is made that the population is distributed uniformly throughout the entire area under study. It should be realized that some situations deviate considerably from this assumption and that the indicated solution may be very approximate in extreme cases. When this occurs, it would seem appropriate either to investigate shifts between service facilities in the values of λ and s or to partition the population into areas of more uniform density and obtain separate solutions.

COMPLETED FORMULATION OF MODEL 3

Definitions: Same as before, plus the definitions for the travel-time models.

Given: $\mu, C_w, C_{s3}, C_f, \lambda_p, a, v$.

To find: λ, s.

Objective: Minimize $E(C_3) = (C_f + sC_{s3})/\lambda + C_w[W + E(T)]$, subject to $\lambda = \lambda_p/n$, where $n = 1, 2, \cdots$.

For example, if travel-time model 1 is used, then

$$E(C_3) = \frac{C_f + sC_{s3}}{\lambda} + C_w\left[W + \frac{\sqrt{a\lambda}}{v}\right].$$

The method of solution is quite straightforward. Since $L = \lambda W$ (see Sec. 10.3.8), it follows that

$$\lambda E(C_3) = E(C_1) + [C_f + C_w\lambda E(T)] .$$

For a fixed value of λ, the $[C_f + C_w\lambda E(T)]$ term is a constant. It therefore follows that the optimal value of s, given λ, is the same for models 1 and 3. Thus, using model 1 to determine s, given λ, the minimum value of $E(C_3)$ can be calculated for $\lambda = \lambda_p/n$ for $n = 1, 2, \cdots$. Proceeding in this manner, the minimizing value of λ would be found by trial and error, as illustrated in Example 3 of Sec. 11.6. For the case of a Poisson input and exponential service times, the graphical results referenced in Sec. 11.5.3 greatly reduce the computational effort required by this solution procedure.

One important special case of model 3 is where s is restricted to be one, so that only a single server can be assigned to service each of the n portions of the population. For example, each operator might be assigned to service a certain group of automatic or semi-automatic machines. This example often has been analyzed using the exact assumption of a limited source (see Sec. 10.5.6). However, by assuming an unlimited source and negligible travel time, an explicit solution for λ can be obtained. This solution should be quite appropriate in some cases, while in others, like the example involving relatively small calling populations, the expression for λ at least indicates the approximate functional form of the solution. Furthermore, neglecting travel time may be quite reasonable for this case, since a single server would service a relatively small area (and it may actually be the server that does the traveling involved, in which case his travel time should be included in service time). The formulation and the derivation of the solution for λ follow.

FORMULATION OF MODEL 3b

Special case of model 3 with the following restrictions:

(1) $s = 1$. (Therefore, set $C_f = 0$ so that C_{s3} denotes the total cost of service per service facility per unit time.)
(2) $v = \infty$, i.e., travel time is negligible.
(3) Poisson input.
(4) Variance of service times, σ^2, is fixed and known, although the distribution is arbitrary.

Therefore,

$$E(C_{3b}) = \frac{C_{s3}}{\lambda} + C_w W ,$$

where Sec. 10.5.2 indicates that

$$W = \lambda\left[\frac{\mu^2\sigma^2 + 1}{2\mu(\mu - \lambda)}\right] + \frac{1}{\mu} \cdot$$

Solution for Model 3b: The optimal value of λ is

$$\lambda^* = \frac{\mu}{1 + \sqrt{\dfrac{C_w}{C_{s3}} \cdot \dfrac{1}{2}(\mu^2\sigma^2 + 1)}} \cdot$$

Derivation: Set

$$\frac{dE(C_{3b})}{d\lambda} = 0 .$$

Therefore,

$$\begin{aligned}\frac{dE(C_{3b})}{d\lambda} &= -\frac{C_{s3}}{\lambda^2} + C_w\left[\lambda\frac{\mu^2\sigma^2 + 1}{2\mu(\mu - \lambda)^2} + \frac{\mu^2\sigma^2 + 1}{2\mu(\mu - \lambda)}\right] \\ &= -\frac{C_{s3}}{\lambda^2} + C_w\left[\frac{\mu^2\sigma^2 + 1}{2(\mu - \lambda)^2}\right] \\ &= 0 .\end{aligned}$$

Hence,

$$-2C_{s3}(\mu - \lambda)^2 + C_w(\mu^2\sigma^2 + 1)\lambda^2 = 0 .$$

Solving this quadratic equation in λ and simplifying,

$$\lambda = \mu \frac{-1 \pm \sqrt{\frac{C_w}{C_{s3}} \cdot \frac{1}{2} (\mu^2\sigma^2 + 1)}}{\frac{C_w}{C_{s3}} \cdot \frac{1}{2} (\mu^2\sigma^2 + 1) - 1}.$$

Considering separately the cases where the denominator is positive and where it is negative, the conclusion is drawn in both cases that the $\pm$ sign must be a $+$ sign in order for the requirement, $0 < \lambda < \mu$, to hold. With a $+$ sign, this expression simplifies to $\lambda = \lambda^*$ after factoring the denominator and then canceling the numerator. For the case where the original denominator was zero, i.e., where the quadratic equation reduces to a linear equation, both the linear equation and λ^* reduce to $\lambda = \frac{1}{2}\mu$. Therefore, $\lambda = \lambda^*$ is the general expression which satisfies the necessary condition for a minimum (see Appendix 2). Furthermore, $d^2E(C_{3b})/d\lambda^2 > 0$ for $\lambda < \mu$, so that $\lambda = \lambda^*$ must be a global minimum, as was to be shown.

11.5.6 Unknown μ, λ, and s

If the situation should arise where μ, λ, and s are all decision variables, a solution may be obtained by combining models 2 and 3. For a fixed value of $\lambda = \lambda_p/n$, where n is a positive integer, the optimal μ and s can be obtained from model 2. By repeating this for various values of n (and therefore of λ) and computing the corresponding minimum expected total costs, the over-all optimal solution can be found by trial and error from model 3.

11.5.7 Priority-Discipline Cost Models

When the service discipline is based on a priority system as discussed in Sec. 10.7, a relatively minor change must be made in the preceding cost models. The use of priorities implies that the cost of waiting is different for the various priority classes. Therefore, for models 1 and 2, replace C_wL by

$$\sum_{k=1}^{N} C_kL_k ,$$

where C_k is the cost of waiting per unit time for a member of priority class k (and where the L_k and N are as defined in Sec. 10.7). For model 3, it is more meaningful to let n (the number of service facilities) be the decision variable rather than λ, since there is now a distinct mean arrival rate λ_k for each priority class. Such a revised version of model 3 is given below.

FORMULATION OF MODEL 3P

Definitions: As given for model 3 and in Sec. 14.7, plus the following.
C_k = cost of waiting per unit time for a member of priority class k, for $k = 1, 2, \cdots, N$.

R_k = expected number of members of the entire kth priority class that require service per unit time, for $k = 1, 2, \cdots, N$.
$E(C_{3P})$ = expected total variable cost per unit time.
Given: $\mu, C_{s3}, C_f, v, A; R_k, C_k$, for $k = 1, 2, \cdots, n$.
To find: n, s.
Objective: Minimize

$$E(C_{3P}) = n(C_f + sC_{s3}) + n \sum_{k=1}^{N} C_k\lambda_k[W_k + E(T)] ,$$

where

$$E(T) = \frac{\sqrt{\frac{A}{n}}}{v} \qquad \text{for travel-time model 1 ,}$$

$$\text{and } \lambda_k = R_k/n, \qquad \text{for } k = 1, 2, \cdots, N.$$

Model 3P is based on the same assumptions as model 3, plus the assumption that each priority class is distributed uniformly throughout the population. The solution procedure is the same as for model 3.

11.6 ILLUSTRATIVE PROBLEMS

Example 1

An airline maintenance base only has facilities for overhauling one airplane engine at a time. Therefore, in order to return the airplanes into use as soon as possible, the policy has been to stagger the overhauling of the four engines of each airplane. In other words, only one engine is overhauled each time an airplane comes into the shop. Under this policy, airplanes have arrived according to a Poisson process at a mean rate of one per day. The time required for an engine overhaul (once work has begun) has an exponential distribution with a mean of $\frac{1}{2}$ day.

A proposal has been made to change the policy so as to overhaul all four engines consecutively each time an airplane comes into the shop. It is pointed out that, although this would quadruple the expected service time, each plane would need to come into the shop only one-fourth times as often.

Use queueing theory to compare the two alternatives on a meaningful basis.

Solution

On the basis of the information provided, there is no apparent difference in service costs between the two alternatives. Therefore, any differences must be in the costs that are attributable to having airplanes waiting. Since the alternatives have different mean arrival rates, the expected cost of waiting per unit time is a fixed multiple of L but not of W. Hence, if C_w is the cost of waiting per unit time per airplane, C_wL would be the expected cost of waiting per unit time. Thus, a comparison of the two alternatives reduces to a comparison of their respective values of L as given by queueing theory.

Let the unit of time be a day. For the status quo alternative, the mean arrival rate is $\lambda = 1$, and the expected service time is $1/\mu = \frac{1}{2}$, so that the mean service rate is $\mu = 2$. Since only one airplane engine (calling unit) is serviced at a time, a single-server queueing model is indicated. The queueing system has a Poisson input and exponential service times, so the model of Sec. 10.5.1 should be used. Thus,

$$L = \frac{\lambda}{\mu - \lambda} = \frac{1}{2 - 1} = 1$$

for the status quo alternative.

If the proposal were adopted, the calling units (airplanes) would still be serviced by only a single server. Furthermore, $\lambda = \frac{1}{4}$, $1/\mu = 2$, and $\rho = \lambda/\mu = \frac{1}{2}$, just as for the status quo, so it appears at first glance that L would not change. However, beware of a hasty choice of the queueing model! It is true that one would expect the airplanes to continue to arrive at random, i.e., according to a Poisson input. However, the service-time distribution would no longer be exponential. Service now consists of a sequence of four service phases (overhauling four engines), each of which has an exponential distribution. Therefore, the total service time is a sum of four identical exponential random variables. As discussed in Sec. 10.5.4, this sum has an Erlang distribution with $k = 4$ (assuming that the random variables are mutually independent). Hence, one should use the model of Sec. 10.5.4 rather than the exponential model of Sec. 10.5.1 in order to evaluate the proposal. Thus,

$$L = \frac{k+1}{2k} \frac{\lambda^2}{\mu(\mu - \lambda)} + \frac{\lambda}{\mu} = \frac{5}{8} \frac{\frac{1}{16}}{\frac{1}{2}\left(\frac{1}{2} - \frac{1}{4}\right)} + \frac{1}{2}$$

$$= \frac{13}{16}$$

for the proposal, which would give a significant reduction in waiting costs over the status quo.

Therefore, unless there are other overriding considerations, the proposal should be adopted.

Example 2

Solve the tool crib example given in Sec. 10.2, assuming a Poisson input and exponential service times.

Solution

Using one hour as the unit of time, the expected time between arrivals is $1/\lambda = 50/3600$, and the expected service time is $1/\mu = 60/3600$, so $\rho = \lambda/s\mu = 1.2/s$. Since λ and μ are known, whereas s is the decision variable, cost model 1 should be used; the appropriate queueing model obviously is the one presented in Sec. 10.6.1. The given cost data indicate that $C_{s1} =$ \$3 and $C_w =$ \$7. The consequent computational results are summarized below.

s	sC_{s1}	P_0	L	C_wL	$E(C_1)$
2	\$ 6	0.250	1.875	\$13.12	\$19.12
3	\$ 9	0.294	1.294	\$ 9.06	\$18.06
4	\$12	0.300	1.216	\$ 8.51	\$20.51

Therefore, the tool crib should have three clerks since this minimizes expected total cost per hour.

The results quoted in Sec. 10.2 were obtained by using a $7\frac{1}{2}$-hour day as the unit of time and $[(s - \lambda/\mu)C_{s1} + C_wL_q]$ as the objective function. The reader may verify these results for himself and note that the cost differences between the alternatives are the same as yielded by model 1 when the same unit of time is used.

Example 3

A certain company is designing a new plant. It has been decided to install one or more tool cribs in the factory area of 300,000 square feet. From previous experience, it is known that the time required by a tool crib clerk to service a caller has an exponential distribution with a mean of one-half minute. Judging from the anticipated number of employees in the entire factory area, it is also predicted that the employees would require this service at random but at a mean rate of two employees per minute.

The net cost to the company of each tool crib clerk is about \$3 per hour. The capital recovery costs, upkeep costs, etc., associated with each tool crib provided is estimated to be \$3 per working hour. The cost of an employee waiting is estimated to be \$6 per hour.

Employees walk at a speed of about three miles per hour. Travel-time model 1 is considered to be a reasonable idealization of the mode of travel, etc. The employees requiring tool crib service will be distributed quite uniformly throughout the factory area. Therefore, the tool cribs will be assigned an equal number of clerks and will service employees over roughly equal areas.

Determine the number of tool cribs and the number of clerks at each crib which will minimize expected total cost.

Solution

Each tool crib will have a Poisson input and exponential service times, so the queueing model of Sec. 10.6.1 should be used. The mean arrival rate at each crib, λ, and the number of clerks at each crib, s, are the decision variables, so cost model 3 is appropriate.

It is essential that the same unit of time and of distance be used consistently for all components of the model. Arbitrarily select one hour as the unit of time and one foot as the unit of distance. The given parameters for cost model 3 then become

$$\mu = 120/\text{hr.}, \qquad C_f = \$3/\text{hr.},$$
$$C_w = \$6/\text{hr.}, \qquad \lambda_p = 120/\text{hr.},$$
$$C_{s3} = \$3/\text{hr.}, \qquad a = 2500 \text{ sq. ft.},$$
$$v = 15{,}840 \text{ ft./hr.}$$

The consequent computational results are summarized in the following table.

n	λ	s	W	T	$\dfrac{C_f + sC_{s3}}{\lambda}$	$C_w(W + E(T))$	$E(C_3)$
1	120	1	∞	0.0346	\$0.050	∞	∞
1	120	2	0.0111	0.0346	\$0.075	\$0.274	\$0.349
1	120	3	0.0087	0.0346	\$0.100	\$0.260	\$0.360
2	60	1	0.0167	0.0244	\$0.100	\$0.247	\$0.347
2	60	2	0.0089	0.0244	\$0.150	\$0.200	\$0.350
3	40	1	0.0125	0.0199	\$0.150	\$0.194	\$0.344
3	40	2	0.0086	0.0199	\$0.225	\$0.171	\$0.396
4	30	1	0.0111	0.0173	\$0.200	\$0.170	\$0.370

Therefore, the indicated optimal solution is to provide three tool cribs, each with a single clerk, at an expected total variable cost of \$0.344 per unit serviced. However, the narrowness of the margin over alternative solutions indicates that a more detailed analysis would be required to more positively identify the best solution. Any further investigation apparently should concentrate on the travel-time analysis since the travel-time cost is a dominant part of the total cost in this case. Finally, it appears that the alternative of providing two tool cribs, one with two clerks servicing about two-thirds of the factory and the other with one clerk servicing the remainder, should also be considered.

Example 4

Plans are currently being developed for a new factory. One department has been allocated a large number of automatic machines of a certain type, and it is now desired to determine how many machines should be assigned to each operator for servicing (loading, unloading, adjusting, setup, etc.). For the purpose of this analysis, the following information has been provided.

The running time (time between completing service and requiring service again) of each machine has an exponential distribution with a mean of 120 minutes. The service time has an exponential distribution with a mean of 6 minutes. The net cost to the company of each operator would be about $3 per hour. It is estimated that the cost or imputed cost because a machine is idle waiting for service or being serviced would be $30 per hour.

An operator must attend to his own machines; he cannot give help to or receive help from other operators.

How many machines should be assigned to each operator?

Solution

Even though there will be a number of operators, each group of machines will be serviced by only one of them, so that a single-server queueing model must be used. Conceptually, each operator constitutes a single-server service facility with its own calling population.

Since the number of machines assigned to each operator will be finite, each service facility will have a limited input source, i.e., a finite calling population. The only single-server queueing model of this type given in Chapter 10 is the one in Sec. 10.5.6. Fortunately, the assumptions regarding the input process and service-time distribution are satisfied, so this model is applicable. Hence, the problem can be solved by trial and error by evaluating various values of M, the number of machines assigned to each operator. However, the computational effort required to obtain the necessary information is relatively extensive (except when using the tabulated results referenced in Sec. 10.6.4). Therefore, it would be very desirable to obtain an initial approximation of the optimal value of M in order to reduce the number of values that need to be evaluated.

The optimal value of λ can be approximated very readily by assuming an unlimited source, so that the mean arrival rate λ to each service facility is independent of the line length. If only their running time is considered, each machine calls for service according to a Poisson distribution at a mean rate of 1/2 times per hour. Therefore, when M machines are assigned to each operator, it is reasonable to approximate the actual input process by a Poisson input with a mean rate per hour of $\lambda = M/2$. Thus, λ may now be used as the decision variable for the problem. Since the number of servers s is restricted to one, and the calling units (machines) do no traveling, cost model 3b becomes applicable. Continuing to use one hour as the unit of time, the given parameters for model 3b are $\mu = 10$, $C_w = \$30$, $C_{s3} = \$3$, and (since $1/\mu^2$ is the variance of the exponential distribution) $\sigma^2 = 1/100$. Therefore, the desired approximation of the optimal value of λ is

$$\begin{aligned}\lambda &= \frac{10}{1 + \sqrt{\frac{30}{3} \cdot \frac{1}{2}\left(100 \frac{1}{100} + 1\right)}}\\ &= \frac{10}{1 + \sqrt{10}}\\ &\doteq 2.40 .\end{aligned}$$

Hence, the optimal value of M is approximately $M = 2\lambda = 4.8$, or, rounding to the nearest integer, $M = 5$.

The stage is now set for finding the optimal solution by using the exact assumption of a limited source as described by the queueing model of Sec. 10.5.6. Under this assumption, the mean arrival rate to a service facility is not independent of line length, so cost model 3 cannot be used. However, it will be easy to develop a similar cost model which is applicable. Since the underlying objective is to minimize the expected total variable cost of service and waiting for all machines, it is essential that the objective function adopted be a fixed multiple of this quantity. For this reason, a criterion such as expected cost per hour per operator is not valid (since the total number of operators changes as the decision variable, M, changes). On the other hand, expected cost per hour per machine is a valid objective function, and it will be used here [denoted by $E(C)$]. Thus, the objective is to minimize

$$E(C) = \frac{C_{s3} + C_w L}{M},$$

where C_{s3} and C_w are the cost parameters used by cost model 3b. Hence, $C_{s3} = \$3$ and $C_w = \$30$, so that

$$E(C) = \frac{\$3 + \$30L}{M}.$$

Let λ denote the mean arrival rate of each individual running machine. Section 10.5.6 then yields

$$L = M - \frac{\mu}{\lambda}(1 - P_0),$$

where

$$\frac{1}{P_0} = \sum_{n=0}^{M} \frac{M!}{(M-n)!}\left(\frac{\lambda}{\mu}\right)^n.$$

Since $\lambda = 1/2$ and $\mu = 10$, the following computational results are obtained.

M	P_0	L	$E(C)$
4	0.81093	0.2186	\$2.390
5	0.76436	0.2872	\$2.323
6	0.71814	0.3628	\$2.314
7	0.67233	0.4466	\$2.343

Therefore, on the basis of available information, the optimal decision is to assign six machines to each operator at an expected cost of \$2.314 per hour per machine. It is interesting to note that this solution is slightly different from the one obtained by assuming an unlimited source, but that the improvement in expected cost is very small.

SELECTED REFERENCES

1. Bowman, Edward H., and Fetter, Robert F. (eds.), *Analyses of Industrial Operations*, Irwin, Homewood, Illinois, 1959, Part III.
2. Buffa, Elwood S., *Readings in Production and Operations Management*, Wiley, New York, 1966, papers 12–15.
3. Hillier, Frederick S., "The Application of Waiting Line Theory to Industrial Problems," *Journal of Industrial Engineering*, **15,** No. 1, 3–8 (1964).
4. Morse, Philip M., *Queues, Inventories, and Maintenance*, Wiley, New York, 1958.
5. Saaty, Thomas L., *Elements of Queueing Theory*, McGraw-Hill, New York, 1961, chap. 14.
6. Wolff, Ronald W., "Problems of Statistical Inference for Birth and Death Queueing Models," *Operations Research*, **13,** No. 2, 343–357 (1965).

PROBLEMS

1. Consider a queueing system with a Poisson input, where the server must perform two distinguishable tasks in sequence for each calling unit, so the total service time is the sum of the two task times (which are statistically independent).

(a) Suppose that the first task time has an exponential distribution with a mean of one minute, and the second task time has an Erlang distribution with a mean of three minutes and with the shape parameter $k = 3$. Which queueing theory model should be used to represent this system?

(b) Suppose that Part (a) is modified so that the first task time also has an Erlang distribution with the shape parameter $k = 3$ (but with the mean still equal to one minute). Which queueing theory model should be used to represent this system?

2. A certain single-server queueing system has been under observation in order to determine which theoretical queueing model should be used to represent this system. The following service times (in minutes) have been recorded:

0.47, 0.22, 1.37, 0.67, 0.38, 2.80, 0.03, 0.85, 0.72, 0.27, 1.40, 0.32, 0.55, 0.13, 0.25, 2.20, 0.81, 1.05, 0.18, 0.61, 0.37, 1.72, 0.74, 0.48, 0.15.

(a) Use a statistical procedure to test the hypothesis that the service-time distribution is exponential.
(b) Assuming that the service-time distribution is indeed exponential, estimate the mean service rate μ.

3. It is believed that a certain queueing system has an Erlang service-time distribution. A sample of actual service times (in minutes) has been recorded, yielding a sample mean of 2.48 and a sample variance of 1.55. Use this information to estimate the shape parameter k.

4. A certain queueing system has a Poisson input with a mean arrival rate of two calling units per hour. The service-time distribution is exponential with a mean of 0.4 hours. The marginal cost of providing each server is \$4 per hour, where it is estimated that the cost which is incurred by having each calling unit idle (i.e., in the queueing system) is \$100 per hour. Determine the number of servers that should be assigned to the system in order to minimize the expected total cost per hour.

5. A railroad considers it necessary to paint its cars once a year. Alternative 1 is to provide two paint shops where painting is done by hand (one car at a time) for a total annual cost of \$150,000. The painting time for a car has an exponential distribution with a mean of six hours. Alternative 2 is to provide one spray shop involving an annual cost of \$200,000. In this case, the painting time for a car has an exponential distribution with a mean of three hours. For both alternatives, the cars arrive according to a Poisson input with a mean arrival rate of one every eight hours. The cost of idle time per car is \$30 per hour. Which alternative should the railroad choose? Assume that the paint shops are always open, i.e., they work $(24)(365) = 8760$ hours per year.

6. An airline maintenance base wishes to make a change in its overhaul operation. The present situation is that only one airplane can be repaired at a time, and the expected repair time is 36 hours, whereas the expected time between arrivals is 48 hours. This has led to frequent and prolonged delays in repairing incoming planes, even though the base operates continuously. The average cost of an idle plane to the airline is \$1000 per hour. It is estimated that each plane goes into the maintenance shop six times per year. It is believed that the input process for the base is Poisson and that the probability distribution of repair times is exponential. Alternative A is to provide a duplicate maintenance shop so that two planes can be repaired simultaneously. The cost, depreciated over a period of five years, is \$300,000 per airplane per year.

Alternative B is to replace the present maintenance equipment by the most efficient (and expensive) equipment available, thereby reducing the expected repair time to 24 hours. The cost, depreciated over a period of five years, is \$400,000 per airplane yer year.

Which alternative should the airline choose?

7. A single crew is provided for unloading and/or loading each truck that arrives at the loading dock of a warehouse. These trucks arrive according to a Poisson input process at a mean rate of one per hour. The time required by a crew to unload and/or load a truck has an exponential distribution (regardless of the crew size). The expected time required by a one-man crew would be two hours.

The cost of providing each additional member of the crew is \$5 per hour. The cost that is attributable to having a truck not in use (i.e., a truck standing at the loading dock) is estimated to be \$20 per hour.

(a) Assume that the mean service rate of the crew is proportional to its size. What should the size be in order to minimize the expected total cost per hour?
(b) Assume that the mean service rate of the crew is proportional to the square root of its size. What should the size be in order to minimize expected total cost per hour?

8. Consider cost model 2b. Verify that the minimizing value of μ occurs at the unique value of μ (for $\mu > \lambda$) which satisfies the equation,

$$C_{s2}(1+\Delta)\mu^{\Delta} - \frac{\lambda C_w}{(\mu-\lambda)^2}\left[1 + \left(\frac{1-k}{k}\right)\frac{\lambda}{\mu}\left(2-\frac{\lambda}{\mu}\right)\right] = 0\,.$$

9. Consider a factory whose floor area is 160,000 square feet. Suppose that four service facilities of a certain kind are provided in the factory, that the employees use them at a total mean rate of eight employees per minute. The employees are distributed uniformly throughout the factory, and they walk to and from the nearest facility at an average speed of three miles per hour.

Compare travel-time models 1, 2, and 3 in terms of their prediction of the expected travel time, both ways, for an employee visiting a service facility.

10. Consider the derivation of $E(T)$, given in Sec. 11.5.5, for the travel-time models.

(a) For travel-time model 2, indicate how the initial expression given for $E(T)$ is obtained.
(b) For travel-time model 3, indicate how the initial expression given for $E(T)$ is obtained.

11. Consider a generalized version of travel-time model 1 where the area is rectangular and the service facility is not necessarily in the center of the area, as depicted in the following graphical representation.

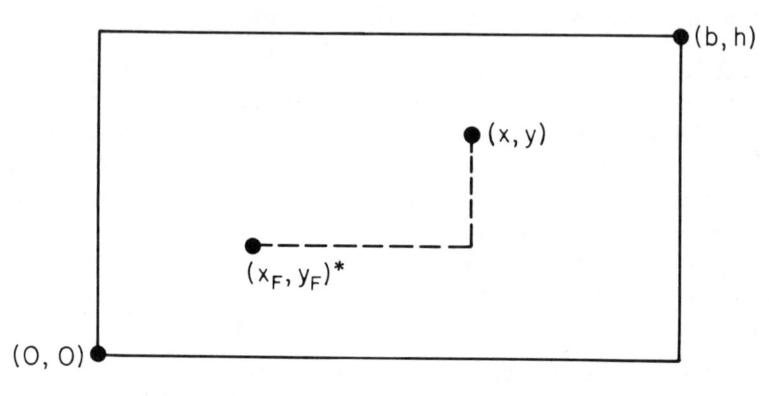

* (x_F, y_F) is the location of the service facility.

Derive the expected travel time, $E(T)$, for this model. Your equation for $E(T)$ should be in terms of v (average velocity), x_F, y_F, b, and h.

12. A new factory is being planned, and one decision to be made is how many tool cribs to provide. Thus far, it has only been decided that there should be a large number of small tool cribs, each with a single clerk, so as to avoid excessive wasted time in walking to and from the crib. The following data have been obtained for analyzing the problem further.

The mechanics assigned to a tool crib would arrive for service according to a Poisson input process (as for an infinite calling population), with each mechanic coming about once every 100 minutes on the average. The time required to service each mechanic has an Erlang distribution with the shape parameter $k = 4$ and with a mean of one minute. The cost of providing each tool crib, including the clerk, is estimated to be \$10 per hour. The estimated cost associated with a mechanic waiting at a tool crib is \$5 per hour.

Ignoring the cost of idle time due to walking to and from the tool crib, determine how many mechanics should be assigned to each tool crib in order to minimize expected total cost.

13. A certain large shop doing light fabrication work uses a single central storage facility (dispatch station) for material in-process storage.

The typical procedure is that each employee personally delivers his finished work (by hand, tote box, or hand cart) and receives new work and materials at the facility. While this procedure had worked well in earlier years when the shop was smaller, it appears that it may now be advisable to divide the shop into two semi-independent parts, with a separate storage facility for each one. You have been assigned the job of comparing the use of two facilities and of one facility from a cost standpoint.

The factory has the shape of a rectangle 150 yards by 100 yards. Thus, letting one yard be the unit of distance, the (x, y) coordinates of the corners would be (0, 0), (150, 0), (150, 100), and (0, 100). Using this coordinate system, the existing facility is located at (50, 50), and the location available for the second facility is (100, 50).

Each facility would be operated by a single clerk. The time required by a clerk to service a caller has an exponential distribution with a mean of two minutes. Employees arrive at the present facility according to a Poisson input process at a mean rate of 20 per hour. The employees are rather uniformly distributed throughout the shop, and if the second facility were installed, each employee would normally use the nearer of the two facilities. Employees walk at an average speed of about three miles per hour. All aisles are parallel to the outer walls of the shop. The net cost of providing each facility is estimated to be about \$10 per hour, plus \$5 per hour for the clerk. The estimated total cost of an employee being idled by traveling or waiting at the facility is \$10 per hour.

Given the preceding cost factors, which alternative minimizes expected total cost?

14. A certain job shop has been experiencing long delays in jobs going through the turret lathe department because of inadequate capacity. The foreman contends that five machines are required, as opposed to the three machines that he now has. However, because of pressure from management to hold capital expenditures down, only one additional machine will be authorized unless there is solid evidence that a second one is necessary.

This shop does three kinds of jobs, namely, government jobs, commercial jobs, and standard products. Whenever a turret lathe finishes a job, it starts a government job if one is waiting; if not, it starts a commercial job if any are waiting; if not, it starts on a standard product if any are waiting. Jobs of the same type are taken on a first-come-first-served basis.

Although much overtime work is required currently, management wants the turret lathe department to operate on an 8-hour, 5-day-a-week basis. The probability distribution of the time required by a turret lathe for a job appears to be approximately exponential with a mean of ten hours. Jobs come into the shop according to a Poisson input process, but at a mean rate of seven per week for government jobs, five per week for commercial jobs, and two per week for standard products. (These figures are expected to remain the same for the indefinite future.)

It is worth about \$300, \$150, and \$30 to avoid a delay of one additional (working) day in a government job, commercial job, and a standard job, respectively. The incremental capitalized cost of providing each turret lathe (including the operator, etc.) is estimated to be \$100 per working day.

Determine the number of additional turret lathes that should be obtained in order to minimize expected total cost.

CHAPTER 12

Inventory Theory[65]

12.1 INTRODUCTION

The problem of determining inventory policies is certainly not new. Industrial firms have been faced with this problem since their beginnings. It is only within the last decade or so that it has been approached by using the new quantitative technique of representation by means of a mathematical model, a method conducive to optimization. An inventory can be defined as a stock of goods which is held for the purpose of future production or sales. Since inventories constitute an alternative to production, or purchase in the future, the choice among policies depends upon their relative "profitability." Some of the costs that determine this profitability are: (1) the costs of ordering or manufacturing, (2) holding or storage costs, (3) unsatisfied demand or shortage penalty costs, (4) revenues, (5) salvage costs, and (6) discount rate.

The cost of ordering or manufacturing an amount z can be represented by a function $c(z)$. The simplest form of this function is one which is directly proportional to the amount ordered, i.e., $c \cdot z$, where c represents the unit price paid. Another common assumption is that $c(z)$ is composed of two parts, a term which is directly proportional to the amount ordered and a term which is constant K, for z positive and zero for $z = 0$. For this case, if z is positive the ordering, or production cost, is given by $K + c \cdot z$. K is often referred to as the setup cost and generally includes the administrative cost of ordering, the preliminary labor and other expenses of starting a production run, etc. There are other assumptions that can be made about this ordering function, but this chapter is restricted to the two cases described above.

[65] Equations are numbered in this chapter for the first time in the text. This is done because frequent reference to equations is required.

The holding or storage costs represent the costs associated with the storage of the inventory until it is sold or used. They may include the cost of space, insurance, protection, taxes attributed to storage, etc. This cost may be a function of the maximum quantity held during a period, the average amount held, or the cumulated excess of supply over demand. The latter viewpoint is usually taken in this chapter.

The unsatisfied demand or shortage penalty cost is incurred when the stock of the commodity proves to be inadequate to meet the demand. This cost depends upon the structure of the model. One such case occurs when the demand exceeds the available inventory, and it is met by a priority shipment, or is not met at all. The penalty cost can be viewed as the difference between the cost of priority shipment and the cost of routine delivery, or, in the situation where the unsatisfied demand is lost, as the loss in revenue. This case is known as "no backlogging." The second case of demand not being fulfilled out of stock assumes that it is satisfied when the commodity next becomes available. The penalty cost can be interpreted as the loss of customer's good will and his subsequent reluctance to do business with the firm. This case is known as "backlogging" of unsatisfied demand. This unsatisfied demand cost is usually a function of the excess of demand over supply.

The revenue cost may or may not be included in the model. If it is assumed that both the price and the demand of the product are not under the control of the company, the revenue from sales is independent of the firm's inventory policy and may be neglected except for the situation in which the firm cannot meet the demand and the sale is lost. In this no-backlogging case, the situation can be handled by including the loss in revenue in the unsatisfied demand penalty cost.

The salvage value of an item is the value of a leftover item at the termination of the inventory period. If the inventory policy is carried on for an indefinite number of periods, and there is no obsolescence, there are no leftover items. What is left over at the end of one period is the amount available at the beginning of the next period. On the other hand, if the policy is to be carried out for only one period, the salvage value represents the disposal value of the item to the firm, say, the selling price. The negative of the salvage value is called the salvage cost. If there is a cost associated with the disposal of an item, the salvage cost may be positive. Since the storage costs generally are assumed to be a function of excess of supply over demand, the salvage costs can be combined with this cost and, hence, are usually neglected in this chapter.

Finally, the discount rate takes into account the time value of money. When a firm ties up capital in inventory, it is prevented from using this money for alternative purposes. In particular, it could invest this money in secure investments, say, government bonds, and have a return on investment, a year hence, of, say, 4%. Thus, a dollar invested today would be worth $1.04 a year hence, or alternatively, a dollar profit a year hence is equivalent to $\alpha = 1/1.04$ dollars today. The quantity α is known as the discount factor. Thus, in considering "profitability" of an inventory policy, the profit or costs a year hence should be multiplied by α, two years hence, by α^2, etc.

Of course, the choice of discounting on a yearly basis is arbitrary, but it is clear that for short periods α may be assumed to be 1, but for long horizons α should not be neglected.

Inventory models may be classified into two categories, depending upon whether the demand for a period is known (deterministic demand) or whether it is a random variable having a known probability distribution (non-deterministic or random demand).

12.2 DETERMINISTIC INVENTORY MODELS

This section is concerned with inventory problems where the actual demand for a period is known. Several models are considered, beginning with the economic lot size models.

12.2.1 Economic Lot Size Models

The most common inventory problem faced by industry concerns the situation where stock levels are depleted with time and then are replenished by the arrival of new items. A simple model representing this situation is given by the economic lot size model. Items are assumed to be withdrawn continuously and at a known constant rate denoted by a. It is further assumed that items are ordered in equal numbers, Q at a time, and production is instantaneous. The only costs to be considered are the setup cost, K, charged at the beginning of the period, a production cost (or purchase cost) of c dollars per item, and an inventory holding cost of h dollars per item per unit of time. The inventory problem is to determine how often to make a production run, and what size it should be in order that the cost per unit of time is a minimum. It will first be assumed that shortages are not allowed, and then this assumption will be relaxed. The problem is summarized in Fig. 12.1.

The ordering cost per order is given by

$$\begin{cases} 0, & \text{if } Q = 0 \\ K + cQ, & \text{if } Q > 0\,, \end{cases}$$

and the holding cost per period is given by

$$h \int_0^{Q/a} Q(t)dt = h \int_0^{Q/a} (Q - at)dt = hQ^2/2a\,.$$

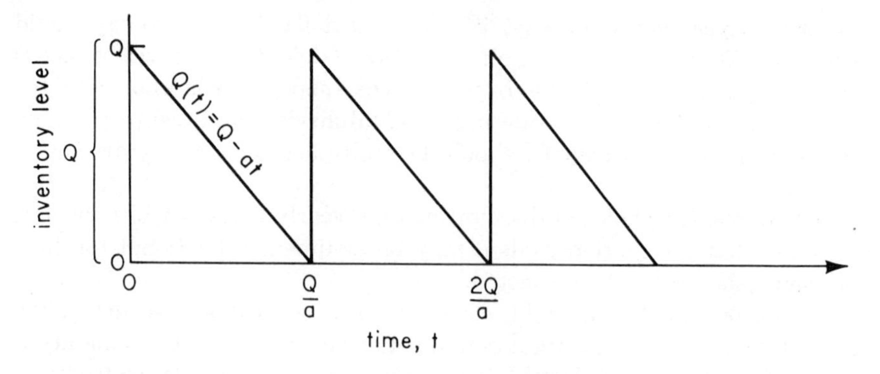

FIGURE 12.1. Diagram of inventory level as a function of time—no shortages permitted.

Therefore the total cost per period is

$$K + cQ + hQ^2/2a\,, \tag{1}$$

and the total cost per unit of time is

$$T = \frac{K + cQ + hQ^2/2a}{Q/a} = aK/Q + ac + hQ/2\,. \tag{2}$$

It is evident that the value of Q, say, Q^*, which minimizes T is found from $dT/dQ = 0$. $dT/dQ = -aK/Q^2 + h/2 = 0$, so that

$$Q^* = \sqrt{2aK/h}\,, \tag{3}$$

which is the well-known economic lot size result. Similarly, the time it takes to diminish this optimum value of Q^*, say, t^*, is given by

$$t^* = Q^*/a = \sqrt{2K/ah}\,. \tag{4}$$

If shortages are allowed and are priced out at a cost of u dollars for each unit of demand unfilled for one unit of time, a similar result can be obtained. Denote by S the stock on hand at the beginning of a period. The problem is summarized in Fig. 12.2.

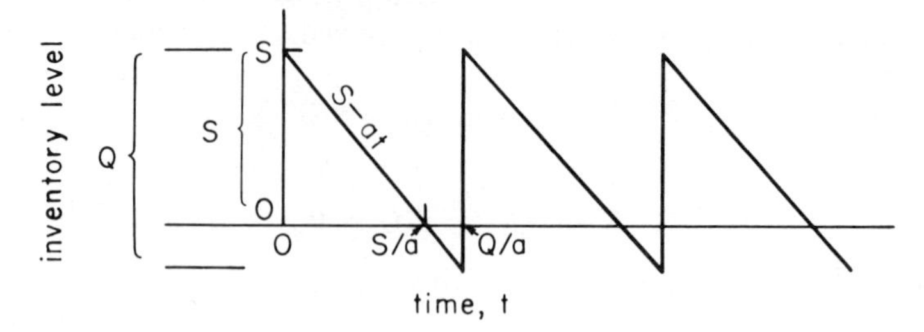

FIGURE 12.2. Diagram of inventory level as a function of time—shortages permitted.

The ordering cost per order is given by

$$\begin{cases} 0, & \text{if } Q = 0 \\ K + cQ, & \text{if } Q > 0\,. \end{cases}$$

The holding cost per period is given by

$$h \int_0^{S/a} (S - at)dt = hS^2/2a\,,$$

and the shortage cost per period is given by

$$u \int_0^{Q/a - S/a} at\, dt = u(Q - S)^2/2a\,.$$

Therefore, the total cost per period is

$$K + cQ + hS^2/2a + u(Q - S)^2/2a\,, \tag{5}$$

and the total cost per unit of time is

$$T = \frac{K + cQ + hS^2/2a + u(Q - S)^2/2a}{Q/a} \tag{6}$$

$$= aK/Q + ac + hS^2/2Q + u(Q - S)^2/2Q\,.$$

The optimum values of S, say, S^*, and Q, say, Q^*, are found from

$$\frac{\partial T}{\partial S} = \frac{\partial T}{\partial Q} = 0.$$

$$\frac{\partial T}{\partial S} = hS/Q - u(Q - S)/Q = 0.$$

$$\frac{\partial T}{\partial Q} = -aK/Q^2 - hS^2/2Q^2 + u(Q - S)/Q - u(Q - S)^2/2Q^2 = 0.$$

Solving these equations simultaneously leads to

$$S^* = \sqrt{2aK/h}\,\sqrt{u/(u + h)}\,, \tag{7}$$

$$Q^* = \sqrt{2aK/h}\,\sqrt{(u + h)/u}\,. \tag{8}$$

The optimal period length, t^*, is given by

$$t^* = Q^*/a = \sqrt{2K/ah}\,\sqrt{(u + h)/u}\,. \tag{9}$$

Further, from Fig. 12.2, the fraction of time that no shortage exists is given by

$$\frac{S^*}{a} \Big/ \frac{Q^*}{a} = u/(u + h)\,,$$

which is independent of K. Note that if it is assumed (as was done) that the production (or purchase) cost of an item is constant throughout all time periods, it does not appear in the optimal solution. This is evident since no matter what policy is used, the same quantity is required, and, hence, this cost is fixed. The same remarks hold for revenue so that it, too, can be neglected.

12.2.2 Production Planning

In the last section, the economic lot size model was explored. The results were dependent upon the assumption of a constant demand rate and a constant order (or production) quantity. When this is relaxed, i.e., when the amounts required from period to period are allowed to vary, the square root formula no longer assures a minimum cost solution.

Consider the following model due to Wagner and Whitin.[66] As before, the only costs to be considered are the setup cost, K, charged at the beginning of the period, a production cost (or purchase cost) of c dollars per item, and an inventory holding cost of h dollars per item which is charged (arbitrarily) at the beginning of the time period. In addition, r_i, $i = 1, 2, \cdots, n$, represents the requirements at time i, and it is assumed that these requirements must be met. Initially there is no stock on hand. For a horizon of n periods, the inventory problem is to determine how much should be produced at the beginning of each time period (assumed to be instantaneous) so as to minimize the total cost incurred over the n periods. The problem is best illustrated by the following example. Let the setup cost K be \$2, the production cost c be \$1 per item, and the inventory holding cost be 20 cents per item. There are four periods to be considered. The requirements are $r_1 = 3$, $r_2 = 2$, $r_3 = 3$, and $r_4 = 2$. The problem is to determine how much to produce in each period, satisfying the requirements, and minimizing the total cost. A solution, though not optimal, is given in Fig. 12.3. This policy calls for producing 3 items at the beginning of the first period, 6 items at the beginning of the second period, and 1 item at the beginning of the fourth period.

The following general result characterizes optimal policies.

For an arbitrary demand requirement, a fixed setup cost and linear production and holding costs, there is an optimum policy which orders only when the stock is zero.

In order to show why this result is true, choose any policy. Consider the time from the beginning of a period when production from zero is made to the first time production is made when the stock is not zero. For the policy given in Fig. 12.3 this interval starts at the beginning of period 2 and ends at the beginning of period 4 when one item is produced. This time period is also shown by the solid lines in Fig. 12.4.

[66] H. M. Wagner and T. M. Whitin, "Dynamic Version of The Economic Lot Size Model," *Management Science*, **5**, No. 1, 89–96 (1958).

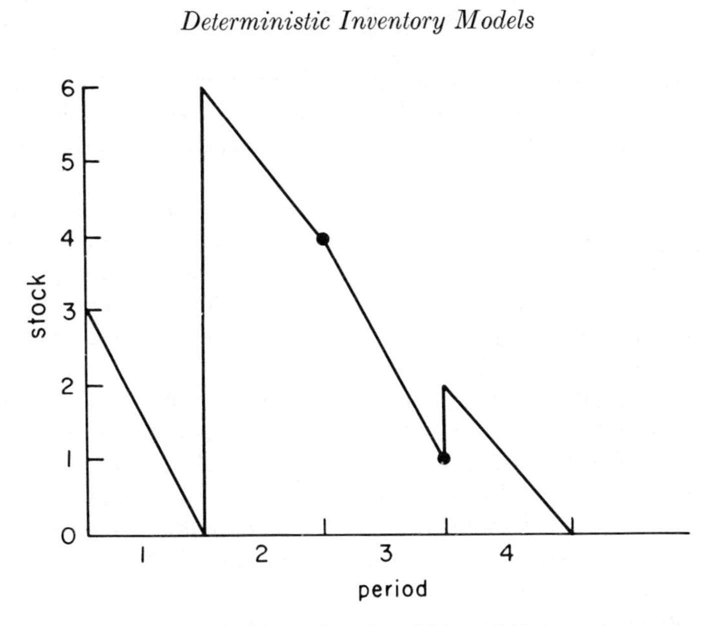

FIGURE 12.3. Production schedule which satisfies requirements.

Consider the alternate policy which implies production of 5 items at the beginning of period 2 and production of 2 items at the beginning of period 4. This policy is shown by the dotted lines in Fig. 12.4. This policy, B, dominates policy A in that the total cost is smaller. The setup costs for both of

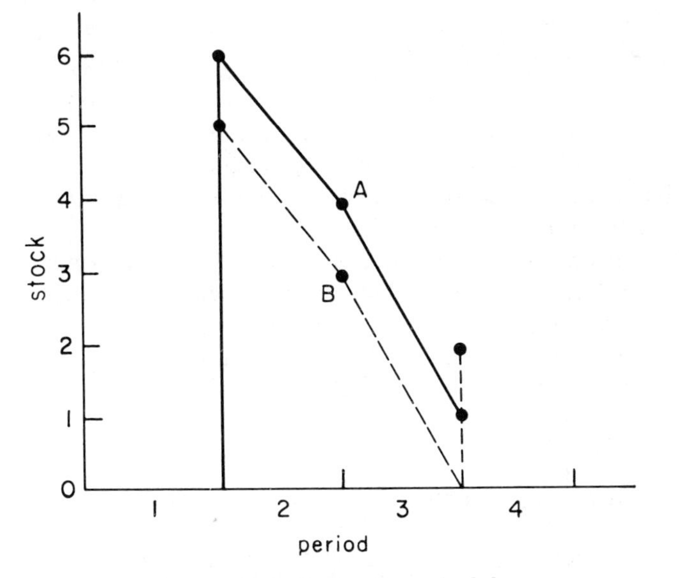

FIGURE 12.4. Production schedules.

these policies are the same, and the production costs are the same. It is evident that the holding cost for B is smaller than that for A since there is always less stock on hand. Therefore, B is better than A so that A cannot be optimal.

This characterization of optimal policies can be used to determine which policies are not optimal, but it cannot be used to find the optimal policy. Of course, one method for solving the optimization problem is to enumerate all the 2^{n-1} combinations of either ordering or not ordering in each period. This is rather cumbersome, even for moderate-sized n. Hence, a more efficient algorithm is desirable.

Suppose an optimal policy is presented. If the time of the *last* production is known for this optimal policy (it has to be when the inventory is zero), the total cost of the previous periods must be a minimum for this reduced problem since the over-all policy is optimal. Therefore, in the previously mentioned example, if the last production for the optimal policy takes place at the beginning of the third period (inventory is zero at this point), all that remains is to determine the optimal policy for the two-period problem having a requirement of 3 units for the first period and 2 units for the second period.

Let C_i denote the cost for the first i periods using an optimal policy, $i = 1, 2, \cdots, n$. A recursive expression for C_n is given by

$$C_n = \underset{j=1,2,\cdots,n}{\text{minimum}} [C_{j-1} + K + c(r_j + \cdots + r_n) + h\{r_j + 2r_{j+1} + 3r_{j+2} + \cdots + (n - j + 1)r_n\}], \tag{10}$$

where j can be viewed as an index which indicates the time (beginning of the period) of the last production. $C_0 = 0$, $c(r_j + \cdots + r_n)$ is the cost of the last production, and the quantity $h\{\quad\}$ is the total holding cost of the inventory after the last production. This latter cost is easily verified by noting that if the last production was as the beginning of the jth period, the holding cost for that period is $h(r_j + r_{j+1} + \cdots + r_{n-1} + r_n)$, the holding cost incurred at the beginning of the $j + 1$ period is $h(r_{j+1} + r_{j+2} + \cdots + r_{n-1} + r_n)$, $\cdots$, and the holding cost incurred at the beginning of the nth period is $h(r_n)$. Summing these costs leads to h times the expression in braces. Thus, in order to find the optimal policy, together with its associated cost, requires finding $C_1, C_2, \cdots, C_{n-1}$ before C_n is obtained.

Returning to the example, first consider the one-period problem (order for the first period only).

$$C_1 = C_0 + 2 + 1(3) + \frac{1}{5}(3) = 0 + 2 + 3 + 0.6 = 5.6\,.$$

For the two-period problem, there are two cases to consider, i.e., the last order may be placed at the beginning of the first period, or the last order may be placed at the beginning of the second period. In expression (10), j may range over 1 or 2, resulting in the costs $C_2^{(1)}$ or $C_2^{(2)}$, respectively. C_2 is then the minimum of $C_2^{(1)}$ and $C_2^{(2)}$. These are reflected by the policies given in Fig. 12.5.

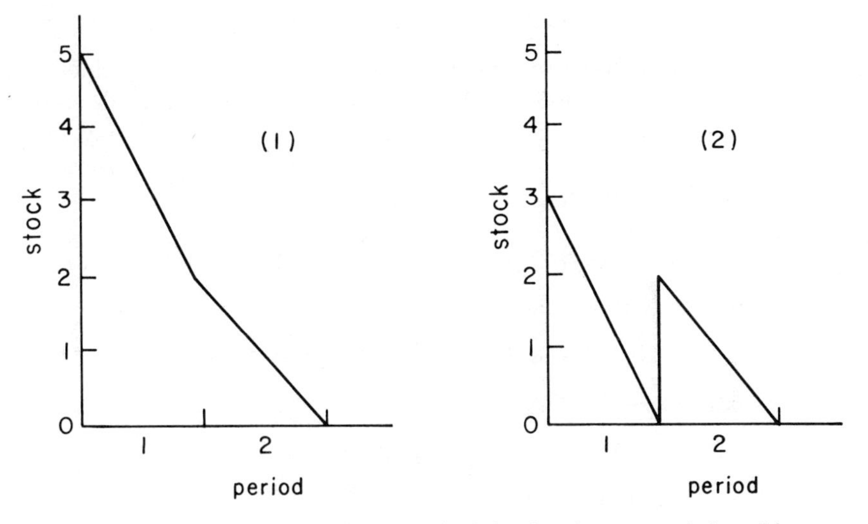

FIGURE 12.5. Alternate production schedules for the two-period problems.

$$C_2^{(1)} = C_0 + 2 + 1(3 + 2) + \frac{1}{5}\{3 + 2(2)\} = 0 + 2 + 5 + 1.4 = 8.4\,,$$

and

$$C_2^{(2)} = C_1 + 2 + 1(2) + \frac{1}{5}\{2\} = 5.6 + 2 + 2 + .4 = 10\,.$$

Hence,

$$C_2 = \min\,(8.4,\, 10) = 8.4\,.$$

For the three-period problem, there are three cases to consider, i.e., the last order may be placed at the beginning of the first period, second period, or the third period. In expression (10), j may range over 1, 2, or 3, resulting in the costs $C_3^{(1)}$, $C_3^{(2)}$, or $C_3^{(3)}$, respectively. C_3 is then the minimum of $C_3^{(1)}$, $C_3^{(2)}$, and $C_3^{(3)}$.

$$\begin{aligned} C_3^{(1)} &= C_0 + 2 + 1(3 + 2 + 3) + \frac{1}{5}\{3 + 2(2) + 3(3)\} \\ &= 0 + 2 + 8 + 3.2 = 13.2\,, \\ C_3^{(2)} &= C_1 + 2 + 1(2 + 3) + \frac{1}{5}\{2 + 2(3)\} \\ &= 5.6 + 2 + 5 + 1.6 = 14.2\,, \end{aligned}$$

and

$$\begin{aligned} C_3^{(3)} &= C_2 + 2 + 1(3) + \frac{1}{5}\{3\} \\ &= 8.4 + 2 + 3 + 0.6 = 14\,. \end{aligned}$$

Hence,

$$C_3 = \min\,(13.2,\ 14.2,\ 14) = 13.2\,.$$

Finally, for the four-period problem, there are four cases to consider i.e., the last order may be placed at the beginning of the first period, second period, third period, or the fourth period. In expression (10), j may range over 1, 2, 3, or 4, resulting in the costs $C_4^{(1)}$, $C_4^{(2)}$, $C_4^{(3)}$, or $C_4^{(4)}$, respectively. C_4 is then the minimum of $C_4^{(1)}$, $C_4^{(2)}$, $C_4^{(3)}$, and $C_4^{(4)}$.

$$\begin{aligned} C_4^{(1)} &= C_0 + 2 + 1(3 + 2 + 3 + 2) + \frac{1}{5}\{3 + 2(2) + 3(3) + 4(2)\} \\ &= 0 + 2 + 10 + 4.8 = 16.8\,, \\ C_4^{(2)} &= C_1 + 2 + 1(2 + 3 + 2) + \frac{1}{5}\{2 + 2(3) + 3(2)\} \\ &= 5.6 + 2 + 7 + 2.8 = 17.4\,, \\ C_4^{(3)} &= C_2 + 2 + 1(3 + 2) + \frac{1}{5}\{3 + 2(2)\} \\ &= 8.4 + 2 + 5 + 1.4 = 16.8\,, \end{aligned}$$

and

$$\begin{aligned} C_4^{(4)} &= C_3 + 2 + 1(2) + \frac{1}{5}\{2\} \\ &= 13.2 + 2 + 2 + 0.4 = 17.6\,. \end{aligned}$$

Hence,

$$C_4 = \min\,(16.8,\ 17.4,\ 16.8,\ 17.6) = 16.8\,,$$

so that the optimal production schedule is to produce all the items at the beginning of the first period or produce 5 units at the beginning of the first period and 5 units at the beginning of the third period.

It should be noted that the unit cost c is irrelevant to the problem because over all the time periods, all policies use the same number of items at the same total cost. Hence, this cost could have been neglected, and the same optimal policies would have been obtained.

The characterization of the optimal policy, and the subsequent algorithm for finding an optimal policy, depended upon the assumption that the holding and production costs were linear. This constraint can be relaxed to include concave production and holding costs. In fact, any increasing function of the holding cost will serve as an alternative condition if the production cost is linear. However, these alternate conditions require a modification in the algorithm for finding an optimal policy. If the production cost function is denoted by $c[\cdot]$ and holding cost function by $h[\cdot]$, the recursive expression for C_n becomes

$$C_n = \min_{j=1,2,\cdots,n} \{C_{j-1} + K + c[r_j + \cdots + r_n] + h[r_j + r_{j+1} + \cdots + r_n] + h[r_{j+1} + r_{j+2} + \cdots + r_n] + \cdots + h[r_n]\}, \quad (11)$$

where $C_0 = 0$.

A natural extension of the production planning model is to permit shortages to occur. This has been studied by Zangwill,[67] and differs from the model in Sec. 12.2.2 in that shortage costs are incurred for each unit of demand unfilled for one unit of time. Zangwill characterizes the form of the optimal policy and gives an efficient recursive relationship for finding the optimal policy. These results apply when the production costs, holding costs, and shortage costs, per period, are concave functions (thereby including the case of linear costs).

Other results have been obtained for this production planning model under the assumption that the production, holding, and shortage costs are convex. Convex production costs arise, for example, where there are several sources of limited production at different unit costs in a period. If one uses these sources up to capacity in order of ascending unit cost (as is optimal), the resulting production cost is convex in the total amount produced. Such an assumption about the production cost precludes the use of the setup charge.

12.2.3 **Inventory Issuing Policies**

The previous sections have been concerned with ordering decisions, i.e., the selection of the quantities and the times of procurement or production of a product. There are situations where the "value" of an item depends upon its age, such as items in storage which "deteriorate" with age. Consider the following model. A stockpile consists of n items. Associated with the ith item is an age (length of time in the stockpile) S_i for $i = 1, 2, \cdots, n$. The field life of an item is a function, $L(S)$, of the age of the item upon issue to the field. When an item's usefulness or life in the field is ended, a replacement is issued from the stockpile. Items are to be issued successively until the stockpile is depleted. The problem of interest is to find the order of item issue which maximizes the total field life obtained from the stockpile.

If a complete knowledge of the function $L(S)$ is available, then optimal policies for any given situation can be obtained either by a consideration of all $n!$ different orderings and the consequent selection of the best, or by using an algorithm which will lead to the solution. For large n (and even moderately sized n), heavy numerical calculations are involved. Furthermore, in the usual circumstances there is only limited knowledge available

[67] W. I. Zangwill, "A Deterministic Multi-Period Production Scheduling Model with Backlogging," *Management Science*, **13**, No. 1, 105–119 (1966).

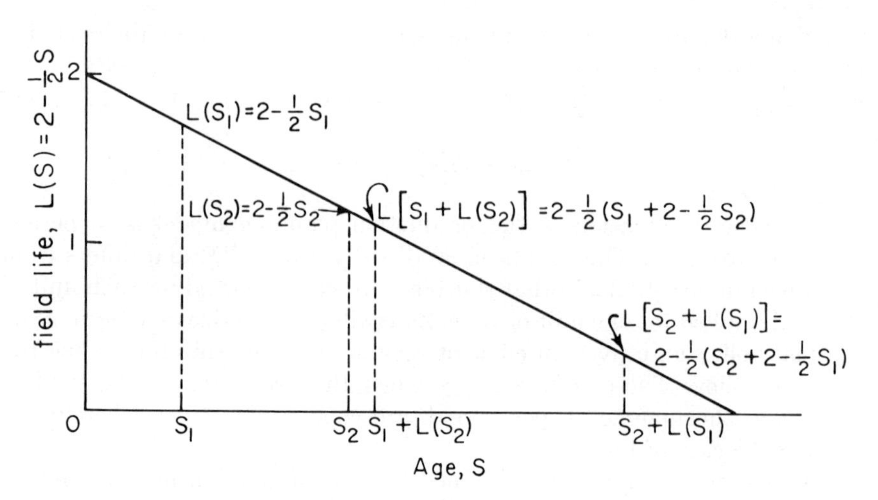

FIGURE 12.6. Field life function.

about the function $L(S)$ and the ages (S_i), e.g., general shape of $L(S)$ and possibly the ranking of the S_i, making it impossible to use these techniques to find an optimal policy.

As a simple example, suppose there are two batteries in a stockpile of ages S_1 and S_2 $(S_2 > S_1)$. S_1 is the younger of the two, S_2 is the older. There are two possible issuing policies, S_1 followed by S_2 or S_2 followed by S_1. The former policy is a *LIFO* (last in, first out) policy, whereas the latter is a *FIFO* (first in, first out) policy.

The *total field life* following a *LIFO* policy for two items is given by

$$L(S_1) + L[S_2 + L(S_1)] ,$$

and the total field life following a *FIFO* policy is given by

$$L(S_2) + L[S_1 + L(S_2)] .$$

FIFO is then an optimal policy if

$$L(S_2) + L[S_1 + L(S_2)] \geq L(S_1) + L[S_2 + L(S_1)] ; \qquad (12)$$

otherwise, *LIFO* is an optimal policy.

Assume that the field life function for the life of batteries is given by $L(S) = 2 - (1/2)S$, where the life is measured in units of months. This field life function is shown in Fig. 12.6.

Substituting into equation (12), it becomes evident that *FIFO* is the optimal policy for the S_2 and S_1 shown in Fig. 12.6 since

$$2 - \frac{1}{2}S_2 + 2 - \frac{1}{2}\left(S_1 + 2 - \frac{1}{2}S_2\right) > 2 - \frac{1}{2}S_1 + 2 - \frac{1}{2}\left(S_2 + 2 - \frac{1}{2}S_1\right) .$$

In fact, FIFO is always an optimal policy for all S_1 and S_2 ($S_2 > S_1$), provided that the slope, b, in the field life function, $a + bS$, is greater than or equal to minus one. This is shown as follows. Suppose S_2 is such that $L(S_2) > 0$, and $b \geq -1$. The left-hand side of expression (12) equals $L(S_1) + L[S_2 + L(S_2)]$. Furthermore, $L(S_1) + L[S_2 + L(S_2)] > L(S_1) + L[S_2 + L(S_1)]$ so that expression (12) holds and *FIFO* is optimal. If S_2 is such that $L(S_2) = 0$, then expression (12) holds immediately, and again *FIFO* is optimal.

Conditions for the optimality of *FIFO* have been presented for the case of two items. However, the more interesting situation occurs when there are n items in stock (and $n!$ possible issuing policies).

If $L(S) = a + bS$ and $b \geq -1$, then FIFO (issue oldest item from those remaining in the inventory) is an optimal policy for $n \geq 2$.

This result can be shown as follows. The function to be maximized by choosing an optimal issue policy may be written in the form $Q(x) = x + a + b\ (x + S^*)$, where x denotes the field life resulting from the use of the first $(n - 1)$ items issued, and S^* is the initial age of the nth item issued. $a + b(x + S^*)$ is then the field life resulting from the nth item issued. Using an induction argument, assume *FIFO* is the best policy when there are $(n - 1)$ items in the inventory, and then show that it must also be the best policy when there are n items in the inventory. If $b = -1$, then $Q(x) = L(S^*) = a - S^*$, which is a maximum when $S^* = S_1$. If $b > -1$, then $Q(x)$ is maximized by making x (the field life resulting from the use of the first $(n - 1)$ items issued) as large as possible. By the induction assumption, x is maximized by using a *FIFO* policy on the first $(n - 1)$ items issued. Now, if the issuing policy is such that S_1 is not issued last, it follows that in maximizing x it will be issued next to last. At this point in time there are only two items left. It has already been shown that for $n = 2$, *FIFO* is optimal so that the issuing policy could be improved by interchanging the order of issue of the remaining two items (S_1 then being used last). Thus, the optimal policy must be of the form where the oldest item is issued. last. This being established, the *FIFO* result is obtained from the application, again, of the induction assumption.

More general field life functions have been considered. Lieberman[68] has shown that *if $dL(S)/dS \geq -1$ and $L(S)$ is a concave function on the interval where $L(S)$ is strictly positive, then FIFO is optimal for $n \geq 2$.* The condition $dL(S)/dS \geq -1$ has the interpretation that an item "ages" at least as fast in the field as on the shelf. More precisely, if two items are initially at the same age and if the first is issued before the second, then the first will complete its useful field life no later than the second.

[68] G. J. Lieberman, "LIFO vs FIFO in Inventory Depletion Management," *Management Science,* **5,** No. 1, 102–105 (1958).

Derman and Klein[69] have shown that *if $L(S)$ is a convex function and if LIFO is an optimal policy when $n = 2$, then LIFO is an optimal policy for $n > 2$.* Lieberman[68] has shown that *if $dL(S)/dS \geq -1$ and if LIFO is an optimal policy when $n = 2$, then LIFO is an optimal policy for $n > 2$.* Finally, Bomberger[70] has shown that *if the inverse of the field life function, i.e., $L^{-1}(S)$, is concave increasing, then LIFO is optimal for $n \geq 2$.*

Thus, it has been pointed out that conditions exist where either *LIFO* or *FIFO* are optimal issuing policies from among the $n!$ possible policies, and these conditions require only limited knowledge about the form of the field life function, $L(S)$, and the ages, S_i, e.g., general shape of $L(S)$ and possibly the ranking of the S_i.

12.3 STOCHASTIC INVENTORY MODELS

This section is concerned with inventory problems where the demand for a period is a random variable having a known probability distribution. Both single-period models and multi-period models are analyzed.

12.3.1 A Single-Period Model with No Setup Cost

The following inventory model is to be considered. Items are produced (or purchased) for a single period at a cost of c dollars per item. The holding cost is given by h dollars per item, and the selling price is given by p dollars per unit. Denote by y the quantity produced (or purchased) at the beginning of the period, and let D be a random variable which denotes the demand during the period. $\varphi_D(\xi)$ is the probability density function of D. It is assumed that the demand is continuous (often resulting in an approximation since demand is generally discrete). Discrete demand can be used, but the expressions become slightly more difficult to solve analytically. Furthermore, the differences in numerical values will be small, provided the demands are relatively large.

This model can represent the inventory of an item, such as a toy, which becomes obsolete quickly. If the item is unavailable, the sale is lost by the manufacturer who is interested in maximizing his expected profits. This is a single-period problem in that production takes place only once, say before Christmas, and will never be repeated.

The amount sold is given by

$$\left.\begin{array}{ll} D, & \text{if } D < y \\ y, & \text{if } D \geq y \end{array}\right\} = \min\,(D, y)\,.$$

[69] C. Derman and M. Klein, "Inventory Depletion Management," *Management Science,* **5,** No. 4, 450–456 (1958).

[70] E. Bomberger, "Optimal Inventory Depletion Policies," *Management Science,* **7,** No. 3, 294–303 (1961).

Initially, it is assumed that there is no holding cost. Using the notation previously introduced,

$$\text{profit} = P(y) = \begin{cases} pD - cy, & \text{if } y > D \\ py - cy, & \text{if } y \leq D \end{cases} = p \min (D, y) - cy ,$$

and the expected profit is given by

$$\begin{aligned} \text{expected profit} &= E[P(y)]^{71} \\ &= \int_0^y p\xi\varphi_D(\xi)d\xi + \int_y^\infty py\varphi_D(\xi)d\xi - cy . \\ &= \int_0^\infty p \min (\xi, y)\varphi_D(\xi)d\xi - cy . \end{aligned} \tag{13}$$

Before solving (13) for the optimal y, note that it can be written as

$$\begin{aligned} E[P(y)] = \int_0^\infty p\xi\varphi_D(\xi)d\xi - \int_y^\infty p\xi\varphi_D(\xi)d\xi \\ + \int_y^\infty py\varphi_D(\xi)d\xi - cy . \end{aligned} \tag{14}$$

Hence,

$$E[P(y)] = pE(D) - \left\{ \int_y^\infty p(\xi - y)\varphi_D(\xi)d\xi + cy \right\}, \tag{15}$$

where $E(D)$ is the expected value of the demand. Thus, maximizing $E[P(y)]$ is equivalent to minimizing the expression in braces in (15), i.e.,

$$E[C(y)] = \int_y^\infty p(\xi - y)\varphi_D(\xi)d\xi + cy , \tag{16}$$

since $pE(D)$ is just a constant. The interpretation of (16) is rather interesting. cy is just the total cost of ordering y units. The integral,

$$\int_y^\infty p(\xi - y)\varphi_D(\xi)d\xi ,$$

is positive and can be viewed as the expected cost of this shortage, the revenue foregone because of shortage, or the unsatisfied demand cost due to the demand exceeding the amount produced. If additional costs are incurred

[71] The notation introduced in Chapter 3 is being followed. If X is a random variable having density function $f_X(y)$, and $g(X)$ is a function of X, then

$$E[g(X)] = \int_{-\infty}^\infty g(y)\, f_X(y)\, dy .$$

Thus, profit is a random variable since it is a function of the random variable demand, and, hence, the expected profit is given by (13).

when a shortage exists, and it is also a linear function of the amount of the shortage, the p value appearing in braces in (15) can be replaced by the total of the two costs.

Finally, from (13), (15), and (16)

$$E[P(y)] = pE(D) - E[C(y)]\,,$$

or the expected profit is equal to p times the expected demand minus both the expected shortage and production costs. Maximizing expected profit then is equivalent to minimizing expected total costs.

This latter objective function is useful in considering the spare parts problem. Suppose a new missile is to be built, which will be obsolete in a year, and all spare parts are to be manufactured as part of production. The government is interested in minimizing its total expected costs (profit *not* being a motive), and the aforementioned model is appropriate. Whereas earlier,

$$\int_y^\infty p(\xi - y)\varphi_D(\xi)d\xi \tag{17}$$

represented the expected revenue foregone because of shortage of stock, in the spare parts problem, this quantity can now represent the expected cost of supplying the parts at a later time if a shortage occurs.

Thus far, it has been assumed that the holding cost is zero. If this assumption is relaxed, the holding cost can generally be charged in two ways—at the beginning of the period or at the end of the period. In the former situation, the cost is charged on the total purchase, and, therefore, the holding cost is just hy. Thus, the production cost can be modified to be a production plus a holding cost, i.e., $(c + h)y$, and the previous equations hold. When the holding cost is charged at the end of the period (as will be assumed from here on), it will be a function of the excess of production over the demand; i.e.,

$$H(y) = \begin{cases} h(y - D), & \text{if } y \geq D \\ 0, & \text{if } y < D\,. \end{cases}$$

The expected holding cost becomes

$$E[H(y)] = \int_0^y h(y - \xi)\varphi_D(\xi)d\xi\,. \tag{18}$$

Thus, equations (13), (15), and (17) become, respectively,

$$\begin{aligned} E[P(y)] &= \int_0^y p\xi\varphi_D(\xi)d\xi + \int_y^\infty py\varphi_D(\xi)d\xi - \int_0^y h(y - \xi)\varphi_D(\xi)d\xi - cy \\ &= \int_0^\infty p \min(\xi, y)\varphi_D(\xi)d\xi - \int_0^y h(y - \xi)\varphi_D(\xi)d\xi - cy\,, \end{aligned} \tag{13'}$$

$$E[P(y)] = pE(D) - \left\{ \int_y^\infty p(\xi - y)\varphi_D(\xi)d\xi \right.$$
$$\left. + \int_0^y h(y - \xi)\varphi_D(\xi)d\xi + cy \right\}, \tag{15'}$$

and

$$E[P(y)] = pE(D) - E[C(y)] - E[H(y)]. \tag{17'}$$

Thus, in the presence of holding costs, if it is desired to maximize profits, expression (13′) or (15′) can be maximized. If it is desired to minimize costs, it is necessary to minimize the expression in braces in (15′) or minimize $E[C(y)] + E[H(y)]$. A useful result for finding policies which maximize profits or minimize costs is as follows.

Let D be a random variable having a density function

$$\begin{cases} \varphi_D(\xi), & \text{if } \xi \geq 0 \\ 0, & \text{otherwise}. \end{cases}$$

Denote by $\Phi(a)$ the cumulative distribution function, i.e.,

$$\Phi(a) = \int_0^a \varphi_D(\xi)d\xi .$$

Let $g(\xi, y)$ be defined as

$$g(\xi, y) = \begin{cases} c_1(y - \xi), & \text{if } y > \xi,\ c_1 > 0 \\ c_2(\xi - y), & \text{if } y \leq \xi,\ c_2 > 0, \end{cases} \tag{19}$$

and

$$G(y) = \int_0^\infty g(\xi, y)\varphi_D(\xi)d\xi + cy,\ 0 < c. \tag{20}$$

Then $G(y)$ is minimized at $y = y^0$, where y^0 is the solution to

$$\Phi(y^0) = \frac{c_2 - c}{c_1 + c_2}. \tag{21}$$

In order to see why the value of y^0 in (21) minimizes $G(y)$ note that by definition

$$G(y) = c_1 \int_0^y (y - \xi)\varphi_D(\xi)d\xi + c_2 \int_y^\infty (\xi - y)\varphi_D(\xi)d\xi + cy .$$

Taking the derivative and setting it equal to zero leads to

$$\frac{dG(y)}{dy} = c_1 \int_0^y \varphi_D(\xi)d\xi - c_2 \int_y^\infty \varphi_D(\xi)d\xi + c = 0. \tag{22}$$

This implies that

$$c_1\Phi(y^0) - c_2[1 - \Phi(y^0)] + c = 0\,,$$

since

$$\int_0^\infty \varphi_D(\xi)d\xi = 1\,.$$

Solving this expression results in

$$\Phi(y^0) = \frac{c_2 - c}{c_1 + c_2}\cdot$$

Checking the second derivative indicates that

$$\frac{d^2G(y)}{dy^2} = (c_1 + c_2)\varphi_D(y) \geq 0 \tag{23}$$

for all y so that the result is obtained.

To apply this result, it is sufficient to show that the quantity in braces in (15′), i.e.,

$$\int_y^\infty p(\xi - y)\varphi_D(\xi)d\xi + \int_0^y h(y - \xi)\varphi_D(\xi)d\xi + cy\,, \tag{24}$$

has the form of $G(y)$.

Clearly $c_1 = h$, $c_2 = p$, and $c = c$ so that, from (21), the optimum quantity to order, y^0, is that value which satisfies

$$\Phi(y^0) = \frac{p - c}{p + h}\cdot \tag{25}$$

As an illustration, suppose the demand, D, for a spare airplane part has an exponential distribution with parameter $1/50$, i.e.,

$$\varphi_D(\xi) = \begin{cases} \dfrac{1}{50}\,e^{-\xi/50}, & \xi \geq 0 \\ 0, & \text{otherwise}\,. \end{cases}$$

This airplane will be obsolete in one year, and, hence, all production is to take place at the present time. The production costs now are \$1000 per item, i.e., $c = 1000$, but they become \$10,000 per item if they must be supplied at later dates, i.e., $p = 10{,}000$. The holding costs, charged on the excess after the end of the period, are \$100 per item. The problem is to determine the required number of spare parts.

Since the demand density is exponential,

$$\Phi(a) = \int_0^a \frac{1}{50}\,e^{-\xi/50}\,d\xi = 1 - e^{-a/50}\,.$$

Substituting into (25) yields

$$1 - e^{-y^0/50} = \frac{10{,}000 - 1000}{10{,}000 + 100} = \frac{9000}{10{,}100} = \frac{90}{101}$$

or

$$y^0 = 50 \ln \frac{101}{11} = 111 .$$

As a variation of the above problem, suppose that the initial stock level is given by x, and the problem is to determine how much is to be made available, y, at the beginning of the period. Thus, $(y - x)$ is to be ordered so that

$$\text{amount available } (y) = \text{initial stock } (x) + \text{amount produced } (y - x) .$$

The cost equations (13′) and (15′) remain identical except for the terms that were previously cy. These terms now become $c(y - x)$. Thus, maximizing $E[P(y)]$ is equivalent to minimizing the expression in braces in (15′) with $c(y - x)$ replacing cy, i.e.,

$$\min_{y \geq x} \left[c(y - x) + \int_y^\infty p(\xi - y)\varphi_D(\xi)d\xi + \int_0^y h(y - \xi)\varphi_D(\xi)d\xi \right] . \qquad (26)$$

The constraint that $y \geq x$ must be added since it is assumed that items on hand at the beginning of the period cannot be depleted or returned. The optimum policy is described as follows.

The inventory policy which satisfies, for $p > c$,

$$\min_{y \geq x} \left[-cx + \left\{ \int_y^\infty p(\xi - y)\varphi_D(\xi)d\xi + \int_0^y h(y - \xi)\varphi_D(\xi)d\xi + cy \right\} \right] \qquad (27)$$

is given by $y = \begin{cases} y^0 \\ x \end{cases}$ *so that*

if $x < y^0$ *order up to* y^0 *(order* $y^0 - x$*),*
if $x \geq y^0$ *do not order,*

where y^0 *satisfies*

$$\Phi(y^0) = \frac{p - c}{p + h} .$$

In order to see why this policy is optimal, note that the expression in braces in (27) is a $G(y)$ as defined in (20) with $c_1 = h$, $c_2 = p$, and $c = c$. Hence (27) can be written as

$$\min_{y \geq x} [-cx + G(y)] . \qquad (28)$$

It is clear that $-cx$ is a constant so that it is sufficient to find the y which minimizes the expression

$$\min_{y \geq x} G(y) \,. \tag{29}$$

From (21) or (25), the value y^0, which minimizes $G(y)$, satisfies

$$\Phi(y^0) = \frac{p - c}{p + h} \cdot$$

Furthermore, from (23), $G(y)$ must be a convex function since

$$\frac{d^2G(y)}{dy^2} \geq 0 \,.$$

From (22)

$$\lim_{y \to 0} \frac{dG(y)}{dy} = c - p,$$

which is negative,[72] and

$$\lim_{y \to \infty} \frac{dG(y)}{dy} = h + c,$$

which is positive. Hence, $G(y)$ must be as shown in Fig. 12.7.

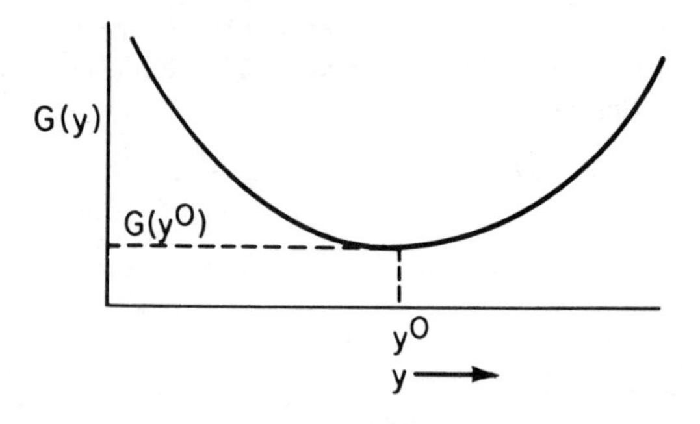

FIGURE 12.7. Graph of $G(y)$.

Thus, the optimal policy must be given by the following:

if $x < y^0$ order up to y^0 since y^0 can be achieved together with the minimum value $G(y^0)$,

if $x \geq y^0$ do not order since any $G(y)$, with $y > x$, must exceed $G(x)$.

In the previous example, if the number of spare parts on hand was 50, the optimal policy is to order up to 111 (which implies ordering 61 additional parts). On the other hand, if the number of spare parts on hand was 120, the optimum policy is not to order.

[72] If $c - p$ is non-negative, $G(y)$ will be a monotone increasing function. This implies that the item should not be stocked, i.e., $y^0 = 0$.

Similar results for these models can be obtained for other than linear holding and shortage penalty costs. Denote the holding cost by

$$\begin{cases} h(y - D), & \text{if } y \geq D \\ 0, & \text{if } y < D\,, \end{cases} \tag{30}$$

where $h(\cdot)$ is a mathematical function, not necessarily linear.

Similarly, the shortage penalty cost can be denoted by

$$\begin{cases} p(D - y), & \text{if } D \geq y \\ 0, & \text{if } D < y\,, \end{cases} \tag{31}$$

where $p(\cdot)$ is also a function, not necessarily linear.

Thus, the total expected cost is given by

$$c(y - x) + \int_y^{\infty} p(\xi - y)\varphi_D(\xi)d\xi + \int_0^y h(y - \xi)\varphi_D(\xi)d\xi\,, \tag{32}$$

where x is the amount on hand.

If $L(y)$ is defined as the expected holding plus shortage costs, i.e.,

$$L(y) = \int_y^{\infty} p(\xi - y)\varphi_D(\xi)d\xi + \int_0^y h(y - \xi)\varphi_D(\xi)d\xi\,, \tag{33}$$

then expression (32) can be written as

$$c(y - x) + L(y)\,. \tag{34}$$

The optimal policy is obtained by minimizing expression (34), subject to the constraint that $y \geq x$, i.e.,

$$\min_{y \geq x} [c(y - x) + L(y)]\,. \tag{35}$$

If $L(y)$ is strictly convex [*a sufficient condition being that* (30) *and* (31) *each are convex and* $\varphi_D(\xi) > 0$], *then the optimum policy is given by*

$$\begin{cases} \textit{if } x < y^0, & \textit{order up to } y^0\,, \\ \textit{if } x \geq y^0, & \textit{do not order}\,, \end{cases} \tag{36}$$

where y^0 is the value of y which satisfies the expression

$$\frac{dL(y)}{dy} + c = 0\,. \tag{37}$$

This result follows by observing that (35) is a convex function in x.

12.3.2 A Single-Period Model with a Setup Cost

Consider the same model as in the previous section, but with a setup cost, K, for ordering. To begin with, assume that the expected holding and penalty costs are each linear, i.e.,

$$L(y) = p \int_y^\infty (\xi - y)\varphi_D(\xi)d\xi + h \int_0^y (y - \xi)\varphi_D(\xi)d\xi . \tag{38}$$

Thus, the total expected cost incurred if one orders up to y is given by

$$\begin{cases} K + c(y - x) + L(y), & \text{if } y > x \\ L(x), & \text{if } y = x . \end{cases} \tag{39}$$

It is also clear that $cy + L(y)$ is the expression in braces in (27) and, hence, is what was previously called $G(y)$ and appears in Fig. 12.7. This is reproduced in Fig. 12.8.

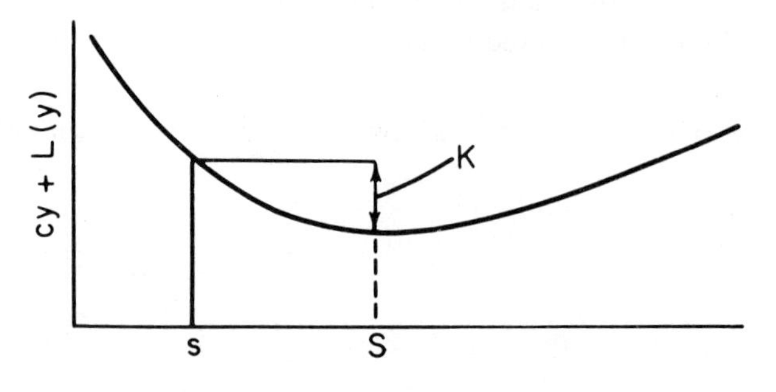

FIGURE 12.8. Graph of $cy + L(y)$.

Define S as the value of y which minimizes $cy + L(y)$, and define s as the smallest value of y for which $cs + L(s) = K + cS + L(S)$. From Fig. 12.8 it is evident that if $x > S$, then $K + cy + L(y) > cx + L(x)$ for all $y > x$. Hence, $K + c(y - x) + L(y) > L(x)$, where the left-hand side of the inequality represents the expected total cost if one orders up to y, and the right-hand side of the inequality represents the expected total cost if no ordering occurs. Hence, the optimum policy indicates that if $x > S$, do not order. If $s \leq x \leq S$, it is again evident from Fig. 12.8 that

$$K + cy + L(y) \geq cx + L(x) \qquad \text{for all } y > x$$

so that

$$K + c(y - x) + L(y) \geq L(x) .$$

Again no ordering is less expensive than ordering.

Finally, if $x < s$, it follows from Fig. 12.8 that

$$\min_{y \geq x} [K + cy + L(y)] = K + cS + L(S) < cx + L(x) ,$$

or

$$\min_{y \geq x} [K + c(y - x) + L(y)] = K + c(S - x) + L(S) < L(x) ,$$

so that it pays to order. The minimum cost is incurred if one orders up to S.

Thus, the optimum ordering policy can be summarized as follows:

$$\begin{cases} \textit{if } x < s, & \textit{order up to } S \\ \textit{if } x \geq s, & \textit{do not order}\,. \end{cases} \tag{40}$$

The value of S is obtained from (25), *i.e.*,

$$\Phi(S) = \frac{p - c}{p + h}, \tag{41}$$

and s is the smallest value which satisfies the expression

$$cs + L(s) = K + cS + L(S)\,. \tag{42}$$

This (s, S) policy, or two-bin inventory policy, has had extensive use in industry.

Referring to the example of the previous section,

$$y^0 = S = 111\,.$$

If $K = 2000$, s is obtained from

$$\begin{aligned} 1000s + 10{,}000 \int_s^\infty (\xi - s)\, \frac{1}{50}\, e^{-\xi/50}\, d\xi + 100 \int_0^s (s - \xi)\, \frac{1}{50}\, e^{-\xi/50}\, d\xi \\ = 2000 + 1000(111) + 10{,}000 \int_{111}^\infty (\xi - 111)\, \frac{1}{50}\, e^{-\xi/50}\, d\xi \\ + 100 \int_0^{111} (111 - \xi)\, \frac{1}{50}\, e^{-\xi/50}\, d\xi\,, \end{aligned}$$

so that

$$s = 97\,.$$

It may be of interest to solve this problem, in general, when the distribution of demand, D, is exponential, i.e.,

$$\varphi_D(\xi) = \frac{1}{\lambda}\, e^{-\xi/\lambda}\,.$$

From (25),

$$1 - e^{-S/\lambda} = \frac{p - c}{p + h} \text{ or } S = \lambda \ln \frac{h + p}{h + c}\,. \tag{43}$$

For any y,

$$\begin{aligned} cy + L(y) &= cy + h \int_0^y (y - \xi)\, \frac{1}{\lambda}\, e^{-\xi/\lambda}\, d\xi \\ &\quad + p \int_y^\infty (\xi - y)\, \frac{1}{\lambda}\, e^{-\xi/\lambda}\, d\xi \\ &= (c + h)y + \lambda(h + p)e^{-y/\lambda} - \lambda h\,. \end{aligned} \tag{44}$$

Therefore, from (42) through (44),

$$(c + h)\, s + \lambda\, (h + p)\, e^{-s/\lambda} - \lambda h$$
$$= K + (c + h)\, S + \lambda\, (h + p)\, e^{-S/\lambda} - \lambda h\,,$$

or

$$(c + h)\, s + \lambda\, (h + p)\, e^{-s/\lambda} = K + (c + h)\, S + \lambda\, (c + h)\,. \tag{45}$$

Letting $\Delta = S - s$, and from (43) and (45),

$$e^{\Delta/\lambda} = \frac{K}{\lambda(c + h)} + \frac{\Delta}{\lambda} + 1\,. \tag{46}$$

If Δ/λ is close to zero, $e^{\Delta/\lambda}$ can be expanded into a Taylor series around zero. If the terms beyond the quadratic term are neglected, (46) becomes

$$1 + \frac{\Delta}{\lambda} + \frac{\Delta^2}{2\lambda^2} = \frac{K}{\lambda(c + h)} + \frac{\Delta}{\lambda} + 1\,,$$

so that

$$\Delta = \sqrt{(2\lambda\, K)/(c + h)}\,. \tag{47}$$

In the example, substituting into (47) leads to

$$\Delta = \sqrt{(2)\ (50)\ (2000)/(1000 + 100)} = 14\,,$$

so that $s = 97$. Clearly, $\Delta/\lambda = 14/50$ is small so that the approximation is fairly good. This is evident from the closeness of the results using (47) with the exact result found previously.

Again it is evident that these results can be extended easily to any strictly convex expected holding and penalty cost, $L(y)$. This results in a strictly convex $cy + L(y)$ similar to Fig. 12.8. Hence, the optimum ordering policy is of the form:

$$\begin{cases} \textit{if } x < s, & \textit{order up to } S \\ \textit{if } x \geq s, & \textit{do not order}\,, \end{cases} \tag{48}$$

where S is the value of y which satisfies

$$c + \frac{dL(y)}{dy} = 0\,, \tag{49}$$

and s is the smallest value which satisfies the expression

$$cs + L(s) = K + cS + L(S)\,. \tag{50}$$

It has been tacitly assumed that minimizing costs are equivalent to maximizing profits. In a model concerned with minimizing costs, the penalty for unsatisfied demand usually represents the cost incurred in backlogging the unsatisfied demand. In a model concerned with maximizing profits where unsatisfied demand is lost, there are two interpretations of this penalty cost, i.e., (1) the revenue foregone by not satisfying demand and (2) the other costs incurred because of shortages such as loss of good will, etc. This second cost is denoted by $p(D - y)$, which need not be linear. If the revenue is now denoted by r dollars per item sold, the revenue is given by $r \min(D, y)$. Thus, the expected profit is

$$E[P(y)] = rE(D) - \left\{ \int_y^\infty p(\xi - y)\varphi_D(\xi)d\xi + \int_0^y h(y - \xi)\varphi_D(\xi)d\xi \right.$$

$$\left. + c(y - x) + r\int_y^\infty (\xi - y)\varphi_D(\xi)d\xi \right\}$$

$$= rE(D) - \left\{ L(y) + c(y - x) + r\int_y^\infty (\xi - y)\varphi_D(\xi)d\xi \right\}. \quad (51)$$

Let

$$\mathfrak{L}(y) = L(y) + r\int_y^\infty (\xi - y)\varphi_D(\xi)d\xi ,$$

so that

$$E[P(y)] = rE(D) - \{\mathfrak{L}(y) + c(y - x)\} . \quad (52)$$

Hence, maximizing expected profit in (52) is equivalent to minimizing

$$\mathfrak{L}(y) + c(y - x) ,$$

subject to the constraint that $y \geq x$. Furthermore, if $L(y)$ is strictly convex, so is $\mathfrak{L}(y)$. Therefore, (48) through (50) hold with $L(y)$ replaced by $\mathfrak{L}(y)$.

12.3.3 A Two-Period Dynamic Inventory Model with No Setup Cost

The inventory models with random demand previously considered were concerned with a single period. A natural extension of these models is to a horizon of more than one period. To illustrate the ideas, a two-period problem is considered first. Suppose a run of a particular part is to be made twice before the part becomes obsolete. Assume that the production (or purchase) leads to immediate delivery; shortages at the end of the first period must be made up, if they exist (backlogging of orders is possible at the end of the first period, but not at the end of the second period); no disposal of stock is permitted. Furthermore, the demands, D_1, D_2, for the two periods are independent, identically distributed random variables having density $\varphi_D(\xi)$. The purchase cost is linear, i.e., cz where z is the amount ordered, and the expected (one period) holding plus shortage penalty cost, $L(y)$, is strictly convex [which is the case if each is linear and $\varphi_D(\xi) > 0$].[73]

The solution to this problem is not to use the optimal one-period solution twice. Smaller costs can be achieved by viewing the problem from a

[73] The penalty for unsatisfied demand must be interpreted as the "loss of good will" and not the cost of "priority shipment" since shortages are backlogged (except at the end of the horizon when they are lost).

two-period dynamic programming viewpoint. Order the time periods backwards so that the beginning of time-period 2 implies that there are two periods left in the horizon. Similarly, the beginning of time-period 1 implies that there is one period left in the horizon (the last period is beginning). The problem is to find critical numbers which describe the optimum ordering policy. It will be shown that these are single critical numbers for each period. These numbers will be denoted by y_1^0 and y_2^0. Further, y_1 and y_2 (without the superscript) represent any amount of stock ordered up to at the beginning of the respective period.

Denote by $C_1(x_1)$ the cost of following an optimum policy (minimum cost) when there is one period left in the horizon, and there are x_1 units on hand. Similarly, denote by $C_2(x_2)$ the cost of following an optimum policy (minimum cost) when there are two periods remaining in the horizon, and there are x_2 units on hand. $C_2(x_2)$ is the expression sought since this is obtained by following the optimum policy for the entire (two-period) horizon. In order to obtain $C_2(x_2)$ it is necessary to first find $C_1(x_1)$. From the model in Sec. 12.3.1, the optimal policy for a one-period problem is given by a single critical number found from

$$c + L'(y_1^0) = 0\,, \tag{53}$$

i.e., if x_1 is the amount available at the beginning of the last period (period with a horizon of one), then

$$\begin{cases} \text{order } (y_1^0 - x_1^0), & \text{if } x_1 < y_1^0 \\ \text{do not order}, & \text{if } x_1 \geq y_1^0\,. \end{cases} \tag{54}$$

The cost of this optimum policy can be expressed as

$$C_1(x_1) = \begin{cases} L(x_1), & \text{if } x_1 \geq y_1^0 \\ c(y_1^0 - x_1) + L(y_1^0), & \text{if } x_1 < y_1\,. \end{cases}$$

Note that although y_1^0 is determined from (53), x_1 is a random variable which depends on the amount of stock on hand at the beginning of the period with a horizon of two (after the amount ordered is received), y_2, and the random demand, D_2, for the period, i.e., $x_1 = y_2 - D_2$. Thus,

$$C_1(x_1) = C_1(y_2 - D_2) = \begin{cases} L(y_2 - D_2), & \text{if } y_2 - D_2 \geq y_1^0 \\ c(y_1^0 - y_2 + D_2) + L(y_1^0), & \text{if } y_2 - D_2 < y_1^0\,. \end{cases}$$

Hence, $C_1(x_1)$ is a random variable, and the expected cost following the optimum one-period policy is given by

$$E[C_1(x_1)] = \int_0^\infty C_1(y_2 - \xi)\varphi_D(\xi)d\xi = \int_0^{y_2 - y_1^0} L(y_2 - \xi)\varphi_D(\xi)d\xi$$

$$+ \int_{y_2 - y_1^0}^\infty [c(y_1^0 - y_2 + \xi) + L(y_1^0)]\varphi_D(\xi)d\xi\,. \tag{55}$$

Note that since shortages are permitted, $(y_2 - \xi)$ can be negative; further note that $E[C_1(x_1)]$ is just a function of y_2 and y_1^0, with y_1^0 obtained from (53).

At the beginning of period 2 (when two periods remain in the horizon and y_2 is ordered), the costs incurred consist of the purchase cost, $c(y_2 - x_2)$, and the expected holding and shortage costs, $L(y_2)$. Thus, the expected cost of following the optimal policy for the two-period horizon is given by

$$C_2(x_2) = \min_{y_2 \geq x_2} \{c(y_2 - x_2) + L(y_2) + E[C_1(x_1)]\} . \tag{56}$$

where $E[C_1(x_1)]$ is given by expression (55). Again note that $C_2(x_2)$ is just a function of x_2, the amount of stock on hand. Furthermore, it is easily shown that the expression in the braces of (56) is strictly convex, so that there is a unique minimum, with this minimum occuring at y_2^0. Hence, the optimal policy is as follows:

At the beginning of period 2,

$$\begin{cases} \textit{order up to } y_2^0 \ (\textit{order } y_2^0 - x_2), & \textit{if } x_2 < y_2^0 \\ \textit{do not order}, & \textit{if } x_2 \geq y_2^0 \, . \end{cases}$$

At the beginning of period 1,

$$\begin{cases} \textit{order up to } y_1^0 \ (\textit{order } y_1^0 - x_1), & \textit{if } x_1 < y_1^0 \\ \textit{do not order}, & \textit{if } x_1 \geq y_1^0 \, . \end{cases}$$

If a discount factor α is incurred at the beginning of period 1, $C_2(x_2)$ is given by

$$C_2(x_2) = \min_{y_2 \geq x_2} \{c(y_2 - x_2) + L(y_2) + \alpha E[C_1(x_1)]\} , \tag{57}$$

where $0 \leq \alpha \leq 1$.

Consider the following example: The cost of producing an item is \$10 per item ($c = 10$). If any excess inventory remains at the end of a period, it is charged at \$10 per item ($h = 10$); if no excess appears, there is no holding charge. If a shortage occurs within a period, there is a penalty cost of \$15 per item ($p = 15$). The density function of demand is given by

$$\varphi_D(\xi) = \begin{cases} \dfrac{1}{10}, & \text{if } 0 \leq \xi \leq 10 \\ 0, & \text{otherwise} . \end{cases}$$

It is necessary to find the optimum two-period policy. For linear costs, equation (53) becomes

$$\Phi(y_1^0) = \frac{p - c}{p + h} = \frac{15 - 10}{15 + 10} = \frac{1}{5} .$$

Hence, since $\Phi(y_1^0) = y_1^0/10$,

$$y_1^0 = 2 .$$

Furthermore,

$$L(z) = \int_z^{10} \frac{15(\xi - z)}{10}\, d\xi + \int_0^z \frac{10(z - \xi)}{10}\, d\xi$$
$$= 75 - 15z + (5/4)z^2 .$$

From (55)

$$E[C_1(x_1)] = \int_0^{y_2-2} [75 - 15(y_2 - \xi) + (5/4)(y_2 - \xi)^2] \frac{1}{10}\, d\xi$$
$$+ \int_{y_2-2}^{10} [10(2 - y_2 + \xi) + 75 - (15)(2) + (5/4)2^2] \frac{1}{10}\, d\xi$$
$$= \int_0^{y_2-2} [75 - 15(y_2 - \xi) + (5/4)(y_2 - \xi)^2] \frac{1}{10}\, d\xi$$
$$+ \int_{y_2-2}^{10} [70 - 10(y_2 - \xi)] \frac{1}{10}\, d\xi$$
$$= (y_2)^3/24 - (y_2)^2/4 - 19y_2/2 + 359/3 .$$

Thus, from (56)

$$C_2(x_2) = \min_{y_2 \geq x_2} \{10(y_2 - x_2) + 75 - 15y_2 + (5/4)(y_2)^2$$
$$+ (y_2)^3/24 - (y_2)^2/4 - 19y_2/2 + 359/3\}$$
$$= \min_{y_2 \geq x_2} \{-10x_2 + (y_2)^3/24 + (y_2)^2 - 29y_2/2 + 584/3\} .$$

Taking the derivative, with respect to y_2, of the expression in braces and setting it equal to zero lead to

$$\frac{d\{\ \ \}}{dy_2} = \left[-29/2 + 2y_2^0 + \frac{1}{8}(y_2^0)^2\right] = 0 ,$$

so that

$$y_2^0 = 5.42 \qquad \text{(discarding the negative root)} .$$

Substituting $y_2^0 = 5$ and $y_2^0 = 6$ into $C_2(x_2)$ leads to a smaller value with $y_2^0 = 5$. Thus, the optimal policy can be described as follows: If the initial amount of stock on hand does not exceed 5, order up to 5 units (order $5 - x_2$ units). Otherwise, do not order. After a period has elapsed, and at the beginning of the last period, if the amount on hand does not exceed 2 units, order up to 2 units (order $2 - x_1$ units, where x_1 may be negative).

12.3.4 **Multi-Period Dynamic Inventory Model with No Setup Cost**

This model is an extension of the one considered in the previous section. Suppose there exists an horizon of n periods for which it is required to determine the optimum inventory policy. As before, assume that the production leads to immediate delivery; shortages must be made up, if they exist except at the final period when they are lost (backlogging of orders is possible); no disposal of stock is permitted. Furthermore, the demands for the n periods are independent, identically distributed random variables having density $\varphi_D(\xi)$. The purchase cost is linear, i.e., cz where z is the amount ordered, and the expected (one period) holding plus shortage penalty cost, $L(y)$, is strictly convex. α is the cost discounting factor, $0 < \alpha < 1$. Again, the periods are ordered backwards so that the beginning of time period n implies that there are n periods left in the horizon.

As noted in the two-period problem, the penalty for unsatisfied demand must be interpreted as the "loss of good will," rather than the cost of "priority shipment," because shortages are backlogged except at the end of the horizon when they are lost. Since it has been assumed that this penalty cost is independent of the period, technically it is improper to view this penalty cost as having elements attributable to making up the unsatisfied demand because the unsatisfied demand in the final period is lost. However, if the number of periods is large, and $\alpha < 1$, the seriousness of such an error is negligible.

$C_n(x_n)$ is defined as the minimum expected cost associated with having x_n units on hand now and n periods to go before terminating the process. Similarly, define $C_{n-1}(x_{n-1})$, $C_{n-2}(x_{n-2})$, $\cdots$, $C_2(x_2)$, $C_1(x_1)$.

At the beginning of period n, a decision about the inventory is made, i.e., $y_n - x_n$ is ordered ($y_n \geq x_n$), and a cost incurred. This is given by

$$c(y_n - x_n) + L(y_n) \,. \tag{58}$$

During this nth period, a demand, D_n, occurs so that at the beginning of the $(n - 1)$ period, the amount on hand, x_{n-1}, is a random variable equal to $(y_n - D_n)$. If an optimum policy is carried on from the beginning of period $(n - 1)$ to the end of the process, the discounted (discounted to the beginning of period n) expected minimum cost of the future $(n - 1)$ periods is given by

$$\alpha E[C_{n-1}(x_{n-1})] = \alpha E[C_{n-1}(y_n - D_n)] = \alpha \int_0^\infty C_{n-1}(y_n - \xi)\varphi_D(\xi)d\xi \,. \tag{59}$$

Thus, the expected cost of following the optimal policy for the n period horizon is obtained from (58) and (59), and is given by

$$C_n(x_n) = \min_{y_n \geq x_n} \{c(y_n - x_n) + L(y_n) + \alpha E[C_{n-1}(y_n - D_n)]\} \,, \tag{60}$$

where

$$C_0(x_0) = 0 \,.$$

From this dynamic programming formulation, in principle it is possible to reach a solution by first finding $C_1(x_1)$, given $C_0(x_0) = 0$, then finding

$C_2(x_2)$ from a knowledge of $C_1(x_1)$, and so on until $C_n(x_n)$ is obtained. This is rather cumbersome, and some qualitative results would be useful.

This model has the following properties, which are stated without proof, but can be found in the work of Arrow, Karlin, and Scarf. (See "selected references" at the end of the chapter.)

(1) The optimum ordering policy in each period is a single critical number, $y_n^0, y_{n-1}^0, \cdots, y_2^0, y_1^0$.

(2) $y_1^0 \leq y_2^0 \leq \cdots \leq y_{n-1}^0 \leq y_n^0 \cdots \leq y^0$, where y^0 satisfies

$$L'(y^0) + c(1 - \alpha) = 0 . \tag{61}$$

Thus, the critical numbers are monotonic.

(3) For every x, the sequence $C_n(x)$ converges. Hence, one may define a function

$$C(x) = \lim_{n \to \infty} C_n(x) .$$

(4) The limit function satisfies the equation

$$C(x) = \min_{y \geq x} \left\{ c(y - x) + L(y) + \alpha \int_0^\infty C(y - \xi)\varphi_D(\xi)d\xi \right\} .$$

(5) The value of y which satisfies (4) is the maximum of y^0 and x, where y^0 is obtained from (61).

(6) $\lim_{n \to \infty} y_n^0 = y^0$.

(7) $\lim_{n \to \infty} \left| \dfrac{y^0 - y_n^0}{\alpha^n} \right| \leq \dfrac{2c}{L''(y^0)}$ · This indicates how fast the y_n^0 converge to y^0.

The solution referred to in (5) for the infinite stage model, which is given by (61), is readily obtained if one is willing to assume that the form of the solution is a single critical number and $x \leq y$.[74] The total cost can be written as

$$c(y - x) + L(y) + \alpha[cD_1 + L(y)] + \alpha^2[cD_2 + L(y)] + \cdots + \alpha^j[cD_j + L(y)] + \cdots ,$$

where D_j is the demand during the jth period (jth from the beginning). Since $D_j \geq 0$, one always orders up to y, and, hence, the expected holding and shortage cost for each period is $L(y)$. The total expected cost is then obtained as

$$cy - cx + L(y)\ (1 + \alpha + \alpha^2 + \cdots) + cE(D)\ \alpha[1 + \alpha + \alpha^2 + \cdots]$$

[74] If $x > y$ and $E(D) > 0$, the Law of Large Numbers assures that eventually $x \leq y$.

or

$$cy - cx + \frac{L(y)}{1 - \alpha} + \frac{cE(D)\alpha}{1 - \alpha}.$$

Taking the derivative with respect to y, and setting it equal to zero, leads to

$$L'(y^0) + c(1 - \alpha) = 0\,.$$

For the example of the two-period model, it is of interest to find y^0 for the infinite-period model. α is now included and is chosen equal to 0.75.

$$L'(y^0) = h\Phi(y^0) - p[1 - \Phi(y^0)] = \frac{10}{10}\,y^0 - 15\left[1 - \frac{y^0}{10}\right] = \frac{5}{2}\,y^0 - 15\,.$$

From (61)

$$\frac{5}{2}\,y^0 - 15 = 10(0.25)$$

or

$$y^0 = 5\,.$$

Hence, the infinite stage model says that if the amount on hand does not exceed five, order up to five units. Furthermore, from property (2) for any finite stage model, the critical numbers are always less than or equal to five.

There is another interesting formulation due to A. F. Veinott, Jr.,[75] which leads to expression (61). Consider an n period model similar to that given earlier, but now assume that stock left over at the end of the final period can be salvaged with a return of the initial purchase cost, c. Similarly, if there is a shortage at this time, the items are supplied also at the purchase price c. These two changes could lead to more realism in the model but, as important, they lead to rather simple optimal policies.

If y_j and x_j are the amount of stock ordered up to and the amount of stock available, respectively, at the beginning of the period with a horizon of j periods, the total cost of producing items (including salvage or backlogging at the end of the horizon, but not holding and shortage costs) can be written as

$$\begin{aligned} c(y_n - x_n) + \alpha\, c(y_{n-1} - x_{n-1}) + \cdots + \alpha^{n-1}\, c(y_1 - x_1) - \alpha^n\, c(y_1 - D_1) \\ = \sum_{k=1}^{n} \alpha^{n-k} c(y_k - x_k) - \alpha^n c(y_1 - D_1)\,, \end{aligned}$$

where D_1 represents the demand during the last period. In general let D_k be the demand during the kth period (horizon of k periods) so that

$$x_k = y_{k+1} - D_{k+1} \text{ for } k = 1, 2, \cdots, n - 1\,.$$

[75] A. F. Veinott, Jr., "The Optimal Inventory Policy for Batch Ordering," *Operations Research,* **13,** No. 3, 424–432 (1965).

The total cost of producing the items may be written as

$$c(y_n - x_n) + \sum_{k=1}^{n-1} \alpha^{n-k} c(y_k - y_{k+1} + D_{k+1}) - \alpha^n \cdot c(y_1 - D_1)$$

$$= cy_n - cx_n + \sum_{k=1}^{n-1} \alpha^{n-k} cy_k - \sum_{k=1}^{n-1} \alpha^{n-k} cy_{k+1}$$

$$+ \sum_{k=1}^{n-1} \alpha^{n-k} cD_{k+1} - \alpha^n cy_1 + \alpha^n cD_1$$

$$= -cx_n + \sum_{k=1}^{n} \alpha^{n-k} cy_k - \sum_{k=0}^{n-1} \alpha^{n-k} cy_{k+1} + \sum_{k=0}^{n-1} \alpha^{n-k} cD_{k+1}$$

$$= -cx_n + (1 - \alpha) \sum_{k=1}^{n} \alpha^{n-k} cy_k + \sum_{k=0}^{n-1} \alpha^{n-k} cD_{k+1} .$$

The expected total cost of production is then given by

$$c\left\{-x_n + (1 - \alpha) \sum_{k=1}^{n} \alpha^{n-k} y_k + E\left[\sum_{k=1}^{n} \alpha^{n-k+1} D_k\right]\right\}$$

$$= c(1 - \alpha) \sum_{k=1}^{n} \alpha^{n-k} y_k + \left\{-cx_n + cE(D) \sum_{k=1}^{n} \alpha^{n-k+1}\right\} .$$

Notice that the bracketed quantity on the right, in the expression for the expected total cost of production, depends in no way on the decision variables $y_1, \cdots, y_n$, and hence may be ignored in the minimization that follows.

Since the expected holding and shortage costs in period j are given by $L(y_j)$, the total expected cost is given by

$$\sum_{t=1}^{n} \alpha^{t-1} G(y_{n-t+1}) + \left[-cx_n + cE(D) \sum_{t=1}^{n} \alpha^t\right],$$

where

$$G(y_j) = (1 - \alpha)\, cy_j + L(y_j) .$$

To minimize this total expected cost one need only minimize

$$\sum_{t=1}^{n} \alpha^{t-1} G(y_{n-t+1}) .$$

If it can be shown that this sum is minimized term by term, i.e.,

$$\min_{y \geq x} G(y) = \begin{cases} G(y^0), & \text{if } y^0 > x \\ G(x), & \text{if } y^0 \leq x\,, \end{cases}$$

where y^0 is defined through

$$G'(y^0) = (1 - \alpha)\, c + L'(y^0) = 0\,,$$

the following result holds.

The optimal ordering policy for the n period and infinite-period models is a single critical number policy of the form

$$\left.\begin{array}{ll} \textit{order up to } y^0, & \textit{if } x_t < y^0 \\ \textit{do not order}, & \textit{if } x_t \geq y^0 \end{array}\right\} \quad \textit{for all } t\,,$$

where y^0 satisfies expression (61), *i.e.,*

$$L'(y^0) + c(1 - \alpha) = 0\,.$$

In order to show that y^0 does indeed have this property note that under the assumption that $L(y)$ is strictly convex, $G(y)$ must also be strictly convex and appear as shown in Fig. 12.9.

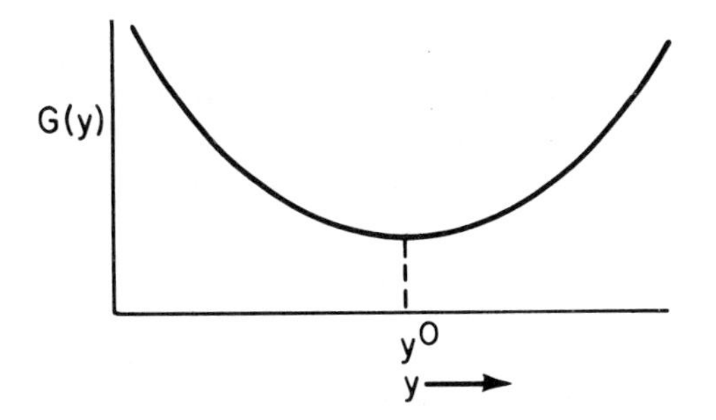

FIGURE 12.9. Plot of the $G(y)$ function.

Now, consider any policy other than the single critical number policy described above. Let $y_n, y_{n-1}, \cdots, y_1$ be the inventory levels associated with it and $y'_n, y'_{n-1}, \cdots, y'_1$ the inventory levels associated with the single critical number policy.

CASE 1

Suppose $y'_j \leq y^0$.
The single critical number policy calls for ordering up to y^0 so that $G(y'_j) = G(y_0)$.

Hence,

$$G(y_j') \leq G(y_j) .$$

CASE 2

Suppose $y_j' > y^0$.
If $y_j' > y^0$, so is every other earlier y'. In fact,

$$y_n' \geq y_{n-1}' \geq \cdots \geq y_j' .$$

Hence, no ordering ever took place under the single critical number policy so that $x_j' = x_n - D_n - D_{n-1} - \cdots - D_{j+1}$.
Furthermore,

$$x_j = x_n - D_n - D_{n-1} - \cdots - D_{j+1} + \text{any amount ordered}$$

so that

$$y_j \geq x_j \geq x_j' = y_j'$$

or

$$y_j \geq y_j' .$$

Hence,

$$G(y_j) \geq G(y_j') .$$

In both cases, the inventory levels associated with following the single critical number policy lead to total expected costs which are no greater (and possibly smaller) than that obtained by following a different policy. Hence, the single critical number policy must be optimal.

The results are extended to the infinite-case model by simply letting $n \to \infty$ in the last expression.

The results are rather striking, since the slight modification in the model leads to the same single critical number for *all* periods, both finite and infinite. It should also be noted that for the infinite stage model, the two models, with or without including salvage value, are equivalent because of the discount factor.

12.3.5 A Multi-Period Dynamic Inventory Model with Setup Cost

This model is identical with that given in Sec. 12.3.4, except that a setup cost K is incurred whenever an order takes place. The dynamic programming formulation is similar to expression (60) with the setup cost added, i.e.,

$$C_n(x_n) = \min_{y_n \geq x_n} \left\{ K\delta(y_n - x_n) + c(y_n - x_n) + L(y_n) + \alpha \int_0^\infty C_{n-1}(y_n - \xi)\varphi_D(\xi)d\xi \right\}, \quad (62)$$

where

$$K\delta(y_n - x_n) = \begin{cases} K, & \text{if } y_n > x_n \\ 0, & \text{if } y_n = x_n , \end{cases}$$

and $C_0(x_0) = 0$. In principle, from this formulation it is possible to reach a solution. However, this is rather cumbersome, and no simple solutions exist, even for $n = \infty$. However, the form of the optimal policy can be characterized. The following result was obtained by H. Scarf.[76]

If $L(y)$ is convex, then the optimum policy in period n is

$$\begin{array}{ll} \textit{order up to } S_n (\textit{order } S_n - x_n), & \textit{if } x_n < s_n \\ \textit{do not order}, & \textit{if } x_n \geq s_n . \end{array}$$

This is the familiar (s, S) policy alluded to earlier in the discussion of one-period models. As previously mentioned, unfortunately exact computations of s_n and S_n for the finite- or infinite-horizon model are extremely difficult. However, the importance of this result cannot be minimized. Even if the exact s_n and S_n are unknown, it is important to know that one should consider using policies of this form, rather than a policy from another class.

12.3.6 **Dynamic Inventory Models with Revenue**

In the previous dynamic models, it was assumed that there was no revenue, and the optimum inventory policy was concerned with minimizing costs rather than maximizing profits. In this section, revenue is included, and an optimal policy is sought which minimizes costs minus revenue. This is equivalent to maximizing profits (revenue minus costs). It is assumed that backlogging is permissible, and that revenue is counted when the stock is delivered, rather than when the order is placed. Thus, three situations must be considered:

(1) The initial stock at the beginning of a period is non-negative. The revenue for that period is just

$$r \int_0^\infty \min (y, \xi) \varphi_D(\xi) d\xi .$$

(2) The initial stock at the beginning of a period is negative, but the amount of stock ordered up to, y, is non-negative. Here the revenue for that period is now

$$-rx + r \int_0^\infty \min (y, \xi) \varphi_D(\xi) d\xi .$$

[76] H. Scarf, "The Optimality of (s, S) Policies for the Dynamic Inventory Problem," *Proceedings of the First Stanford Symposium on Mathematical Methods in the Social Sciences*, Stanford University Press, Stanford, Calif., 1960.

(3) The initial stock at the beginning of a period is negative, and the amount of stock ordered up to, y, is negative. In this case the revenue for that period is now

$$r(y - x)\,.$$

Note that, in all three cases, the revenue can be represented as

$$-r \min\,(x, 0) + r \int_0^y \xi \varphi_D(\xi) d\xi + ry \int_y^\infty \varphi_D(\xi) d\xi\,. \tag{63}$$

Hence,

$$\begin{aligned} C_n(x_n) = \min_{y_n \geq x_n} \Bigg\{ & K\delta(y_n - x_n) + c(y_n - x_n) + L(y_n) \\ & - \left[-r \min\,(x_n, 0) + r \int_0^{y_n} \xi \varphi_D(\xi) d\xi + ry_n \int_{y_n}^\infty \varphi_D(\xi) d\xi \right] \\ & + \alpha \int_0^\infty C_{n-1}(y_n - \xi) \varphi_D(\xi) d\xi \Bigg\}. \end{aligned} \tag{64}$$

Equation (64) looks somewhat like (62) [with a new $L(y_n)$], except for the term $r \min\,(x_n, 0)$. However, (64) can be rewritten as

$$\begin{aligned} C_n(x_n) - r \min\,(x_n, 0) = \min_{y_n \geq x_n} \Bigg\{ & K\delta(y_n - x_n) + c(y_n - x_n) + L(y_n) \\ & - \left[ry_n \int_{y_n}^\infty \varphi_D(\xi) d\xi - r \int_{y_n}^\infty \xi \varphi_D(\xi) d\xi + rE(D) \right] \\ & + \alpha \left[\int_0^\infty C_{n-1}(y_n - \xi) \varphi_D(\xi) d\xi - r \int_{y_n}^\infty (y_n - \xi) \varphi_D(\xi) d\xi \right. \\ & \left. + r \int_{y_n}^\infty (y_n - \xi) \varphi_D(\xi) d\xi \right] \Bigg\}, \end{aligned} \tag{65}$$

where

$$r \int_{y_n}^\infty (y_n - \xi) \varphi_D(\xi) d\xi = \int_0^\infty r \min\,(y_n - \xi, 0) \varphi_D(\xi) d\xi\,.$$

Thus, if

$$f_n(x_n) = C_n(x_n) - r \min\,(x_n, 0), \tag{66}$$

and

$$\mathfrak{L}(y_n) = L(y_n) - rE(D) + r(1 - \alpha) \int_{y_n}^\infty (\xi - y_n) \varphi_D(\xi) d\xi\,, \tag{67}$$

then (65) can be written as

$$f_n(x_n) = \min_{y_n \geq x_n} \left\{ K\delta(y_n - x_n) + c(y_n - x_n) + \mathcal{L}(y_n) + \alpha \int_0^\infty f_{n-1}(y_n - \xi)\varphi_D(\xi)d\xi \right\}. \quad (68)$$

This is the familiar dynamic programming equation previously encountered. Thus, if $f_0(x_0)$ is defined as $-r \min(x_0, 0)$, and $L(y)$ is strictly convex, $\mathcal{L}(y)$ is also strictly convex so that all the previous results about (s, S) policies or single critical number policies are applicable and can be obtained from (67).

12.3.7 Dynamic Inventory Models with Lead Times

Up to this point, it has been assumed that stock is obtained instantaneously after ordering. This assumption is now relaxed, and a lead time, λ, between the placing and receiving of an order is considered. λ is assumed constant over time and independent of the size of the order. Again, backlogging is permitted. One-period costs are a function of the stock on hand at the beginning of the period *after* delivery of old orders but before the placing of a new one. Under these assumptions, it can be shown that the optimal policy can be obtained from

$$f_n(u_n) = \min_{y_n \geq u_n} \left\{ K\delta(y_n - u_n) + c(y_n - u_n) + \alpha^\lambda \int_0^\infty L(y_n - \eta)\varphi_D^{(\lambda)}(\eta)d\eta + \alpha \int_0^\infty f_{n-1}(y_n - \xi)\varphi_D(\xi)d\xi \right\}, \quad (69)$$

where u_n represents the amount of stock on hand at the beginning of period n, plus the amount on order in the next $\lambda - 1$ periods. $\varphi_D^{(\lambda)}(\eta)$ is the density of the sum of λ demands where demands are independent, identically distributed random variables each having density $\varphi_D(\xi)$.

It is evident that (69) is the familiar zero lead time equation with a modified expected holding and shortage cost $\mathcal{L}(y)$, where

$$\alpha^\lambda \mathcal{L}(y) = \alpha^\lambda \int_0^\infty L(y - \eta)\varphi_D^{(\lambda)}(\eta)d\eta . \quad (70)$$

The optimal policies for this model are exactly the same as the zero lead time models given previously. For example, for the infinite-stage dynamic inventory model with no setup cost, the critical number is obtained from the solution of

$$L'(y^0) + c(1 - \alpha) = 0 .$$

The solution to this problem with a λ period lead time is found from

$$\alpha^\lambda \mathcal{L}'(y^0) + c(1 - \alpha) = 0 ,$$

where $\alpha^{\lambda}\mathcal{L}(y)$ is obtained from (70). If $\varphi_D(\xi)$ is exponential with parameter μ, then $\varphi_D^{(\lambda)}(\eta)$ has a gamma distribution with parameters μ and λ.

12.3.8 (k, Q) Policies for a Multi-Period Dynamic Inventory Model

In Sec. 12.3.4, a general multi-period dynamic inventory model with no setup cost was considered. In this section, an additional constraint is placed on the ordering policy, i.e., each order for stock must be some non-negative integral multiple of Q, a fixed positive constant.

As before, the demands for the n periods are assumed to be independent, identically distributed random variables having density $\varphi_D(\xi)$. The purchase cost is linear, and the expected (one period) holding plus shortage penalty cost, $L(y)$, is strictly convex. α is the cost discounting factor, $0 < \alpha < 1$. At the beginning of each period the system is reviewed. An order may be placed for any non-negative integral multiple of Q, a fixed positive number. Thus, orders must be placed in multiples of some standard batch size, e.g., a case, a truck load, etc. When the demand exceeds the inventory on hand, the excess demand is backlogged until it is subsequently filled by a delivery. In addition, it is assumed that stock left over at the end of the final period n can be salvaged with a return of the initial purchase cost, c. Similarly, if there is a shortage at this time, the items are backlogged also at the purchase price c. This model is considered by A. F. Veinott, Jr.[77] He shows that a (k, Q) policy is optimal. A (k, Q) policy is described as follows:

If at the beginning of a period the stock on hand is less than k, an order should be placed for the smallest multiple of Q that will bring the stock level to at least k (and probably higher); otherwise, an order should not be placed. The same parameter k is used in each period.

The parameter k is chosen as follows: Let y^0 be the minimum of $G(y) = (1 - \alpha)cy + L(y)$ which must be convex and as shown in Fig. 12.10. Then k is any number for which $k \leq y^0 \leq k + Q$ and $G(k) = G(k + Q)$. Referring to Fig. 12.10, if a "ruler" of length Q is placed horizontally into the "valley," k is found to be that value of the abscissa, to the left of y^0, where the "ruler" intersects the "valley." Note that if the initial inventory on hand lies in R_1, then Q is ordered; if it lies in R_2, then $2Q$ is ordered, etc.

The arguments required to show that the (k, Q) policy is optimal are almost identical with those presented in Sec. 12.3.4 for Veinott's formulation of the single critical number model, and so they are not presented here.

It should be noted that the same value of the parameter, k, is used for

[77] A. F. Veinott, Jr., "The Optimal Inventory Policy for Batch Ordering," *Operations Research*, **13,** No. 3, 424–432 (1965).

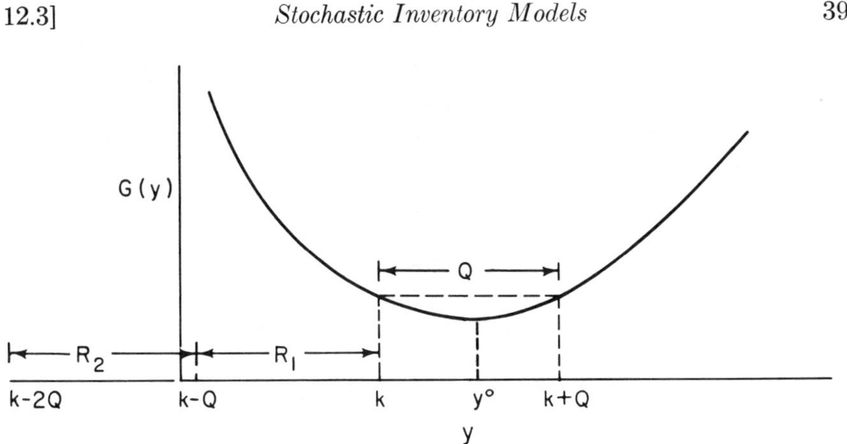

FIGURE 12.10. Plot of the $G(y)$ function.

each period of a finite horizon model, as well as for the infinite horizon model. In the latter situation, this is the same optimal policy that would have been obtained if salvage costs and backlogging *at the last period* were omitted.

12.3.9 **Multi-Product Inventory Models**

The previous sections dealt with inventory systems for single product models. However, most real inventory systems involve many products with various types of interactions such as joint storage and budget limitations, product substitutability, etc. However, an important motivation for the study of single product models is that it provides insight into solving multi-product problems, and, furthermore, it is often possible to "factor" an N-product problem into N one-product problems without loss of optimality. (This occurs if the demand and cost for each product can be treated independently of the other products.) There has been recent work on multi-product models in which such "factorization" is not possible. In these models, stocks of a single product at different locations or echelons of a supply system can also be conveniently viewed at stocks of different products.[78] In a recent paper, Veinott[79] proposed a multi-product model which is a direct anolog of the single product multi-period dynamic inventory model with no setup cost, introduced in Sec. 12.3.4. This multi-product model considers N products and m different classes of demands for these products. The demand classes in a period may be classified by such char-

[78] An excellent summary of the status of inventory theory is given in a paper by A. F. Veinott, Jr., "The Status of Mathematical Inventory Theory," *Management Science*, **12,** No. 11, 745–777 (1966).

[79] A. F. Veinott, Jr., "Optimal Policy for a Multi-Product, Dynamic Non-Stationary Inventory Problem," *Management Science*, **12,** No. 3, 206–222 (1965).

acteristics as time of occurrence, essentiality, products desired, acceptable substitutes, etc. Under the usual restrictions on the form of the costs, the optimal policy is a single critical number policy for each product, i.e., if x_{ik} is the amount on hand of product k at period i, order up to y_{ik} if $x_{ik} < y_{ik}$; otherwise, do not order (assuming initially that $x_{1k} \leq y_{1k}$ for all k).

This model has many useful applications. For example, suppose there are two products, with product 1 serving as a substitute for product 2, and all unsatisfied demands are lost. By appropriately choosing a stocking policy, which for this model supplies unsatisfied demand for product 2 with excess stock from product 1, if available, the optimal critical numbers can be obtained. This example can be interpreted as a two-echelon, inventory model with demands for a single product which cannot be satisfied at echelon 2 being transmitted up to echelon 1.

A second application concerns two products which serve as substitutes for each other. Again, all unsatisfied demands are assumed to be lost. The stocking policy supplies unsatisfied demand for one product with excess stock from the other, if available. This example can be interpreted as a two-location inventory model with an end-of-period redistribution of excess stock (if any) at one location to satisfy a shortage (if one exists) at the other location.

A different variation of the two-product inventory models was presented by Iglehart.[80] Inventories of product 2 are maintained to provide capability for production of product 1. For example, if product 1 is a car, product 2 might be machinery or labor. An optimal policy describes the amount of product 1 and product 2 to produce in period i in order to minimize the total cost, subject to certain constraints.

An important deficiency of the multi-echelon structures mentioned previously is that delivery lead time is assumed to be zero. Clark and Scarf[81] have discovered that, for certain series echelon structure, it is possible to permit a delivery lag between echelons and still obtain a computationally feasible solution.

SELECTED REFERENCES

1. Arrow, K. J., Karlin, S., and Scarf, H., *Studies in the Mathematical Theory of Inventory and Production*, Stanford Univ. Press, Stanford, Calif., 1958.
2. Buchan, J., and Koenigsberg, E., *Scientific Inventory Management*, Prentice Hall, Englewood Cliffs, N.J., 1963.
3. Hadley, G., and Whitin, T., *Analysis of Inventory Systems*, Prentice Hall, Englewood Cliffs, N.J., 1963.

[80] D. Iglehart, "Capital Accumulation and Production for the Firm Optimal Dynamic Policies," *Management Science*, **12**, No. 3, 193–205 (1965).

[81] A. Clark and H. Scarf, "Optimal Policies for a Multi-Echelon Inventory Problem," *Management Science*, **6**, No. 4, 475–490 (1960).

4. Starr, M., and Miller, D., *Inventory Control: Theory and Practice,* Prentice Hall, Englewood Cliffs, N.J., 1962.
5. Veinott, A. F., "The Status of Mathematical Inventory Theory," *Management Science,* **12,** No. 11, 745–777 (1966).

PROBLEMS

1. Suppose that the demand for a product is 25 units per month, and the items are withdrawn uniformly. The setup cost each time a production run is made is \$15. The production cost is \$1 per item, and the inventory holding cost is \$.30 per item per month.

(a) Assuming shortages are not allowed, determine how often to make a production run, and what size it should be.
(b) If shortages cost \$1.50 per item per month, determine how often to make a production run, and what size it should be.

2. Suppose the requirement for the next five months is given by $r_1 = 2$, $r_2 = 4$, $r_3 = 2$, $r_4 = 2$, and $r_5 = 3$. The setup cost is \$3, the production cost is \$1, and the holding cost is \$.25. Determine the optimal production schedule satisfying the monthly requirements.

3. Solve problem 2 assuming that the production costs are given by $\$2(1 + \log_e X)$, where X is the amount produced in a month.

4. A bread manufacturer distributes bread to grocery stores daily. It makes a profit of 20 cents per loaf sold provided that it is disposed of as fresh bread (sold on the day it is baked). The company has a store outlet that sells bread which is a day or more old at a loss of 5 cents per loaf. If the demand has a uniform distribution between 1000 and 2000 loaves, find the optimal daily number of loaves that the manufacturer should produce.

5. Find the optimal ordering policy for one period, where the demand has probability density $\varphi_D(\xi) = \frac{1}{25} e^{-\xi/25}$, and the costs are:

setup cost $= 15$,
price $= 1$ per unit ordered,
holding cost $= \frac{3}{10}z$ when $z \geq 0$,
shortage cost $= \frac{3}{2}z^2$ when $z < 0$, where z is the quantity left in stock after the demand (negative values of z imply a shortage).

6. Find the optimal ordering policy for a one-period model, where the demand has a probability density

$$\varphi_D(\xi) = \begin{cases} \dfrac{1}{20}, & \text{if } 0 \leq \xi \leq 20 \\ 0, & \text{otherwise}, \end{cases}$$

and the costs are:

holding = \$1 per item,
shortage = \$2 per item,
revenue = \$5 per item (negative cost),
setup = \$10,
production = \$2 per item.

7. Consider the following inventory model which is a single-period model with known density of demand $\varphi_D(\xi) = e^{-\xi}$ for $\xi > 0$ and zero elsewhere. There are two costs connected with the model. The first cost is the purchase cost and is given by $c \cdot (y - x)$. The second cost is the unsatisfied demand cost and is just a constant, p (independent of the amount of unsatisfied demand).

(a) If x units are available and goods are ordered up to y, write down the expression for the expected loss and describe completely the optimal policy.
(b) If a fixed cost K is also incurred whenever you order, describe the optimal policy.

8. Using the approximation for finding the optimal policy for a single-period model when the density of demand has an exponential distribution (Sec. 12.3.2), find this policy when

$$\varphi_D(\xi) = \begin{cases} \frac{1}{25} e^{-\xi/25}, & \text{if } \xi \geq 0 \\ 0, & \text{otherwise}, \end{cases}$$

and the costs are:

holding = \$.30 per item,
shortage = \$1.50 per item,
purchase price = \$1 per item,
setup = \$15.

9. There are production processes for which the difference between the cost of producing the maximum number of units allowed by some capacity restriction and the cost of producing any number of units less than this maximum is negligible, i.e., ordering is by batches. Consider a one-stage model where the only two costs are holding costs given by

$$h(y - D) = \left(\frac{3}{10}\right)(y - D)$$

and the penalty cost for unsatisfied demand given by

$$p(D - y) = \left(\frac{3}{2}\right)(D - y) .$$

The density function for demand is given by

$$\varphi_D(\xi) = \begin{cases} \dfrac{e^{-\xi/25}}{25}, & \text{for } \xi \geq 0 \\ 0, & \text{otherwise}, \end{cases}$$

If you order, you must order in batches of 50 units of product, and this quantity is delivered instantaneously. Thus, if x denotes the quantity on hand, and you do not order, then $y = x$. If you order one batch, then $y = x + 50$. Let $G(y)$ denote the total expected cost of this inventory problem when there are y units available for the period (after you have ordered).

(a) Write down the expression for $G(y)$.
(b) What is the optimal ordering policy?

10. In a single-stage inventory situation ordering must be in batches of size b, i.e., order $b, 2b, 3b, \cdots$. Suppose that for a fixed amount, x, of material on hand, the expected loss is given by $G(x)$.

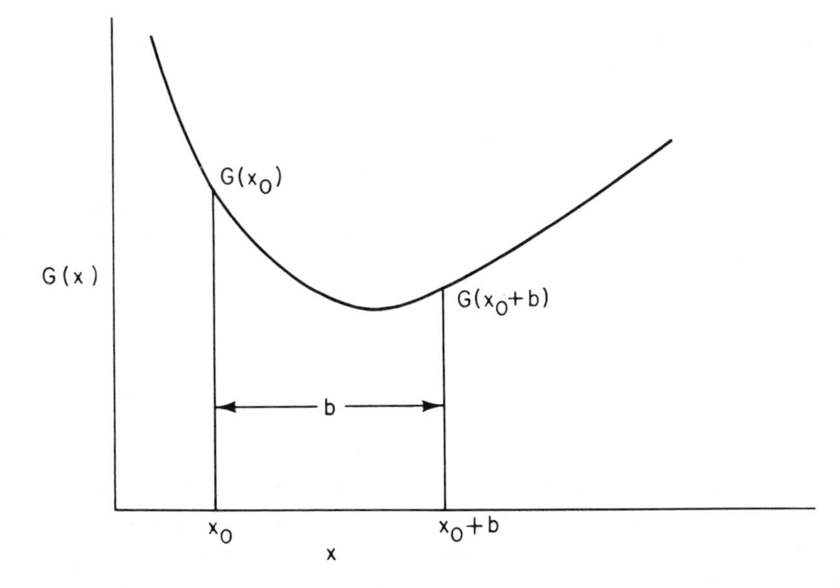

If b units are ordered, the expected loss is given by $G(x + b)$. For example, if $x = x_0$ and no ordering is done, the loss incurred is $G(x_0)$, whereas, if b units are ordered, the loss is $G(x_0 + b)$. In the above figure, it is clearly better to order the b units. Describe the optimal ordering procedure.

11. Find the optimal one- and two-period policies for the following inventory. Demands are independent with common density $\varphi_D(\xi) = 1/10$, $0 < \xi < 10$. Orders may be placed at the start of each period without setup cost and at a price of $c = 10$. There is a holding cost of 10 per unit remaining in stock at the end of each period and a penalty cost of 15 per unit quantity backlogged. Use a discount factor $\alpha = 3/4$ in the two-period case.

12. Find the optimal inventory policy for the following two-period model. Let the density of the demand D be given by

$$\varphi_D(\xi) = \begin{cases} \dfrac{1}{25}\, e^{-\xi/25}, & \text{if } \xi \geq 0 \\ 0, & \text{otherwise}, \end{cases}$$

and the costs are:

holding = \$.30 per item,
shortage = \$1.50 per item,
purchase price = \$1 per item.

13. Solve problem 12 for a two-period model using a discount factor of $\alpha = .90$.

14. Determine the optimum inventory policy when the goods are to be ordered at the end of every month from now on. The cost of ordering up to y when x is available is given by $2(y - x)$. Similarly, the cost of not satisfying a consumer demand of D is given by $5(D - y)$. The density function for the random variable, demand, is given by $\varphi_D(\xi) = e^{-\xi}$. The storage costs are given by $(y - D)$ and represent the expense of storing unsold stock. The total profit is given by $100\,D$. The losses at each succeeding stage are equivalent to a loss of 95% of that at the previous stage.

15. Solve problem 12 for an infinite-period model using a discount factor of $\alpha = .90$.

16. Consider an infinite-period inventory model in which the demands are independent and identically distributed random variables. Denote the expected demand in a period by μ. Assume the cost of ordering z units $(z \geq 0)$ is $C \cdot z$ $(C > 0)$. Let $\alpha (0 < \alpha < 1)$ be the discount factor. Assume that all unsatisfied demand is backlogged. Finally, suppose that when y is the inventory on hand after ordering but before the occurrence of a demand of size D in a period, a cost $(y - D)^2$ is incurred. When $y > D$, the cost is a charge for carrying the inventory; when $y < D$, the cost is a charge for backlogging demand.

(a) Describe the optimal ordering policy and give simple formulas for its parameters in terms of C, α, and μ.
(b) Suppose there is a one-period lead time in delivery. Describe the optimal ordering policy and give simple formulas for its parameters in terms of C, α, and μ.

17. Find the optimal (k, Q) policy for problem 9 for an infinite-period model using a discount factor of $\alpha = .95$.

18. In Sec. 12.3.1, the critical number y^0 for the optimal ordering policy for a single-period model was shown to satisfy the equation,

$$\int_0^{y^0} \varphi_D(\xi)d\xi = \Phi(y^0) = \frac{p - c}{p + h},$$

when the ordering, shortage, and holding costs are linear, and the demand D is a continuous random variable with density function $\varphi_D(\xi)$. Similarly, in Sec. 12.3.4, the critical number y^0 for the optimal ordering policy for an infinite-period model was shown to satisfy the equation,

$$\int_0^{y^0} \varphi_D(\xi)d\xi = \Phi(y^0) = \frac{p - c(1 - \alpha)}{p + h}.$$

Show that these results are valid for demands which are discrete random variables, provided that the integral is replaced by a summation. If rounding for integers is required, round up to the nearest integer.

CHAPTER 13

Markov Chains and Their Applications

13.1 INTRODUCTION

In earlier chapters, emphasis was placed on representing a physical process by a mathematical model. This mathematical model has often had stochastic phenomena associated with it so that a study of stochastic behavior has become necessary. A stochastic process is defined to be simply an indexed collection of random variables $\{X_t\}$, where the index t runs through a given set T. Often T is taken to be the set of non-negative integers, and X_t represents a measurable characteristic of interest at time t. For example, the stochastic process, $X_1, X_2, X_3, \cdots$, can represent the collection of daily inventory levels of a given product, or it can represent the collection of daily demands for this product.

There are many stochastic processes that are of interest. A consideration of the behavior of a system operating for some period of time often leads to the analysis of a stochastic process with the following structure. At particular points of time t labelled $0, 1, \cdots$, the system is found in exactly one of a finite number of mutually exclusive and exhaustive categories or *states* labelled $0, 1, \cdots, M$. The points in time may be equally spaced, or their spacing may depend upon the over-all behavior of the physical system in which the stochastic process is *imbedded*, e.g., the time between occurrences of some phenomenon of interest. Although the states may constitute a qualitative as well as quantitative characterization of the system, no loss of generality is entailed by the numerical labels, $0, 1, \cdots, M$, which are used henceforth to denote the possible states of the system. Thus, the mathematical representation of the physical system is that of a stochastic process $\{X_t\}$, where the random variables are observed at $t = 0, 1, 2, \cdots$, and where each random variable may take on any one of the $(M + 1)$ integers, $0, 1, \cdots, M$. These integers are a characterization of the $(M + 1)$ states of the process.

As an example, consider the following inventory problem. A camera store stocks a particular model camera which can be ordered weekly. Let $D_1, D_2, \cdots$, represent the demand for this camera during the first week, second week, $\cdots$, respectively. It is assumed that the D_i are independent and identically distributed random variables having a known probability distribution. Let X_0 represent the number of cameras on hand at the outset, X_1 the number of cameras on hand at the end of week one, X_2 the number of cameras on hand at the end of week two, etc. Assume that $X_0 = 3$. On Saturday night the store places an order which is delivered in time for the opening of the store on Monday. The store uses the following (s, S) ordering policy. If the number of cameras on hand at the end of the week is less than $s = 1$ (no cameras in stock), the store orders (up to) $S = 3$. Otherwise, the store does not order (if there are any cameras in stock, no order is placed). It is assumed that sales are lost when demand exceeds the inventory on hand. Thus, $\{X_t\}$ for $t = 0, 1, \cdots$, is a stochastic process of the form described above. The possible states of the process are the integers, 0, 1, 2, 3, representing the possible number of cameras on hand at the end of the week. In fact, the random variables X_t are clearly dependent and may be evaluated iteratively by the expression,

$$X_{t+1} = \begin{cases} \max\{(3 - D_{t+1}), 0\}, & \text{if } X_t < 1 \\ \max\{(X_t - D_{t+1}), 0\}, & \text{if } X_t \geq 1, \end{cases}$$

for $t = 0, 1, 2, \cdots$. This example is used for illustrative purposes throughout many of the following sections. The next section further defines the type of stochastic process considered in this chapter.

13.2 MARKOV CHAINS

Assumptions regarding the joint distribution of $X_0, X_1, \cdots$, are necessary in order to obtain analytical results. One assumption which leads to analytical tractability is that the stochastic process is a Markov chain (defined below), which has the following key property. A stochastic process $\{X_t\}$ is said to have the *Markovian property* if $P\{X_{t+1} = j | X_0 = k_0, X_1 = k_1, \cdots, X_{t-1} = k_{t-1}, X_t = i\} = P\{X_{t+1} = j | X_t = i\}$ for $t = 0, 1, \cdots$ and every sequence, $i, j, k_0, k_1, \cdots, k_{t-1}$.

This Markovian property can be shown to be equivalent to stating that the conditional probability of any future "event," given any past "event" and the present state $X_t = i$, is *independent* of the past "event" and depends only on the present state of the process. The conditional probabilities, $P\{X_{t+1} = j | X_t = i\}$, are called transition probabilities. If, for each i and j,

$$P\{X_{t+1} = j | X_t = i\} = P\{X_1 = j | X_0 = i\}, \qquad \text{for all } t = 0, 1, \cdots,$$

then the (one-step) transition probabilities are said to be *stationary* and are usually denoted by p_{ij}. Thus, having stationary transition probabilities imply that the transition probabilities do not change in time. The existence of stationary (one-step) transition probabilities also implies that, for each i, j, and $n(n = 1, 2, \cdots)$,

$$P\{X_{t+n} = j | X_t = i\} = P\{X_n = j | X_0 = i\},$$

for all $t = 0, 1, \cdots$. These conditional probabilities are usually denoted by $p_{ij}^{(n)}$[82] and are called n-step transition probabilities. Thus, $p_{ij}^{(n)}$ is just the conditional probability that the random variable X, starting in state i, will be in state j after exactly n steps (time units).

Since the $p_{ij}^{(n)}$ are conditional probabilities, they must satisfy the properties,

$$p_{ij}^{(n)} \geq 0, \qquad \text{for all } i \text{ and } j, \text{ and } n = 1, 2, \cdots$$

$$\sum_{j=0}^{M} p_{ij}^{(n)} = 1, \qquad \text{for all } i \text{ and } n = 1, 2, \cdots.$$

A convenient notation for representing the transition probabilities is the matrix form,

$$\mathbf{P}^{(n)} = \begin{bmatrix} p_{00}^{(n)} & \cdots & p_{0M}^{(n)} \\ \cdot & & \cdot \\ \cdot & & \cdot \\ \cdot & & \cdot \\ p_{M0}^{(n)} & \cdots & p_{MM}^{(n)} \end{bmatrix}, \qquad \text{for } n = 1, 2, \cdots.$$

It is now possible to define a Markov chain. A stochastic process $\{X_t\}$ $(t = 0, 1, \cdots)$ is said to be a *finite-state Markov chain*[83] if it has the following:

(1) a finite number of states,
(2) the Markovian property,
(3) stationary transition probabilities,
(4) a set of initial probabilities, $P\{X_0 = i\}$ for all i.

Returning to the inventory example developed in the preceding section, it is easily seen that $\{X_t\}$, where X_t is the number of cameras in stock at the end of the tth week (before an order is received), is a Markov chain. Now consider how to obtain the (one-step) transition probabilities, i.e., the elements of the (one-step) *transition matrix*,

$$\mathbf{P} = \begin{bmatrix} p_{00} & p_{01} & p_{02} & p_{03} \\ p_{10} & p_{11} & p_{12} & p_{13} \\ p_{20} & p_{21} & p_{22} & p_{23} \\ p_{30} & p_{31} & p_{32} & p_{33} \end{bmatrix}$$

[82] For $n = 1$, $p_{ij}^{(1)}$ is denoted by p_{ij}.

[83] The definitions of Markovian property and Markov chain are more restrictive than the usages of these terms in the literature since the discussion is confined to a discrete time parameter and finite-state space.

assuming that each D_t has a Poisson distribution with parameter $\lambda = 1$.

In order to obtain p_{00}, it is necessary to evaluate $P\{X_t = 0|X_{t-1} = 0\}$. If $X_{t-1} = 0$, then $X_t = \max\{(3 - D_t), 0\}$. Therefore, if $X_t = 0$, then the demand during the week has to be three or more. Hence, $p_{00} = P\{D_t \geq 3\}$. This is just the probability that a Poisson random variable with parameter $\lambda = 1$ takes on a value of 3 or more, which is obtained from Table A5.4 of Appendix 5, so that $p_{00} = .08$. $p_{10} = P\{X_t = 0|X_{t-1} = 1\}$ can be obtained in a similar way. If $X_{t-1} = 1$, then $X_t = \max\{(1 - D_t), 0\}$. In order that $X_t = 0$, the demand during the week has to be one or more. Hence, $p_{10} = P\{D_t \geq 1\} = .632$ (from Table A5.4 of Appendix 5). To find $p_{21} = P\{X_t = 1|X_{t-1} = 2\}$, note that $X_t = \max\{(2 - D_t), 0\}$ if $X_{t-1} = 2$. Therefore, if $X_t = 1$, then the demand during the week has to be exactly one. Hence, $p_{21} = P\{D_t = 1\} = .368$ (from Table A5.4 of Appendix 5). The remaining entries are obtained in a similar manner, which yield the following (one-step) transition matrix,

$$\mathbf{P} = \begin{bmatrix} .080 & .184 & .368 & .368 \\ .632 & .368 & 0 & 0 \\ .264 & .368 & .368 & 0 \\ .080 & .184 & .368 & .368 \end{bmatrix}$$

13.3 CHAPMAN–KOLMOGOROV EQUATIONS

In the previous section, the n-step transition probability $p_{ij}^{(n)}$ was introduced. This transition probability can be useful when the process is in state i and the probability that the process will be in state j n periods later is desired. The *Chapman–Kolmogorov equations* provide a method for computing these n-step transition probabilities. These equations are

$$p_{ij}^{(n)} = \sum_{k=0}^{M} p_{ik}^{(v)} p_{kj}^{(n-v)}, \qquad \text{for all } i, j, n, \text{ and } 0 \leq v \leq n\,.$$

These equations merely point out that, in going from state i to state j in n steps, the process will be in some state k after exactly v (less than n) steps. Thus, $p_{ik}^{(v)} p_{kj}^{(n-v)}$ is just the conditional probability that, starting from state i, the process goes to state k after v steps and then to state j in $n - v$ steps. Therefore, summing these conditional probabilities over all possible k must yield $p_{ij}^{(n)}$. The special cases of $v = 1$ and $v = n - 1$ lead to the expressions,

$$p_{ij}^{(n)} = \sum_{k=0}^{M} p_{ik} p_{kj}^{(n-1)}$$

and

$$p_{ij}^{(n)} = \sum_{k=0}^{M} p_{ik}^{(n-1)} p_{kj}\,,$$

for all i, j, n. It then becomes evident that the n-step transition probabilities can be obtained from the one-step transition probabilities recursively. This recursive relationship is best explained in matrix notation (see Appendix 3). For $n = 2$, these expressions become

$$p_{ij}^{(2)} = \sum_{k=0}^{M} p_{ik}p_{kj} \qquad \text{for all } i, j.$$

Note that the $p_{ij}^{(2)}$ are the elements of the matrix $\mathbf{P}^{(2)}$. However, it must also be noted that these elements

$$\sum_{k=0}^{M} p_{ik}p_{kj}$$

are obtained by multiplying the matrix of one-step transition probabilities by itself, i.e.,

$$\mathbf{P}^{(2)} = \mathbf{P} \cdot \mathbf{P} = \mathbf{P}^2.$$

More generally, it follows that the matrix of n-step transition probabilities can be obtained from the expression

$$\mathbf{P}^{(n)} = \mathbf{P} \cdot \mathbf{P} \cdots \mathbf{P} = \mathbf{P}^n = \mathbf{P}\mathbf{P}^{n-1} = \mathbf{P}^{n-1}\mathbf{P}.$$

Thus, the n-step transition probability matrix can be obtained by computing the nth power of the one-step transition matrix. For values of n which are not too large, the n-step transition matrix can be calculated in the manner described above. However, when n is large, such computations are often tedious, and, furthermore, round-off errors may cause inaccuracies.

Returning to the inventory example, the two-step transition matrix is given by

$$\mathbf{P}^{(2)} = \mathbf{P}^2 = \begin{bmatrix} .080 & .184 & .368 & .368 \\ .632 & .368 & 0 & 0 \\ .264 & .368 & .368 & 0 \\ .080 & .184 & .368 & .368 \end{bmatrix} \begin{bmatrix} .080 & .184 & .368 & .368 \\ .632 & .368 & 0 & 0 \\ .264 & .368 & .368 & 0 \\ .080 & .184 & .368 & .368 \end{bmatrix}$$

$$= \begin{bmatrix} .249 & .286 & .300 & .165 \\ .283 & .252 & .233 & .233 \\ .351 & .319 & .233 & .097 \\ .249 & .286 & .300 & .165 \end{bmatrix} \text{[84]}$$

Thus, given that there is one camera left in stock at the end of a week, the probability is .283 that there will be no cameras in stock two weeks later, i.e., $p_{10}^{(2)} = .283$. Similarly, given that there are two cameras left in stock at the end of a week, the probability is .097 that there will be three cameras in stock two weeks later, i.e., $p_{23}^{(2)} = .097$.

[84] Note that round-off errors already appear in the row corresponding to state 1.

The four-step transition matrix can also be obtained as follows.

$$\mathbf{P}^{(4)} = \mathbf{P}^4 = \mathbf{P}^2 \cdot \mathbf{P}^{(2)} = \begin{bmatrix} .249 & .286 & .300 & .165 \\ .283 & .252 & .233 & .233 \\ .351 & .319 & .233 & .097 \\ .249 & .286 & .300 & .165 \end{bmatrix} \begin{bmatrix} .249 & .286 & .300 & .165 \\ .283 & .252 & .233 & .233 \\ .351 & .319 & .233 & .097 \\ .249 & .286 & .300 & .165 \end{bmatrix}$$

$$= \begin{bmatrix} .289 & .286 & .261 & .164 \\ .282 & .285 & .268 & .166 \\ .284 & .283 & .263 & .171 \\ .289 & .286 & .261 & .164 \end{bmatrix}$$

Thus, given that there is one camera left in stock at the end of a week, the probability is .282 that there will be no cameras in stock four weeks later, i.e., $p_{10}^{(4)} = .282$. Similarly, given that there are two cameras left in stock at the end of a week, the probability is .171 that there will be three cameras in stock four weeks later, i.e., $p_{23}^{(4)} = .171$.

It has previously been pointed out that the one-step or n-step transition probabilities are conditional probabilities, e.g., $P\{X_n = j | X_0 = i\} = p_{ij}^{(n)}$. If the unconditional probability $P\{X_n = j\}$ is desired, it is necessary to have specified the probability distribution of the initial state. Denote this probability distribution by $Q_{X_0}(i)$, where

$$Q_{X_0}(i) = P\{X_0 = i\}, \qquad \text{for } i = 0, 1, \cdots, M .$$

It then follows that

$$P\{X_n = j\} = Q_{X_0}(0)p_{oj}^{(n)} + Q_{X_0}(1)p_{1j}^{(n)} + \cdots + Q_{X_0}(M)p_{Mj}^{(n)} .$$

In the inventory example, it was assumed that initially there were three units in stock, i.e., $X_0 = 3$. Thus,

$$Q_{X_0}(0) = Q_{X_0}(1) = Q_{X_0}(2) = 0, \qquad \text{and } Q_{X_0}(3) = 1 .$$

Hence, the (unconditional) probability that there will be three cameras in stock two weeks after the inventory system began is .165, i.e., $P\{X_2 = 3\} = (1)p_{33}^{(2)}$. If, instead, it were given that $Q_{X_0}(i) = 1/4$ for $i = 0, 1, 2, 3$, then

$$P\{X_2 = 3\} = \left(\frac{1}{4}\right) .165 + \left(\frac{1}{4}\right) .233 + \frac{1}{4}(.097) + \frac{1}{4}(.165) = .165 .$$

The fact that the same answer is obtained using these two initial probability distributions is purely coincidental.

13.4 FIRST PASSAGE TIMES

The preceding section dealt with finding n-step transition probabilities [i.e., given that the process is in state i, determining the (conditional) probability that the process will be in state j after n periods]. It is often desirable to make probability statements about the number of transitions made by the process in going from state i to state j *for the first time.* This length of time is called the *first passage time* in going from state i to state j. When $j = i$, this first passage time is just the number of transitions until the process returns to the initial state i. In this case, the first passage time is called the *recurrence time* for state i.

To illustrate these definitions, reconsider the inventory example developed in the preceding sections. Recall that the initial inventory (X_0) contains three cameras. Suppose that it turns out that there are two cameras at the end of the first week (X_1 takes on the value 2), one camera at the end of the second week (X_2 takes on the value 1), no cameras in stock at the end of the third week (X_3 takes on the value 0), three cameras at the end of the fourth week (X_4 takes on the value 3), and one camera at the end of the fifth week (X_5 takes on the value 1). In this case, the first passage time in going from state 3 to state 1 is 2 weeks, the first passage time in going from state 3 to state 0 is 3 weeks, and the recurrence time of state 3 is 4 weeks.

In general the first passage times are random variables and, hence, have probability distributions associated with them. These probability distributions depend upon the transition probabilities of the process. In particular, let $f_{ij}^{(n)}$ denote the probability that the first passage time from state i to j is equal to n. It can be shown that these probabilities satisfy the following recursive relationships.

$$\begin{aligned} f_{ij}^{(1)} &= p_{ij}^{(1)} = p_{ij}, \\ f_{ij}^{(2)} &= p_{ij}^{(2)} - f_{ij}^{(1)} p_{jj}, \\ &\vdots \\ f_{ij}^{(n)} &= p_{ij}^{(n)} - f_{ij}^{(1)} p_{jj}^{(n-1)} - f_{ij}^{(2)} p_{jj}^{(n-2)} \cdots - f_{ij}^{(n-1)} p_{jj}. \end{aligned}$$

Thus, the probability of a first passage time from state i to state j in n steps can be computed recursively from the one-step transition probabilities. In the inventory example, the probability distribution of the first passage time in going from state 3 to state 0 is obtained as follows:

$$\begin{aligned} f_{30}^{(1)} &= .080 \\ f_{30}^{(2)} &= (.249) - (.080)(.080) = .243 \\ &\vdots \end{aligned}$$

For fixed i and j, the $f_{ij}^{(n)}$ are non-negative numbers such that

$$\sum_{n=1}^{\infty} f_{ij}^{(n)} \leq 1.$$

Unfortunately, this sum may be strictly less than one, which implies that a process initially in state i may never reach state j. When the sum does equal one, $f_{ij}^{(n)}$ (for $n = 1, 2, \cdots$) can be considered as a probability distribution for the random variable, the first passage time.

If $i = j$ and

$$\sum_{n=1}^{\infty} f_{ii}^{(n)} = 1 ,$$

then state i is called a *recurrent state*, since this implies that once the process is in state i, it will return to state i. A special case of a recurrent state is an *absorbing state*. A state i is said to be an *absorbing state* if the (one-step) transition probability, p_{ii}, equals one. Thus, if a state is an absorbing state, the process will never leave it once it enters.

If

$$\sum_{n=1}^{\infty} f_{ii}^{(n)} < 1 ,$$

then state i is called a *transient state*, since this implies that once the process is in state i, there is a strictly positive probability that it will never return to state i.

It is not generally possible to calculate the probabilities of first passage time for all n so that it is not always evident whether a state should be classified as recurrent or transient. For example, although all states in the inventory example are recurrent (as shown in Sec. 13.5), it is not simple to prove that

$$\sum_{n=1}^{\infty} f_{ii}^{(n)} = 1 .$$

As another example, suppose that a Markov process has the following transition matrix:

$$\mathbf{P} = \text{State}\ \begin{array}{c} \\ 0 \\ 1 \\ 2 \\ 3 \\ 4 \end{array} \begin{array}{c} \text{State} \\ \begin{array}{ccccc} 0 & 1 & 2 & 3 & 4 \end{array} \\ \left[\begin{array}{ccccc} \frac{1}{4} & \frac{3}{4} & 0 & 0 & 0 \\ \frac{1}{2} & \frac{1}{2} & 0 & 0 & 0 \\ 0 & 0 & 1 & 0 & 0 \\ 0 & 0 & \frac{1}{3} & \frac{2}{3} & 0 \\ 1 & 0 & 0 & 0 & 0 \end{array}\right] \end{array}$$

It is evident that state 2 is an absorbing state (and, hence, a recurrent state) since once the process enters state 2 (third row of the matrix), it will never leave. States 3 and 4 are transient states since once the process is in state 3 there is a positive probability that it will never return. The probability is 1/3 that the process will go from state 3 to state 2 on the first step. Once the process is in state 2, it remains in state 2. Once a process leaves state 4, it can never return. States 0 and 1 are recurrent states. As indicated earlier, in order to show that states 1 and 2 are recurrent, it is sufficient to show that

$$\sum_{n=1}^{\infty} f_{00}^{(n)} = 1 \quad \text{and} \quad \sum_{n=1}^{\infty} f_{11}^{(n)} = 1 .$$

This is generally difficult, and an alternative test is desired. A necessary and sufficient condition that state i be recurrent is that

$$\sum_{n=1}^{\infty} p_{ii}^{(n)}$$

should diverge. Unfortunately, this criterion is also difficult to apply, so that another criterion is given in Sec. 13.5. However, observe that the n-step transition matrix always has the appearance,

$$\mathbf{P}^{(n)} = \begin{bmatrix} * & * & 0 & 0 & 0 \\ * & * & 0 & 0 & 0 \\ 0 & 0 & 1 & 0 & 0 \\ 0 & 0 & * & * & 0 \\ * & * & 0 & 0 & 0 \end{bmatrix},$$

where the symbol * represents positive numbers. Hence, it is intuitively evident that, once the process is in state 0, it will return to state 0 (possibly passing through state 1) after some number of steps. A similar argument holds for state 1.

Whereas, calculating $f_{ij}^{(n)}$ for all n may be difficult, it is relatively simple to obtain the expected first passage time from state i to state j. Denote this expectation by μ_{ij}, which is defined by the expressions,

$$\mu_{ij} = \begin{cases} \infty, & \text{if } \sum_{n=1}^{\infty} f_{ij}^{(n)} < 1 \\ \sum_{n=1}^{\infty} n f_{ij}^{(n)}, & \text{if } \sum_{n=1}^{\infty} f_{ij}^{(n)} = 1 . \end{cases}$$

Whenever

$$\sum_{n=1}^{\infty} f_{ij}^{(n)} = 1 ,$$

then μ_{ij} satisfies uniquely the equation,

$$\mu_{ij} = 1 + \sum_{k \neq j} p_{ik}\mu_{kj} .$$

For the inventory example, these equations can be used to compute the expected time until the cameras are out of stock, assuming the process is started when three cameras are available, i.e., the expected first passage time, μ_{30}, can be obtained. Assuming that all of the states are recurrent (as is shown soon), the system of equations leads to the expressions,

$$\begin{aligned} \mu_{30} &= 1 + p_{31}\mu_{10} + p_{32}\mu_{20} + p_{33}\mu_{30} , \\ \mu_{20} &= 1 + p_{21}\mu_{10} + p_{22}\mu_{20} + p_{23}\mu_{30} , \\ \mu_{10} &= 1 + p_{11}\mu_{10} + p_{12}\mu_{20} + p_{13}\mu_{30} , \end{aligned}$$

or

$$\begin{aligned} \mu_{30} &= 1 + .184\mu_{10} + .368\mu_{20} + .368\mu_{30} , \\ \mu_{20} &= 1 + .368\mu_{10} + .368\mu_{20} , \\ \mu_{10} &= 1 + .368\mu_{10} . \end{aligned}$$

The simultaneous solution to this system of equations is

$$\begin{aligned} \mu_{10} &= 1.58 \text{ weeks} , \\ \mu_{20} &= 2.51 \text{ weeks} , \\ \mu_{30} &= 3.50 \text{ weeks} , \end{aligned}$$

so that the expected time until the cameras are out of stock is 3.50 weeks. In making these calculations μ_{20} and μ_{10} are also obtained.

When $j = i$, the expected first passage time is called the *expected recurrence time.* The recurrent state is called a *null recurrent* state if $\mu_{ii} = \infty$, and it is called a positive recurrent state if $\mu_{ii} < \infty$. In a finite state Markov chain there are no null recurrent states (only positive recurrent states and transient states).

13.5 LONG-RUN PROPERTIES OF MARKOV CHAINS

13.5.1 Introduction

In Sec. 13.3, the four-step transition matrix for the inventory example was obtained. It will now be instructive to examine the eight-step transition probabilities given by the matrix,

$$\mathbf{P}^{(8)} = \mathbf{P}^8 = \mathbf{P}^4 \cdot \mathbf{P}^4 = \begin{bmatrix} .286 & .285 & .264 & .166 \\ .286 & .285 & .264 & .166 \\ .286 & .285 & .264 & .166 \\ .286 & .285 & .264 & .166 \end{bmatrix}$$

Notice the rather remarkable fact that each of the four rows has identical entries. This implies that the probability of being in state j after 8 weeks appears to be independent of the initial level of inventory. Before exploring this further, it is necessary to examine the structure of the Markov chain.

It has already been noted that a Markov chain is completely characterized by the (one-step) transition probabilities p_{ij} and the probability distribution of the initial states $Q_{X_0}(i)$; the former determined whether a state was classified as recurrent or transient. Using the properties of conditional probability and Markov chains, the following expression is obtained.

$$P\{X_0 = i_0, X_1 = i_1, \cdots, X_n = i_n\} = Q_{X_0}(i_0)p_{i_0 i_1}\, p_{i_1 i_2} \cdots p_{i_{n-1}\, i_n},$$

for all $i_0, i_1, \cdots, i_n$, and n. It then follows that the conditional probability of the event,

$$\{E|X_0 = i_0\} = \{X_0 = i_0, X_1 = i_1, \cdots, X_n = i_n|X_0 = i_0\}, \text{ for } Q_{X_0}(i_0) > 0,$$

is given by the expression,

$$P\{E|X_0 = i_0\} = P\{X_0 = i_0, X_1 = i_1, \cdots, X_n = i_n|X_0 = i_0\}$$
$$= p_{i_0 i_1} p_{i_1 i_2} \cdots p_{i_{n-1}\, i_n}.$$

If $Q_{X_0}(i_0) = 0$, the above expression is still taken as the definition for this conditional probability.

If $P\{E|X_0 = i_0\}$ is strictly positive, the sequence of states, $i_0, i_1, \cdots, i_n$, is said to form a *path* from i_0 to i_n, and that i_n is accessible from i_0 in n steps. Since $p_{ij}^{(n)}$ is the conditional probability of being in state j after n steps, starting in state i, $p_{i_0 i_n}^{(n)}$ is just the sum of the conditional probabilities of going from i_0 to i_n in n steps along all n-step paths from i_0 to i_n. Hence, state i is defined to be *accessible* from j if and only if $p_{ij}^{(n)} > 0$ for *some* n. In the inventory example $p_{ij}^{(2)} > 0$ for all i, j, so that every state is accessible from every other state. Obviously, a sufficient condition for *all* states to be accessible is that there exists a value of n not dependent on i and j for which $p_{ij}^{(n)} > 0$ for all i and j. If state i is accessible from state j and, in addition, state j is accessible from state i, then states i and j are said to *communicate*. All states that communicate with each other are said to belong to one *class*. Thus, the states of a Markov chain may consist of one or more classes. Furthermore, a state may not belong to any class. The transition matrix presented in Sec. 13.4 contains three classes. States 0 and 1, recurrent states, form one class in that they communicate with one another. State 2 is an absorbing (and recurrent) state and, hence, forms a class since it communicates with itself. State 3, a transient state, communicates with itself and also forms a class. State 4, also a transient state, belongs to no class.

In a finite-state Markov chain, the members of a class are either all transient states or all positive recurrent states. Many Markov chains encountered in practice consist entirely of states which all communicate with each other; these form single classes containing only positive recurrent states.[85] As indicated above, in order to determine if all states of a chain communicate with each other, it is sufficient to show that there exists a value of n not dependent on i and j for which $p_{ij}^{(n)} > 0$ for all i and j. This is, then, the alternative criterion for determining if states are recurrent that was alluded to in Sec. 13.4. In the inventory example, $p_{ij}^{(2)}$ is positive for all i and j, so that all states communicate and thereby form a single class. This class must contain states which are all positive recurrent.

A final property of Markov chains that must be considered before discussing its long-run behavior is the property of *periodicities*. A state i is said to have period t ($t > 1$) if $p_{ii}^{(n)} = 0$ whenever n is not divisible by t, and t is the smallest integer with this property. For example, it may be possible for the process to enter state i only at the time, 0, 2, 4, $\cdots$, in which case this state has period 2. If there are two consecutive numbers, s and $(s + 1)$, such that the process can be in state i at times s and $(s + 1)$, the state is said to have period one and is called an *aperiodic* state. If state i in a class is aperiodic, then all states in the class are aperiodic. Positive recurrent states which are aperiodic are called *ergodic* states. Several results related to the long-run behavior of finite-state Markov processes follow.

13.5.2 Steady-State Probabilities

If states i and j are ergodic and belong to one class, then it can be shown that

$$\lim_{n \to \infty} p_{ij}^{(n)} = \pi_j ,$$

where the π_j's uniquely satisfy the following "steady-state" equations:

$$\pi_j > 0 ,$$

$$\pi_j = \sum_{i=0}^{M} \pi_i p_{ij}, \qquad \text{for } j = 0, 1, \cdots, M ,$$

$$\sum_{j=0}^{M} \pi_j = 1 .$$

The π_j's are called the steady-state probabilities of the Markov chain and are equal to the reciprocal of the expected recurrence time, i.e.,

$$\pi_j = \frac{1}{\mu_{jj}}, \qquad \text{for } j = 0, 1, \cdots, M .$$

The term "steady-state" probability means that the probability of finding the process in a certain state, say, j, after a large number of transitions tends to the value π_j, independent of the initial probability distribution

[85] The only possible alternative for such a chain is that it contains all transient states, which is not possible for a finite-state Markov chain.

defined over the states. It is important to note that "steady-state" probability does *not* imply that the process settles down into one state. On the contrary, the process continues to make transitions from state to state, and, at any step n, the transition probability from state i to state j is still p_{ij}.

The π_j's can also be interpreted as stationary probabilities (not to be confused with stationary transition probabilities). If the initial absolute probability of being in state j is given by π_j (i.e., $P\{X_0 = j\} = \pi_j$) for all j, then the absolute probability of finding the process in state j at time $n = 1, 2, \cdots$, is also given by π_j (i.e., $P\{X_n = j\} = \pi_j$).

It should be noted that the steady-state equations consist of $(M + 2)$ equations in $(M + 1)$ unknowns. Since it has a unique solution, at least one equation must be redundant and can, therefore, be deleted. It cannot be the equation

$$\sum_{j=0}^{M} \pi_j = 1 ,$$

since $\pi_j = 0$ for all j will satisfy the other $(M + 1)$ equations. Furthermore, the solutions to the other $(M + 1)$ steady-state equations have a unique solution up to a multiplicative constant, and it is this final equation that forces the solution to be a probability distribution.

Returning to the inventory example, the steady-state equations can be expressed as

$$\begin{aligned}
\pi_0 &= \pi_0 p_{00} + \pi_1 p_{10} + \pi_2 p_{20} + \pi_3 p_{30} , \\
\pi_1 &= \pi_0 p_{01} + \pi_1 p_{11} + \pi_2 p_{21} + \pi_3 p_{31} , \\
\pi_2 &= \pi_0 p_{02} + \pi_1 p_{12} + \pi_2 p_{22} + \pi_3 p_{32} , \\
\pi_3 &= \pi_0 p_{03} + \pi_1 p_{13} + \pi_2 p_{23} + \pi_3 p_{33} , \\
1 &= \pi_0 + \pi_1 + \pi_2 + \pi_3 .
\end{aligned}$$

Substituting values for p_{ij} into these equations leads to the equations,

$$\begin{aligned}
\pi_0 &= (.080)\pi_0 + (.632)\pi_1 + (.264)\pi_2 + (.080)\pi_3 , \\
\pi_1 &= (.184)\pi_0 + (.368)\pi_1 + (.368)\pi_2 + (.184)\pi_3 , \\
\pi_2 &= (.368)\pi_0 + (.368)\pi_2 + (.368)\pi_3 , \\
\pi_3 &= (.368)\pi_0 + (.368)\pi_3 , \\
1 &= \pi_0 + \pi_1 + \pi_2 + \pi_3 .
\end{aligned}$$

Solving the last four equations provides the simultaneous solutions,

$$\begin{aligned}
\pi_0 &= .285 , \\
\pi_1 &= .285 , \\
\pi_2 &= .264 , \\
\pi_3 &= .166 ,
\end{aligned}$$

which are essentially the results that appear in the matrix $\mathbf{P}^{(8)}$. Thus, after many weeks the probability of finding zero, one, two, and three cameras in stock tends to .285, .285, .264, and .166, respectively. The corresponding expected recurrence times are

$$\mu_{00} = \frac{1}{\pi_0} = 3.51 \text{ weeks},$$

$$\mu_{11} = \frac{1}{\pi_1} = 3.51 \text{ weeks},$$

$$\mu_{22} = \frac{1}{\pi_2} = 3.79 \text{ weeks},$$

$$\mu_{33} = \frac{1}{\pi_3} = 6.02 \text{ weeks}.$$

There are other important results concerning steady-state probabilities. In particular, if i and j are recurrent states belonging to different classes, then

$$p_{ij}^{(n)} = 0, \qquad \text{for all } n.$$

This result follows from the definition of a class.

Similarly, if j is a transient state, then

$$\lim_{n \to \infty} p_{ij}^{(n)} = 0, \qquad \text{for all } i.$$

This implies that the probability of finding the process in a transient state after a large number of transitions tends to zero.

13.5.3 Expected Average Cost per Unit Time

The previous section dealt with Markov chains whose states were ergodic (positive recurrent and aperiodic). If the requirement that the states be aperiodic is relaxed, then the limit,

$$\lim_{n \to \infty} p_{ij}^{(n)},$$

may not exist. To illustrate this, consider the two-state transition matrix,

$$\mathbf{P} = \begin{bmatrix} 0 & 1 \\ 1 & 0 \end{bmatrix}.$$

If the process starts in state 0 at time 0, it will be in state 0 at times 2, 4, $6 \cdots$, and in state 1 at times 1, 3, $5 \cdots$. Thus, $p_{00}^{(n)} = 1$ if n is even, and $p_{00}^{(n)} = 0$ if n is odd, so that

$$\lim_{n \to \infty} p_{00}^{(n)}$$

does not exist. However, the following limit always exists. If states i and j are positive recurrent and belong to one class, then

$$\lim_{n \to \infty} \left\{ \frac{1}{n} \sum_{k=1}^{n} p_{ij}^{(k)} \right\} = \pi_j,$$

where the π_j's satisfy the steady-state equations presented in Sec. 13.5.2.

This result is extremely important in computing the long-run average cost per unit time associated with a Markov chain. Suppose that a cost (or other penalty function) $C(X_t)$ is incurred when the process is in state X_t at time t, for $t = 0, 1, 2, \cdots$. Note that $C(X_t)$ is a random variable which takes on any one of the values, $C(0), C(1), \cdots, C(M)$, and the function $C(\cdot)$ is independent of t. The expected average cost incurred over the first n periods is given by the expression,

$$E\left[\frac{1}{n}\sum_{t=1}^{n} C(X_t)\right].$$

Using the result that

$$\lim_{n\to\infty}\left\{\frac{1}{n}\sum_{k=1}^{n} p_{ij}^{(k)}\right\} = \pi_j ,$$

it is simple to show that the (long-run) *expected average cost per unit time* is given by

$$\lim_{n\to\infty}\left\{E\left[\frac{1}{n}\sum_{t=1}^{n} C(X_t)\right]\right\} = \sum_{j=0}^{M} C(j)\pi_j .$$

As an example, suppose the camera store finds that a storage charge is being allocated for each camera remaining on the shelf at the end of the week. The cost is charged as follows: If $X_t = 0$, then $C(0) = 0$. If $X_t = 1$, then $C(1) = 2$. If $X_t = 2$, then $C(2) = 8$. Finally, if $X_t = 3$, then $C(3) = 18$. The long-run expected average holding cost per week can then be obtained from the preceding equation, i.e.,

$$\lim_{n\to\infty}\left\{E\left[\frac{1}{n}\sum_{t=1}^{n} C(X_t)\right]\right\} = 0(.285) + 2(.285) + 8(.264) + 18(.166) = 5.67 .$$

It should be noted that an alternative measure to the (long-run) expected average cost per unit time is the (long-run) *actual average cost per unit time*. It can be shown that this latter measure is given by

$$\lim_{n\to\infty}\left\{\frac{1}{n}\sum_{t=1}^{n} C(X_t)\right\} = \sum_{j=0}^{M} \pi_j C(j)$$

for almost all paths of the process. Thus, either measure leads to the same result. These results can also be used to interpret the meaning of the π_j's. To do this, let

$$C(X_k) = \begin{cases} 1, & \text{if } X_k = j \\ 0, & \text{if } X_k \neq j . \end{cases}$$

The (long-run) expected fraction of times the system is in state j is then given by

$$\lim_{n \to \infty} \left\{ E \left[\frac{1}{n} \sum_{t=1}^{n} C(X_t) \right] \right\} = \lim_{n \to \infty} \{E[\text{fraction of times the system is in state } j]\}$$

$$= \pi_j \,.$$

Similarly, π_j can also be interpreted as the (long-run) actual fraction of times that the system is in state j.

13.5.4 Expected Average Cost per Unit Time for Complex Cost Functions

In the preceding section, the cost function was based solely on the state that the process is in at time t. In many important problems encountered in practice, the cost may depend upon another random variable as well as upon the state that the process is in. For example, in the inventory example developed in this chapter suppose that the costs to be considered are the ordering cost and the penalty cost for unsatisfied demand (storage costs will be ignored). It is reasonable to assume that the number of cameras ordered depends only upon the state of the process (the number of cameras in stock) when the order is placed. The cost for unsatisfied demand may be assumed to depend upon the demand during the week as well as upon the state of the process at the beginning of the week. The charges for period t will be made at the end of the week and will include the cost of the order delivered on the Monday of that week and the cost of unsatisfied demand during the week. Thus, the cost incurred for period t can be described as a function of X_{t-1} and D_t, i.e., $C(X_{t-1}, D_t)$. Note that the demands D_t, $D_{t+1}, \cdots$, during successive weeks are assumed to be independent and identically distributed random variables. Furthermore, recall that the (s, S) policy, $(1, 3)$, is being used. X_{t-1}, the stock level at the end of period $t - 1$ (before ordering), is defined iteratively by the expression given in Sec. 13.1. Thus, it follows that $(X_0, X_1, X_2, \cdots, X_{t-1})$ and D_t are independent random variables because $X_0, X_1, X_2, \cdots, X_{t-1}$ are functions only of $X_0, D_1, \cdots, D_{t-1}$, which are independent of D_t. Under these conditions, it can be shown that the (long-run) *expected average cost per unit time* is given by

$$\lim_{n \to \infty} \left\{ E \left[\frac{1}{n} \sum_{t=1}^{n} C(X_{t-1}, D_t) \right] \right\} = \sum_{j=0}^{M} k(j)\pi_j \,,$$

where

$$k(j) = E[C(j, D_t)] \,.$$

Similarly, the (long-run) actual average cost per unit time is given by

$$\lim_{n \to \infty} \left\{ \frac{1}{n} \sum_{t=1}^{n} C(X_{t-1}, D_t) \right\} = \sum_{j=0}^{M} k(j)\pi_j .$$

Suppose that the following costs are associated with the (s, S) inventory policy given earlier. If $z > 0$ cameras are ordered, the cost incurred is $10 + 50z$ dollars. If no cameras are ordered, no ordering cost is incurred. For each unit of unsatisfied demand (lost sales), there is a penalty of \$50 per unit. If the $(s = 1, S = 3)$ ordering policy is followed, the cost in week t is given by $C(X_{t-1}, D_t)$, where

$$C(X_{t-1}, D_t) = \begin{cases} 10 + (50)(3) + 50 \max \{(D_t - 3), 0\}, & \text{if } X_{t-1} < 1 \\ 50 \max \{(D_t - X_{t-1}), 0\}, & \text{if } X_{t-1} \geq 1 . \end{cases}$$

for $t = 1, 2, \cdots$.
Hence,

$$C(0, D_t) = 160 + 50 \max \{(D_t - 3), 0\} ,$$

so that

$$\begin{aligned} k(0) &= E[C(0, D_t)] = 160 + 50E[\max \{(D_t - 3), 0\}] \\ &= 160 + 50[1P_D(4) + 2P_D(5) + 3P_D(6) + \cdots] , \end{aligned}$$

where $P_D(i)$ is the probability that a Poisson random variable, with parameter $\lambda = 1$, equals i. Hence, $k(0) = 161.2$. Similar calculations lead to the results,

$$\begin{aligned} k(1) = E[C(1, D_t)] &= 50E[\max \{(D_t - 1), 0\}] \\ &= 50[1P_D(2) + 2P_D(3) + 3P_D(4) + \cdots] \\ &= 18.4 , \end{aligned}$$

$$\begin{aligned} k(2) = E[C(2, D_t)] &= 50E[\max \{(D_t - 2), 0\}] \\ &= 50[1P_D(3) + 2P_D(4) + 3P_D(5) + \cdots] \\ &= 5.2 , \end{aligned}$$

and

$$\begin{aligned} k(3) = E[C(3, D_t)] &= 50E[\max \{(D_t - 3), 0\}] \\ &= 50[1P_D(4) + 2P_D(5) + \cdots] \\ &= 1.2 . \end{aligned}$$

Thus, the (long-run) expected average inventory cost per week is given by

$$\sum_{j=0}^{3} k(j)\pi_j = (161.2)(.285) + (18.4)(.285) + (5.2)(.264) + (1.2)(.166) = 47.96 .$$

This is the cost associated with the (s, S) policy, $(s, S) = (1, 3)$. The cost of other (s, S) policies can be evaluated in a similar way in order to identify the policy that minimizes the expected average inventory cost per week.

The results of this section were presented only in terms of the inventory example. However, the (non-numerical) results still hold for other problems as long as the following conditions are satisfied:

(1) $\{X_t\}$ is a Markov chain whose states are positive recurrent and belong to one class.
(2) Associated with this Markov chain is a sequence of random variables, $\{D_t\}$, each of which is independent and identically distributed.
(3) A cost, $C(X_t, D_t)$,[86] is incurred at time t, for $t = 0, 1, 2, \cdots$.
(4) The sequence $(X_0, X_1, X_2, \cdots, X_t)$ must be independent of D_t.

In particular, if these conditions are satisfied, then

$$\lim_{n\to\infty} \left\{ E\left[\frac{1}{n} \sum_{t=1}^{n} C(X_t, D_t) \right] \right\} = \sum_{j=0}^{M} k(j)\pi_j ,$$

where

$$k(j) = E[C(j, D_t)] .$$

Furthermore,

$$\lim_{n\to\infty} \left\{ \frac{1}{n} \sum_{t=1}^{n} C(X_t, D_t) \right\} = \sum_{j=0}^{M} k(j)\pi_j ,$$

for almost all paths of the process.

13.6 A REPLACEMENT POLICY MODEL

The following problem is an example of a model that uses the concepts described in the previous sections.[87] Suppose that a unit is inspected at equally spaced points in time, and that after each inspection it is classified into one of 4 states, 0, 1, 2, 3. A unit is in state 0 if and only if it is new. A unit is in state 3 if and only if it is inoperative. A unit in state 1 or 2 is operative, but will "soon" become inoperative. Let the times of inspection be denoted by $t = 0, 1, \cdots$. If a replacement is made, the unit is inoperative for a period. (This can be interpreted as the time necessary to effect the replacement.) Let X_t denote the observed state of the unit in use at time

[86] In the inventory example, the cost incurred was $C(X_{t-1}, D_t)$ rather than $C(X_t, D_t)$. Whether X_t or X_{t-1} is used is unimportant, provided that condition 4 is satisfied.

[87] C. Derman, "On Optimal Replacement Rules When Changes of State are Markovian," in *Mathematical Optimization Techniques*, edited by R. Bellman, University of California Press, Berkeley and Los Angeles, 1963, Chapter 9, pp. 201–210.

t. The replacement policy to be followed is to replace a unit only when it becomes inoperative. Assume that $\{X_t\}$ is a Markov chain with transition matrix given by

$$\mathbf{P} = \begin{bmatrix} 0 & \frac{7}{8} & \frac{1}{8} & 0 \\ 0 & \frac{3}{4} & \frac{1}{4} & 0 \\ 0 & 0 & \frac{1}{2} & \frac{1}{2} \\ 1 & 0 & 0 & 0 \end{bmatrix}.$$

A cost of \$200 is incurred if the unit is replaced after becoming inoperative. Otherwise, no cost is incurred.

By noting that $p_{ij}^{(4)} > 0$ for all i and j, it is evident that every state is positive recurrent and belongs to one class. The steady-state equations can be written as

$$\begin{aligned} \pi_0 &= \pi_3 , \\ \pi_1 &= \frac{7}{8}\pi_0 + \frac{3}{4}\pi_1 , \\ \pi_2 &= \frac{1}{8}\pi_0 + \frac{1}{4}\pi_1 + \frac{1}{2}\pi_2 , \\ \pi_3 &= \frac{1}{2}\pi_2 , \\ 1 &= \pi_0 + \pi_1 + \pi_2 + \pi_3 . \end{aligned}$$

The simultaneous solution is

$$\begin{aligned} \pi_0 &= \frac{2}{15} , \\ \pi_1 &= \frac{7}{15} , \\ \pi_2 &= \frac{4}{15} , \\ \pi_3 &= \frac{2}{15} . \end{aligned}$$

Hence, the (long-run) expected average cost per unit time is given by

$$\pi_3(200) = \frac{2}{15}(200) = \$26.67 .$$

Suppose that the replacement policy is modified so that a replacement is made if the process is in states 1, 2, or 3. The cost structure is now changed so that the cost is only \$100 if the replacement is made from states 1 or 2.

The transition matrix must now be modified to reflect this change in replacement policy as follows.

$$\mathbf{P} = \begin{bmatrix} 0 & \frac{7}{8} & \frac{1}{8} & 0 \\ 1 & 0 & 0 & 0 \\ 1 & 0 & 0 & 0 \\ 1 & 0 & 0 & 0 \end{bmatrix}.$$

It must be noted that this chain is periodic. The system is in state 0 at time 0, 2, 4, $\cdots$. Furthermore, states 0, 1, and 2 form a class, and state 3 belongs to no class. Since the process starts in state 0, state 3 can be eliminated from consideration. However, as indicated in Sec. 13.4.2, the

$$\lim_{n\to\infty} \left\{ \frac{1}{n} \sum_{k=1}^{n} p_{ij}^{(k)} \right\}$$

exists and satisfies the steady-state equations. These equations are then written as

$$\begin{aligned} \pi_0 &= \pi_1 + \pi_2 , \\ \pi_1 &= \frac{7}{8} \pi_0 , \\ \pi_2 &= \frac{1}{8} \pi_0 , \\ 1 &= \pi_0 + \pi_1 + \pi_2 . \end{aligned}$$

The simultaneous solution is

$$\pi_0 = \frac{1}{2}, \quad \pi_1 = \frac{7}{16}, \quad \pi_2 = \frac{1}{16}.$$

Thus, the (long-run) expected average cost per unit time is given by $\frac{7}{16}(100) + \frac{1}{16}(100) = \$50$. This expected cost is greater than the expected cost of the first policy (replace only when the unit is inoperative).

13.7 OPTIMAL MARKOVIAN DECISION RULES

In the above replacement policy example there are four different replacement policies that must be considered. For this example, there remain only two to evaluate, i.e., replace when the system is in states 2 or 3 and replace when the system is in states 1 or 3. However, if the number of states, $M + 1$, is large, there are 2^{M-1} different policies that must be evaluated (replacement is always made in state M and never made in state 0), and an algorithm for finding the optimal solution is desirable. Manne[88] has provided an algorithm for solving the following general problem. (The replacement policy example is a special case of this model.)

Consider a system with a finite number $(M + 1)$ of states $i = 0, 1, \cdots, M$. The state of the system is observed at times $t = 0, 1, \cdots$. At these times one of K possible decisions (denoted by d_k, for $k = 1, 2, \cdots, K$) must be made. This decision, d_k, which depends on the past history of the system, may be based on a specified probability distribution over the set of decisions. In the replacement policy example, $K = 2$, i.e., replace or not replace. Thus, the decision-maker makes decision d_1 (replace) with probability a, and decision d_2 (not replace) with probability $(1 - a)$. As a joint result of the current state i of the system, and the decision d_k chosen, two things occur. An expected cost, c_{ik}, is incurred. The system moves to a new state j with transition probability given by $p_{ij}(k)$. The sequence of observed states $X_0, X_1, \cdots$ and the sequence of decisions $\Delta_0, \Delta_1, \cdots$ is called a Markovian Decision Process. Derman[89] has shown that the optimal decision rule depends only upon the last state observed, i.e., he shows that

$$P\{\Delta_t = d_k | X_0, X_1, \cdots, X_t = i\} = P\{\Delta_t = d_k | X_t = i\} = D_{ik} .$$

When the process is in state i, D_{ik} represents a probability distribution over the set of decisions. Derman has shown that $D_{ik} = 0$ or 1 (decisions are non-randomized), which implies that the same decision k is made whenever the system is in state i. Thus, for the replacement policy example, the decision to replace or not replace the unit depends only upon the last state observed, and either $D_{i1} = 0$ and $D_{i2} = 1$ (do not replace), or $D_{i1} = 1$ and $D_{i2} = 0$ (replace). However, in the present formulation, it is advantageous to consider D_{ik} to have a non-degenerate probability distribution (not just 0 or 1) defined over all possible decisions d_k for $k = 1, 2, \cdots, K$, with

$$\sum_{k=1}^{K} D_{ik} = 1 .$$

The problem of interest is to choose D_{ik} for $i = 0, 1, 2, \cdots, M$ and $k = 1, 2, \cdots, K$ so that the (long-run) expected average cost per unit time is minimized. The solution is obtained by solving the following linear programming problem.

[88] A. Manne, "Linear Programming and Sequential Decisions," *Management Science*, **6,** No. 3, 259–267 (1960).

[89] C. Derman, "On Sequential Decisions and Markov Chains," *Management Science*, **9,** No. 1, 16–24 (1962).

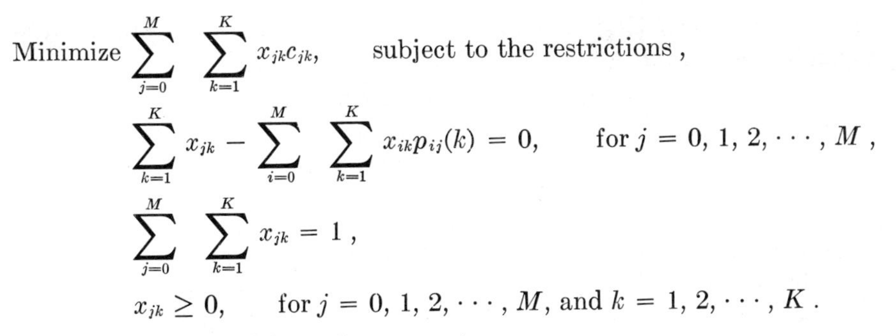

Minimize $\sum_{j=0}^{M} \sum_{k=1}^{K} x_{jk} c_{jk}$, subject to the restrictions ,

$$\sum_{k=1}^{K} x_{jk} - \sum_{i=0}^{M} \sum_{k=1}^{K} x_{ik} p_{ij}(k) = 0, \qquad \text{for } j = 0, 1, 2, \cdots, M,$$

$$\sum_{j=0}^{M} \sum_{k=1}^{K} x_{jk} = 1,$$

$$x_{jk} \geq 0, \qquad \text{for } j = 0, 1, 2, \cdots, M, \text{ and } k = 1, 2, \cdots, K.$$

The D_{jk} are obtained from the expression,

$$D_{jk} = \frac{x_{jk}}{\sum_{k=1}^{K} x_{jk}}, \qquad \text{for } j = 0, 1, 2, \cdots, M, \text{ and } k = 1, 2, \cdots, K.$$

x_{jk} can be interpreted as the (long-run) probability of being in state j and making decision k.

13.8 A WATER RESOURCE MODEL

A multi-purpose dam is used for generating electric power as well as for flood control. The capacity of the dam is 3 units. The probability distribution of the quantity of water, W_t, which flows into the dam during month t (for $t = 1, 2, \cdots$) is given by $P_W(k)$, where

$$P_W(0) = P\{W = 0\} = \frac{1}{6}$$

$$P_W(1) = P\{W = 1\} = \frac{1}{3}$$

$$P_W(2) = P\{W = 2\} = \frac{1}{3}$$

$$P_W(3) = P\{W = 3\} = \frac{1}{6}.$$

If the water in the dam exceeds the capacity of 3 units, the excess water is released through the spillways. For the purpose of generating electric power, 2 units of water are required and released at the end of each month. If there are less than 2 units in the dam, all the water available is released.

Let X_t denote the amount of water in the dam at time t *after* the water is released. Assume that the dam is empty when $t = 0$. Then X_{t+1} is defined recursively by $X_{t+1} = \min\{1, (X_t + W_{t+1} - 2)^+\}$, for $t = 0, 1, \cdots$, where the symbol A^+ is defined as

$$A^+ = \begin{cases} A, & \text{if } A > 0 \\ 0, & \text{if } A \leq 0. \end{cases}$$

It is evident that $\{X_t\}$ is a Markov chain with transition probabilities given by the matrix,

$$\mathbf{P} = \begin{bmatrix} \frac{5}{6} & \frac{1}{6} \\ \frac{1}{2} & \frac{1}{2} \end{bmatrix}$$

Note that there are only two values for the state space, i.e., 0 and 1. Given that the dam is empty at time 0, there can never be more than 1 unit in the dam *after* the water is released. Each element of the transition matrix is positive, and, hence, all states are positive recurrent and belong to one class. The steady-state equations are given by

$$\begin{aligned} \pi_0 &= \frac{5}{6}\pi_0 + \frac{1}{2}\pi_1 , \\ \pi_1 &= \frac{1}{6}\pi_0 + \frac{1}{2}\pi_1 , \\ 1 &= \pi_0 + \pi_1 . \end{aligned}$$

The simultaneous solution of these equations yields

$$\begin{aligned} \pi_0 &= \frac{3}{4}, \\ \pi_1 &= \frac{1}{4}. \end{aligned}$$

In general, for any two-by-two transition matrix, the steady-state equations lead to

$$\begin{aligned} \pi_0 &= p_{10}/(p_{10} + p_{01}) , \\ \pi_1 &= p_{01}/(p_{10} + p_{01}) . \end{aligned}$$

Suppose that excess water which overflows the spillways is used for irrigation purposes and is worth \$100,000 per unit per month. Similarly, when less than 2 units are released, additional water must be purchased for generating electric power, at a price of \$200,000 per unit per month. The (long-run) expected average cost per month is desired. The conditions given in Sec. 13.4.3 that are necessary for

$$\lim_{n \to \infty} \left\{ E\left[\frac{1}{n} \sum_{t=1}^{n} C(X_{t-1}, W_t) \right] \right\}$$

to equal

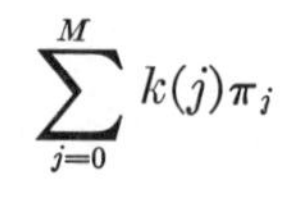

$$\sum_{j=0}^{M} k(j)\pi_j$$

are satisfied and, hence,

$$k(j) = E[C(j, W_t)], \qquad \text{for } j = 0, 1 .$$

It is necessary to calculate $C(j, W_t)$. If there is no water in the dam at time $(t - 1)$ and $W_t = 0$, then 2 units of water must be purchased; if $W_t = 1$, then 1 unit must be purchased; if $W_t = 2$ or 3, no additional water is required. Furthermore, no savings are obtained by water overflowing the spillways. Hence,

$$k(0) = E[C(0, W_t)] = (200{,}000)(2)\frac{1}{6} + (200{,}000)(1)\frac{1}{3} = 133{,}333 .$$

If there is one unit of water in the dam at time $(t - 1)$ and $W_t = 0$, then 1 unit of water must be purchased; if $W_t = 1$ or 2, no additional water is required; if $W_t = 3$, then 1 unit is saved for irrigation purposes. Hence,

$$k(1) = E[C(1, W_t)] = (200{,}000)(1)\frac{1}{6} - (100{,}000)(1)\frac{1}{6} = 16{,}667 .$$

Therefore the (long-run) expected average cost per unit time is given by

$$\left(\frac{3}{4}\right)(133{,}333) + \left(\frac{1}{4}\right)(16{,}667) = \$104{,}167 .$$

There are other release policies that should be evaluated, i.e., release 0, 1, or 3 units, in order to find an optimal policy. This can be done by enumeration, or by using the linear programming technique suggested in Sec. 13.5.

13.9 POLICY IMPROVEMENT TECHNIQUE FOR FINDING OPTIMAL PROCEDURES

There exist criteria, other than the expected average cost per unit time, for evaluating policies. Consider a system with a finite number $(M + 1)$ of states $i = 0, 1, \cdots M$. The state of the system is observed at times $t = 0, 1, \cdots$. At these times, one of K possible decisions (denoted by d_k, for $k = 1, 2, \cdots, K$) must be made. The decision d_k may depend on the past history of the system. As a joint result of the current state i of the system and the decision d_k chosen, two things occur. The system moves to a new state j with transition probability given by $p_{ij}(k)$. A reward (or cost) $r_{ij}(k)$ is associated with the transition from i to j. A discount factor $\alpha < 1$ is specified so that the present value of one unit of income m periods in the future is α^m. A rule for making a sequence of decisions is sought which maximizes the present value of the total expected reward for a system.

It can be shown that, for Markovian decision processes, only (nonrandomized) decisions which depend on the last state observed need be considered. A *policy* R is a rule that specifies which one of the K possible decisions, d_k, is to be made when the system is in state i (for $i = 0, 1, 2, \cdots, M$). Thus, a policy R is just a sequence of decisions, $d_0(R)$, $d_1(R)$, $\cdots$, $d_M(R)$, where each $d_i(R)$ is one of the K possible decisions, d_k.

Denote by $p_{ij}[d_i(R)]$ the transition probability of going from state i to state j when decision $d_i(R)$ is made while operating under policy R. Let $r_{ij}[d_i(R)]$ be the reward associated with the transition from state i to state j when decision $d_i(R)$ is made while operating under policy R. For a given policy R, $V_i(R)$ is defined as the present value of the total expected reward for a system starting in state i. It can be shown that $V_i(R)$ satisfies the following recursive relation:

$$V_i(R) = q_i[d_i(R)] + \alpha \sum_{j=0}^{M} p_{ij}[d_i(R)]V_j(R), \qquad \text{for } i = 0, 1, \cdots, M ,$$

where

$$q_i[d_i(R)] = \sum_{j=0}^{M} p_{ij}[d_i(R)]r_{ij}[d_i(R)] .$$

R. Howard (see "selected references" at the end of the chapter) has presented an algorithm that can be used to evaluate these policies without complete enumeration. This procedure, which is called the Policy Improvement Technique, can be summarized as follows.

Step 1:

For an arbitrarily chosen policy R, use $p_{ij}[d_i(R)]$ and $q_i[d_i(R)]$ to solve the set of equations,

$$V_i(R) = q_i[d_i(R)] + \alpha \sum_{j=0}^{M} p_{ij}[d_i(R)]V_j(R), \qquad \text{for } i = 0, 1, \cdots, M ,$$

for all present values $V_i(R)$.

Step 2:

Find the alternative policy R' such that, for each state i, $d_i(R')$ is the decision that makes

$$q_i[d_i(R')] + \alpha \sum_{j=0}^{M} p_{ij}[d_i(R')]V_j(R)$$

a maximum, using the present values $V_j(R)$ just computed from the previous policy. Then R' becomes the new policy and $d_i(R')$ becomes the new decision in the ith state, $q_i[d_i(R')]$ becomes $q_i[d_i(R)]$, and $p_{ij}[d_i(R')]$ becomes $p_{ij}[d_i(R)]$, and step 1 is repeated with this policy R'.

The iteration cycle will be able to make policy improvements until the policies on two successive iterations are identical. At this point it has found the optimal policy, and the procedure is completed. (The policy is optimal in the sense of maximizing the present value of the total expected reward.)

As an example of the Policy Improvement Technique, consider the following model. An expensive complex electronic unit is manufactured by a team of operators. The company has classified its team of operators into the categories of operators and senior operators. It takes a month for a team to produce a unit. When the operators use the machines, the probability is .2 that the machines break down, requiring a major overhaul (it will be assumed that such an overhaul, if necessary, can be postponed until *after* the unit is completed and the overhaul can be finished over a weekend). When the senior operators use the machines, the probability is .1 that the machines break down. The company's unit profit is $10,000 minus the cost of labor and repairs. A major overhaul costs $5,000, primarily due to the cost of replacement parts. The labor charges are $2,000 and $3,000 for the operators and senior operators, respectively, for each unit produced. The discount factor is .995 per month. The system can be assumed to be in one of two states, 0 or 1. State 0 implies that the machines have just been overhauled. State 1 implies that the machines have been operated for at least one month without an overhaul. Let X_t $(t = 0, 1, 2, \cdots)$ denote the state of the system after a unit is completed and *after* the overhaul, if required, has been made. A policy corresponds to an assignment of a team to the machines for each state of the system. It is evident that $\{X_t\}$ is a Markov chain. Hence, there are 4 possible policies that the company can use. Policy R_1 will represent the assignment of operators to the machines when the process is in state 0 or state 1. Policy R_2 will represent the assignment of operators to the machines when the process is in state 0, and the assignment of senior operators to the machines when the process is in state 1. Policy R_3 will represent the reverse of policy 2. Policy R_4 will represent the assignment of senior operators to the machines when the process is in state 0 or state 1. For this example, direct enumeration is simple, and can be accomplished. However, the Policy Improvement Technique will be used for illustrative purposes.

In order to begin step 1 of the Policy Improvement Technique, it is necessary to choose a policy arbitrarily. Let this be policy R_4. The transition matrix for this policy is given by

$$\mathbf{P} = \begin{bmatrix} .1 & .9 \\ .1 & .9 \end{bmatrix}.$$

The reward (profit) corresponding to the system being in state 0 when starting from state 0, $r_{00}[d_0(R_4)]$, is given by

$$10{,}000 - 3{,}000 - 5{,}000 = 2{,}000\,.$$

The other rewards are given by

$$r_{01}[d_0(R_4)] = 7{,}000,\ r_{10}[d_1(R_4)] = 2{,}000, \text{ and } r_{11}[d_1(R_4)] = 7{,}000\,.$$

Hence,

$$q_0[d_0(R_4)] = p_{00}[d_0(R_4)]\, r_{00}[d_0(R_4)] + p_{01}[d_0(R_4)]\, r_{01}[d_0(R_4)] = 6{,}500\,,$$

and

$$q_1[d_1(R_4)] = p_{10}[d_1(R_4)]\, r_{10}[d_1(R_4)] + p_{11}[d_1(R_4)]\, r_{11}[d_1(R_4)] = 6{,}500\,.$$

The following equations must be solved.

$$V_0(R_4) = q_0[d_0(R_4)] + .995\{p_{00}[d_0(R_4)]\, V_0(R_4) + p_{01}[d_0(R_4)]\, V_1(R_4)\}\,, \text{ and}$$
$$V_1(R_4) = q_1[d_1(R_4)] + .995\{p_{10}[d_1(R_4)]\, V_0(R_4) + p_{11}[d_1(R_4)]\, V_1(R_4)\}\,.$$

Thus,

$$V_0(R_4) = 6{,}500 + .0995V_0(R_4) + .8955V_1(R_4)\,,$$
$$V_1(R_4) = 6{,}500 + .0995V_0(R_4) + .8955V_1(R_4)\,.$$

The simultaneous solution to this system of equations yields

$$V_0(R_4) = 1{,}300{,}000$$

and

$$V_1(R_4) = 1{,}300{,}000\,.$$

Step 2 can now be applied. It is necessary to find the alternative policy R' which has the property that $m_0 = d_0(R')$ and $m_1 = d_1(R')$ are the decisions that maximize $Z_0[m_0]$ and $Z_1[m_1]$, respectively,
where

$$Z_0[m_0] = q_0[m_0] + .995\{p_{00}[m_0](1{,}300{,}000) + p_{01}[m_0](1{,}300{,}000)\}\,,$$

and

$$Z_0[m_1] = q_1[m_1] + .995\{p_{10}[m_1](1{,}300{,}000) + p_{11}[m_1](1{,}300{,}000)\}\,.$$

In order to find $d_0(R')$, it is necessary to evaluate $p_{00}[m_0]$, $p_{01}[m_0]$, $q_0[m_0]$, and $Z_0[m_0]$ for all possible values of m_0. When the system is in state 0, there are two possible decisions that can be made, namely, to use operators, (which will be denoted by $m_0 = 1$) or to use senior operators (which will be denoted by $m_0 = 2$). Hence, the following results are obtained.

m_0	$p_{00}[m_0]$	$p_{01}[m_0]$	$q_0[m_0]$	$Z_0[m_0]$
1	.2	.8	7,000	1.3005×10^6
2	.1	.9	6,500	1.3000×10^6

It is evident that $d_0(R') = m_0 = 1$ (use operators) is the decision that maximizes $Z_0[m_0]$.

In order to find $d_1(R')$, it is necessary to evaluate $p_{10}[m_1]$, $p_{11}[m_1]$, $q_1[m_1]$, and $Z_1[m_1]$ for all possible values of m_1. When the system is in state 1 there are two possible decisions that can be made, namely, to use operators (which will be denoted by $m_1 = 1$) or to use senior operators (which will be denoted by $m_1 = 2$). Hence, the following results are obtained.

m_1	$p_{10}[m_1]$	$p_{11}[m_1]$	$q_1[m_1]$	$Z_1[m_1]$
1	.2	.8	7,000	1.3005×10^6
2	.1	.9	6,500	1.3000×10^6

It is evident that $d_1(R') = m_1 = 1$ (use operators) is the decision that maximizes $Z_1[m_1]$. Thus, since $d_0(R') = d_1(R') = 1$, policy R' is policy R_1 and at least one more iteration is required since the starting policy was R_4.

The equations that must be solved are the following.

$$V_0(R_1) = q_0[d_0(R_1)] + .995\{p_{00}[d_0(R_1)]V_0(R_1) + p_{01}[d_0(R_1)]V_1(R_1)\}\ ,$$
$$V_1(R_1) = q_1[d_1(R_1)] + .995\{p_{10}[d_1(R_1)]V_0(R_1) + p_{11}[d_1(R_1)]V_1(R_1)\}\ .$$

The simultaneous solution to these equations yields

$$V_0(R_1) = V_1(R_1) = 1{,}400{,}000\ .$$

Step 2 can now be applied. It is necessary to find the alternative policy R' which has the property that $m_0 = d_0(R')$ and $m_1 = d_1(R')$ are the decisions that maximize $Z_0[m_0]$ and $Z_1[m_1]$, respectively, where

$$Z_0[m_0] = q_0[m_0] + .995\{p_{00}[m_0](1{,}400{,}000) + p_{01}[m_0](1{,}400{,}000)\}\ ,$$

and

$$Z_1[m_1] = q_1[m_1] + .995\{p_{10}[m_1](1{,}400{,}000) + p_{11}[m_1](1{,}400{,}000)\}\ .$$

The values of $q_0[m_0]$, $q_1[m_1]$, $p_{00}[m_0]$, $p_{01}[m_0]$, $p_{10}[m_1]$, and $p_{11}[m_1]$ have already been found in the first iteration so that only $Z_0[m_0]$ and $Z_1[m_1]$ are required. The following values are obtained.

m_0	$Z_0[m_0]$	m_1	$Z_1[m_1]$
1	1.4000×10^6	1	1.4000×10^6
2	1.3995×10^6	2	1.3995×10^6

Thus, $d_0(R') = m_0 = 1$ (use operators) and $d_1(R') = m_1 = 1$ (use operators), so that policy R' is again policy R_1. The policies on two successive iterations are identical so that the optimal policy, R_1, has been found, and the procedure is completed. This optimal policy calls for the use of only operators rather than senior operators.

There are two additional aspects of this algorithm that are pertinent. It is not necessary to start the procedure with step 1. Instead, an initial set of present values may be chosen arbitrarily, and the iteration may be started with step 2. If there is no prior basis for selecting an initial policy in step 1, it is often convenient to start the process with step 2 in the policy improvement technique with all $V_i(R)$ set equal to zero. The initial policy selected will then be the one that maximizes expected immediate reward, a very satisfactory starting point in many cases.

The policy improvement technique was introduced as a procedure that can be used to find optimal policies using the present value of the total expected reward criterion rather than the average expected reward per unit time criterion. However, a simple modification in step 1 enables the procedure to be used for finding optimal procedures under this latter criterion. This modification replaces the equations that must be solved in step 1 by the equations,

$$g(R) + V_1(R) = q_i[d_i(R)] + \sum_{j=0}^{M} p_{ij}[d_i(R)]V_j(R), \qquad \text{for } i = 0, 1, 2, \cdots, M .$$

These equations are solved for all $V_i(R)$ and $g(R)$ by setting $V_M(R)$ equal to zero. The two-step iterative procedure outlined earlier is then followed. Of course, α is set equal to one in the equations of step 2 since the average expected reward per unit time criterion precludes the concept of discounting. The final value of $g(R)$ is the average expected reward per unit time for the optimal procedure.

13.10 ABSORPTION STATES

It has been pointed out that a state k is called an absorbing state if $p_{kk} = 1$, so that once the chain visits k it remains there forever. If k is an absorbing state, the first passage probability from i to k is called the probability of absorption into k, having started at i. When there are two or more absorbing states in a chain, and it is evident that the process will be absorbed into one of these states, it is desirable to find these probabilities of absorption. These probabilities can be obtained by solving a system of linear equations. Suppose that the Markov chain is such that ultimately one of the absorbing states will be reached. If the state k is an absorbing state, then the set of absorption probabilities f_{ik} satisfies the system of equations,

$$f_{ik} = \sum_{j=0}^{M} p_{ij} f_{jk}, \qquad \text{for } i = 0, 1, \cdots, M ,$$

subject to the conditions,

$$f_{kk} = 1\,,$$
$$f_{ik} = 0, \qquad \text{if state } i \text{ is recurrent and } i \neq k\,.$$

Absorption probabilities are important in "random walks." A *random walk* is a Markov chain with the property that if the system is in a state i, then in a single transition the system either remains at i or moves to one of the states immediately adjacent to i. For example, a random walk often is used as a model for situations involving gambling. To illustrate, suppose that two players, each having two dollars, agree to keep playing a game betting a dollar at a time until one is broke. The amount of money that player A has after n plays of the game forms a Markov chain with transition matrix,

$$\mathbf{P} = \begin{bmatrix} 1 & 0 & 0 & 0 & 0 \\ 1-p & 0 & p & 0 & 0 \\ 0 & 1-p & 0 & p & 0 \\ 0 & 0 & 1-p & 0 & p \\ 0 & 0 & 0 & 0 & 1 \end{bmatrix}.$$

If p represents the probability of A winning a single encounter, then the probability of absorption into state 0 (A losing all his money) can be obtained from the above system of equations. It can be shown that this leads to the alternate expressions (for general M rather than $M = 4$ as in this example),

$$1 - f_{i0} = \frac{\sum_{m=0}^{i-1} \rho^m}{\sum_{m=0}^{M-1} \rho^m}, \qquad \text{for } i = 1, 2, \cdots, M\,,$$

where $\rho = (1-p)/p$.
For $M = 4$ and $i = 2$, the probability of A going broke is given by

$$f_{20} = \frac{\rho^2 + \rho^3}{1 + \rho + \rho^2 + \rho^3}.$$

13.11 CONTINUOUS PARAMETER MARKOV CHAINS

All of the previous sections assumed that the time parameter t was discrete (i.e., $t = 0, 1, 2, \cdots$). Such an assumption is suitable for many problems, but there are certain cases (such as for some queueing models) where a continuous time parameter is required.

Let $\{X(t)\}$, where $t \geq 0$, be a Markov chain with $M+1$ discrete states, $0, 1, \cdots, M$, and stationary transition probability function,

$$p_{ij}(t) = P\{X(t+s) = j | X(s) = i\}, \qquad \text{for } i, j = 0, 1, \cdots, M .$$

This function is assumed to be continuous at $t = 0$ with

$$\lim_{t \to 0} p_{ij}(t) = \begin{cases} 1, & \text{if } i = j \\ 0, & \text{if } i \neq j . \end{cases}$$

Just as the discrete time parameter models satisfy the Chapman–Kolmogorov equations, the continuous time transition probability function also satisfies these equations, i.e., for any state i and j, and positive numbers t and $v (0 \leq v \leq t)$,

$$p_{ij}(t) = \sum_{k=0}^{M} p_{ik}(v) p_{kj}(t-v) .$$

A pair of states i and j are said to communicate if there are times t_1 and t_2 such that $p_{ij}(t_1) > 0$ and $p_{ji}(t_2) > 0$. All states that communicate are said to form a class. If all states in a chain form a single class, then

$$p_{ij}(t) > 0 \text{ for all } t > 0 \text{ and all states } i \text{ and } j .$$

Furthermore,

$$\lim_{t \to \infty} p_{ij}(t) = \pi_j$$

always exists and is independent of the initial state of the chain, for $i = 0, 1, \cdots, M$. The π_j satisfy the equations,

$$\pi_j = \sum_{i=0}^{M} \pi_i p_{ij}(t), \qquad \text{for } j = 0, 1, \cdots, M, \quad \text{and for every } t \geq 0 .$$

Just as the one-step transition probabilities played a major role in describing the Markov process for a discrete time parameter chain, the analogous role for a continuous time parameter chain is played by the transition intensities. The *transition intensity* is defined by

$$u_j = -\frac{d}{dt} p_{jj}(0) = \lim_{t \to 0} \frac{1 - p_{jj}(t)}{t}, \qquad \text{for } j = 0, 1, \cdots, M ,$$

and

$$u_{ij} = \frac{d}{dt} p_{ij}(0) = \lim_{t \to 0} \frac{p_{ij}(t)}{t}, \qquad \text{for all } i \neq j ,$$

provided that these limits exist and are finite. u_j is called the *intensity of passage*, given that the Markov chain is in state j, and u_{ij} is called the *intensity of transition* to state j from the state i.

These transition intensities also satisfy the equation,

$$\pi_j u_j = \sum_{i \neq j} \pi_1 u_{ij}, \qquad \text{for } j = 0, 1, \cdots, M.$$

The transition intensities can be interpreted as follows. The probability of transition from state i to j during the interval of length Δt, $p_{ij}(\Delta t)$, is equal to $u_{ij}\Delta t$ plus a remainder which, when divided by Δt, tends to zero as $\Delta t \to 0$. Similarly, $1 - p_{jj}(\Delta t)$, the probability of a transition from a state j to some other state during the interval of length Δt, is equal to $u_j\Delta t$ plus a remainder which, when divided by Δt, tends to zero as $\Delta t \to 0$. Thus, for small Δt, the probabilities of transition within a time interval of length Δt are essentially proportional to Δt, the proportionality constants being the transition intensities.

As an example, consider the following repairman problem which was discussed in Sec. 10.5.6. There are M machines serviced by a single repairman. A machine which breaks down is serviced immediately unless the repairman is servicing another machine, in which case a waiting line is formed. A system is said to be in state n if n machines are not working. If the process is in state n, where $1 \leq n \leq M$, this means that one machine is being serviced and $(n - 1)$ are in the waiting line waiting to be repaired. If the process is in state 0, then all machines are working, and the repairman is idle. Let $X(t)$ be the number of machines not working at time t. Suppose the transition intensities satisfy the condition that if i and j are states such that $|i - j| \geq 2$, then $u_{ij} = 0$. It can be shown that $\{X(t)\}$ is a continuous parameter Markov process which changes states only through transitions from a state to its immediate neighbors. The transition intensities can be written as

$$u_{j,j+1} = (M - j)\lambda, \qquad \text{if } j = 0, 1, 2, \cdots M,$$

$$u_{j,j-1} = \begin{cases} \mu, & \text{if } j = 1, 2, \cdots, M \\ 0, & \text{if } j = 0, \end{cases}$$

$$u_j = \begin{cases} (M - j)\lambda + \mu, & \text{if } j = 1, \cdots, M \\ M\lambda, & \text{if } j = 0. \end{cases}$$

(To simplify the notation, λ is being used rather than λ_1, which was introduced in Sec. 10.5.6.) More explicitly,

$$\lim_{t \to 0} \left\{ \frac{p_{j,j+1}(t)}{t} \right. = (M - j)\lambda, \qquad \text{for } j = 0, 1, 2, \cdots, M,$$

$$\lim_{t \to 0} \left\{ \frac{p_{j,j-1}(t)}{t} \right. = \begin{cases} \mu, & \text{for } j = 1, 2, \cdots, M \\ 0, & \text{for } j = 0 , \end{cases}$$

$$\lim_{t \to 0} \left\{ \frac{1 - p_{jj}(t)}{t} \right. = \begin{cases} (M - j)\lambda + \mu, & \text{for } j = 1, 2, \cdots, M \\ M\lambda, & \text{for } j = 0 . \end{cases}$$

Thus, these equations indicate that in a small time interval the number of machines working either decreases by one, increases by one, or stays the same. The conditional probability of an increase of 1 is denoted by $(M - j)\lambda$. The conditional probability of a decrease by 1 is denoted by μ. Substituting these results into the system of equations which the π_j satisfy, i.e.,

$$\pi_j u_j = \sum_{i \neq j} \pi_i u_{ij} ,$$

the following system of equations is obtained.

$$\pi_0 M\lambda = \pi_1 \mu ,$$

$$\pi_j[(M - j)\lambda + \mu] = \pi_{j-1}(M - j + 1)\lambda + \pi_{j+1}\mu , \text{ for } j = 1, \cdots, M - 1 ,$$

$$\pi_M \mu = \pi_{M-1}\lambda , \qquad \text{for } j = M .$$

Solving this system of equations leads to the steady-state probability distribution of $X(t)$ given in Sec. 10.5.6, i.e.,

$$P_0 = 1 \Big/ \sum_{j=0}^{M} \left[\frac{M!}{(M - j)!} \left(\frac{\lambda}{\mu} \right)^j \right]$$

$$P_j = \frac{M!}{(M - j)!} \left(\frac{\lambda}{\mu} \right)^j P_0, \qquad \text{for } j = 1, 2, \cdots, M .$$

SELECTED REFERENCES

1. Barlow, R. E., and Proschan, F., *Mathematical Theory of Reliability,* Wiley, New York, 1965.
2. Chung, K. L., *Markov Chains with Stationary Transition Probabilities,* Springer-Verlag, Berlin, 1960.
3. Feller, W., *An Introduction to Probability Theory and Its Applications,* Wiley, New York, 2nd ed., 1957.
4. Howard, R., *Dynamic Programming and Markov Processes,* M.I.T. Press, Cambridge, Mass., 1960.
5. Kemeny, J. G., and Snell, J. L., *Finite Markov Chains,* Van Nostrand, Princeton, N.J., 1959.
6. Parzen, E., *Stochastic Processes,* Holden-Day, San Francisco, 1962.

PROBLEMS

1. Suppose that a communications network transmits numbers in a binary system, i.e., 0 or 1. In passing through the network, there is a probability, q, that the number will be received incorrectly at the next stage. If X_0 denotes the number entering the system, X_1 the number recorded after the first transmission, X_2 the number recorded after the second transmission, $\cdots$, then $\{X_n\}$ is a Markov chain. Find the one-step and steady-state transition matrix.

2. A transition matrix P is said to be doubly stochastic if the sum over each column equals one, i.e.,

$$\sum_{i=0}^{M} p_{ij} = 1 \qquad \text{for all } j .$$

If such a chain is aperiodic and consists of $M + 1$ states, all of which belong to one class, show that

$$\pi_j = \frac{1}{M+1}, \qquad \text{for } j = 0, 1, \cdots, M .$$

3. A particle moves on a circle through points which have been marked 0, 1, 2, 3, 4 (in a clockwise order). The particle starts at point 0. At each step it has probability q of moving to the right (clockwise) and $1 - q$ to the left (counterclockwise). Let $X_n (n \geq 0)$ denote its location on the circle. $\{X_n\}$ is a Markov chain.

(a) Find the transition probability matrix.
(b) Find the steady-state probabilities.

4. Evaluate the expected average inventory cost per week for the inventory example introduced in Sec. 13.5.4 using the (s, S) policy, $(s, S) = (2, 3)$.

5. For the replacement policy example given in Sec. 13.6, find the (long-run) expected average cost per unit time for the replacement policy which replaces the unit when (a) it is in state 2 or 3, (b) when it is in state 1 or 3.

6. For the replacement policy example given in Sec. 13.6, formulate the linear programming problem that must be solved in order to find the optimal solution. Do not solve numerically.

7. Evaluate the other three water release policies for the water resource model given in Sec. 13.8, using the expected average cost per unit time criterion.

8. Using the average cost per unit time criterion (no discounting), find the optimal policy for the example concerning assignment of machine operators presented in Sec. 13.9.

9. Consider the inventory example introduced in Sec. 13.1. Instead of following an (s, S) policy, a (q, Q) policy will be used. If the stock level at the end of each period is less than $q = 2$ units, $Q = 2$ additional units will be ordered. Otherwise, no ordering will take place. This is a (q, Q) policy with $q = 2$ and $Q = 2$. Let X_t denote the number of units on hand at the end of the tth period. Assume that demand which is not filled results in lost sales. $\{X_n\}$ is a Markov chain (assume $X_0 = 0$). Using the cost values and demand distribution given for the inventory example in the text:

(a) find the steady-state probabilities
(b) find the long-run expected average cost per unit time.

10. Consider the following (k, Q) inventory policy. Let $D_1, D_2, \cdots$ be the demand for a product in periods $1, 2, \cdots$, respectively. If the demand during a period exceeds the number of items available, this unsatisfied demand is backlogged, i.e., it is filled when the next order is received. Let $Z_n (n = 0, 1, \cdots)$ denote the amount of inventory on hand minus the number of units backlogged before ordering at the end of period $n (Z_n = 0)$. If Z_n is zero or positive, no orders are backlogged. If Z_n is negative, then $-Z_n$ represents the number of backlogged units and no inventory is on hand. If at the beginning of period n, $Z_n < k = 1$, an order is placed for $2m$ (Qm in general) units, where m is the smallest integer such that $Z_n + 2m \geq 1$. (The amount ordered is the smallest integral multiple of 2, which brings the level to at least 1 unit.) Let D_n be independent and identically distributed random variables taking on the values, 0, 1, 2, 3, 4, each with probability 1/5. Let X_n denote the amount of stock on hand *after* ordering at the end of period n ($X_0 = 2$). It is evident that

$$X_n = \begin{cases} X_{n-1} - D_n + 2m, & \text{if } X_{n-1} - D_n < 1 \\ X_{n-1} - D_n, & \text{if } X_{n-1} - D_n \geq 1 \end{cases} \qquad (n = 1, 2, \cdots),$$

and $\{X_n\} (n = 0, 1, \cdots)$ is a Markov chain with only 2 states, 1 and 2. [The only time that ordering will take place is when $Z_n = 0, -1$, or -2, in which case 2, 2, and 4 units are ordered, respectively, leaving $X_n =$ 2, 1, 2, respectively. In general for any (k, Q) policy, the possible states are $k, k + 1, k + 2, \cdots, k + Q - 1$.]

(a) Find the one-step transition matrix.
(b) Find the stationary probabilities (see problem 2).
(c) Suppose that the ordering cost is given by $(4 + 2m)$ if an order is placed and zero otherwise. The holding cost per period is Z_n if $Z_n \geq 0$

and zero otherwise. The shortage cost per period is $-4Z_n$ if $Z_n < 0$ and zero otherwise. Find the (long-run) expected average cost per unit time.

11. An important unit consists of two components placed in parallel. The unit performs satisfactorily if one of the two components is operating. A component breaks down in a given period with probability q. Assume that the component breaks down only at the end of a period. When this occurs, the parallel component takes over, if available, beginning at the next period. Only one serviceman is assigned to service each component in need of repair, and it takes two periods to complete the servicing. Let X_t be a vector consisting of two elements, U and V. U represents the number of components operating at the end of the tth period. V takes on the value 1 if the serviceman requires only one additional period to complete a repair, if he is so engaged, and zero otherwise. Thus, the state space consists of the four states, (2, 0), (1, 0), (0, 1), and (1, 1). For example, the state (1, 1) implies that one component is operative and the other component needs an additional period for repair before becoming operative. Denote these four states by 0, 1, 2, 3, respectively. $\{X_t\}$ $(t = 0, 1, \cdots)$ is a Markov chain [Assume that X_0 is the vector (2, 0), i.e., $X_0 = 0$] with transition matrix,

$$\mathbf{P} = \begin{bmatrix} 1-q & q & 0 & 0 \\ 0 & 0 & q & 1-q \\ 0 & 0 & 0 & 1 \\ 1-q & q & 0 & 0 \end{bmatrix}.$$

(a) What is the probability that there is a waiting line of length 1 (a unit needing service but not being worked on) at the end of a current service period?
(b) What are the steady-state probabilities?
(c) If it costs \$10,000 per period when the unit is inoperable (both components down), and zero otherwise, what is the (long-run) expected average cost per period?

12. Using the policy improvement technique, find the optimal policy for the example concerning assignment of machine operators presented in Sec. 13.9. Use the costs and probabilities given except for the following changes. When the process is in state 1, the transition probabilities become

$$p_{10} = .5 \text{ and } p_{11} = .5 \qquad \text{for the operators,}$$

while

$$p_{10} = .2 \text{ and } p_{11} = .8 \qquad \text{for the senior operators.}$$

13. Consider a single-server queueing system in which customers arrive according to a Poisson input process with parameter λ (see Sec. 10.4.3), and the service times for the respective calling units are independent and identically distributed random variables. For $n = 1, 2, \cdots$, let X_n denote the number of calling units in the system at the moment, t_n, when the nth calling unit to be served (over a certain time interval) has finished being served. The sequence of time, $\{t_n\}$, corresponding to the moments when successive calling units depart service are called *regeneration points.* Furthermore, $\{X_n\}$, which represents the number of calling units in the system at the corresponding sequence of time $\{t_n\}$, is a Markov chain, and is known as an *imbedded Markov chain.* Imbedded Markov chains are useful for studying the properties of continuous time parameter stochastic processes.

Now consider the particular special case where the service time of successive calling units is a fixed constant, say, 10 minutes, and the mean arrival rate is one every 50 minutes. In order to obtain a *finite* number of states, assume as an approximation that, if there are 4 calling units in the system, the system becomes saturated so that additional arrivals are turned away. Therefore, $\{X_n\}$ is an imbedded Markov chain with states 0, 1, 2, or 3. (Since there are never more than 4 calling units in the system, there can never be more than 3 in the system at a regeneration point.) Since the system is observed at successive departures, X_n can never decrease by more than 1. Furthermore, the probabilities of transitions which result in increases in X_n are obtained directly from the Poisson distribution.

(a) Find the one-step transition matrix. (In obtaining the transition probability from state 3 to state 3, use the probability of one or more arrivals rather than just one arrival, and similarly for other transitions to state 3.)
(b) Find the steady-state probabilities for the number of calling units in the system at regeneration points.
(c) Compute the expected number of calling units in the queueing system at regeneration points and compare it to the value of L for the model in Sec. 10.5.3.

CHAPTER 14

Simulation

14.1 INTRODUCTION

The technique of simulation has long been an important tool of the designer, whether he be simulating airplane flight in a wind tunnel, simulating plant layouts with scale models of machines, or simulating lines of communication with an organization chart. With the advent of the high-speed digital computer with which to conduct simulated experiments, this technique also has become increasingly important to the operations researcher. Thus, simulation has become an experimental arm of operations research.

The emphasis in the preceding chapters was on formulating and solving mathematical models which represent real systems. One of the main strengths of this approach is that it abstracts the essence of the problem and reveals its underlying structure, thereby providing insight into the cause-and-effect relationships within the system. Therefore, if it is possible to construct a mathematical model that is both a reasonable idealization of the problem and amenable to solution, this analytical approach usually is superior to simulation. However, many problems are so complex that they cannot be solved analytically. Thus, even though it tends to be a relatively expensive procedure, simulation often provides the only practical approach to a problem.

Within operations research, simulation typically also involves the construction of a model which is largely mathematical in nature. Rather than directly describing the over-all behavior of the system, the simulation model describes the operation of the system in terms of individual events of the individual components of the system. In particular, the system is divided into elements whose behavior can be predicted, at least in terms of probability distributions, for each of the various possible states of the system and its inputs. The interrelationships between the elements also are built into the model. Thus, simulation provides a means of dividing the model-building job into smaller component parts (where it may be possible to formulate each of these parts by methods described in other chapters), and then combining these parts in their natural order and allowing the computer to present the effect of their interaction on each other. After constructing the model, it is then activated (by generating input data) in order to simulate the actual operation of the system and record its aggregate behavior. By repeating this for the various alternative design configurations and comparing their performances, one can identify the most promising configurations. Because of statistical error, it is impossible to guarantee that the configuration yielding the best simulated performance is indeed the optimal one, but it should be at least near-optimal if the simulated experiment was designed properly.

Thus, simulation typically is nothing more or less than the technique of performing sampling experiments on the model of the system. The experiments are done on the model rather than on the real system itself only because the latter would be too inconvenient, expensive, and time-consuming. Otherwise, simulated experiments should be viewed as virtually indistinguishable from ordinary statistical experiments, so that they also should be based upon sound statistical theory. Even though simulated experiments usually are executed on a digital computer, this is only because of the vast amount of calculating required, rather than any inherent relationship.

14.2 ILLUSTRATIVE EXAMPLES

Example 1

Suppose you were offered the chance to play a game whereby you would repeatedly flip an unbiased coin until the difference between the number of heads tossed and the number of tails tossed is three. You would be required to pay $1.00 for each flip of the coin, but you would receive $8.00 at the end of each play of the game. You are not allowed to quit during a play of a game. Thus, you win money if the number of flips required is less than eight, but you lose money if more than eight flips are required. How would you decide whether or not to play this game?

The chances are quite good that one would try simulation, although it might not be called by that name. (There is also an analytical solution for this game, although it is not a particularly elementary one.) In this case, simulation would amount to nothing more than playing the game alone many times until it becomes clear whether it is worthwhile playing for stakes. Half an hour spent in repeatedly flipping a coin and recording the earnings or losses that would have resulted might be sufficient.

How would this simulated experiment be executed on a digital computer? Although the computer cannot flip coins, it can generate numbers. Therefore, it would generate (or be given) a sequence of random digits, each of which would correspond to a flip of a coin. (The generation of random numbers is discussed in Sec. 14.3.2.) The probability distribution for the outcome of a flip is, of course, that the probability of a head is 1/2 and the probability of a tail is 1/2. Since there are ten possible values of a random digit, each having a probability of 1/10, five of these values (say, 0, 1, 2, 3, 4) would be assigned an association with a head, and the other five (say, 5, 6, 7, 8, 9) with a tail. Thus, the computer would simulate the playing of the game by examining each new random digit generated and labeling it a head or a tail according to its value. It would continue doing this, recording the outcome of each simulated play of the game, as long as desired.

To illustrate the computer approach to this simulated experiment, suppose that the computer had generated the following sequence of random digits:

8, 1, 3, 7, 2, 7, 1, 6, 5, 5, 7, 9, 0, 0, 3, 4, 3, 5, 6, 8, 5,
8, 9, 4, 8, 0, 4, 8, 6, 5, 3, 5, 9, 2, 5, 7, 9, 7, 2, 9, 3, 9,
8, 5, 8, 9, 2, 5, 7, 6, 9, 7, 6, 0, 7, 3, 9, 8, 2, 7, 1, 0, 3,
2, 6, 2, 7, 1, 3, 7, 0, 4, 4, 1, 8, 3, 2, 1, 3, 9, 5, 9, 0, 5,
0, 3, 8, 7, 8, 9, 5, 4, 0, 8, 3, 8, 0, 1.

Thus, denoting a head by H and a tail by T, the first simulated play of the game is $T\ H\ H\ T\ H\ T\ H\ T\ T\ T$, requiring 11 simulated flips of a coin. The subsequent simulated plays of the game require 5, 5, 9, 7, 7, 5, 3, 17, 5, 5, 3, 9, and 7 simulated flips, respectively, for an over-all average of 7. This sample average would seem to indicate that, on the average, one should win about $1.00 for each play of the game. Therefore, if one does not have a relatively high aversion to risk, it appears that he should choose to play this game, preferably a large number of times. However, beware! One of the common errors in the use of simulation is that conclusions are based on overly small samples because the statistical analysis was inadequate or totally lacking. In this case, the sample standard deviation is 3.67, so that the estimated standard deviation of the sample average is 0.98. Therefore, even if it is assumed that the probability distribution of the number of flips required for a play of the game is a normal distribution (which is a gross assumption since the true distribution is skewed), any reasonable confidence interval for the true mean of this distribution would extend far above 8. Hence, a much larger sample is required in order to draw a valid conclusion at a reasonable level of statistical significance. Unfortunately, since the standard deviation of a sample average is inversely proportional to the square root of the sample size, a large increase in the sample size is required to yield a relatively small increase in the precision of the estimate of the true mean. In this case, it appears that perhaps an additional 100 simulated plays of the game would be adequate.

It so happens that the true mean of the number of flips required for a play of this game is 9. Thus, in the long run, one actually would lose about $1.00 for each play of the game.

Example 2

Consider the single-server queueing theory model with Poisson input and exponential service times that was discussed in Sec. 10.5.1. Although this model already has been solved analytically, it will be instructive to consider how to use simulation to study it.

To summarize the physical operation of the system, arriving customers (calling units) enter the queue, eventually are serviced by the server, and then leave. Thus, it is necessary for the simulation model to describe and synchronize the arrival of customers and the servicing of customers. The two methods for handling such synchronization in a digital computer are called synchronous timing and asynchronous timing. They will be described in turn.

With synchronous timing the following two-step procedure is used, beginning with the system in its initial state at a given point in time. First, advance time by a small fixed amount; add one to a register which serves as the "master clock" for the system in order to record the passage of this time. Second, update the system by determining what events occurred during this elapsed time unit and what the resulting state of the system is. Repeat these two steps for as many time units as desired.

For the queueing theory model under consideration, only two types of events can occur during each of these elapsed time units, namely, one or more customers can arrive and one or more customers can complete being served. Furthermore, the probability of two or more arrivals or of two or more service completions during a time unit is negligible for this model if the time unit is relatively short. Thus, the only two possible events during a time unit that need to be investigated are the arrival of one customer and the completion of service for one customer. Each of these events has a known probability. Therefore, just as in Example 1, in order to simulate whether an event occurs or not, the computer only needs to generate a random number. For example, suppose that the probability that a customer will arrive during an elapsed time unit is 0.007. The computer would need to generate one of the 1,000 possible three-digit numbers (000, 001, · · · , 999) at random. By associating seven of the possible numbers (say, 000, · · · , 006) with the event occurring, and the remaining numbers with the event not occurring, the random number generated determines the actual simulated outcome for that time unit. If a customer were in the process of being served, the computer would be programmed to use this same method to determine if a simulated service completion occurs or not during the elapsed time unit, given the probability of such a completion. However, if no customer were being served, the computer would decide automatically that no service completion had occurred during the elapsed time unit. To implement this, the computer would use an indicator which would be given one of two numerical values, depending upon whether the server was busy servicing a customer or not. Similarly, a counter would be used to record the current number of customers in the queue waiting to be served.

Thus, updating the system after an elapsed time unit amounts to updating the numbers that should be inserted into the indicator and the counter. At the same time, the computer would record the desired information about the aggregate behavior of the system during this time unit. For example, it could record the number of customers in the queueing system and the waiting time of any customer who just completed his wait. If it is sufficient to estimate only the mean rather than the probability distribution of each of these random variables, the computer would merely add the value (if any) for the current time unit to a cumulative sum. The sample averages would be obtained after the simulation run is completed by dividing these sums by the total elapsed time and the total number of customers, respectively.

Asynchronous timing differs from synchronous timing in that the master clock is increased by a variable amount rather than by a fixed amount each time. Conceptually, the asynchronous timing procedure is to keep the system running until an event occurs, at which point the computer pauses momentarily to record the change in the system. To implement this conceptual idea, the computer actually proceeds by keeping track of when the next few simulated events are scheduled to occur, jumping in simulated time to the next imminent event, and updating the system. This cycle is repeated as many times as desired.

For this example, the computer needs to keep track of two future events, namely, when the next customer will arrive and when the server will finish servicing his current customer (if any). These times are obtained by taking a random observation from the probability distribution of the time between arrivals and of service times, respectively. As before, the computer takes such a random observation by generating and using a random number. (The technique for doing this is discussed subsequently in Sec. 14.3.3.) Thus, each time an arrival or service completion occurs, the computer first determines how long it will be until the next time that this event will occur, and then adds this to the current clock time. This sum is then stored in a computer file. To determine which event will occur next, the computer merely finds the minimum of the clock times stored in the file.

Several pertinent questions about how to conduct a simulation study of this type still remain to be answered. These answers are presented in a broader context in subsequent sections.

14.3 FORMULATING AND IMPLEMENTING A SIMULATION MODEL

14.3.1 Constructing the Model

The first step in a simulation study is to develop a model representing the system to be investigated. It is apparent that this requires the analyst to become thoroughly familiar with the operating realities of the system and with the objectives of the study. Given this, the analyst probably would attempt to reduce the real system to a logical flow diagram. The system is thereby broken down into a set of components linked together by a master flow diagram, where the components themselves may be broken down into subcomponents, etc. Ultimately, the system is decomposed into a set of elements for which operating rules may be given. These operating rules predict the events that will be generated by the corresponding elements, perhaps in terms of probability distributions. After specifying these elements, rules, and logical linkages, the model should be thoroughly tested piece by piece. This can be done by performing the proposed simulation on a desk calculator, and checking whether each input is received from the appropriate source and each output is acceptable to the next submodel. If any information is available regarding the aggregate behavior of some form of the real system, it is also worthwhile to verify that this behavior is predicted reasonably well by the corresponding simulated system.

It should be emphasized that, like any operations research model, the simulation model need not be a completely realistic representation of the real system. In fact, it appears that most simulation models err on the side of being overly realistic rather than overly idealized. With the former approach, the model easily degenerates into a mass of trivia and meandering details, so that a great deal of programming and computer time is required to obtain a small amount of information. Furthermore, failing to strip away trivial factors to get down to the core of the system may obscure the significance of those results that are obtained.

If the behavior of an element cannot be predicted exactly, given the state of the system, it is better to take random observations from the probability distributions involved than to use averages to simulate this performance. This is true even when one is only interested in the average aggregate performance of the system, since combining average performances for the invidivual elements may result in something far from average for the over-all system.

One question that may arise when choosing probability distributions for the model is whether to use frequency distributions of historical data or to seek the theoretical probability distribution which best fits these data. The latter alternative usually is preferable since it would seem to come closer to predicting expected future performance rather than reproducing the idiosyncracies of a certain period of the past.

14.3.2 Generating Random Numbers

As the examples in Sec. 14.2 demonstrated, implementing a simulation model requires random numbers in order to obtain random observations from probability distributions. One method for generating such random numbers is to use a physical device such as a spinning disc or an electronic randomizer. Several tables of random numbers have been generated in this way, including one containing one million random digits published by the Rand Corporation. An excerpt from the Rand table is given at the end of this section.

Various relatively sophisticated statistical procedures have been proposed for testing whether a sequence of numbers constitutes a sample of random numbers of not.[90] Basically, the requirements are that each successive number in the sequence must have an equal probability of taking on any one of the possible values, and it must be statistically independent of the other numbers in the sequence.

If a digital computer is to be used for executing the simulation, the random numbers it needs could be fed into the computer from one of the available tables. (In fact, the Rand table already is available on punched cards.) However, it is more common to have the computer itself generate the random numbers. There is a number of methods for doing this, of which the most popular are the additive and multiplicative congruential methods. One example of these methods is described briefly in order to illustrate this type of approach.

The multiplicative congruential method obtains the $(n + 1)$st random number, x_{n+1}, from the nth random number, x_n, by using the recurrence relation,

$$x_{n+1} \equiv kx_n(\text{modulo } m) ,$$

where k and m are positive integers ($k < m$). This mathematical notation signifies that x_{n+1} is the remainder when kx_n is divided by m. In other words, x_{n+1} is that number between 0 and m which differs from kx_n by an integer multiple of m. The first random number, x_1, is obtained by selecting any

[90] The interested reader is referred to reference 7 at the end of the chapter for a description of these tests and for more details about the generation of random numbers.

large integer for x_0 and using this recurrence relation. Then, x_2 is obtained from x_1, x_3 from x_2, etc. For example, suppose that $x_0 = 3$, $k = 7$, and $m = 10$ (so that the x_{n+1} will be integers ranging from 0 and 9). Thus, $(7)(3)/10 = (20 + 1)/10$ so that $x_1 = 1$. Similarly, $(7)(1)/10 = (0 + 7)/10$ so that $x_2 = 7$; $(7)(7)/10 = (40 + 9)/10$ so that $x_3 = 9$, etc. In this way, the entire sequence, 1, 7, 9, 3, 1, 7, 9, 3, 1, $\cdots$, is obtained. This is obviously not a valid sequence of random numbers since only four of the ten possible numbers (0, 1, $\cdots$, 9) ever appear. Furthermore, the sequence is cyclic with cycles of length four, which is not satisfactory if more than four random numbers are required. As this demonstrates, great discretion must be exercised in selecting the combination of k, m, and x_0 to use. Considerable mathematical analysis has revealed only a few combinations that will yield satisfactory sequences. One of these is $k = 455, 470, 314$ and $m = 2, 147, 483, 647 = (2^{31} - 1)$, so that

$$x_{n+1} \equiv 455, 470, 314 x_n \text{ modulo } (2^{31} - 1) ,$$

where x_0 can be any integer in the range, $1 \leq x_0 \leq 2, 147, 483, 646$. The resulting sequences are guaranteed to have cycles of length 2, 147, 483, 646

TABLE 14.1 Table of Random Digits*

09656	96657	64842	49222	49506	10145	48455	23505	90430	04180
24712	55799	60857	73479	33581	17360	30406	05842	72044	90764
07202	96341	23699	76171	79126	04512	15426	15980	88898	06358
84575	46820	54083	43918	46989	05379	70682	43081	66171	38942
38144	87037	46626	70529	27918	34191	98668	33482	43998	75733
48048	56349	01986	29814	69800	91609	65374	22928	09704	59343
41936	58566	31276	19952	01352	18834	99596	09302	20087	19063
73391	94006	03822	81845	76158	41352	40596	14325	27020	17546
57580	08954	73554	28698	29022	11568	35668	59906	39557	27217
92646	41113	91411	56215	69302	86419	61224	41936	56939	27816
07118	12707	35622	81485	73354	49800	60805	05648	28898	60933
57842	57831	24130	75408	83784	64307	91620	40810	06539	70387
65078	44981	81009	33697	98324	46928	34198	96032	98426	77488
04294	96120	67629	55265	26248	40602	25566	12520	89785	93932
48381	06807	43775	09708	73199	53406	02910	83292	59249	18597
00459	62045	19249	67095	22752	24636	16965	91836	00582	46721
38824	81681	33323	64086	55970	04849	24819	20749	51711	86173
91465	22232	02907	01050	07121	53536	71070	26916	47620	01619
50874	00807	77751	73952	03073	69063	16894	85570	81746	07568
26644	75871	15618	50310	72610	66205	82640	86205	73453	90232

* Reproduced with permission from The Rand Corporation, *A Million Random Digits with 100,000 Normal Deviates*. Copyright, The Free Press, Glencoe, Ill., 1955, top of p. 182.

(which is adequate since the required number of random numbers presumedly is less than this), where each integer in the range from 1 to 2, 147, 483, 646 appears exactly once in each cycle. Then, if the computer actually needs four digit random numbers (0000 to 9999), it would be instructed to take, say, the last four digits (except that the number would be rejected if the preceding digits were 214748).

Strictly speaking, the numbers generated by the computer should not be called random numbers since they are predictable and reproducible (which sometimes is advantageous). Therefore, they are sometimes given the name pseudo-random numbers. However, the important point is that they satisfactorily play the role of random numbers in the simulation if the method used to generate them is valid.

14.3.3 **Generating Random Observations from a Probability Distribution**

Given a sequence of random numbers, how can one generate a sequence of random observations from a given probability distribution?

For simple discrete distributions, one answer is quite evident as demonstrated by the examples of Sec. 14.2. Merely allocate the possible values of a random number to the various numbers in the probability distribution in direct proportion to the respective probabilities of those numbers. For example, consider the probability distribution of the outcome of a throw of two dice. It is well known that the probability of throwing a two is 1/36 (as is the probability of a twelve), the probability of a three is 2/36, etc. Therefore, 1/36 of the possible values of a random number should be associated with throwing a two, 2/36 of the values with throwing a three, etc. Thus, if two digit random numbers are being used, 72 of the 100 values would be selected for consideration, so that a random number would be rejected if it took on any one of the other 28 values. Then, two of the 72 possible values (say, 00 and 01) would be assigned an association with throwing a two, four of them (say, 02, 03, 04, and 05) would be assigned to throwing a three, etc.

For more complicated distributions, the answer still is essentially the same although the procedure is slightly more involved. The first step is to construct the cumulative distribution function, $F(x) = P\{X \leq x\}$, where X is the random variable involved. This can be done by writing the equation for this function, or by graphically plotting the function, or by developing a table giving the value of x for uniformly spaced values of $F(x)$ from 0 to 1. The second step is to generate a random decimal number between 0 and 1. This is done by obtaining a random integer number having the desired number of digits (including any leading zeros) and then placing a decimal point in front of it. The final step is to set $P\{X \leq x\}$ equal to the random decimal number, and solve for x. This value of x is the desired random observation from the probability distribution. This procedure is illustrated in Fig. 14.1 for the case where the cumulative distribution function is plotted graphically and the random decimal number happens to be .5269.

When the given probability distribution is continuous, the procedure outlined above actually approximates this continuous distribution by a discrete distribution whose irregularly spaced points have equal probabilities. However, this is not particularly serious since the approximation can be made as accurate as desired by using a sufficiently large number of

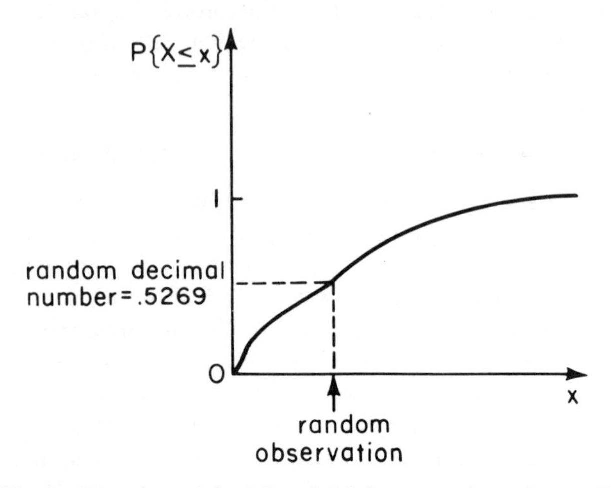

FIGURE 14.1. Illustration of procedure for obtaining a random observation from a given probability distribution.

digits for the random number. Perhaps the greatest danger is that the approximation will be adequate everywhere except in the extreme tails of the distribution. For example, suppose that three digit random numbers are being used. Then, the values of $P\{X \leq x\}$ that will be sampled range from 0.000 to 0.999. However, it may be that those rare occurrences when the actual value taken on by X falls outside the range permitted in the simulation would have a critical impact on the system. One refinement that would rectify this is to generate a second random number whenever the first one is (for the case of three-digit random numbers) 000 or 999 in order to select a value of $P\{X \leq x\}$ within the range from 0.000000 to 0.000999 or from 0.999000 to 0.999999.

Although the graphical procedure illustrated by Fig. 14.1 is convenient if the simulation is done manually, the digital computer must revert to some alternative approach such as the two mentioned earlier. One of these involved using a table of the cumulative distribution function. Having the computer do this is essentially equivalent to using the graphical procedure manually. The disadvantages of this table look-up approach are the great amount of work required to develop the required tables and the limitations on accuracy due to computer storage limitations. The other approach mentioned earlier requires writing the equation for the cumulative distribution function and then solving for the point where this function equals the random decimal number. This approach leads to a simple explicit solution for several important probability distributions, as illustrated below for the exponential and Erlang distributions. For other cases, time-consuming numerical methods would be required to obtain the solution. Fortunately, for each of several important probability distributions, special techniques have been developed for efficiently generating random observations from that particular distribution. Two of the simplest of these techniques that are applicable to the normal distribution and the chi-square distribution, respectively, are described at the end of this section.

Consider the exponential distribution, which has the cumulative distribution function,

$$P\{X \leq x\} = 1 - e^{-\mu x}, \qquad \text{for } x \geq 0\,,$$

where $1/\mu$ is the mean of the distribution. Applying the procedure outlined above, set this function equal to a random decimal number between 0 and 1. Since the complement of such a random number is itself a random number, this is equivalent to setting

$$e^{-\mu x} = R.N.\,,$$

where $R.N.$ denotes a random decimal number between 0 and 1. Therefore, taking the natural logarithm of both sides,

$$\ln(e^{-\mu x}) = \ln(R.N.)\,,$$

so that

$$-\mu x = \ln(R.N.)\,,$$

which yields

$$x = \frac{\ln(R.N.)}{-\mu}$$

as the desired random observation from the exponential distribution. (It should be noted that other more complicated techniques have also been developed for the exponential distribution, which may be faster for the computer to use than calculating a logarithm.)

A natural extension of the above procedure can also be used to generate a random observation from an Erlang (gamma) distribution. As indicated in Sec. 10.5.4, the sum of k independent exponential random variables, each with mean $1/k\mu$, has the Erlang distribution with shape parameter k and mean $1/\mu$. Therefore, given a sequence of k random decimal numbers between 0 and 1, $(R.N.)_1, (R.N.)_2, \cdots, (R.N.)_k$, the desired random observation from the Erlang distribution is

$$x = \sum_{i=1}^{k} \frac{\ln(R.N.)_i}{-k\mu},$$

which reduces to

$$x = -\frac{1}{k\mu} \ln \left\{ \prod_{i=1}^{k} (R.N.)_i \right\},$$

where $\prod$ denotes multiplication.

A particularly simple technique for generating a random observation from a normal distribution is obtained by applying the Central Limit Theorem (presented in Sec. 3.15). A future random decimal number actually is a random variable with a uniform (rectangular) distribution from 0 to 1 and with mean 1/2 and standard deviation $1/\sqrt{12}$. Therefore, this theorem implies that the sum of n random decimal numbers has approximately a normal distribution with mean $n/2$ and standard deviation $\sqrt{n/12}$. Thus, if $(R.N.)_1$, $(R.N.)_2, \cdots, (R.N.)_n$ are a sample of random decimal numbers, then

$$x = \frac{\sigma}{\sqrt{n/12}} \sum_{i=1}^{n} (R.N.)_i + \left(\mu - \frac{n}{2} \frac{\sigma}{\sqrt{n/12}}\right)$$

is a random observation from an approximately normal distribution with mean μ and standard deviation σ. This approximation is an excellent one (except in the tails of the distribution) even with small values of n. Thus, values of n from 5 to 10 often are used; $n = 12$ also is a convenient value since it eliminates the square-root terms from the above expression.

Various other approximate or exact techniques for generating random observations from a normal distribution have also been developed.

A simple method for handling the chi-square distribution (see Table 3.1) is to use the fact that it is obtained by summing squares of standardized normal random variables. Thus, if $y_1, y_2, \cdots, y_n$ are a sample of random observations from a normal distribution with mean 0 and standard deviation 1, such as could be obtained (approximately) by the technique described above, then

$$x = \sum_{i=1}^{n} y_i^2$$

is a random observation from a chi-square distribution with n degrees of freedom.

14.3.4 **Preparing a Simulation Program**

A number of detailed decisions confront the person who must write the computer program for executing a simulation. These are discussed quite extensively in reference 1 cited at the end of this chapter. Although such a discussion is beyond the scope of this book, it is worthwhile to mention several major considerations in preparing a simulation program.

The basic purpose of most simulation studies is to compare alternatives. Therefore, the simulation program must be flexible enough to readily accommodate the alternatives that will be considered. Since it often is impossible to predict exactly what interesting alternatives will be uncovered during the course of the study, it is essential that flexibility and provision for rapid, simple modifications be built into the program.

Most of the instructions in a simulation program are logical operations, whereas the relatively little actual arithmetic work required usually is of a very simple type. This should be reflected in the choice of computer equipment and programming language to be used.

The considerations mentioned above actually provided part of the motivation for an important breakthrough in the art of simulation that occurred during the early 1960's, namely, the development of general simulation programming languages. These languages are designed especially to expedite the type of programming (and reprogramming) unique to simulation. Their specific purposes include the following. One objective is to provide a convenient means of describing the elements that commonly appear in simulation models. A second is to expedite changing the design configuration of the system being simulated, so that a large number of configurations (including some suggested during the course of the study) can be considered easily. Another service provided by the simulation languages is some type of internal timing and control mechanism, with related commands, to assist in the kind of bookkeeping that is required when executing a simulation run. They also are designed to conveniently obtain data and statistics on the aggregate behavior of the system being simulated. Finally, these languages provide simple operational procedures, such as introducing changes into the simulation model, initializing the state of the model, altering the kind of output data to be generated, and stacking a series of simulation runs.

For all of these reasons, a simulation program almost always should be written in one of these simulation languages rather than a general programming language. The tremendous savings in programming time ordinarily provided by the simulation languages usually compensates for any slight loss in computer running time. Some of the best known of the early general simulation languages are SIMSCRIPT, GPSS, and DYNAMO.[91]

Finally, it should be emphasized that the strategy of the simulation study should be planned carefully before finishing the simulation program.

[91] A comparison of these languages is given by Howard S. Krasnow and Reino A. Merikallio, "The Past, Present, and Future of General Simulation Languages," *Management Science*, **11,** No. 2, 236–267 (1964).

Merely letting the computer compile masses of data in a blind search for attractive alternatives is far from adequate. Simulation basically is a means for conducting an experimental investigation. Therefore, just as with a physical experiment, careful attention should be given to the construction of a theory or formal hypothesis to be tested and to the skillful design of a statistical experiment that will yield valid conclusions. This is the subject of discussion in Secs. 14.4 and 14.5.

14.4 EXPERIMENTAL DESIGN FOR SIMULATION

14.4.1 Selecting a Statistical Procedure

The underlying statistical theory applicable to simulated experimentation is essentially indistinguishable from that for physical experimentation. Thus, the design of a simulated experiment should be based upon the large body of knowledge comprising the science of statistics, which was surveyed briefly in Chapter 4.

There are, however, differences between physical and simulated experimentation regarding the emphasis placed on using the various types of statistical procedures. Physical experiments frequently involve testing hypotheses about the value of a population parameter or about whether several population means are equal. Simulated experiments typically place more emphasis on optimization. It probably is taken for granted that alternative design configurations have different population means for the index of performance of the system. Instead, the objective of the simulation study probably is to find the alternative yielding the greatest mean index of performance. Hence, multiple decision tests and complete or partial ordering procedures frequently are appropriate for simulated experiments. Furthermore, sequential procedures tend to be useful, both because the evolution of the experiment may be difficult to predict and because a simulated experiment often can be resumed relatively easily.

Another difference between these two types of experiments is the degree to which the conditions (under which alternatives are compared) can be made as identical as possible. Only simulated experiments can control the variability in the behavior of the elements of the system during the course of the experiment. By reproducing the same sequence of random numbers for each alternative simulated, it usually is possible to reproduce an identical sequence of events. This sharpens the contrast between alternatives by reducing the residual variation in the differences in the aggregate performance of the system, so that much smaller sample sizes are required to detect statistically significant differences. Therefore, this approach usually is far superior to generating new random numbers for each alternative. The fact that reproducing the same random numbers does not yield statistically independent results should not be of great concern. The correct procedure for comparing only two alternatives is to pair the results regarding the aggregate performance of the system that were produced by the same events. Since these pairs of results are obtained under the same experimental conditions, the differences between them become the relevant sample observations. This sample would be used to test the hypothesis that the mean of these differences is zero and to obtain a confidence interval estimate of this mean. This would thereby indicate whether there is a statistically significant difference between the means of the performance index of the system for the two alternatives. If more than two alternatives need to be compared, no completely satisfactory statistical procedure is available if the same random numbers are being reproduced for each alternative simulated. One can still make a sequence of comparisons of pairs of alternatives, but only by reducing the probability that all of the comparisons will yield the correct conclusion. Nevertheless, this procedure (illustrated in Sec. 14.6.1) probably is still preferable to using different random numbers for each alternative and thereby obtaining statistically independent samples with relatively large variances.

Often it is possible to express the alternatives in terms of the values of one or more continuous design variables. In these cases, there actually is an infinite number of alternatives (although the differences among some of them are minute). Since it would be impossible to simulate all of them, it is necessary to take a selective sample of these alternatives and then estimate the value of the design variables that will maximize some index of performance for the system. There now exists considerable literature giving efficient procedures for experimentally determining the maximum of a mathematical function to within a specified accuracy.[92]

14.4.2 **Variance Reducing Techniques**

It is axiomatic that one should attempt to obtain as much and as precise information as possible from the amount of simulation that can be done. Unfortunately, there has been a tendency in practice to apply simulation uncritically without giving adequate thought to the efficiency of the experimental design. This has been true despite the fact that considerable progress has been made on developing special techniques for increasing the precision (i.e., decreasing the variance) of sample estimators.

These variance reducing techniques often are called Monte Carlo techniques (a term sometimes applied to simulation in general). Since these techniques tend to be rather sophisticated, it is not possible to explore them deeply here. However, an attempt is made to impart the flavor of these techniques and the great increase in precision they sometimes provide.

[92] A survey of the procedures available for this problem is given by Douglass J. Wilde, *Optimum Seeking Methods*, Prentice-Hall, Englewood Cliffs, N.J., 1963.

This is done by presenting several of the more elementary techniques by means of a simple illustrative example.

Consider the exponential distribution whose parameter has a value of one. Thus, its probability density function is $f(x) = e^{-x}$, as shown in Fig. 14.2, and its cumulative distribution function is $F(x) = 1 - e^{-x}$. It is well known that the mean of this distribution is one. However, suppose that this were not known and that it is desired to estimate this mean by using simulation. How should it be done? Although this problem is too simple to be typical of those where simulation is required, it does provide a useful platform for exhibiting certain rather general variance reducing techniques

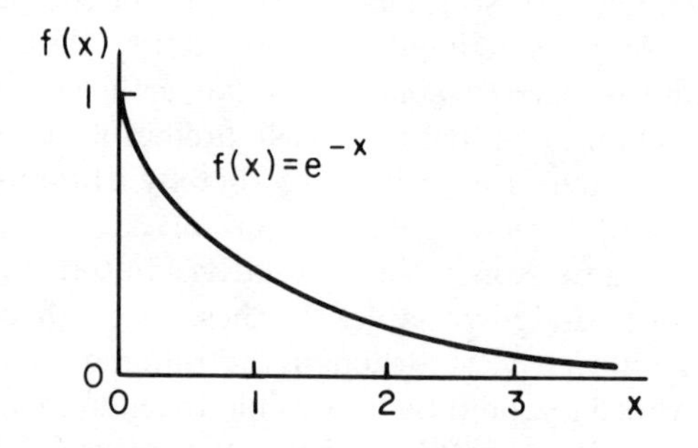

FIGURE 14.2. Probability density function for examples.

To provide a standard of comparison, consider first the straightforward simulation approach, sometimes called the *crude Monte Carlo* technique. As described in Sec. 14.3.3, this approach begins by generating some random decimal numbers, setting each of them equal to the cumulative distribution function $[F(x)]$, and solving these equations individually in order to obtain random observations from the probability distribution. Thus, let $\xi_1, \xi_2, \cdots, \xi_n$ denote these random decimal numbers (between 0 and 1), and let the function $g(\xi)$ denote the value of x which is the solution to the equation, $F(x) = \xi$, given the value of ξ. The average of the random observations,

$$\text{sample average} = \frac{1}{n} \sum_{i=1}^{n} g(\xi_i) \, ,$$

is the desired estimator of the mean of the distribution. Since $F(x) = 1 - e^{-x}$ for the particular distribution under consideration, it is easy to verify that

$$g(\xi) = -\ln(1 - \xi)$$

for this case. (This expression is used in order to facilitate comparison with the other Monte Carlo techniques, even though it was mentioned in Sec. 14.3.3 that $-\ln \xi$ also could be used.)

A demonstration of the crude Monte Carlo technique is given in Table 14.2 for $n = 10$, where the random decimal numbers were obtained from a portion of Table 14.1. (These same random numbers also are used to illustrate the other Monte Carlo techniques in order to sharpen the comparison.)

TABLE 14.2. Example for Crude Monte Carlo Technique

i	ξ_i *	$g(\xi_i) = -\ln(1 - \xi_i)$
1	0.495	0.684
2	0.335	0.408
3	0.791	1.568
4	0.469	0.633
5	0.279	0.328
6	0.698	1.199
7	0.013	0.014
8	0.761	1.433
9	0.290	0.343
10	0.693	1.183
	Total =	7.793
	Estimate of mean =	0.779

* Actually, 0.0005 was added to the indicated value for each of the ξ_i so that the range of their possible values would be from 0.0005 to 0.9995 rather than from 0.000 to 0.999.

Notice that the sample average is 0.779, as opposed to the true mean of 1.000. However, because the standard deviation of the sample average happens to be $1/\sqrt{n}$, or $1/\sqrt{10}$ in this case (as could be estimated from the sample), an error of this amount or larger would occur approximately one-half of the time. Furthermore, since the standard deviation of a sample average always is inversely proportional to $\sqrt{n}$, this sample size would need to be quadrupled in order to reduce this standard deviation by one-half. These somewhat disheartening facts suggest the need for other techniques which would obtain such estimates more precisely and more efficiently.

A relatively simple Monte Carlo technique for obtaining better estimates is *stratified sampling*. There are two shortcomings of the crude Monte Carlo approach that are rectified by stratified sampling. First, by the very nature of randomness, a random sample may not provide a particularly uniform cross section of the distribution. For example, the random sample given in Table 14.2 has no observations between 0.014 and 0.328 even though the probability that a random observation will fall inside this interval is greater than 1/4. Second, certain portions of a distribution may be more critical than others for obtaining a precise estimate, but random sampling gives no special priority to obtaining observations from these portions. For example, the tail of an exponential distribution is especially critical in determining its mean. However, the random sample in Table 14.2 includes no observations larger than 1.568, even though there is at least a small probability of much larger values. This is the basic explanation for this particular sample average being far below the true mean. Stratified sampling circumvents these difficulties by dividing the distribution into portions called strata, where each stratum would be sampled individually with disproportionately heavy sampling of the more critical strata.

It is convenient to specify the strata in terms of the cumulative distribution function, $F(x)$. Thus, if there are m strata, the first stratum would be from $F(x) = \alpha_0 = 0$ to $F(x) = \alpha_1$, the second from $F(x) = \alpha_1$ to $F(x) = \alpha_2$, etc., until the last stratum would be from $F(x) = \alpha_{m-1}$ to $F(x) = \alpha_m$. Then, if the ith observation is to be drawn from the jth stratum, this random observation would be the value of x which is the solution of the equation,

$$F(x) = \xi_i',$$

where ξ_i' is a random decimal number between α_{j-1} and α_j. Using the notation introduced for the crude Monte Carlo technique, this random observation is just $g(\xi_i')$. To obtain ξ_i', one generates a random decimal number between 0 and 1, ξ_i, and then calculates

$$\xi_i' = \alpha_{j-1} + (\alpha_j - \alpha_{j-1})\xi_i .$$

In addition to defining the strata, it is necessary to specify the number of observations to be drawn from each stratum; denote these numbers by $n_1, n_2, \cdots, n_m$, and their sum by n. One rule for choosing them is to make n_j proportional to the product of the probability of a random observation falling inside the jth stratum times the standard deviation within this stratum.

Given the random observations, $g(\xi_1'), g(\xi_2'), \cdots, g(\xi_n')$, from the various strata, what is the desired estimate of the mean of the distribution? It certainly would not be correct to use the unweighted sample average, since certain portions of the distribution have been sampled more than others. Recall that $(\alpha_j - \alpha_{j-1})$ is the probability that a random observation will fall inside the jth stratum, whereas, n_j/n is the actual fraction of the observations drawn from that stratum. Therefore, if the ith observation is drawn from the jth stratum, that observation should be divided by the sampling weight,

$$w_i = \frac{\left(\frac{n_j}{n}\right)}{\alpha_j - \alpha_{j-1}} = \frac{n_j}{(\alpha_j - \alpha_{j-1})n}.$$

Hence, the resulting unbiased estimator of the mean of the distribution is

$$\text{weighted sample average} = \frac{1}{n}\sum_{i=1}^{n} \frac{g(\xi_i')}{w_i}.$$

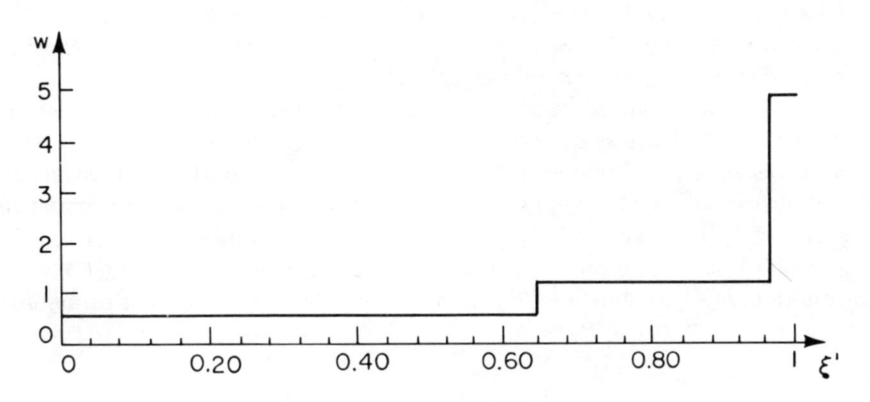

FIGURE 14.3. Sampling weights in example for stratified sampling.

To illustrate the stratified sampling approach for the distribution under consideration, suppose that $m = 3$, that $\alpha_0 = 0$, $\alpha_1 = 0.64$, $\alpha_2 = 0.96$, $\alpha_3 = 1$, and that $n_1 = 4$, $n_2 = 4$, $n_3 = 2$. These three strata were

TABLE 14.3. Example for Stratified Sampling

i	ξ_i	ξ_i'	$g(\xi_i') = -\ln(1 - \xi_i')$	w_i	$\frac{g(\xi_i')}{w_i}$
1	0.495	0.317	0.381	$\frac{5}{8}$	0.610
2	0.335	0.215	0.242	$\frac{5}{8}$	0.387
3	0.791	0.507	0.707	$\frac{5}{8}$	1.131
4	0.469	0.300	0.357	$\frac{5}{8}$	0.571
5	0.279	0.729	1.306	$\frac{5}{4}$	1.045
6	0.698	0.864	1.995	$\frac{5}{4}$	1.596
7	0.013	0.644	1.033	$\frac{5}{4}$	0.826
8	0.761	0.884	2.154	$\frac{5}{4}$	1.723
9	0.290	0.9716	3.561	5	0.712
10	0.693	0.9877	4.398	5	0.880
				Total =	9.481
				Estimate of mean =	0.948

chosen to correspond to observations approximately from 0 to 1, from 1 to 3, and from 3 to infinity, respectively. The values of the n_j were chosen to roughly satisfy the rule given earlier for selecting these numbers. Thus, the sampling weights on the respective strata—$w_1 = 4/(0.64)10 = \frac{5}{8}$, $w_2 = \frac{5}{4}$, and $w_3 = 5$—reflect the relative importance of these strata in determining the mean. These weights are shown in Fig. 14.3, and the resulting sample data are given in Table 14.3. Notice that, even though the same original random numbers are being used, the estimate of the mean (0.948) is much closer to the true value of the mean (1) than was the estimate obtained by the crude Monte Carlo technique. This is an accurate reflection of the relative efficiency of the two estimators in general.

Importance sampling is a Monte Carlo technique that is essentially an extension of the stratified sampling approach. Consider Fig. 14.3. Since an observation corresponding to $\xi' = 0.90$ is more important for estimating the mean than one corresponding to $\xi' = 0.70$, for example, why should the same sampling weights be placed on both? Importance sampling rectifies this shortcoming by replacing the constant weights shown in Fig. 14.3 by a function, $h(\xi')$, as shown in Fig. 14.4. More precisely, $h(\xi')$ is the probability

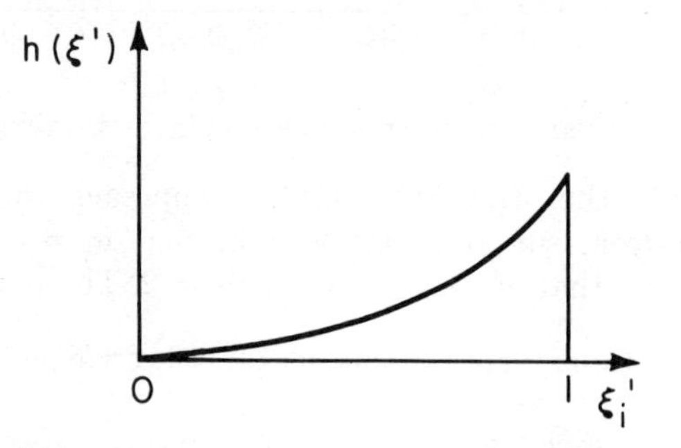

FIGURE 14.4. Probability density function of sampling weights for importance sampling.

density function of the number ξ' that will be used to obtain the observation $g(\xi')$. Thus, two steps are required to obtain an observation from the original probability distribution of interest. First, a random observation ξ' is generated from the probability distribution defined by $h(\xi')$ by using a method such as that described in Sec. 14.3.3. Second, ξ' is used to play the role of a random decimal number in order to generate an observation $g(\xi')$ from the original distribution. This procedure ensures that most of the observations will come from the most important portions of the distribution. To compensate for this, each observation $g(\xi')$ should be divided by its sampling weight $h(\xi')$. This yields

$$\text{weighted sample average} = \frac{1}{n} \sum_{i=1}^{n} \frac{g(\xi_i')}{h(\xi_i')}$$

as the estimator of the mean.

Since the magnitude of $g(\xi')$ for a given value of ξ' is a measure of the importance of obtaining an observation corresponding to ξ', $h(\xi')$ should be chosen to be as close to proportional to $g(\xi')$ as possible. In other words, the objective when choosing $h(\xi')$ is to make $g(\xi')/h(\xi')$ as close to constant as possible. The ideal choice would be $h(\xi') = g(\xi')/\text{mean}$, but this is impossible since the mean is not known. However, by having $h(\xi')$ mimic $g(\xi')$ as much as possible, the variance of $g(\xi')/h(\xi')$ will be much smaller than that of $g(\xi')$ alone, whereas the mean of $g(\xi')/h(\xi')$ always equals the mean to be estimated [since ξ' is a random variable whose probability density function is $h(\xi')$]. Therefore, averaging some observations of $g(\xi')/h(\xi')$ provides a relatively precise estimator of the mean of the original distribution.

In practice, the shape of the $g(\xi')$ function may not be known very closely. However, even letting the shape of the $h(\xi')$ function crudely approximate that of $g(\xi')$ may help considerably. To illustrate this, consider the exponential distribution of Fig. 14.2. Even without knowing the analytical expression for $g(\xi')$, a little thought about this distribution suggests that $g(\xi')$ increases approximately linearly for small values of ξ' and more than linearly for large values of ξ'. Therefore, even the linear probability density function, $h(\xi') = 2\xi'$ (for $0 \leq \xi' \leq 1$), mimics $g(\xi')$ considerably more closely than $h(\xi') = 1$ (which is what the crude Monte Carlo technique uses in effect). Using $h(\xi') = 2\xi'$ yields the results shown in Table

TABLE 14.4. Example for Importance Sampling

i	ξ_i	$\xi_i' = \sqrt{\xi_i}$	$g(\xi_i') = -\ln(1 - \xi_i')$	$h(\xi_i') = 2\xi_i'$	$\frac{g(\xi_i')}{h(\xi_i')}$
1	0.495	0.704	1.217	1.408	0.864
2	0.335	0.579	0.865	1.158	0.747
3	0.791	0.890	2.207	1.780	1.241
4	0.469	0.685	1.155	1.370	0.843
5	0.279	0.529	0.753	1.058	0.712
6	0.698	0.836	1.808	1.672	1.081
7	0.013	0.116	0.123	0.232	0.530
8	0.761	0.873	2.064	1.746	1.183
9	0.290	0.539	0.774	1.078	0.718
10	0.693	0.833	1.790	1.666	1.073
				Total =	8.992
				Estimate of mean =	0.899

14.4. Notice that the estimate of the mean (0.899) is much closer to the mean than that for crude Monte Carlo. Furthermore, by selecting $h(\xi')$ more carefully, this estimator can be considerably improved so that it would compare favorably with that for stratified sampling. For example, even the simple function, $h(\xi') = 3(\xi')^2$ (for $0 \leq \xi' \leq 1$), would yield an estimate of 0.954.

The *control variate* method is another Monte Carlo technique for reducing the variation of the sample observations in order to increase the precision of the estimator of the mean. However, rather than dividing $g(\xi)$ by a similar function, the control variate method is to subtract such a function instead. To compensate for this, the expected value (in the statistical sense) of this function is then added to the average of the resulting sample observations in order to obtain the desired estimate. Thus, considering ξ (without a subscript) as a random variable with a uniform distribution from 0 to 1, the estimator is

$$\text{adjusted sample average} = E\{h_c(\xi)\} + \frac{1}{n}\sum_{i=1}^{n}[g(\xi_i) - h_c(\xi_i)],$$

where $h_c(\xi)$ is a function of ξ (not necessarily a probability density function) that approximates the $g(\xi)$ function. This $h_c(\xi)$ function is called the control variate for $g(\xi)$.

To illustrate the control variate method for the exponential distribution under consideration, let $h_c(\xi) = 3\xi^2$ (for $0 \leq \xi \leq 1$). This choice for the $h_c(\xi)$ function is a reasonable one since its general shape resembles that of $g(\xi)$, although it is only one of many that could have been used. Since

TABLE 14.5. Example for Control Variate Method

i	ξ_i	$g(\xi_i) = -\ln(1 - \xi_i)$	$h_c(\xi_i) = 3\xi_i^2$	$g(\xi_i) - h_c(\xi_i)$
1	0.495	0.684	0.737	−0.053
2	0.335	0.408	0.338	+0.070
3	0.791	1.568	1.879	−0.311
4	0.469	0.633	0.661	−0.028
5	0.279	0.328	0.234	+0.094
6	0.698	1.199	1.464	−0.265
7	0.013	0.014	0.005	+0.009
8	0.761	1.433	1.740	−0.307
9	0.290	0.343	0.253	+0.090
10	0.693	1.183	1.443	−0.260
			Total =	−0.961
		Estimate of mean =	1.000 − 0.096 =	0.904

$$E\{h_c(\xi)\} = \int_0^1 3\xi^2(1)d\xi = 1 \,,$$

the data shown in Table 14.5 lead to an estimate of 0.904 for the mean of the distribution.

It has just been seen that the control variate method involves obtaining random observations of the difference of two random variables [$g(\xi)$ and $h_c(\xi)$] which have a high positive correlation. By contrast, the *antithetic variate* method involves obtaining random observations of the sum of two random variables which have a high negative correlation. More precisely, the estimator is

$$\text{combined sample average} = \frac{1}{n}\sum_{i=1}^{n}\frac{1}{2}\left[g(\xi_i) + h_a(\xi_i)\right] ,$$

where $h_a(\xi)$ is a function of the random variable ξ such that $h_a(\xi)$ has a high negative correlation with $g(\xi)$, and the expected value of $h_a(\xi)$ equals the mean to be estimated [as does the expected value of $g(\xi)$]. Thus, since $h_a(\xi)$ tends to be above the mean whenever $g(\xi)$ is below it, and vice versa, their average tends to be considerably closer to the mean than $g(\xi)$ alone.

The simplest example of the antithetic method is provided by letting $h_a(\xi) = g(1 - \xi)$. Since $g(\xi)$ increases as ξ increases, $g(\xi)$ and $g(1 - \xi)$ will be negatively correlated. Thus, for the distribution under consideration, the desired estimate would be obtained as shown in Table 14.6.[93]

TABLE 14.6. Example for Antithetic Variate Method

i	ξ_i	$g(\xi_i) = -\ln(1 - \xi_i)$	$h_a(\xi_i) = -\ln \xi_i$
1	0.495	0.684	0.702
2	0.335	0.408	1.092
3	0.791	1.568	0.234
4	0.469	0.633	0.756
5	0.279	0.328	1.275
6	0.698	1.199	0.359
7	0.013	0.014	4.305
8	0.761	1.433	0.272
9	0.290	0.343	1.236
10	0.693	1.183	0.366
	Total:	7.793	10.597
	Estimate of mean	$= \frac{1}{2}(0.779 + 1.060)$	$= 0.920$

[93] It should be noted that $2n$ calculations of a logarithm were required in this case, in contrast to the n that were required by each of the preceding techniques. Therefore, since the calculation of a logarithm would dominate the computation time on a digital computer, the precision of this estimator should be compared with the others only when they are based on $2n$ rather than n random numbers.

This illustrative example has suggested that the variance reducing techniques provide a much more precise estimator of the mean than does straightforward simulation. These results definitely were not a coincidence, as a derivation of the variance of the estimators would show. In comparison with straightforward simulation, these techniques do indeed provide a much more precise estimator with the same amount of computer time, or as precise an estimator with much less computer time. Despite the fact that additional analysis is required to incorporate one or more of these techniques into the simulation study, the rewards should not be foregone readily.

Although this example was a particularly simple one, it is often possible, though more difficult, to apply these techniques to much more complex problems. For example, suppose that the objective of the simulation study is to estimate the mean waiting time of customers in a queueing system (such as those described in Chapter 10). Since both the probability distribution of time between arrivals and the probability distribution of service times are involved, and since consecutive waiting times are not statistically independent, this problem appears to be beyond the capabilities of the variance reducing techniques. However, as has been described in detail elsewhere,[94] some of these techniques can indeed be applied to this type of problem very advantageously.[95]

14.5 TACTICAL PROBLEMS

14.5.1 Starting Conditions and Equilibrium

Many simulation studies are concerned with investigating systems that operate continually in a steady-state condition. Unfortunately, a simulation model cannot be operated this way; it must be started and stopped. Because of the artificiality introduced by the abrupt beginning of operation, the performance of the simulated system does not become representative of the corresponding real world system until it, too, has reached a steady-state condition. Therefore, the data obtained during this initial period of operation should be excluded from consideration. Furthermore, the simulated system should be started in a state as representative of steady-state conditions as possible in order to minimize the required length of this initial period.

As indicated in Sec. 10.3.7 for the case of queueing systems, a steady-state condition implies that the state of the system has become independent of the initial state and of the elapsed time since the start-up of the system. In other words, a system essentially reaches a steady-state condition when

[94] S. Ehrenfeld and S. Ben-Tuvia, "The Efficiency of Statistical Simulation Procedures," *Technometrics*, **4**, No. 2, 257–275 (1962).

[95] The sophisticated reader who wishes to study the theory and application of these (and other) variance reducing techniques in greater depth should find reference 3, cited at the end of this chapter, instructive.

the probability distribution of its state essentially reaches a limiting equilibrium distribution. Thus, it is the probability distribution of the state of the system, and not the particular value of the state in a given run (or even the mean value), that determines when the system has reached a steady-state condition. It should also be recognized that steady state is a limiting condition that may be approached but never actually attained exactly.

It is relatively difficult to estimate how long a simulated system must be operated in order to essentially reach a steady-state condition. This usually requires making a number of preliminary pilot runs from the same starting point and comparing the observed distribution of the state of the system at various ages. The insight thereby obtained into how rapidly the distribution "settles down" into an equilibrium usually provides the least unsatisfactory basis available for making this estimate.

The time required to essentially reach a steady-state condition depends considerably upon the selection of the starting conditions. Although it is common to begin the simulation run with the simulated system having no initial workload, this choice usually is an unfortunate one. Starting the run with the simulated system in a more typical state accelerates the approach to a steady-state condition. When comparing alternative design configurations, it is probably preferable to use the same starting conditions for all of them in order to avoid the possibility of biasing the comparisons.

14.5.2 **Determining Sample Sizes**

The choice of the sample sizes to be used for the simulated experiments is one of the most important decisions to be made in planning a simulation study. It is completely inappropriate to select these sample sizes arbitrarily and then assume that the estimates thereby obtained are sufficiently precise to yield valid conclusions. Instead, it is essential that a statistical analysis be conducted to determine the required sample sizes.

Suppose that it is desired to estimate the mean of some measure of the system's performance. Assume that the observations of this measure are statistically independent with a common normal distribution. In this case, a confidence interval for the mean can be obtained quite easily by the procedure described in Sec. 4.6.1 (for the case where the standard deviation is unknown). This interval can be made as small as desired by making the sample size sufficiently large. As the expression for the confidence interval indicates, the required number of observations (after the simulated system has essentially reached a steady-state condition) can be predicted by obtaining an estimate of the standard deviation of the observations from pilot runs or from the early observations.

Unfortunately, because of the nature of the problems for which simulation is used, the observations from a simulated experiment are likely to be highly correlated. For example, there is a high correlation between the waiting times of consecutive customers in a queueing system. Furthermore, many measures of performance are such that the simulated experiment yields this measure continuously as a function of time rather than as a sequence of separate observations. For example, the number of customers in a queueing system is one such measure. How can one estimate the required length of the over-all simulation run if either or both of these complications arise?

Two simple methods are available for circumventing these complications. One method is to execute a series of completely separate and independent runs of equal length, and use the average measure of performance for each run (excluding the initial stabilization period) as an individual observation. This provides a sequence of statistically independent observations. Furthermore, since they are averages, these observations should tend to have an approximately normal distribution because of relevant versions of the Central Limit Theorem (see Sec. 3.15) for dependent random variables. Therefore, a confidence interval for the mean can be obtained by the standard procedure mentioned above.

The main disadvantage of the approach just described is that each of the runs requires an initial stabilization period for approaching a steady-state condition, so that much of the simulation time is unproductive. The second method eliminates this disadvantage by making the runs consecutively, using the ending condition of one run as the steady-state starting condition for the next run. In other words, there is only one continuous over-all simulation run which (except for the one initial stabilization period) is divided for bookkeeping purposes into a series of equal portions (runs). The average measure of performance for each portion is then treated as an individual observation. The price paid for thereby eliminating the extra stabilization periods is that these observations may not be statistically independent. However, by making each of the portions sufficiently long, the correlation between these observations hopefully can be made relatively negligible. If so, the confidence interval for the mean can be obtained just as before.

For both methods, the over-all simulation run should be divided in such a way as to provide approximately 10 to 15 observations. The required length of the individual runs or portions can then be estimated by using pilot runs or early results to predict the size of the confidence interval for various lengths.

It was pointed out in Sec. 14.4.1 that, when comparing two alternative systems, the preferred procedure is to reproduce the same sequence of random numbers for both simulations. The corresponding results regarding the performance of the two systems would then be paired and the differences between these paired results would be used as the sample observations. In this case, the mean being estimated is the mean of the difference of the measure of performance for the two systems. However, the earlier discussion about estimating the mean of the measure of performance of a single system applies to this case as well. This is illustrated by a numerical example in Sec. 14.6.1.

14.6 FURTHER EXAMPLES

14.6.1 Example 3

Plans are being made for a new shopping center with several adjacent service stations. The problem to be considered concerns one of these service stations. This station will include several gasoline pumps and a single hydraulic lift for lubricating cars. The future owner wishes to know how much land he should purchase for his site. In particular, he wants to determine how many parking spaces he should provide for cars waiting to be lubricated.

For purposes of analyzing this problem, the following assumptions are made. Potential customers arriving to have their cars lubricated will turn away and go to another service station if and only if there are no empty parking spaces available. Once a customer has stopped, he will leave his car until it has been serviced. If the customer has not returned yet when his car is ready, it will be parked nearby in the shopping center parking lot. Potential customers will arrive randomly (i.e., according to a Poisson input process) at a mean rate of 32 per day. The time required to service a car has an exponential distribution where the mean service rate is 40 per day. The profit for each car serviced will be about $1.00. The capitalized cost of the land, etc., for each parking space would be approximately $0.40 per day. The objective is to determine the number of parking spaces that maximizes expected net profit.

Upon attempting to formulate the mathematical model for this problem, it soon becomes clear that a queueing theory model is applicable. In particular, the hydraulic lift and its operator are the server, whereas the cars waiting in the parking spaces constitute the customers waiting in the queue. Thus, there is a single server, with a Poisson input, exponential service times, and a finite queue. Therefore, the appropriate queueing theory model is the one discussed in Sec. 10.5.5.

Let P denote the expected net profit per day, so that the objective is to maximize P. Notice that one expression for P is

$$P = (1.00)(32)(1 - P_{N+1}) - 0.40N ,$$

where N is the number of parking spaces, and P_{N+1} is the probability of having $(N + 1)$ customers in the system so that all N parking spaces are occupied (so that arriving customers will turn away). Since an expression for

P_{N+1} was obtained in Sec. 10.5.5 (with $N + 1 = M$), it is straightforward to identify the maximum of P by trial and error.

It also is relatively straightforward to apply simulation to this problem. With this approach, the appropriate expression for P is

$$P = 1.00S - 0.40N ,$$

where S is the expected number of customers serviced per day. By using simulation to estimate S for various values of N, the optimal value of N can be estimated.

Since the underlying mathematical model for this problem is very similar to that for Example 2, the approach for formulating and implementing the simulation model is essentially the same as described in Sec. 14.2 and elaborated upon in Sec. 14.3. Sections 14.4 and 14.5 discussed in general terms how to use such a simulation model to analyze problems such as this one. The procedure used for one actual simulation study of this problem is described below.[96]

The first step was to run the simulation model for various values of N in order to obtain preliminary estimates of the corresponding values of P. These estimates revealed that $N = 5, 6, 7$, and 8 were the candidates for the optimal value of N, with $N = 6$ and 7 as the prime candidates. This preliminary investigation also was used to determine reasonable starting conditions, to estimate the time required for the simulated system to essentially reach a steady-state condition, and to estimate the required sample sizes. The next step was to execute long simulation runs for each of these four values of N. Each of these runs was continued for 1500 simulated days after the system essentially reached a steady-state condition, where these 1500 days were divided for bookkeeping purposes into 15 equal portions of 100 days each. The data recorded were the average net profit for each of the portions. The same sequences of random numbers were used for each of the runs so that the sequences of inter-arrival times and service times would be the same on the respective runs. When comparing the performance for two values of N, the relevant information was the value of d_i, the difference in the average net profit during portion i between the first and second values of N, for $i = 1, 2, \cdots, 15$. For example, consider $N = 7$ and $N = 8$. The estimates of P obtained from the corresponding simulation runs were \$28.045 and \$27.973, respectively, so that the difference was \$0.072. However, this does not prove that the true value of P is larger for $N = 7$ than for $N = 8$. It is necessary to take statistical error into account. By taking the difference for each of the 15 portions, the average difference,

[96] This description is based upon student solutions to a course problem used in the Digital Systems Simulation course offered by the Department of Industrial Engineering and Operations Research, Cornell University, 1963, and in the Data Processing in Operations Research course offered by the Department of Industrial Engineering, Stanford University, 1964.

$$\bar{d} = \frac{1}{n}\sum_{i=1}^{n} d_i = \$0.072 ,$$

and the sample standard deviation of the difference,

$$s = \sqrt{\frac{\sum_{i=1}^{n} (d_i - \bar{d})^2}{n - 1}} = \$0.158 ,$$

were obtained, where the sample size was $n = 15$. Hence, the estimated standard deviation of the average difference is $s/\sqrt{n} = \$0.0408$. Thus, the corresponding t statistic is

$$t = \frac{\bar{d}}{s/\sqrt{n}} = 1.76 ,$$

where 1.76 also happens to be the 95% percentile point of Student's t-distribution with $(n - 1) = 14$ degrees of freedom, as given in Table A5.2 of Appendix 5. Therefore, the hypothesis that the mean difference is zero (i.e., P is the same for $N = 7$ and $N = 8$) is rejected in favor of the alternative hypothesis that the mean difference is positive (i.e., P for $N = 7$ is larger than P for $N = 8$) at the 5% level of statistical significance.

Proceeding in the same way, it was found that P for $N = 6$ is larger than P for $N = 5$ at an acceptable level of statistical significance. This left only $N = 6$ and $N = 7$ to be compared to determine which value of N maximizes P. The simulation runs had yielded \$28.068 and \$28.045 as the estimates of P for $N = 6$ and $N = 7$, respectively. Taking the differences for the corresponding portions of the runs, it was found that the average difference was $\bar{d} = \$0.023$, and the sample standard deviation of the difference was $s = \$0.171$. Thus, the estimated standard deviation of the average difference is $\$0.171/\sqrt{15} = \$0.0442$, so that the t statistic is only $t = 0.023/0.0442 = 0.52$. Therefore, the hypothesis that $N = 6$ and $N = 7$ have the same value of P cannot be rejected at any reasonable level of statistical significance, so that the difference in the estimated values of P is not statistically significant. To distinguish between the true values of P would require much longer simulation runs (approximately ten times as long); it probably is not worth the effort. The conclusion is that 6 and 7 parking spaces essentially tie for maximizing expected net profit, so that the owner should select either one of these two alternatives on the basis of the intangibles involved.

14.6.2 **Example 4**

The system that probably has been simulated most frequently is the type of process-organized manufacturing facility commonly called the "job shop." A primary characteristic of a job shop is the great diversity of jobs to be performed. A job shop primarily produces to custom orders, so that the same job may never be done twice. Each job will have a different set and sequence of operations to be performed. Hence, the task of planning, scheduling, and controlling the work being done in a job shop is very complex. As a result, only very limited analytical procedures are available for helping to perform this task. Therefore, it has been common to resort to simulation for guidance.

The main considerations in designing and operating a job shop are the cost of having idle machine and labor capacity, the cost of carrying in-process inventory, and the importance of meeting specified order completion due dates. Unfortunately, these considerations tend to conflict with each other. One can have a low cost of idle machine and labor capacity by providing only a minimum amount of machinery and manpower. However, this would result in considerable work waiting to be done and, therefore, large in-process inventories and difficulty in meeting completion due dates. On the other hand, one can essentially guarantee meeting realistic completion due dates by providing so much machine and labor capacity that orders usually would not have to wait to be processed. However, this would result in excessive costs for idle machine and labor capacity. Therefore, it is necessary to strive for an economic compromise between these considerations.

After the job shop has been designed, the primary objective in the daily operation of the shop is to schedule the work so that specified order completion due dates can be met. This task is greatly complicated by the wide variety of orders to be processed, by the variability of the processing times, and by interruptions of scheduled work due to machine breakdowns or expediting of special orders. As a consequence, it is inevitable that waiting lines consisting of orders will form in front of some of the work centers. The delay of an order at one work center then delays its arrival at succeeding work centers, where additional delays may occur because other orders already are waiting to be processed. It is, therefore, essential that waiting be taken into account in scheduling orders and in setting completion dates. However, since it is essentially impossible to accurately predict how long an order will have to wait at the respective work centers, the goal of accurately scheduling future work on all orders in the shop is a hopeless one. Therefore, the usual procedure is to do no more than estimate future workloads at the various work centers, and to use this information to estimate realistic completion dates and to determine when orders should be released to the shop. When two or more orders are waiting simultaneously at a work center, the decision as to which one to process first is based on the relative urgency of the orders. If a formal rule is used for making this choice, it is called the "dispatch rule." Expediters also are used to monitor the especially urgent orders and to make sure that they receive top priority.

A simulation model of a job shop must take into account all of the operating characteristics described above. To begin, it must generate orders and their attributes. These attributes include an ordered list of the necessary operations, the type of machine required to perform each operation, the actual processing time for each operation, and the completion due date of the order. The simulation program also must release orders to the shop at appropriate times and assign them to the appropriate machines in the specified order. A record is maintained of the current status of each machine by identifying the order being processed (if any) and the orders waiting to be processed. The program also synchronizes the operation of the individual machines and the progress of the individual jobs. In particular, whenever the specified processing time for an operation has elapsed, that order is assigned immediately to its next machine and the next order to be processed is selected by the specified dispatch rule. Finally, the simulation program computes the desired statistics regarding the aggregate performance of the simulated job shop. These statistics should measure such things as the degree of success in meeting due dates, the cost of carrying in-process inventory, and the utilization of machines and labor.

Simulating a job shop can be very helpful in a number of ways. First, when designing a job shop system, simulating a proposed design may suggest improvements by identifying bottlenecks, overloaded work areas, etc. Given an existing system, simulation provides a convenient means for testing suggested changes regarding machine and labor capacity, using overtime, and subcontracting. Simulation also can be used to forecast workloads in the various work areas of the job shop, and thereby develop more realistic schedules and estimated completion dates. Finally, various dispatch rules can be simulated to compare their effect on the performance of the system and thereby determine which one best meets management's objectives.

14.6.3 Typical Applications of Simulation

There have been numerous applications of simulation in industry, in the military, and elsewhere. Some examples of these are listed below in order to illustrate the great versatility of simulation.

(1) Simulation of the operations at a large airport by an airlines company in order to test changes in company policies and practices (e.g., amounts of maintenance capacity, berthing facilities, spare aircraft, etc.).
(2) Simulation of the passage of traffic across a junction with time-sequenced traffic lights in order to determine the best time sequences.
(3) Simulation of a maintenance operation in order to determine the optimal size of repair crews.

(4) Simulation of the flux of uncharged particles through a radiation shield to determine the intensity of the radiation that penetrates the shield.
(5) Simulation of steel-making operations in order to evaluate changes in operating practices and in the capacity and configuration of the facilities.
(6) Simulation of the United States economy in order to predict the effect of economic policy decisions.
(7) Simulation of large-scale military battles in order to evaluate defensive and offensive weapon systems.
(8) Simulation of large-scale distribution and inventory control systems in order to improve the design of these systems.
(9) Simulation of the over-all operation of an entire business firm in order to evaluate broad changes in the policies and operation of the firm, and also to provide a business game for training executives.
(10) Simulation of a telephone communications system in order to determine the capacity of the respective components that would be required to provide satisfactory service at the most economical level.
(11) Simulation of the operation of a developed river basin in order to determine the best configuration of dams, power plants, and irrigation works that would provide the desired level of flood control and water-resource development.
(12) Simulation of the operation of a production line in order to determine the amount of in-process storage space that should be provided.

14.7 **Conclusions**

Simulation is indeed a very versatile tool. However, it is by no means a panacea. Simulation is inherently an imprecise technique. It provides only statistical estimates rather than exact results, and it only compares alternatives rather than generating the optimal one. Furthermore, simulation is a slow and costly way to study a problem. It usually requires a large amount of time and expense for analysis and programming, in addition to considerable computer running time. Simulation models tend to become unwieldy, so that the number of cases that can be run and the accuracy of the results obtained often turn out to be very inadequate. Finally, simulation yields only numerical data about the performance of the system, so that it provides no additional insight into the cause-and-effect relationships within the system except for the clues that can be gleaned from these numbers (and from the analysis required to construct the simulation model). Therefore, it is very expensive to conduct a sensitivity analysis of the parameter values assumed by the model. The only possible way would be to conduct new series of simulation runs with different parameter values, which would tend to provide relatively little information at a relatively great cost.

Despite these limitations, simulation unquestionably has an important place in the theory and practice of operations research. It is an invaluable tool for use on those problems where more satisfactory techniques of analysis have failed.

SELECTED REFERENCES

1. Conway, R. W., "Some Tactical Problems in Digital Simulation," *Management Science,* **10,** No. 1, 47–61 (1963).
2. Conway, R. W., Johnson, B. M., and Maxwell, W. L., "Some Problems of Digital Systems Simulation," *Management Science,* **6,** No. 1, 92–110 (1959).
3. Hammersley, J. M., and Handscomb, D. C., *Monte Carlo Methods,* Methuen, London, 1964.
4. Harling, J., "Simulation Techniques in Operations Research—A Review," *Operations Research,* **6,** No. 3, 307–319 (1958).
5. Jackson, J. R., "Simulation as Experimental Mathematics," Research Report No. 72, Management Sciences Research Project, U.C.L.A., June, 1961.
6. Naylor, T. H., Balintfy, J. L., Burdick, D. S., and Chu, K., *Computer Simulation Techniques,* Wiley, New York, 1966.
7. Tocher, K. D., *The Art of Simulation,* Van Nostrand, Princeton, N.J., 1963.

PROBLEMS

(Random numbers for doing the following problems should be obtained from Table 14.1, using the digits consecutively starting with the top row of the table. Three-digit random numbers are sufficient.)

1. Use the multiplicative congruential method to obtain a sequence of five two-digit random numbers such that $x_{n+1} \equiv 49x_n$ (modulus 131) and $x_0 = 17$.

2. Generate five random observations from each of the following probability distributions.

(a) $P(X = k) = 1/10, 2/10, 4/10, 2/10$, and $1/10$ for $k = 1, 2, 3, 4$, and 5, respectively.

(b) The uniform distribution between 5 and 25, so that the probability density function is

$$f(x) = \begin{cases} \dfrac{1}{20}, & \text{if } 5 \le x \le 25 \\ 0, & \text{otherwise}. \end{cases}$$

(c) The geometric distribution with parameter $p = 0.3$, so that

$$P\{X = k\} = \begin{cases} 0.3(0.7)^{k-1}, & \text{if } k = 1, 2, \cdots \\ 0, & \text{otherwise}. \end{cases}$$

(d) The distribution whose probability density function is

$$f(x) = \begin{cases} 4x^3, & \text{if } 0 \leq x \leq 1 \\ 0, & \text{otherwise}. \end{cases}$$

(e) The distribution whose probability density function is

$$f(x) = \begin{cases} \frac{1}{8}(x - 2), & \text{if } 2 \leq x \leq 6 \\ 0, & \text{otherwise}. \end{cases}$$

(f) The distribution of the sum of four dice.

3. Generate five random observations from each of the following probability distributions.

(a) The exponential distribution with mean = 10.
(b) The Erlang distribution with mean = 10 and shape parameter $k = 4$ (i.e., standard deviation = 5).
(c) The normal distribution with mean = 10 and standard deviation = 5. (Use the Central Limit Theorem and 12 random numbers to obtain each observation.)

4. The game of craps requires the player to throw two dice one or more times until a decision has been reached as to whether he wins or loses. He wins if the first throw results in a sum of 7 or 11 or, alternatively, if the first sum is 4, 5, 6, 8, 9, or 10, and the same sum reappears before a sum of 7 has appeared. Conversely, he loses if the first throw results in a sum of 2, 3, or 12 or, alternatively, if the first sum is 4, 5, 6, 8, 9, or 10, and a sum of 7 appears before the first sum reappears.

(a) Simulate 20 plays of this game in order to estimate the probability of winning. Also calculate an approximate 95% confidence interval for this probability.
(b) Given n plays of the game, the expected value and standard deviation of the proportion of wins are approximately 0.493 and $0.5/\sqrt{n}$, respectively. How many simulated plays are required in order to have a probability of at least 0.95 that the estimated probability of winning will be less than 0.5?

5. Consider the single-server queueing theory model with Poisson input and exponential service times that was discussed in Sec. 10.5.1 and

Example 2 of Sec. 14.2. Suppose that the mean arrival rate is 3 per hour and the mean service rate is 5 per hour, and that it is desired to estimate the mean waiting time by using simulation. Perform the simulation briefly (approximately 20 arrivals), and then outline how you would proceed to obtain this estimate.

(a) Use asynchronous timing.
(b) Use synchronous timing with one minute as the time unit.

6. A company has been having a maintenance problem with a certain complex piece of equipment. This equipment contains four identical vacuum tubes that have been the cause of the trouble. The problem is that the tubes fail fairly frequently, thereby forcing the equipment to be shut down while making a replacement. The current practice is to replace tubes only when they fail. However, a proposal has been made to replace all four tubes whenever any one of them fails in order to reduce the frequency with which the equipment must be shut down. The objective is to compare these two alternatives on a cost basis.

The pertinent data are the following. For each tube, the operating time until failure has approximately a normal distribution with a mean of 600 hours and a standard deviation of 100 hours. The equipment must be shut down for one hour in order to replace one tube, or for two hours in order to replace all four tubes. The total cost associated with shutting down the equipment and replacing tubes is $6.00 per hour plus $8.00 for each new tube.

Using reasonable starting conditions, simulate the operation of the two alternative policies for 3,000 hours of simulated time. Use the result to make a preliminary comparison of the alternatives on a cost basis, and then outline how you would proceed further to solve this problem.

7. A manufacturing company has three planers for cutting flat surfaces in large work pieces of two different types. The time required to perform each job varies somewhat, depending largely upon the number of passes that must be made. In particular, for both types of work pieces, the time required by a planer has approximately the following probability distribution.

Time	*Probability*
20 min.	0.20
25 min.	0.34
30 min.	0.17
35 min.	0.11
40 min.	0.07
45 min.	0.05
50 min.	0.03
55 min.	0.02
60 min.	0.01

The two types of work pieces are brought to the planer department on an alternating basis at a constant rate of one piece every ten minutes, so that three of each type are completed per hour on the average.

Unfortunately, the planer department has had a difficult time keeping up with its workload. Frequently, there are a number of work pieces waiting for a free planer. This has seriously disrupted the production schedule for the subsequent operations, thereby greatly increasing the cost of in-process inventory as well as the cost of idle equipment and resulting lost production. Therefore, the proposal has been made to obtain one additional planer in order to relieve this bottleneck.

It is estimated that the total incremental cost (including capital recovery cost) associated with obtaining and operating another planer would be \$30.00 per hour. (This takes into account the fact that, even with an additional planer, the total running time for all the planers will remain the same.) It is also estimated that the total cost associated with work pieces having to wait to be processed is \$40.00 per work piece per hour and \$15.00 per work piece per hour for work pieces of the first and second types, respectively. Because of this difference in costs, work pieces of the first type always are given priority over those of the second type. In other words, if a planer becomes free when work pieces of both types are waiting, a work piece of the first type always is chosen to be processed next.

Simulate the operation of the two alternative policies (the status quo or obtaining one additional planer) for 1,100 minutes of simulated time. Use the first 100 minutes for attempting to essentially reach a steady-state condition, and then gather the relevant data for each of the subsequent 10 periods of 100 minutes each. Use the same sequence of random numbers for both alternatives. Compare these alternatives on a total cost basis, and state your conclusions in statistical terms.

8. Two alternatives are being compared by using simulation with the same sequence of random numbers for both. After essentially reaching a steady-state condition, the measure of performance (which should be made as large as possible) for each of the subsequent ten periods was 176, 153, 181, 172, 167, 185, 162, 149, 170, and 188 for the first alternative, and 172, 152, 168, 176, 161, 177, 162, 146, 172, and 177 for the second alternative. Compare these two alternatives, and state your conclusions in statistical terms.

9. Consider the probability distribution whose probability density function is

$$f(x) = \begin{cases} \dfrac{2}{x^3}, & \text{if } 1 \leq x \leq \infty \\ 0, & \text{otherwise}. \end{cases}$$

The problem is to perform a simulated experiment, with the help of variance reducing techniques, for estimating the mean of this distribution. To provide a standard of comparison, also derive the mean analytically.

For each of the following cases, generate ten observations and calculate the resulting estimate of the mean.

(a) Use the crude Monte Carlo method.
(b) Use stratified sampling with $m = 3$, $\alpha_0 = 0$, $\alpha_1 = 0.6$, $\alpha_2 = 0.9$, $\alpha_3 = 1$, $n_1 = 3$, $n_2 = 3$, $n_3 = 4$.
(c) Use importance sampling with $h(\xi') = e^{\xi'}/(e - 1)$.
(d) Use the control variate method with $h_c(\xi) = 1 + \frac{1}{2}\xi + \frac{3}{8}[\ln(1 - \xi)]^2$.
(e) Use the antithetic variable method with $h_a(\xi) = g(1 - \xi)$.

10. One product produced by a certain company requires that bushings be drilled into a metal block and that cylindrical shafts be inserted into the bushings. The shafts are required to have a radius of at least 1.0000 inches, but as little larger than this as possible. In actuality, the probability distribution of what the radius of a shaft will be (in inches) has the probability density function,

$$f_S(x) = \begin{cases} 1000e^{-1000(x-1.0000)}, & \text{if } x \geq 1.0000 \\ 0, & \text{otherwise}. \end{cases}$$

Similarly, the probability distribution of what the radius of a bushing will be (in inches) has the probability density function,

$$f_B(x) = \begin{cases} 100, & \text{if } 1.0000 \leq x \leq 1.0100 \\ 0, & \text{otherwise}. \end{cases}$$

The clearance between a bushing and a shaft is the difference in their radii. Since they are selected at random, there occasionally is interference (i.e., negative clearance) between a bushing and a shaft that were to be mated. The objective is to determine how frequently this will happen under the current probability distribution.

Perform a simulated experiment for estimating the probability of interference. Notice that almost all cases of interference will occur when the radius of the bushing is much closer to 1.0000 in. than to 1.0100 in. Therefore, it appears that an efficient experiment would generate most of the simulated bushings from this critical portion of the distribution. Take this into account in Parts (b) and (c). For each of the following cases, generate 20 observations and calculate the resulting estimate of the probability of interference.

(a) Use the crude Monte Carlo method.
(b) Develop and apply a stratified sampling approach to this problem.
(c) Develop and apply an importance sampling approach to this problem.

11. Consider Example 3, which was described in Sec. 14.6.1. Suppose that the estimate of the cost for each parking space is revised from $0.40 per day to $0.80 per day. Write the simulation program for this problem for any accessible digital computer. Then perform a simulation study to determine how many parking spaces should be provided.

12. Consider Example 4, which was described in Sec. 14.6.2. Develop a flow diagram which outlines the simulation model for this problem. Include a description of the form in which relevant information is maintained, of how this information is up-dated and used, and of how the activities of the simulated system are synchronized.

13. Select any of the typical applications of simulation listed in Sec. 14.6.3 and develop a simulation model for this type of problem.

Part V

TECHNIQUES: ADVANCED TOPICS IN MATHEMATICAL PROGRAMMING

Advanced Topics in Linear Programming

15.1 DUALITY THEORY

15.1.1 Complementarity

Section 5.7.1 introduced the important concept of duality and its ramifications. In particular, it was pointed out that associated with every linear programming problem is another intimately related linear programming problem called the dual. This relationship and its implications will now be explored in detail. The notation and results given in Sec. 5.7.1 continue to be used here.

The fundamental theorem of duality theory is the "Dual Theorem" (see Theorem 5.2), which was stated but not proved in Sec. 5.7.1. Such a proof is given here after certain relevant results have been developed.

Lemma 1: $Z_x \leq Z_y$ for any feasible solutions of the primal and dual problems.

Proof: Assume that $(x_1, x_2, \cdots, x_n)$ and $(y_1, y_2, \cdots, y_m)$ are feasible solutions of the primal problem and the dual problem, respectively. The primal and dual constraints imply that

$$\begin{aligned} Z_x = \sum_{j=1}^{n} x_j c_j &\leq \sum_{j=1}^{n} x_j \sum_{i=1}^{m} a_{ij} y_i \\ &= \sum_{i=1}^{m} y_i \sum_{j=1}^{n} a_{ij} x_j \\ &\leq \sum_{i=1}^{m} y_i b_i = Z_y , \end{aligned}$$

which completes the proof of the lemma.

The above lemma does not prove the Dual Theorem because it is still possible that $Z_x < Z_y$ for all feasible solutions. What remains is to show that there exist feasible solutions such that $Z_x = Z_y$. This is done soon.

As suggested in Sec. 5.7.1, the relationship between the primal and dual problems is even more intimate than indicated by the Dual Theorem. Not only are the optimal solutions closely related, but there also exists a similar complementarity between basic solutions of the primal and dual problems. Since the simplex method automatically identifies the complementary dual basic solution, solving one problem (primal or dual) by the simplex method automatically solves the other problem. It is instructive to begin by demonstrating how the simplex method is able to identify the complementary optimal solution, and then how it identifies the complementary basic solutions in general. The significance of complementarity is indicated in subsequent sections.

In order to simplify the notation, the proofs in this section assume that the initial set of equations for solving the primal problem by the simplex method is the following:

$$
\begin{array}{llr}
(0) & Z_x - c_1x_1 - c_2x_2 - \cdots - c_nx_n & = 0 \\
(1) & a_{11}x_1 + a_{12}x_2 + \cdots + a_{1n}x_n + x_{n+1} & = b_1 \\
(2) & a_{21}x_1 + a_{22}x_2 + \cdots + a_{2n}x_n \qquad + x_{n+2} & = b_2 \\
 & \vdots & \\
(m) & a_{m1}x_1 + a_{m2}x_2 + \cdots + a_{mn}x_n \qquad\qquad + x_{n+m} & = b_m .
\end{array}
$$

This is certainly the case when the primal problem is in the form given at the beginning of Sec. 5.7.1 (i.e., all of the constraints are inequalities) and all of the b_i are positive. However, if some of the b_i are negative, so that additional (artificial) variables are introduced, it is evident that any such artificial variables are irrelevant to the analysis. Similarly, the analysis is essentially unchanged if some of the constraints are equations, so that the corresponding slack variables actually are artificial variables. In particular, if the two-phase method is used, the only change in the above set of equations is that the indicated equation (0) is not introduced and updated until the beginning of Phase 2, which does not affect the analysis. If the Big M method is used instead, a proper interpretation of the notation is required for the stated results to hold, as indicated in Problem 3.

In addition, let $(z_j - c_j)$ denote the coefficient of x_j in the current equation (0) obtained by the simplex method, where $j = 1, 2, \cdots, n + m$ (so that, under the above assumptions, $c_j = 0$ for $j = n + 1, \cdots, n + m$). Similarly, let $(z_j^* - c_j)$ denote the coefficient of x_j in the final equation (0), i.e., the one obtained when an optimal solution has been reached by the simplex method, so this equation would look as follows.

$$(0)\quad Z_x + (z_1^* - c_1)x_1 + (z_2^* - c_2)x_2 + \cdots + (z_n^* - c_n)x_n + z_{n+1}^* x_{n+1} + \cdots + z_{n+m}^* x_{n+m} = Z_x^* .$$

Thus, z_j^* is just the net amount by which the original coefficient of x_j in equation (0), $-c_j$, has been increased in the process of executing the simplex method.

This interpretation of z_j^* has an important implication when $j > n$. Note that, in the original set of equations, x_{n+i} has a coefficient of one in equation (i) and a coefficient of zero in all of the other equations. Therefore, exactly z_{n+i}^* times the original equation (i) must have been added (directly or indirectly[97]) to the original equation (0) in the process of executing the simplex method. This immediately implies the following lemma.

Lemma 2:
$$Z_x^* = \sum_{i=1}^{m} z_{n+i}^* b_i ,$$
$$z_j^* = \sum_{i=1}^{m} z_{n+i}^* a_{ij}, \qquad \text{for } j = 1, 2, \cdots, n .$$

These two key facts play an important role in the following analysis.

Theorem 15.1: Suppose that an optimal solution of the primal problem has been obtained by the simplex method. Then an optimal value of the ith dual variable equals the coefficient of the ith slack variable of the primal problem in the final equation (0), i.e.,

$$y_i^* = z_{n+i}^* , \qquad \text{for } i = 1, 2, \cdots, m .$$

Proof: The procedure is to show that the solution, $(y_1, y_2, \cdots, y_m) = (z_{n+1}^*, z_{n+2}^*, \cdots, z_{n+m}^*)$, is feasible for the dual problem, and then that it is at least as good as any other feasible solution (i.e., it is optimal).

According to the test for optimality for the primal problem (see Sec. 5.5), all coefficients in the final equation (0) are necessarily non-negative. Therefore,

$$z_{n+i}^* \geq 0, \qquad \text{for } i = 1, 2, \cdots, m ,$$

which fulfills the non-negativity restrictions for the dual problem, and

$$(z_j^* - c_j) \geq 0, \qquad \text{for } j = 1, 2, \cdots, n .$$

By using Lemma 2 to substitute for z_j^*, it now follows that

$$\sum_{i=1}^{m} z_{n+i}^* a_{ij} \geq c_j , \qquad \text{for } j = 1, 2, \cdots, n ,$$

[97] Adding equation (i) to equation (j) "indirectly" refers here, and hereafter, to adding equation (j) to other equations which are subsequently added (directly or indirectly) to equation (i).

which fulfills the remaining restrictions for the dual problem. Hence, $(z^*_{n+1}, z^*_{n+2}, \cdots, z^*_{n+m})$ is feasible for this problem.

Since Lemma 1 implies that

$$Z^*_x \leq \sum_{i=1}^{m} b_i y_i$$

for any feasible solution of the dual problem, and

$$Z^*_x = \sum_{i=1}^{m} b_i z^*_{n+i}$$

by Lemma 2, it now follows that $(z^*_{n+1}, z^*_{n+2}, \cdots, z^*_{n+m})$ is optimal for the dual problem, as was to be proved.

Corollary: The Dual Theorem (see Theorem 5.2).

Proof: Since both the primal problem and the dual problem are assumed to possess finite feasible solutions, Lemma 1 implies that there exists a finite optimal solution for both problems. Theorem 15.1 established that

$$Z^*_y = \sum_{i=1}^{m} b_i z^*_{n+i},$$

whereas Lemma 2 indicates that

$$Z^*_x = \sum_{i=1}^{m} b_i z^*_{n+i},$$

so that

$$Z^*_x = Z^*_y,$$

as claimed by the Dual Theorem.

Slack variables, y_{m+j} $(j = 1, \cdots, n)$, are now introduced for the dual problem in order to identify dual basic solutions and to indicate a further relationship between the primal and dual problems. Thus,

$$\sum_{i=1}^{m} a_{ij} y_i - y_{m+j} = c_j,$$

or, equivalently,

$$-\sum_{i=1}^{m} a_{ij} y_i + y_{m+j} = -c_j, \qquad \text{for } j = 1, \cdots, n.$$

Theorem 15.2: Suppose that an optimal solution of the primal problem has been obtained by the simplex method. Then an optimal value of the jth slack variable for the dual problem equals the coefficient of the jth variable of the primal problem in the final equation (0), i.e.,

$$y^*_{m+j} = z^*_j - c_j\,, \qquad \text{for } j = 1, \cdots, n\,.$$

Proof: Lemma 2 and Theorem 15.1 yield

$$z^*_j = \sum_{i=1}^{m} a_{ij} z^*_{n+i} = \sum_{i=1}^{m} a_{ij} y^*_i, \qquad \text{for } j = 1, \cdots, n\,.$$

By definition,

$$y^*_{m+j} = \sum_{i=1}^{m} a_{ij} y^*_i - c_j\,, \qquad \text{for } j = 1, \cdots, n\,.$$

Combining these results proves the theorem.

Corollary to Theorems 15.1 and 15.2:

$$\begin{aligned} y^*_i &= 0 \text{ whenever } x^*_{n+i} > 0, \quad \text{for } i = 1, \cdots, m\,. \\ y^*_{m+j} &= 0 \text{ whenever } x^*_j \;\;\; > 0, \quad \text{for } j = 1, \cdots, n\,. \end{aligned}$$

Proof: $x^*_k > 0$ $(k = 1, \cdots, n + m)$ implies that x^*_k is a basic variable, which implies that $z^*_k - c_k = 0$, so the corollary now follows immediately from Theorems 15.1 and 15.2.

Theorem 5.1 implies that this corollary also holds for the optimal primal solution, so that $x^*_j = 0$ whenever $y^*_{m+j} > 0$, and $x^*_{n+i} = 0$ whenever $y^*_i > 0$. These relationships between the two optimal solutions have been given the descriptive name of "complementary slackness."

Theorems 15.1 and 15.2 have identified $(y^*_1, \cdots, y^*_{m+n})$, the dual basic solution which is optimal and therefore complementary to the primal optimal solution. These solutions are complementary in the sense that they yield $Z_x = Z_y$. Similarly, each primal basic solution possesses a complementary dual basic solution such that $Z_x = Z_y$. Theorem 15.3 indicates that the complementary basic solutions are identified in the same way as the complementary optimal solution.

Theorem 15.3: Assume that finite feasible solutions exist for both the primal problem and the dual problem. Suppose that the primal problem is being solved by the simplex method. Let $(x'_1, \cdots, x'_{n+m})$ be the non-optimal basic feasible solution obtained at any particular iteration, and let $(z'_j - c_j)$ be the corresponding coefficient of x'_j in equation (0) for $j = 1, \cdots, n + m$. Consider the following basic (infeasible) solution for the dual problem: $y'_i = z'_{n+i}$ (for $i = 1, \cdots, m$) and $y'_{m+j} = z'_j - c_j$ (for $j = 1, \cdots, n$). Then

$$Z'_x = Z'_y \left(\text{where } Z'_x = \sum_{j=1}^{n} c_j x'_j \quad \text{and} \quad Z'_y = \sum_{i=1}^{m} b_i y'_i \right).$$

Proof: Removing any references to optimality, the proof of Lemma 2 also implies that

$$Z'_x = \sum_{i=1}^{m} z'_{n+i} b_i ,$$

whereas

$$Z'_y = \sum_{i=1}^{m} z'_{n+i} b_i ,$$

by definition, so the desired result follows.

To illustrate Theorems 15.1, 15.2, and 15.3, consider the example of Secs. 5.5 and 5.7.1. Since the final equation (0) for the primal problem is $Z + 3x_4 + x_5 = 36$ (where x_3, x_4, and x_5 are the slack variables), the optimal solution for the dual problem is $y_1^* = 0$, $y_2^* = 3$, $y_3^* = 1$, with $Z_y^* =$

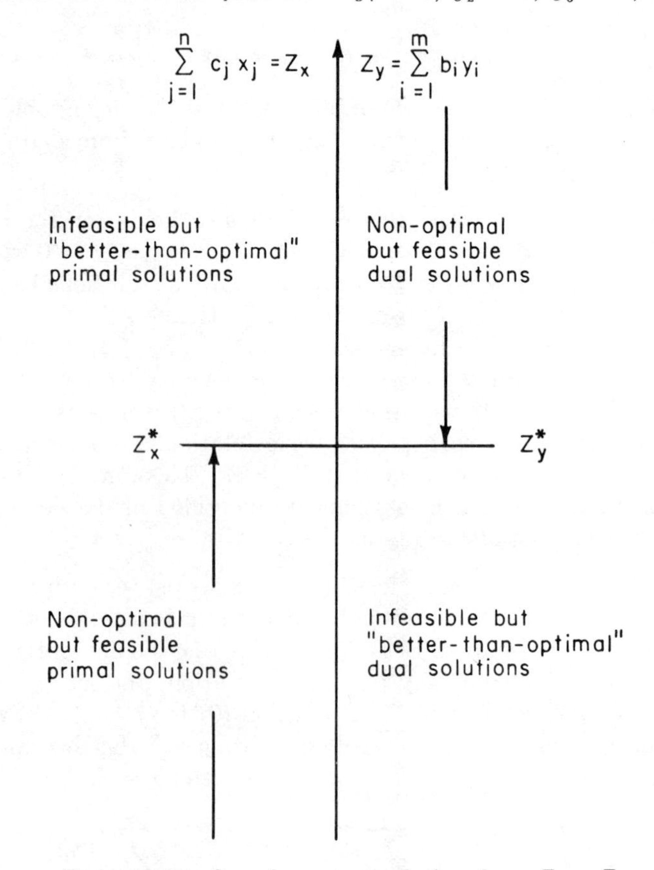

FIGURE 15.1. Complementary solutions have $Z_x = Z_y$.

$4y_1^* + 6y_2^* + 18y_3^* = 36 = Z_x^*$. The optimal values of the slack variables for the dual problem are $y_4^* = 0$ and $y_5^* = 0$. At the first iteration, where $x_1 = 0$, $x_2 = 0$, $x_3 = 4$, $x_4 = 6$, $x_5 = 18$, and equation (0) is $Z - 3x_1 - 5x_2 = 0$, the complementary dual basic solution is $y_1 = 0$, $y_2 = 0$, $y_3 = 0$, $y_4 = -3$, $y_5 = -5$, with $Z_y = 0 = Z_x$. At the second iteration, where $x_1 = 0$, $x_2 = 6$, $x_3 = 4$, $x_4 = 0$, $x_5 = 6$, and equation (0) is $Z - 3x_1 + 5x_4 = 30$, the complementary dual basic solution is $y_1 = 0$, $y_2 = 5$, $y_3 = 0$, $y_4 = -3$, $y_5 = 0$, with $Z_y = 30 = Z_x$.

It is important to notice that *non-optimal but feasible* basic solutions for either problem (primal or dual) are complementary to basic solutions for the other problem, which are *infeasible but "better-than-optimal"* (i.e., the value of the objective function is more favorable than for the optimal solution). This is illustrated in Fig. 15.1. Thus, while the simplex method is dealing directly with non-optimal but feasible basic solutions and working toward optimality in the primal problem, it is simultaneously dealing indirectly with infeasible "better-than-optimal" basic solutions and working toward feasibility in the dual problem. Actually, under certain circumstances to be explored later, it is more convenient to deal directly with infeasible "better-than-optimal" solutions than with feasible solutions. The dual simplex method, presented in the next section, is a procedure for doing this.

15.1.2 The Dual Simplex Method

The dual simplex method deals with the primal problem as if the simplex method were being applied simultaneously to the dual problem. Thus, the dual simplex method deals directly with infeasible but "better-than-optimal" basic solutions and works toward feasibility. The corresponding complementary basic solutions in the dual problem are non-optimal but feasible, and they move toward optimality.

The dual simplex method is very useful in certain special types of situations. Ordinarily, it is easier to find an initial basic feasible solution (by merely selecting the slack variables as basic variables) than it is to find an initial infeasible better-than-optimal basic solution. However, it is occasionally necessary to introduce many artificial variables in order to artificially construct an initial basic feasible solution. In such cases, it may be easier to begin with an infeasible better-than-optimal basic solution and use the dual simplex method. Furthermore, fewer iterations may be required when it is not necessary to drive many artificial variables to zero. The second primary application of the dual simplex method is in conjunction with post-optimality analysis. Suppose that an optimal solution has been obtained by the simplex method, but that it becomes necessary (or of interest for sensitivity analysis) to make minor changes in the model. If the formerly optimal basic solution is no longer feasible, it is often possible to immediately apply the dual simplex method by starting with this basic solution which is now infeasible but better-than-optimal. This usually would lead to the new optimal solution much more quickly than by solving the new problem from the beginning with the simplex method. Post-optimality analysis and some of the cases where the dual simplex method may be applied advantageously are explored in Sec. 15.2.

The dual simplex method is very similar to the simplex method. In fact, once they are started, the only difference is in the criteria used for selecting the entering and leaving basic variables, and for testing for optimality (feasibility). In order to start the dual simplex method, all of the coefficients in equation (0) must be non-negative (so that the basic solution is better-than-optimal). The basic solutions investigated will be infeasible (except for the last one) only because some of the variables are negative. The method continues to decrease the value of the objective function, always retaining non-negative coefficients in equation (0), until all of the variables are non-negative. Such a basic solution is feasible (it satisfies all of the equations) and is, therefore, optimal by the simplex method criterion of non-negative coefficients in equation (0). The details of the dual simplex method are summarized below.

SUMMARY OF DUAL SIMPLEX METHOD

First Iteration: Introduce slack variables as needed to construct a set of equations describing the problem. Find a basic solution such that the coefficients in equation (0) are zero for basic variables and non-negative for non-basic variables. Go to Step 4.

Step 1. Determine the new leaving basic variable: Select the basic variable with the largest negative value.

Step 2. Determine the new entering basic variable: Select the non-basic variable whose coefficient in equation (0) reaches zero first as an increasing multiple of the equation containing the leaving basic variable is added to equation (0). This is done by checking the non-basic variables with negative coefficients in that equation (the one containing the leaving basic variable), and selecting the one with the smallest ratio of the equation (0) coefficient to the absolute value of the coefficient in that equation.

Step 3. Determine the new basic solution: Solve for the basic variables in terms of the non-basic variables by the Gauss–Jordan method of elimination (see Appendix 4), and set the non-basic variables equal to zero.

Step 4. Determine if this solution is feasible (and therefore optimal): Check if all of the basic variables are non-negative. If they are, then this solution is feasible, and therefore optimal, so stop. Otherwise, go to Step 1.

In order to fully understand the dual simplex method, it is important to notice that the method proceeds just as if the simplex method were being applied to the complementary basic solutions in the dual problem. (In fact, this was the motivation for constructing the method as it is.) Step 1, determining the leaving basic variable, is equivalent to determining the entering basic variable in the dual problem. The variable with the largest negative value corresponds to the largest negative coefficient in equation (0) of the dual problem (see Theorems 5.1 and 15.3). Step 2, determining the entering basic variable, is equivalent to determining the leaving basic variable in the dual problem. The coefficient in equation (0) which reaches zero first corresponds to the variable in the dual problem which reaches zero first. The two criteria for optimality are also complementary.

The dual simplex method can now be illustrated by solving the following linear programming problem. Maximize

$$Z = -4x_1 - 6x_2 - 18x_3 ,$$

subject to

$$\begin{aligned} x_1 \qquad\quad &+ 3x_3 \geq 3 \\ x_2 &+ 2x_3 \geq 5 \end{aligned}$$

and

$$x_j \geq 0, \qquad \text{for } j = 1, 2, 3 .$$

(This particular problem was chosen because, as indicated in Sec. 5.7.1, its dual is the problem that was solved by the simplex method in Sec. 5.5.) To begin, the desired initial set of equations is the following:

$$\begin{array}{lrcl} (0) & Z + 4x_1 + 6x_2 + 18x_3 & = & 0 \\ (1) & -\ x_1 \qquad\quad - 3x_3 + x_4 \qquad & = & -3 \\ (2) & -\ x_2 - 2x_3 \qquad + x_5 & = & -5 . \end{array}$$

Notice that all of the coefficients in equation (0) are non-negative, so the solution would be optimal if it were feasible. The initial basic solution is $x_1 = 0$, $x_2 = 0$, $x_3 = 0$, $x_4 = -3$, $x_5 = -5$, with $Z = 0$, which is not feasible because of the negative values. The leaving basic variable is x_5 $(5 > 3)$, and the entering basic variable is x_2 $(6/1 < 18/2)$, which leads to the second set of equations:

$$\begin{array}{lrcl} (0) & Z + 4x_1 \quad + 6x_3 \qquad + 6x_5 & = & -30 \\ (1) & -\ x_1 \quad - 3x_3 + x_4 \qquad & = & -3 \\ (2) & x_2 + 2x_3 \qquad - x_5 & = & 5 . \end{array}$$

The corresponding basic solution is $x_1 = 0$, $x_2 = 5$, $x_3 = 0$, $x_4 = -3$, $x_5 = 0$, with $Z = -30$, which is not feasible. The next leaving basic variable is x_4, and the entering basic variable is x_3.

$$\begin{array}{lllll}
(0) & Z + 2x_1 & & + 2x_4 + 6x_5 = & -36 \\
(1) & \tfrac{1}{3}x_1 & + x_3 & - \tfrac{1}{3}x_4 \qquad = & 1 \\
(2) & -\tfrac{2}{3}x_1 + x_2 & & + \tfrac{2}{3}x_4 - \ x_5 = & 3 .
\end{array}$$

The corresponding basic solution is $x_1 = 0$, $x_2 = 3$, $x_3 = 1$, $x_4 = 0$, $x_5 = 0$, with $Z = -36$, which is feasible and therefore optimal.

Notice that the optimal solution for the dual problem is $y_1^* = 2$, $y_2^* = 6$, $y_3^* = 2$, $y_4^* = 0$, $y_5^* = 0$, as was obtained in Sec. 5.5 by the simplex method. It would be instructive for the reader to trace through the two examples simultaneously and compare the complementary steps.

15.1.3 Economic Interpretation

The concept of duality has a natural economic interpretation which economists find very useful. Recall that, as indicated in Secs. 5.1 and 5.2, linear programming problems involve allocating scarce resources among competing activities. A typical interpretation of the primal problem is that x_j is the level of activity j, c_j is the unit profit from activity j, b_i is the amount of resource i available, and a_{ij} is the amount of resource i consumed by each unit of activity j. Suppose that profit is measured in dollars. Now consider a typical constraint from the corresponding dual problem,

$$a_{1j}y_1 + a_{2j}y_2 + \cdots + a_{mj}y_m \geq c_j .$$

Note that, from the primal problem, the units of c_j are dollars per unit of activity j, and the units of a_{ij} are units of resource i per unit of activity j. Therefore, y_i must have the units of dollars per unit of resource i. In other words, y_i may be interpreted as the *unit price* of resource i in the sense of an implicit or imputed value of the resource to the user. Furthermore,

$$\sum_{i=1}^{m} a_{ij}y_i$$

would then be interpreted as the imputed cost of operating activity j at unit level. The inequality,

$$\sum_{i=1}^{m} a_{ij}y_i \geq c_j ,$$

says that this imputed cost should not be less than the profit that could be obtained from the activity. (Otherwise, the y_i would understate the true implicit values of some of the resources.) The dual objective, minimize

$$Z_y = \sum_{i=1}^{m} b_i y_i ,$$

states that the prices of the resources should be set so as to minimize their total cost to the user. The optimal value of the dual variables, y_i^* ($i = 1, 2,$

$\cdots, m$), then represents the true implicit value[98] per unit of the respective resources. The Dual Theorem, $Z_x^* = Z_y^*$, says that the total cost (implicit value) of the resources equals the total profit from the activities consuming them in an optimal manner.

The Corollary to Theorems 15.1 and 15.2 also contributes to the economic interpretation. It indicates that the implicit value of resource i is zero ($y_i^* = 0$) whenever the supply of that resource is not exhausted by the activities ($x_{n+i} > 0$). In economic terminology, such a resource is a "free good"; the price of goods which are oversupplied must drop to zero by the law of supply and demand. The corollary also indicates that the cost (implicit value) of the resources for one unit of activity j equals the unit profit

$$\left(y_{m+j}^* = 0, \quad \text{so} \quad \sum_{i=1}^{m} a_{ij} y_i^* = c_j\right)$$

whenever that activity j is operated at a positive level ($x_j^* > 0$). Thus, an activity would not be used if the implicit value of the resources required would exceed the profit derived from the activity.

As suggested at the end of Sec. 5.7.1, the interpretation of y_i^* developed above has a very important application. In particular, y_i^* is the rate at which profit would increase (decrease) if the amount of resource i were increased (decreased) over a certain range (namely, the range of b_i over which the original optimal basis is not changed, and, therefore, $y_i^* = z_{n+i}^*$ is not changed). This is easily verified as follows. It was observed when developing Lemma 2 that exactly z_{n+i}^* times the original equation (i) was added (directly or indirectly) to the original equation (0) in the process of obtaining the final equation (0). Therefore, if the original value of b_i were increased (decreased) by an amount k, then Z_x^* would be increased (decreased) by kz_{n+i}^*, assuming the optimal basis remains the same. However, Theorem 15.1 indicates that $y_i^* = z_{n+i}^*$, so that y_i^* does indeed represent the marginal value of resource i.

15.1.4 **Other Practical Applications of Duality**

Duality is a concept and tool of considerable theoretical interest. However, as the preceding (and following) sections indicate, it also has much practical value. This section points out several additional applications.

As indicated by Lemma 2, the value of the objective function for any feasible solution of the dual (primal) problem provides an upper (lower) bound to the optimal value of the objective function for the primal (dual) problem. This fact makes it possible to obtain a good idea of how well (or

[98] Other terms that are sometimes used include incremental value, intrinsic value, shadow price, internal price, and efficiency price.

how much better) one can do by expending the effort required to obtain the optimal solution by the simplex method. To illustrate, consider the example of Sec. 5.5 whose primal and dual formulation is summarized in Sec. 5.7.1. Since the dual constraints are $y_1 + 3y_3 \geq 3$, $y_2 + 2y_3 \geq 5$, and $y_i \geq 0$ ($i = 1, 2, 3$), an immediate feasible dual solution is $y_1 = 3$, $y_2 = 5$, $y_3 = 0$, yielding $Z_y = 4y_1 + 6y_2 + 18y_3 = 42$. Therefore, without investigating any further, it is clear that $Z_x^* \leq 42$. (The true value, obtained by the simplex method, is $Z_x^* = 36$.)

Another application of duality is a direct result of Theorems 5.1 and 15.1. These theorems indicate that solving either the primal or the dual problem automatically solves the other problem. Therefore, if one wishes to identify the optimal primal solution, he may apply the simplex method to whichever problem appears to require less computational effort. Computer time for the simplex method is sensitive primarily to the number of constraints (not counting non-negativity constraints). Since the number of original variables in the primal problem equals the number of constraints in the dual problem, it tends to be more efficient to directly solve the dual problem instead whenever the original form of the primal problem has more constraints than variables ($m > n$).

Another very important application of duality is to the analysis of the effect of changes in the parameters of the problem after the original optimal solution has been obtained. This is the topic of the next section.

15.2 DUALITY AND POST-OPTIMALITY ANALYSIS

15.2.1 Introduction

As discussed in Sec. 5.7.2, the parameters of the model (c_j, a_{ij}, b_i) usually are not known with complete certainty. Therefore, it is often advisable to perform a sensitivity analysis to determine the effect on the optimal solution if particular parameters take on other possible values. Section 15.2.2 explores cases where only a single change is made in the model. Section 15.2.3 discusses how to systematically study making several changes simultaneously. Section 15.4 discusses the formulation of linear programming models where certain of the parameters are explicitly recognized to be random variables. The notation introduced in Sec. 5.2 will continue to be used.

The following example is used for illustrative purposes throughout Sec. 15.2. The primal problem is maximize

$$Z_x = 3x_1 + 5x_2,$$

subject to

$$x_1 \leq 4$$
$$3x_1 + 2x_2 \leq 18$$

and

$$x_j \geq 0, \qquad \text{for } j = 1, 2 .$$

(This is identical to the example of Sec. 5.5, except that the second constraint is omitted.) Applying the simplex method, the initial set of equations is the following:

$$\begin{array}{llcl}
(0) & Z_x - 3x_1 - 5x_2 & & = 0 \\
(1) & x_1 + x_3 & & = 4 \\
(2) & 3x_1 + 2x_2 + x_4 & & = 18\,.
\end{array}$$

The second set of equations yields the optimal solution.

$$\begin{array}{ll}
(0) & Z_x + \frac{9}{2}x_1 + \frac{5}{2}x_4 = 45 \\
(1) & x_1 + x_3 = 4 \\
(2) & \frac{3}{2}x_1 + x_2 + \frac{1}{2}x_4 = 9\,.
\end{array}$$

The optimal solution is $x_1^* = 0$, $x_2^* = 9$, $x_3^* = 4$, $x_4^* = 0$, with $Z_x^* = 45$.

The corresponding dual problem is minimize

$$Z_y = 4y_1 + 18y_2,$$

subject to

$$\begin{aligned} y_1 + 3y_2 &\geq 3 \\ 2y_2 &\geq 5 \end{aligned}$$

and

$$y_i \geq 0, \qquad \text{for } i = 1, 2\,.$$

Introducing slack variables, the constraints become $y_1 + 3y_2 - y_3 = 3$, $2y_2 - y_4 = 5$, and $y_i \geq 0$, for $i = 1, 2, 3, 4$. The optimal dual solution is $y_1 = 0$, $y_2^* = 5/2$, $y_3^* = 9/2$, $y_4^* = 0$, as indicated by the final equation (0) for the primal problem.

The reader may find it instructive to graphically depict the primal and dual problems as they are used and modified in the following sections.

15.2.2 **Single Changes**

15.2.2.1 Change in c_j When x_j^* is Non-Basic

Suppose that the simplex method has obtained an optimal solution, with a particular variable x_j^* as a non-basic variable, and then a change is made in c_j, the coefficient of x_j in the original objective function. This case was discussed briefly in Sec. 5.7.2. As suggested there, if c_j is changed to c_j', the only resulting change in the final set of equations is that $(z_j^* - c_j)$ becomes $(z_j^* - c_j')$. Therefore, it is only necessary to check whether this coefficient is still non-negative. Thus, the previous solution remains optimal as long as $(c_j' - c_j) \leq (z_j^* - c_j)$; otherwise, it becomes necessary to make x_j an entering basic variable and to continue with the simplex method until the new optimal solution has been identified.

It is very useful conceptually to recognize the role of duality in this problem. Changing c_j to c'_j in the primal model also changes the dual model accordingly. However, the dual solution (ignoring its slack variables) which is complementary to the previously optimal primal solution remains the same (since the $z^*_{n+i} = y^*_i$ are not changed). Therefore, asking whether this (still feasible) primal solution is still optimal is equivalent to asking whether the (still optimal or better-than-optimal) complementary dual solution is still feasible. This statement follows immediately from Theorem 15.3, which implies that all of the coefficients in the primal equation (0) are non-negative if and only if all of the dual variables, including the slack variables, are non-negative.

To illustrate, suppose that the primal objective function is changed from $Z_x = 3x_1 + 5x_2$ to $Z_x = 6x_1 + 5x_2$. Is the previously optimal solution ($x^*_1 = 0$, $x^*_2 = 9$, $x^*_3 = 4$, $x^*_4 = 0$) still optimal? Notice that the only change is in the coefficient of x_1, and x^*_1 is non-basic. The only resulting change in the dual model is that the first constraint changes from $y_1 + 3y_2 \geq 3$ to $y_1 + 3y_2 \geq 6$. Is the complementary dual solution ($y^*_1 = 0$, $y^*_2 = 5/2$) still feasible? It is since $y^*_1 + 3y^*_2 = 15/2 \geq 6$, i.e., since $y_3 = z^*_1 - c'_1 = (z^*_1 - c_1) - (c'_1 - c_1) = 9/2 - 3 = 3/2 \geq 0$. Therefore, the primal solution is still optimal. It would remain optimal for $(c'_1 - c_1) \leq 9/2$.

15.2.2.2 CHANGE IN c_j WHEN x^*_j IS BASIC

Now suppose that x^*_j is a basic variable in the optimal solution identified by the simplex method. This case also was discussed in Sec. 5.7.2. To summarize, since $(z^*_j - c'_j) \neq 0$, x^*_j needs to be eliminated from the new final equation (0) before one can check for optimality. This is done in the usual way by subtracting $(z^*_j - c'_j)$ times the equation containing x^*_j as its basic variable from equation (0). The solution is still optimal if all of the coefficients in this modified equation (0) are non-negative. Otherwise, one must continue with more simplex method iterations (starting with the previous optimal solution and the corresponding modified set of equations) in order to obtain the new optimal solution.

The dual problem interpretation of this analysis is the following. The dual model is changed by changing c_j to c'_j. Furthermore, the dual solution which is complementary to the previously optimal primal solution probably is changed for the new model since some of the z^*_{n+i} probably are changed in the modified primal equation (0). The new complementary dual solution must still be optimal or better-than-optimal since the primal solution is still feasible. However, this dual solution need not be feasible, and indeed it will not be if the new $(z^*_i - c_i)$ are negative for any i ($i = 1, 2, \cdots, n + m$). If this solution is not feasible, the complementary primal solution must not be optimal. On the other hand, the primal solution is still optimal if the complementary dual solution is feasible.

To illustrate, suppose that the primal objective function, $Z_x = 3x_1 +$

$5x_2$, is changed to $Z_x = 3x_1 + x_2$. The previous optimal solution was $x_1^* = 0$, $x_2^* = 9$, $x_3^* = 4$, $x_4^* = 0$, so that the variable whose coefficient was changed, x_2^*, is a basic variable. The previous final equation (0) was $Z_x + \frac{9}{2}x_1 + \frac{5}{2}x_4 = 45$. Since the original equation (0) is changed from $Z_x - 3x_1 - 5x_2 = 0$ to $Z_x - 3x_1 - 5x_2 + 4x_2 = 0$, the final equation (0) changes to $Z_x + \frac{9}{2}x_1 + 4x_2 + \frac{5}{2}x_4 = 45$. To eliminate x_2 from this equation, subtract four times equation (2), where equation (2) is $\frac{3}{2}x_1 + x_2 + \frac{1}{2}x_4 = 9$. This yields $Z_x - \frac{3}{2}x_1 + \frac{1}{2}x_4 = 9$ as the new equation (0). Since x_1 has a negative coefficient, the solution is no longer optimal. More simplex iterations are required with x_1 as the next entering basic variable. In the dual problem, the second constraint changes from $2y_2 \geq 5$ to $2y_2 \geq 1$. Furthermore, the complementary dual solution changes to $y_1 = 0$, $y_2 = \frac{1}{2}$, which is not feasible since the first constraint, $y_1 + 3y_2 \geq 3$, is violated. This lack of feasibility also implies that the primal solution is no longer optimal.

15.2.2.3 CHANGE IN b_i

Suppose that, after obtaining the optimal solution, it is decided to change the tightness of the ith constraint by changing b_i to b_i'. If exactly the same calculations were to be repeated, substituting b_i' for b_i, the only possible changes in the final set of equations would be in the right-hand side of the equations. Since the right-hand side is the value of that equation's basic variable, this means that the basic variables for the previous optimal solution may now have new values. Since these values could be negative, this new solution may not be feasible. However, if it is feasible, it must be optimal since $(z_j^* - c_j)$ is unchanged and, therefore, still nonnegative for all j $(j = 1, 2, \cdots, n + m)$. In short, the only question that needs to be investigated when b_i is changed is whether the modified previously optimal solution is still feasible or not. This investigation reduces to determining whether the new values of the basic variables are nonnegative or not.

Recall that x_{n+i}, the slack variable in the equation involving b_i, does not appear in any of the other original equations. This fact makes it simple to determine what multiple of b_i has been added to the right-hand side of the other equations. Let $a_{k,n+i}^*$ denote the coefficient of x_{n+i} in the final equation (k), and let b_k^* denote the right-hand side of this equation, for $k = 1, 2, \cdots, m$. Then, by reasoning analogous to that used in deriving Lemma 2 in Sec. 15.1.1, it follows that, for $k \neq i$, exactly $a_{k,n+i}^*$ times the original equation (i) must have been added (directly or indirectly) to the original equation (k) in the process of executing the simplex method. Therefore,

$$b_k^* = \sum_{i=1}^{m} a_{k,n+i}^* b_i \,, \qquad \text{for } k = 1, 2, \cdots, m \,.$$

(By defining a_{kj}^* in an analogous way, it similarly follows that

$$a_{kj}^* = \sum_{i=1}^{m} a_{k,n+i}^* a_{ij}, \qquad \text{for } k = 1, 2, \cdots, m \quad \text{and} \quad j = 1, 2, \cdots, n,$$

which will be useful in the next section.) Therefore, if b_i is changed to b_i', $a_{k,n+i}^*(b_i' - b_i)$ should be added to the right-hand side of the previous final equation (k) for $k = 1, 2, \cdots, m$, in order to obtain the new final set of equations. (This statement also holds for $k = 0$ if $a_{k,n+i}^*$ is replaced by z_{n+i}^*.) The new value of each basic variable is just the new right-hand side of its equation.

The current roles of the primal and dual problems are just reversed from the case where c_j is changed. Thus, rather than testing for feasibility in the dual and, therefore, optimality in the primal, one now tests for feasibility in the primal and, therefore, optimality in the dual problem. This is only to be expected since b_i plays the same role in the dual model and its dual (the primal) that c_j plays in the primal model and its dual.

The duality theory interpretation suggests what should be done if checking the change in b_i reveals that the modified primal solution is no longer feasible. This state of affairs would imply that the complementary dual solution is feasible but not optimal. Therefore, one would want, in effect, to apply the simplex method to the dual problem, thereby progressing to optimality in the dual problem and to feasibility in the primal problem. As explained in Sec. 15.1.2, this is exactly what is done by applying the dual simplex method to the primal problem. Therefore, one should begin with the modified final primal solution and its corresponding set of equations, and undertake dual simplex method iterations until a feasible solution is obtained. This feasible solution would necessarily also be optimal.

To illustrate the approach when b_i is changed, suppose that the second constraint, $3x_1 + 2x_2 \leq 18$, is changed to $3x_1 + 2x_2 \leq 14$. Thus, $b_2 = 18$ and $b_2' = 14$. Therefore, the final set of equations (shown in Sec. 15.2.1) must be modified as follows:

$$
\begin{array}{llcl}
(0) & Z_x + \frac{9}{2}x_1 \qquad\qquad + \frac{5}{2}x_4 & = & 45 + \frac{5}{2}(14\text{--}18) = 35 \\
(1) & \qquad x_1 \qquad + x_3 & = & 4 \\
(2) & \qquad \frac{3}{2}x_1 + x_2 \qquad + \frac{1}{2}x_4 & = & 9 + \frac{1}{2}(14\text{--}18) = 7.
\end{array}
$$

Hence, the modified solution is $x_1 = 0$, $x_2 = 7$, $x_3 = 4$, $x_4 = 0$, with $Z_x = 35$. The basic variables are non-negative, so this solution is feasible, and it is necessarily still optimal.

15.2.2.4 CHANGE IN a_{ij} WHEN x_j^* IS NON-BASIC

The method for investigating the effect of changing a_{ij} to a_{ij}' when x_j^* is a non-basic variable is similar to that presented in Sec. 15.2.2.1 for the case where c_j is changed. If the calculations yielding the final set of equations are repeated, substituting a'_{ij} for a_{ij}, the only possible changes are in the coefficients of x_j^*. Since x_j^* is non-basic, so that $x_j^* = 0$, the new coefficients in equations other than equation (0) are not relevant for determining the effect of the change in a_{ij}. The same solution must be obtained again, and it must be feasible. The only question is whether it is still optimal. This question is answered by checking the new coefficient of x_j in equation (0). If it is non-negative, the solution must still be optimal. Otherwise, more simplex method iterations are required with the adjusted set of equations, beginning with x_j as the next entering basic variable.

The method of obtaining the coefficients of x_j was suggested in the preceding section. As shown there,

$$a_{kj}^* = \sum_{i=1}^{m} a_{k,n+i}^* a_{ij} , \qquad \text{for } k = 1, 2, \cdots, m .$$

Hence, $a_{k,n+i}^*(a'_{ij} - a_{ij})$ should be added to the current coefficient of x_j in the final equation (k) in order to obtain the new correct coefficient, for $k = 1, 2, \cdots, m$. Similarly, $z_{n+i}^*(a'_{ij} - a_{ij})$ should be added to the current coefficient of x_j in the final equation (0).

The investigation can also be handled directly and simply by dealing only with the dual problem. The only effect on the dual model from the change in a_{ij} is that the jth constraint,

$$\sum_{i=1}^{m} a_{ij} y_i \geq c_j ,$$

is changed accordingly. The complementary dual solution must remain the same since $z_{n+i}^* = y_i^*$ is unchanged ($i = 1, \cdots, m$). Therefore, one need only check the changed constraint to see if it still holds. If it does, the dual solution is still feasible so that the primal solution is still optimal. If the constraint no longer holds, the new value of $y_{m+j}^* = z_j^* - c_j$ is now negative, so that the dual solution is infeasible and the primal solution non-optimal.

To illustrate, suppose that the second constraint in the primal model is changed to $x_1 + 2x_2 \leq 18$. The final set of equations would then become the following:

$$\begin{array}{lllll}
(0) & Z_x - \frac{1}{2}x_1 & & + \frac{5}{2}x_4 & = 45 \\
(1) & \quad x_1 & + x_3 & & = 4 \\
(2) & \frac{1}{2}x_1 + x_2 & & + \frac{1}{2}x_4 & = 9 .
\end{array}$$

Since x_1 now has a negative coefficient in equation (0), the solution is no longer optimal, and simplex iterations should be resumed. The same conclusion is drawn by noticing that the first constraint in the dual problem changes to $y_1 + y_2 \geq 3$, which does not hold for the unchanged complementary dual solution, $y_1 = 0$, $y_2 = 5/2$.

15.2.2.5 CHANGE IN a_{ij} WHEN x_j^* IS BASIC

Investigating a change in a_{ij} is much more difficult when x_j^* is a (non-degenerate) basic variable. The reason is that, since $x_j^* > 0$, all of the changed coefficients of x_j^* in the final set of equations are very relevant for determining the effect of the change in a_{ij}. The previous solution probably will be changed as a result of these changed coefficients, and the new solution need not be feasible since the new values of the basic variables may be negative. Even if it is still feasible, the new solution need not be optimal since equation (0) probably will be changed. In short, this case requires obtaining a modified final set of equations and the corresponding solution, and then investigating both feasibility and optimality.

The first step is to find the new coefficient of x_j^* in each final equation by the method described in the preceding section. This provides the set of equations that would have resulted if all of the simplex method calculations were repeated exactly as before after replacing a_{ij} by its new value. Since x_j^* is a basic variable, the previous final set of equations had zero coefficients for x_j^* in every equation but the one containing x_j^* as its basic variable. This condition must be restored, so modify the new final set of equations algebraically by eliminating x_j^* from every equation except this one. This probably will create changes in equation (0) and in the right-hand side of the equations. If, excluding equation (0), the right-hand sides (the values of the corresponding basic variables) are still non-negative, this solution is still feasible. If the coefficients in the new equation (0) are still non-negative, the new solution is still optimal. If this solution is feasible but not optimal, simplex method iterations would be resumed with the new final set of equations. The dual simplex method may be used if the condition for optimality is satisfied, but the solution is infeasible. If the solution is neither feasible nor "optimal" [according to equation (0)], one may try this procedure again with the set of equations obtained at an earlier iteration (or from some new set of basic variables). There is also the alternative of starting from the beginning with the simplex method.

The effect of changing a_{ij} on the dual problem is to change the jth constraint and the complementary dual solution. This new solution may not be optimal (since the new primal solution may not be feasible), and it may not be feasible (since the new primal solution may not be optimal).

This analysis may be illustrated by supposing that the second constraint is changed to $3x_1 + 4x_2 \leq 18$. This change results in the new final set of equations given below:

$$
\begin{array}{llcl}
(0) & Z_x + \frac{9}{2}x_1 + 5x_2 \qquad + \frac{5}{2}x_4 & = & 45 \\
(1) & \qquad x_1 \qquad + x_3 & = & 4 \\
(2) & \qquad \frac{3}{2}x_1 + 2x_2 \qquad + \frac{1}{2}x_4 & = & 9\,.
\end{array}
$$

Since x_2 is a basic variable, it must be eliminated from every equation but the one in which it is the basic variable [equation (2)]. The result follows:

$$
\begin{array}{llcl}
(0) & Z_x + \frac{3}{4}x_1 \qquad + \frac{5}{4}x_4 & = & \frac{45}{2} \\
(1) & \qquad x_1 \qquad + x_3 & = & 4 \\
(2) & \qquad \frac{3}{4}x_1 + x_2 \qquad + \frac{1}{4}x_4 & = & \frac{9}{2}\,.
\end{array}
$$

This yields the new solution, $x_1 = 0$, $x_2 = \frac{9}{2}$, $x_3 = 4$, $x_4 = 0$. This solution is feasible since the variables are non-negative, and equation (0) indicates that it is optimal. Therefore, changing a_{22} from 2 to 4 has only changed the values of the basic variables of the previous optimal solution without affecting its feasibility or optimality.

15.2.2.6 Addition of a New Constraint

Suppose that, after finding the optimal solution, it is decided that a new constraint should be added to the model. The new constraint can only eliminate previously feasible solutions without adding new ones, so that Z_x^* (the maximum value of the objective function over all feasible solutions) must either decrease or remain unchanged. Consequently, if the previously optimal solution is still feasible, it must still be the best feasible solution, and, therefore, optimal. Hence, it is only necessary to check whether this solution satisfies the new constraint or not. If the constraint is satisfied, the solution must still be optimal. If the constraint is not satisfied, introduce a slack variable and add the resulting equation to the final set of equations. Let the new slack variable be the basic variable for the new equation, and algebraically eliminate any other basic variables that appear in this equation. Equation (0) will still indicate optimality, since it is unchanged, but the solution will be infeasible since the new slack variable will be negative. This is precisely the type of situation where the dual simplex method (see Sec. 15.1.2) should be used to progress to a feasible optimal solution.

To illustrate, suppose that the constraint, $x_2 \leq 6$, is added to the model given in Sec. 15.2.1. Then the previous optimal solution ($x_1^* = 0$, $x_2^* = 9$) is no longer feasible since it violates the new constraint. Therefore, add the equation, $x_2 + x_5 = 6$, to the final set of equations, and eliminate the basic variable x_2. This yields the following:

$$
\begin{array}{llcccccl}
(0) & Z_x + \frac{9}{2}x_1 & & & + \frac{5}{2}x_4 & & = & 45 \\
(1) & x_1 & & + x_3 & & & = & 4 \\
(2) & \frac{3}{2}x_1 & + x_2 & & + \frac{1}{2}x_4 & & = & 9 \\
(3) & -\frac{3}{2}x_1 & & & -\frac{1}{2}x_4 & + x_5 & = & -3\,.
\end{array}
$$

The resulting solution is $x_1 = 0$, $x_2 = 9$, $x_3 = 4$, $x_4 = 0$, $x_5 = -3$, which is infeasible because x_5 violates the non-negativity constraint. However, applying the dual simplex method, starting with this set of equations, soon yields the desired feasible optimal solution.

15.2.2.7 ADDITION OF A NEW VARIABLE

It may be discovered after finding the optimal solution that the linear programming formulation had not considered all of the attractive alternative activities. Considering a new activity requires adding a new variable with the appropriate coefficients to the objective function and constraints of the model. Is there any way to obtain the new optimal solution without restarting the simplex method from the beginning?

It is very easy to check whether the previous optimal solution, combined with the new variable set equal to zero, is still optimal or not. This would make the new variable a non-basic variable, so the coefficients of the other variables would be unchanged in the final set of equations. Therefore, the complementary dual solution ($y_i^* = z_{n+i}^*$) would remain the same. In fact, the only change in the dual model is in the addition of a new constraint corresponding to the new primal variable. Hence, the complementary dual solution remains feasible if and only if the new constraint holds for this solution. If the new constraint does hold, the complementary primal solution is optimal. Otherwise, more simplex method iterations are required on the primal problem, starting with this solution and using the new variable as the next entering basic variable.

If it is necessary to undertake additional simplex iterations, one must first determine what the coefficients of the new variable should be in the last set of equations. The method for doing this has already been described in previous sections. Adding a new variable is really just a special case of changing c_j and a_{ij}, where $j = n$ (letting $n - 1$ be the previous number of decision variables), and the original value of c_n and the a_{in} ($i = 1, 2, \cdots, m$) are zero. Since the new variable x_n is treated like a non-basic variable in the previously optimal solution, the procedures described in Secs. 15.2.2.1 and 15.2.2.4 would be used for finding the coefficients of x_n. Since these procedures only add some number (which may be zero) to the current coefficient in each equation, they may be used successively for each of the $m + 1$ changes in the original coefficients.

To illustrate, suppose that the model of Sec. 15.2.1 is revised[99] to be: maximize

$$Z_x = 3x_1 + 5x_2 + 7x_5 ,$$

subject to

$$\begin{aligned} x_1 \qquad\quad + \ x_5 &\leq 4 \\ 3x_1 + 2x_2 + 2x_5 &\leq 18 \end{aligned}$$

and

$$x_j \geq 0, \qquad \text{for } j = 1, 2, 5 .$$

The first question to be answered is whether appending $x_5 = 0$ to the previous optimal solution, $x_1 = 0$, $x_2 = 9$, will provide the new optimal solution. This is easily answered by referring to the dual problem. The complementary dual solution remains the same, $y_1 = 0$, $y_2 = 5/2$. The only change in the dual model is the addition of a new constraint, $y_1 + 2y_2 \geq 7$, which does not hold for this solution. Since the dual solution is not feasible, the complementary primal solution is not optimal. To find the new optimal solution, begin by modifying the previous final set of equations to include x_5.

$$\begin{aligned}
&(0) \quad Z_x + \frac{9}{2}x_1 \qquad\qquad\qquad + \frac{5}{2}x_4 + \left[-7 + 0(1) + \frac{5}{2}(2)\right]x_5 = 45 \\
&(1) \qquad\quad x_1 \qquad + x_3 \qquad\quad + [\quad 1(1) + 0(2) \quad\ ]\, x_5 = 4 \\
&(2) \qquad \frac{3}{2}x_1 + x_2 \qquad\quad + \frac{1}{2}x_4 + \left[\quad 0(1) + \frac{1}{2}(2) \quad\right]x_5 = 9 .
\end{aligned}$$

The simplex method should now be resumed with x_5 as the next entering basic variable.

15.2.3 **Parametric Linear Programming**

15.2.3.1 Systematic Changes in the c_j

Section 15.2.2 discussed the effect of changing the value of a single c_j. It is often of interest to investigate making simultaneous changes in a number of the c_j. Furthermore, one may be interested in what happens as the magnitude of these simultaneous changes increases. A systematic study of such changes in certain parameters of the linear programming model (whether they be the c_j or other parameters) is the objective of *parametric linear programming*. While this approach is well suited to systematic sensitivity analysis, it is also designed for the situation where there is some flexibility in the parameter values, and one wishes to investigate trade-offs

[99] The new variable added to the model will be called x_5 to avoid confusion with the slack variables introduced for the solution of the original model.

in these values. For example, it may be possible to increase the unit profit from one activity at the expense of another by an appropriate shifting of personnel and equipment. The model and solution procedure for parametric linear programming with variation only in the c_j are described below.

The objective function of the ordinary linear programming model is

$$Z = \sum_{j=1}^{n} c_j x_j .$$

Replace this by

$$Z = \sum_{j=1}^{n} (c_j + \alpha_j \theta) x_j ,$$

where the α_j are given input constants representing the relative rates at which the coefficients are being changed. For any given value of θ, the optimal solution of the corresponding linear programming problem can be obtained by the simplex method. This may have been done already for the original problem where $\theta = 0$. However, the objective is to find the optimal solution of the modified linear programming problem (maximize the new Z subject to the original constraints) as a function of θ. Therefore, the solution procedure will need to be able to determine when and how the optimal solution changes (if it does) as θ increases from zero to any specified positive number.

Suppose that the optimal solution and the corresponding set of equations have been obtained for the original problem ($\theta = 0$) by the simplex method. [As before, let $(z_j^* - c_j)$ denote the coefficient of x_j^* in this optimal equation (0).] It is then easy to find the new equation (0) for this solution when $\theta = 0$ is changed to $\theta = 1$. Merely use the procedures described in Secs. 15.2.2.1 and 15.2.2.2. To summarize, if x_j^* is a non-basic variable, add $(-\alpha_j)$ to the current coefficient of x_j^*. If x_j^* is a basic variable, first add $(-\alpha_j)$ to the current coefficient (zero) and then eliminate it by adding α_j times the equation containing x_j^* as its basic variable to the current equation (0). Repeat this successively for $x_1^*, x_2^*, \cdots, x_n^*$ to obtain the new equation (0). Let $(z_j^* - c_j + \Delta_j)$ denote the coefficient of x_j^* in this new equation (0), for $j = 1, 2, \cdots, n$. Now notice that this coefficient would have become $(z_j^* - c_j + \Delta_j \theta)$, regardless of what θ becomes. This essentially solves the problem. If $\Delta_j \geq 0$ for all j $(j = 1, 2, \cdots, n + m)$, all of the coefficients would remain non-negative for all non-negative values of θ. Hence, the previously optimal solution would remain optimal for $\theta \geq 0$. On the other hand, if $\Delta_j < 0$ for some j, the coefficient $(z_j^* - c_j + \Delta_j \theta)$ for each of these values of j would eventually become negative as θ increases. Hence, the previously optimal solution remains optimal only until one of these coefficients reaches zero. The corresponding θ would equal the minimum value of $[(z_j^* - c_j)/(-\Delta_j)]$ over those j such that $\Delta_j < 0$. Using this value of θ, perform another simplex iteration to identify the next optimal solution, letting the variable whose coefficient reached zero be the entering basic variable. The entire procedure is repeated (treating the new set of equations as if it were the original final set) to determine how much more θ can be increased before the new optimal solution becomes non-optimal. In this way, one can eventually identify the optimal solution over each of a succession of intervals of θ.

This procedure is now illustrated by means of the example of Sec. 15.2.1. Suppose that one wishes to investigate a trade-off between the two activities of this example, whereby the unit profit from activity 1 can be increased by decreasing the unit profit from activity 2 half as much. Thus, the new form of the objective function is

$$Z = (3 + 2\theta)x_1 + (5 - \theta)x_2 ,$$

where Z is to be maximized for given values of θ, subject to the original constraints. The purpose of the following investigation is to identify the optimal solution for each of the positive values of θ.

The optimal solution and the corresponding set of equations have already been found for $\theta = 0$. If θ were now changed to $\theta = 1$, the new equation (0) for this solution would become

$$Z + \left(\frac{9}{2} - 2 - \frac{3}{2}\right) x_1 + \left(\frac{5}{2} - \frac{1}{2}\right) x_4 = 45 - 9 .$$

More generally, the new equation (0) would be

$$Z + \left(\frac{9}{2} - \frac{7}{2}\theta\right) x_1 + \left(\frac{5}{2} - \frac{1}{2}\theta\right) x_4 = 45 - 9\theta$$

for any value of θ. Therefore, the corresponding basic solution is optimal only for $\theta \leq 9/7$. Performing another simplex iteration with $\theta = 9/7$ and with x_1 as the entering basic variable, the new set of equations becomes:

$$\begin{array}{llcl}
(0) & Z + 0\,x_3 + \frac{13}{7}\,x_4 & = & 33\,\frac{3}{7} \\
(1) & x_1 + x_3 & = & 4 \\
(2) & x_2 - \frac{3}{2}\,x_3 + \frac{1}{2}\,x_4 & = & 3 .
\end{array}$$

Thus, the new solution is $x_1 = 4$, $x_2 = 3$, $x_3 = 0$, $x_4 = 0$. When θ is increased one more to $\theta = 16/7$, this equation (0) changes to

$$Z + \left(0 + 2 + \frac{3}{2}\right) x_3 + \left(\frac{13}{7} - \frac{1}{2}\right) x_4 = 33\,\frac{3}{7} + (8 - 3),$$

so that equation (0) for this solution for any θ is

$$Z+\left(0+\frac{7}{2}\left(\theta-\frac{9}{7}\right)\right)x_3+\left(\frac{13}{7}-\frac{1}{2}\left(\theta-\frac{9}{7}\right)\right)x_4=33\frac{3}{7}+5\left(\theta-\frac{9}{7}\right).$$

Since

$$\frac{13/7}{1/2}+\frac{9}{7}=5\,,$$

this solution is optimal only for $9/7 \leq \theta \leq 5$. Using x_4 as the entering basic variable, the next set of equations is obtained at $\theta = 5$.

$$\begin{aligned}
&(0)\quad Z \quad + 0x_2 + 13x_3 \qquad = 52\\
&(1)\qquad x_1 \qquad\quad + \ \ x_3 \qquad = \ \ 4\\
&(2)\qquad\qquad 2x_2 - \ 3x_3 + x_4 = \ \ 6\,.
\end{aligned}$$

The corresponding solution is $x_1 = 4$, $x_2 = 0$, $x_3 = 0$, $x_4 = 6$. Increasing θ one more to $\theta = 6$ changes equation (0) to

$$Z + (0 + 1)x_2 + (13 + 2)x_3 = 52 + 8\,.$$

Thus, equation (0) for this solution is

$$Z + (\theta - 5)x_2 + [13 + 2(\theta - 5)]x_3 = 52 + 8(\theta - 5)$$

for any θ, so that the solution remains optimal for $\theta \geq 5$. This completes the investigation. To summarize, the optimal solutions are: $x_1 = 0$, $x_2 = 9$ for $0 \leq \theta \leq 9/7$, then $x_1 = 4$, $x_2 = 3$ for $9/7 \leq \theta \leq 5$, and then $x_1 = 4$, $x_2 = 0$ for $\theta \geq 5$.

15.2.3.2 SYSTEMATIC CHANGES IN THE b_i

The model and solution procedure for systematically studying changes in the b_i are intimately related to that presented in the preceding section for the c_j. The reason, of course, is that changing the b_i is equivalent to changing the coefficients in the objective function of the dual model. Therefore, the procedure for the primal problem is exactly as if one were simultaneously applying the procedure of the preceding section to the dual problem. While this fact makes it unnecessary to give the details, the procedure will be briefly summarized.

The one modification made in the original linear programming model is that b_i is replaced by $(b_i + \alpha_i\theta)$, for $i = 1, 2, \cdots, m$, where the α_i are given input constants. Thus, the ith constraint becomes

$$\sum_{j=1}^{n} a_{ij}x_j \leq b_i + \alpha_i\theta\,.$$

The goal is to identify the optimal solution as a function of θ.

The solution procedure begins with the optimal solution and corresponding set of equations for $\theta = 0$. It then determines the rate at which the right-hand side of these equations (i.e., the value of the basic variables) changes as θ increases by successively using the procedure of Sec. 15.2.2.3 for $b_1, b_2, \cdots, b_m$. If all of the basic variables remain non-negative for all non-negative values of θ, the corresponding solution will be optimal for $\theta \geq 0$. Otherwise, it remains optimal only until some basic variable has decreased to zero. At this value of θ, obtain the set of equations for the next optimal basic solution by using the dual simplex method, choosing the variable that had reached zero as the leaving basic variable. Continue this procedure for larger values of θ until all of the desired information has been obtained.

Before concluding this discussion of parametric linear programming, two useful results can be stated regarding the way in which the optimal value of the objective function changes as the parameter values change.

Theorem 15.4: Let

$$Z^*(\theta) = \max \sum_{j=1}^{n} c_j x_j ,$$

subject to

$$\sum_{j=1}^{n} a_{ij} x_j \leq b_i + \alpha_i \theta \quad \left(\text{or} \quad \sum_{j=1}^{n} a_{ij} x_j = b_i + \alpha_i \theta \right),$$

for $i = 1, 2, \cdots, m$, and perhaps subject to $x_j \geq 0$, for $j = 1, 2, \cdots, n$. Then $Z^*(\theta)$ is a concave function[100] of θ.

Proof: Consider $\theta_1 < \theta_2$ and $\theta_3 = \lambda\theta_1 + (1 - \lambda)\theta_2$, where $0 \leq \lambda \leq 1$. Let $x_j^{(1)}$, $x_j^{(2)}$, and $x_j^{(3)}$ be the optimal value of x_j ($j = 1, 2, \cdots, n$) for $\theta = \theta_1$, θ_2, and θ_3, respectively. Thus,

$$\lambda Z^*(\theta_1) + (1 - \lambda) Z^*(\theta_2) = \lambda \sum_{j=1}^{n} c_j x_j^{(1)} + (1 - \lambda) \sum_{j=1}^{n} c_j x_j^{(2)}$$

$$= \sum_{j=1}^{n} c_j [\lambda x_j^{(1)} + (1 - \lambda) x_j^{(2)}] .$$

Notice that, if $x_j' = \lambda x_j^{(1)} + (1 - \lambda) x_j^{(2)}$ for $j = 1, 2, \cdots, n$, then $(x_1', x_2', \cdots, x_n')$ is a feasible solution for $\theta = \theta_3$, since

$$\sum_{j=1}^{n} a_{ij} x_j' = \lambda \sum_{j=1}^{n} a_{ij} x_j^{(1)} + (1 - \lambda) \sum_{j=1}^{n} a_{ij} x_j^{(2)}$$

$$\leq \lambda(b_i + \alpha_i\theta_1) + (1 - \lambda)(b_i + \alpha_i\theta_2)$$

$$= b_i + \alpha_i\theta_3, \qquad (\text{for } i = 1, 2, \cdots, m)$$

[100] See Appendix 1 for a definition and discussion of concave and convex functions.

(where $\leq$ becomes $=$ if the ith constraint is an equation), and $x_j \geq 0$ if $x_j^{(1)} \geq 0$ and $x_j^{(2)} \geq 0$. Therefore,

$$\sum_{j=1}^{n} c_j[\lambda x_j^{(1)} + (1 - \lambda)x_j^{(2)}] \leq \sum_{j=1}^{n} c_j x_j^{(3)} ,$$

so that

$$\lambda Z^*(\theta_1) + (1 - \lambda)Z^*(\theta_2) \leq Z^*(\theta_3) .$$

Since this is the condition that defines a concave function, $Z^*(\theta)$ is concave and the theorem is proved.

Corollary: Let

$$Z^*(\theta) = \max \sum_{j=1}^{n} (c_j + \alpha_j\theta)x_j ,$$

subject to

$$\sum_{j=1}^{n} a_{ij}x_j \leq b_i \quad \left(\text{or} \quad \sum_{j=1}^{n} a_{ij}x_j = b_i\right),$$

for $i = 1, 2, \cdots, m$, and perhaps subject to $x_j \geq 0$, for $j = 1, 2, \cdots, n$. Then $Z^*(\theta)$ is a convex function of θ.

The proof of the Corollary is left to the reader (see Problem 11).

Theorem 15.4 and its corollary can be very useful for establishing an upper bound on the optimal value of the objective function after a change is made in the model. For example, suppose that an ordinary linear programming problem of the form shown in Sec. 5.2 has been solved by the simplex method, yielding Z^* as the optimal value of Z and $(y_1^*, y_2^*, \cdots, y_m^*)$ as the optimal dual solution. Then suppose that the b_i are changed to $(b_i + k_i)$, for $i = 1, 2, \cdots, m$, where $k_1, k_2, \cdots, k_m^*$ are given constants. Let Z^{**} be the new (unknown) optimal value of Z. It is easily shown (see Problem 12) that

$$Z^{**} \leq Z^* + \sum_{i=1}^{m} k_i y_i^* .$$

This information could provide considerable guidance on whether such a change in the resource availabilities actually should be made.

15.3 SPECIAL LINEAR PROGRAMMING TECHNIQUES

15.3.1 Secondary Constraints

It occasionally happens that some of the inequality constraints in a linear programming problem appear to be almost superfluous. It may seem unlikely, or even essentially impossible, that these constraints could turn out to be binding (i.e., hold as an equality) on the optimal solution. If these so-called "secondary constraints" represent resource availabilities, past experience may indicate that the amount available should be more than adequate whereas other more limited resources impose the primary restrictions on the solution. Since the number of constraints considered has a major influence on the computational effort, including the secondary constraints throughout the execution of the simplex method usually would be wastefully inefficient. Hence, the alternative procedure that may occur to the reader after reviewing Sec. 15.2.2.6 should significantly reduce computational effort in most cases.

The alternative procedure begins by ignoring the secondary constraints. Find the optimal solution to this new problem where the secondary constraints have been eliminated. Then check whether or not this solution violates any of the secondary constraints. If not, the solution is, of course, optimal for the original problem. On the other hand, if the solution does violate one or more of the secondary constraints, the violated constraints should be introduced into the final set of equations as described in Sec. 15.2.2.6. (Any other secondary constraints that threaten to become binding may also be introduced at this time.) The dual simplex method would then yield the new feasible optimal solution. If additional secondary constraints are now violated, they are introduced and the dual simplex method resumed. Sooner or later, one must obtain the desired optimal solution which satisfies all of the secondary constraints.

It is evident that good judgement must be exercised in selecting the secondary constraints in order for this procedure to be computationally efficient.

15.3.2 **Upper Bounds**

Linear programming problems frequently have many or all of their variables constrained by upper bounds, so that $x_j \leq u_j$ for many or all values of j. Such problems can be solved by the simplex method, of course, but having to include a large number of these constraints greatly increases the computational effort. The special simplicity of these constraints suggests that perhaps they can be taken into account in a more efficient manner.

One method that has been developed is to treat the upper bound constraints somewhat like secondary constraints, applying a modified form of the simplex method only to the remainder of the model. However, rather than initially ignoring the upper bound constraints completely, they are referred to at each iteration to ensure that they are not violated. Thus, the one substantive modification in the simplex method as applied to the remainder of the problem is that each new basic feasible solution is also required to satisfy the upper bound constraints.

Recall that the simplex method selects as the leaving basic variable the one which first becomes infeasible by going negative as the entering basic variable is increased. The modification now made is to select instead the variable which first becomes infeasible in any way, either by going negative or by going over the upper bound, as the entering basic variable is increased. (Notice that one possibility is that the *entering* basic variable may become infeasible first by going over its upper bound, thereby also becoming the leaving basic variable.) If the leaving basic variable reached zero, then proceed as usual with the simplex method. However, if it reached its upper bound instead, then special action must be taken to satisfy the simplex method requirement that all non-basic variables equal zero. Let x_j be the leaving basic variable which reached its upper bound u_j, so that $x_j = u_j$ in the next basic feasible solution. Since $x_j + s_j = u_j$, where $s_j \geq 0$ is a slack variable, replace x_j everywhere in the set of equations by $(u_j - s_j)$. Thus, s_j becomes the new non-basic variable in the next basic feasible solution, whereas x_j is no longer involved in the simplex method manipulations. (The equations should be rearranged so that the constant terms involving u_j are transferred to the right-hand sides.)

Except for the modification described above, the solution procedure is identical to the simplex method. Therefore, a solution is obtained which is optimal for a revised version of the problem and, because of the modification, feasible for the original problem. Since the revised version of the problem is a less constrained form of the original problem, this solution is the desired optimal solution of the original problem.

To illustrate the procedure, consider the example used in Sec. 5.5. The problem is to maximize $Z = 3x_1 + 5x_2$, subject to $3x_1 + 2x_2 \leq 18$, $x_1 \geq 0$, $x_2 \geq 0$, and the upper bound constraints, $x_1 \leq 4$ and $x_2 \leq 6$. The upper bound constraints may be converted to equations, $x_1 + x_3 = 4$ and $x_2 + x_4 = 6$, by introducing non-negative slack variables (x_3 and x_4) in the usual way. However, they are not included in the following set of equations to be manipulated by the simplex method:

$$
\begin{aligned}
&(0) \quad Z - 3x_1 - 5x_2 \qquad\quad = 0 \\
&(1) \qquad\quad 3x_1 + 2x_2 + x_5 = 18\,.
\end{aligned}
$$

The initial basic feasible solution is $x_1 = 0$, $x_2 = 0$, $x_5 = 18$. The negative coefficients in equation (0) indicate that this solution is not optimal, so x_2 is selected in the usual way to be the entering basic variable. However, as one increases x_2 (and thereby decreases x_5) in equation (1), the first variable to become infeasible is x_2 as it increases to a value greater than 6. Hence, rather than remaining in the basis, x_2 becomes the leaving basic variable. Set $x_2 = 6$, and then substitute $x_2 = 6 - x_4$ for x_2 in the equations, so that $x_4 = 0$ becomes the corresponding non-basic variable. Thus, the equations become

$$
\begin{aligned}
&(0) \quad Z - 3x_1 - 5(6 - x_4) &&= 0 \\
&(1) \quad 3x_1 + 2(6 - x_4) + x_5 &&= 18\,,
\end{aligned}
$$

which reduces to

$$
\begin{aligned}
&(0) \quad Z - 3x_1 + 5x_4 &&= 30 \\
&(1) \quad 3x_1 - 2x_4 + x_5 &&= 6\,.
\end{aligned}
$$

The new basic feasible solution is $x_1 = 0$, $x_4 = 0$, $x_5 = 6$ (where $x_4 = 0$ implies $x_2 = 6$ by the second upper bound equation), which is not optimal. The next entering basic variable is x_1, and x_5 is the leaving basic variable since it reaches zero before x_1 reaches its upper bound. Proceeding in the usual way to eliminate the new basic variable yields the following:

$$
\begin{aligned}
&(0) \quad Z + 3\,x_4 + x_5 &&= 36 \\
&(1) \quad x_1 - \frac{2}{3}\,x_4 + \frac{1}{3}\,x_5 &&= 2\,.
\end{aligned}
$$

The corresponding solution, $x_1 = 2$, $x_4 = 0$, $x_5 = 0$, is optimal [all coefficients in equation (0) are non-negative] so that $x_1 = 2$ and $x_2 = 6 - x_4 = 6$ is the desired solution to the original problem, just as was found with somewhat more effort in Sec. 5.5.

15.3.3 **Lower Bounds**

Lower bound constraints can be handled much more conveniently than upper bound constraints. In fact, it is only necessary to make a small adjustment in the problem statement in order to use the simplex method without including these constraints. To show this, consider any linear programming problem containing constraints of the form, $x_j \geq l_j$, where $l_j > 0$. For each such constraint, introduce a new variable y_j such that $x_j = l_j + y_j$, so that y_j measures the amount by which x_j exceeds its lower bound. Now substitute $x_j = l_j + y_j$ for x_j wherever x_j appears in the equations and inequations describing the problem. This new statement of the problem is equivalent to the old one, and it can still be solved by the simplex method. However, the $x_j \geq l_j$ constraints have been replaced by $y_j \geq 0$ constraints, which are automatically taken into account by the simplex method. Therefore, extra computational effort associated with lower bound constraints has been eliminated.

15.3.4 **The Revised Simplex Method**

The original simplex method described in Sec. 5.5 is a straightforward algebraic procedure. However, it is not a particularly efficient computational procedure for electronic digital computers. The problem is that it computes and stores many numbers which are not needed at the current iteration and which may not become relevant for decision-making at subsequent iterations. The only pieces of information relevant at each iteration are the coefficients of the non-basic variables in equation (0), the coefficients of the entering basic variable in the other equations, and the right-hand side of the equations. It would be very useful to have a procedure that could obtain this information efficiently without computing and storing all of the other coefficients.

These considerations motivated the development of the revised simplex method. This method was designed to accomplish exactly the same things as the original simplex method, but in a way which is more efficient for execution on a digital computer. Thus, it is a streamlined version of the original procedure. It computes and stores only the information that is currently needed, and it carries along the essential data in a more compact form.

The revised simplex method explicitly uses matrix manipulations, so it is necessary to describe the problem in matrix notation. (See Appendix 3 for a review of matrices.) Using the matrix form, the linear programming problem formulation given in Sec. 5.2 becomes:[101] maximize

$$x_0 = \mathbf{cx} \, ,$$

subject to

$$\mathbf{Ax} \leq \mathbf{b} \qquad \text{and} \qquad \mathbf{x} \geq \mathbf{0} \, ,$$

where **c** is the row vector,

$$\mathbf{c} = [c_1, c_2, \cdots, c_n] \, ,$$

x, b, and **0** are the column vectors such that

$$\mathbf{x} = \begin{bmatrix} x_1 \\ x_2 \\ \cdot \\ \cdot \\ \cdot \\ x_n \end{bmatrix}, \quad \mathbf{b} = \begin{bmatrix} b_1 \\ b_2 \\ \cdot \\ \cdot \\ \cdot \\ b_m \end{bmatrix}, \quad \mathbf{0} = \begin{bmatrix} 0 \\ 0 \\ \cdot \\ \cdot \\ \cdot \\ 0 \end{bmatrix},$$

and **A** is the matrix,

$$\mathbf{A} = \begin{bmatrix} a_{11} & a_{12} & \cdots & a_{1n} \\ a_{21} & a_{22} & \cdots & a_{2n} \\ \cdot & \cdot & & \cdot \\ \cdot & \cdot & & \cdot \\ \cdot & \cdot & & \cdot \\ a_{m1} & a_{m2} & \cdots & a_{mn} \end{bmatrix}.$$

Now introduce the column vector of slack variables,

[101] In order to emphasize its subsequent interpretation as another basic variable, the notation for the value of the objective function is changed here from Z to x_0.

$$\mathbf{x}_s = \begin{bmatrix} x_{n+1} \\ x_{n+2} \\ \cdot \\ \cdot \\ \cdot \\ x_{n+m} \end{bmatrix},$$

so that the constraints become

$$[\mathbf{A}, \mathbf{I}] \begin{bmatrix} \mathbf{x} \\ \mathbf{x}_s \end{bmatrix} = \mathbf{b} \quad \text{and} \quad \begin{bmatrix} \mathbf{x} \\ \mathbf{x}_s \end{bmatrix} \geq \mathbf{0},$$

where $\mathbf{I}$ is the $m \times m$ identity matrix, and the vector $\mathbf{0}$ now has $(n + m)$ elements.

Recall that the general approach of the simplex method is to obtain one basic feasible solution after another until the optimal solution is reached. One of the key features of the revised simplex method involves the way in which it obtains basic feasible solutions. Recall that a basic solution is a solution of the m equations,

$$[\mathbf{A}, \mathbf{I}] \begin{bmatrix} \mathbf{x} \\ \mathbf{x}_s \end{bmatrix} = \mathbf{b},$$

in which n of the elements of

$$\begin{bmatrix} \mathbf{x} \\ \mathbf{x}_s \end{bmatrix},$$

the non-basic variables, are set equal to zero. Eliminating these n variables by equating them to zero leaves a set of m equations in m unknowns (the basic variables). This set of equations can be denoted by

$$\mathbf{B}\mathbf{x}_B = \mathbf{b},$$

where the vector of basic variables,

$$\mathbf{x}_B = \begin{bmatrix} x_{B1} \\ x_{B2} \\ \cdot \\ \cdot \\ \cdot \\ x_{Bm} \end{bmatrix},$$

is obtained by eliminating the non-basic variables from

$$\begin{bmatrix} \mathbf{x} \\ \mathbf{x}_s \end{bmatrix},$$

and the basis matrix,

$$\mathbf{B} = \begin{bmatrix} B_{11} & B_{12} & \cdots & B_{1m} \\ B_{21} & B_{22} & \cdots & B_{2m} \\ \cdot & \cdot & & \cdot \\ \cdot & \cdot & & \cdot \\ \cdot & \cdot & & \cdot \\ B_{m1} & B_{m2} & \cdots & B_{mm} \end{bmatrix},$$

is obtained by eliminating the columns corresponding to coefficients of nonbasic variables from $[\mathbf{A}, \mathbf{I}]$. (Actually, the elements of $\mathbf{x}_B$, and therefore the columns of $\mathbf{B}$, often are placed in a different order when executing the simplex method.) To solve $\mathbf{B}\mathbf{x}_B = \mathbf{b}$ for the basic solution, notice that premultiplying both sides by $\mathbf{B}^{-1}$,

$$\mathbf{B}^{-1}\mathbf{B}\mathbf{x}_B = \mathbf{B}^{-1}\mathbf{b} ,$$

reduces to

$$\mathbf{I}\mathbf{x}_B = \mathbf{B}^{-1}\mathbf{b} ,$$

so that the basic solution is

$$\mathbf{x}_B = \mathbf{B}^{-1}\mathbf{b} .$$

As seen later, this key fact implies that, at each iteration, all necessary information can be obtained immediately after $\mathbf{B}^{-1}$ has been found.

In order to motivate the procedure, suppose that the original simplex method is being executed, and that the set of equations has been obtained at a given iteration. Given the identity of the basic variables, is there some other way in which the same set of constraint equations could have been obtained? Let x_{Bi} be the basic variable associated with equation (i) for $i = 1, 2, \cdots, m$, and let $\mathbf{B}$ be the corresponding basis matrix (so that column i gives the coefficients of x_{Bi} in the original set of equations). Then, since $\mathbf{x}_B = \mathbf{B}^{-1}\mathbf{b}$, the right-hand side of these constraint equations must be $\mathbf{B}^{-1}\mathbf{b}$. If the original right-hand side, $\mathbf{b}$, has been premultiplied by $\mathbf{B}^{-1}$, then the original left-hand side,

$$[\mathbf{A}, \mathbf{I}] \begin{bmatrix} \mathbf{x} \\ \mathbf{x}_s \end{bmatrix} ,$$

must also have been premultiplied by $\mathbf{B}^{-1}$. Therefore, this set of constraint equations must be

$$\mathbf{B}^{-1} [\mathbf{A}, \mathbf{I}] \begin{bmatrix} \mathbf{x} \\ \mathbf{x}_s \end{bmatrix} = \mathbf{B}^{-1}\mathbf{b} .$$

Thus, it is only necessary to find $\mathbf{B}^{-1}$ in order to determine the set of constraint equations associated with any given set of basic variables. Actually, the revised simplex method does not bother to determine the constraint equations completely, since most of this information is irrelevant. However, it does use this fact about $\mathbf{B}^{-1}$ to quickly obtain the information that *is* relevant.

The above result regarding $\mathbf{B}^{-1}$ and the constraint equations suggests a useful interpretation of the elements of $\mathbf{B}^{-1}$. Using the notation,

$$\mathbf{B}^{-1} = \begin{bmatrix} (\mathbf{B}^{-1})_{11} & (\mathbf{B}^{-1})_{12} & \cdots & (\mathbf{B}^{-1})_{1m} \\ (\mathbf{B}^{-1})_{21} & (\mathbf{B}^{-1})_{22} & \cdots & (\mathbf{B}^{-1})_{2m} \\ \cdot & \cdot & & \cdot \\ \cdot & \cdot & & \cdot \\ \cdot & \cdot & & \cdot \\ (\mathbf{B}^{-1})_{m1} & (\mathbf{B}^{-1})_{m2} & \cdots & (\mathbf{B}^{-1})_{mm} \end{bmatrix},$$

any term in the current equation (i) is obtained by summing the product of $(\mathbf{B}^{-1})_{ij}$ and the corresponding term in the original equation (j), where the sum is over j ($j = 1, 2, \cdots, m$). Therefore, when $i \neq j$, $(\mathbf{B}^{-1})_{ij}$ is just the multiple of the original equation (j) that has been added to equation (i), directly or indirectly, in the process of obtaining the current equation (i).

Having shown how to obtain the set of constraint equations at any iteration, the only preliminary remaining is to develop a method for obtaining the current equation (0) by matrix manipulations. A review of the procedure for constraint equations suggests that the same approach can be used for equation (0) merely by treating it like another constraint equation. Thus, reformulate the problem in an equivalent way as

$$\text{maximize } x_0,$$

subject to

$$x_0 - \sum_{j=1}^{n} c_j x_j = 0\,,$$

$$\sum_{j=1}^{n} a_{ij} x_j + x_{n+i} = b_i\,, \qquad \text{for } i = 1, 2, \cdots, m\,,$$

and

$$x_j \geq 0\,, \qquad \text{for} \qquad j = 1, 2, \cdots, n + m\,.$$

Using matrix notation, this formulation is expressed as

$$\text{maximize } x_0,$$

subject to

$$\begin{array}{c} \\ 1 \\ \\ m \end{array} \left[\begin{array}{c|c|c} 1 & n & m \\ 1 & -\mathbf{c} & \mathbf{0} \\ & & \\ \mathbf{0} & \mathbf{A} & \mathbf{I} \end{array}\right] \begin{bmatrix} x_0 \\ \mathbf{x} \\ \mathbf{x}_s \end{bmatrix} = \begin{array}{c} 1 \\ m \end{array} \begin{bmatrix} 0 \\ \mathbf{b} \end{bmatrix}, \text{ and } \begin{bmatrix} \mathbf{x} \\ \mathbf{x}_s \end{bmatrix} \geq \mathbf{0}\,.$$

(As indicated in Appendix 3, the null matrix $\mathbf{0}$ is assigned however many rows and columns are appropriate each time it is used.) Thus, x_0 may be treated as if it were another basic variable. [It would always be the basic variable for equation (0) since it would never appear in the other equations.] Therefore, rather than finding the basic solution for $\mathbf{x}_B$, one may instead find the basic solution for

$$\begin{bmatrix} x_0 \\ \mathbf{x}_B \end{bmatrix}$$

by the same procedure. Let $\mathbf{B}_0$ be the corresponding expanded basis matrix,

$$\mathbf{B}_0 = \begin{bmatrix} 1 & -c_{B1} & -c_{B2} & \cdots & -c_{Bm} \\ 0 & B_{11} & B_{12} & \cdots & B_{1m} \\ 0 & B_{21} & B_{22} & \cdots & B_{2m} \\ \cdot & \cdot & \cdot & & \cdot \\ \cdot & \cdot & \cdot & & \cdot \\ \cdot & \cdot & \cdot & & \cdot \\ 0 & B_{m1} & B_{m2} & \cdots & B_{mm} \end{bmatrix} = \begin{array}{c} \\ 1 \\ m \end{array} \begin{array}{c|c} 1 & m \\ \hline 1 & -\mathbf{c}_B \\ \hline \mathbf{0} & \mathbf{B} \end{array},$$

where $\mathbf{c}_B = [c_{B1}, c_{B2}, \cdots, c_{Bm}]$, and $-c_{Bi}$ is the coefficient of x_{Bi} in the original equation (0),

$$x_0 - \sum_{j=1}^{n} c_j x_j = 0 .$$

It then follows as before that

$$\begin{bmatrix} x_0 \\ \mathbf{x}_B \end{bmatrix} = \mathbf{B}_0^{-1} \begin{bmatrix} 0 \\ \mathbf{b} \end{bmatrix} .$$

Furthermore,

$$\mathbf{B}_0^{-1} \begin{bmatrix} 1 & -\mathbf{c} & \mathbf{0} \\ \mathbf{0} & \mathbf{A} & \mathbf{I} \end{bmatrix} \begin{bmatrix} x_0 \\ \mathbf{x} \\ \mathbf{x}_s \end{bmatrix} = \mathbf{B}_0^{-1} \begin{bmatrix} 0 \\ \mathbf{b} \end{bmatrix}$$

is the complete set of equations that would have been obtained by the original simplex method in order to identify

$$\begin{bmatrix} x_0 \\ \mathbf{x}_B \end{bmatrix} .$$

Thus, knowing $\mathbf{B}_0^{-1}$ would make all relevant information readily accessible.

The problem can be simplified even further. It has been found that $\mathbf{B}_0^{-1}$ can be obtained by finding only $\mathbf{B}^{-1}$. This becomes clear by applying to the elements of $\mathbf{B}_0^{-1}$ the interpretation given to the elements of $\mathbf{B}^{-1}$. In order to correspond to the numbering of the equations, number the rows and columns of $\mathbf{B}_0^{-1}$ from 0 to m, so that

$$\mathbf{B}_0^{-1} = \begin{bmatrix} (\mathbf{B}_0^{-1})_{00} & (\mathbf{B}_0^{-1})_{01} & \cdots & (\mathbf{B}_0^{-1})_{0m} \\ (\mathbf{B}_0^{-1})_{10} & (\mathbf{B}_0^{-1})_{11} & \cdots & (\mathbf{B}_0^{-1})_{1m} \\ \vdots & \vdots & & \vdots \\ (\mathbf{B}_0^{-1})_{m0} & (\mathbf{B}_0^{-1})_{m1} & \cdots & (\mathbf{B}_0^{-1})_{mm} \end{bmatrix} .$$

Using the same reasoning as before, $(\mathbf{B}_0^{-1})_{ij}$ is the multiple of the original equation (j) that has been added to equation (i), directly or indirectly, in the process of obtaining the current equation (i). Hence, $(\mathbf{B}_0^{-1})_{ij} = (\mathbf{B}^{-1})_{ij}$ for $i = 1, 2, \cdots, m$ and $j = 1, 2, \cdots, m$. Since equation (0) is never multiplied or added to other equations, $(\mathbf{B}_0^{-1})_{00} = 1$ and $(\mathbf{B}_0^{-1})_{i0} = 0$ for $i = 1, 2, \cdots, m$. It remains only to identify $(\mathbf{B}_0^{-1})_{0j}$ for $j = 1, 2, \cdots, m$. Recall that the coefficient of x_{Bi} in equation (0) must be zero since x_{Bi} is a basic variable. Hence, $c_{Bi}x_{Bi}$ must have been added to equation (0) in order to eliminate the original coefficient of $-c_{Bi}$. No current equation contains x_{Bi} except equation (i), where the coefficient of x_{Bi} is one. Therefore, x_{Bi} must have been eliminated from equation (0) by doing the equivalent of adding c_{Bi} times the current equation (i) to equation (0). It was found earlier that the current equation (i) is just the sum over j ($j = 1, 2, \cdots, m$) of $(\mathbf{B}^{-1})_{ij}$ times the original equation (j). Hence, $c_{Bi}(\mathbf{B}^{-1})_{ij}$ times the original equation (j) has been added to equation (0), directly or indirectly, just to eliminate x_{Bi} from equation (0). Since all of the x_{Bi} ($i = 1, 2, \cdots, m$) were eliminated from equation (0), this implies that

$$\sum_{i=1}^{m} c_{Bi}(\mathbf{B}^{-1})_{ij}$$

times the original equation (j) has been added to equation (0), directly or indirectly, in the process of obtaining the current equation (0). Therefore,

$$(\mathbf{B}_0^{-1})_{0j} = \sum_{i=1}^{m} c_{Bi}(\mathbf{B}^{-1})_{ij}, \qquad \text{for } j = 1, 2, \cdots, m.$$

To summarize,

$$\mathbf{B}_0^{-1} = \begin{bmatrix} 1 & \sum_{i=1}^{m} c_{Bi}(\mathbf{B}^{-1})_{i1} & \sum_{i=1}^{m} c_{Bi}(\mathbf{B}^{-1})_{i2} & \cdots & \sum_{i=1}^{m} c_{Bi}(\mathbf{B}^{-1})_{im} \\ 0 & (\mathbf{B}^{-1})_{11} & (\mathbf{B}^{-1})_{12} & \cdots & (\mathbf{B}^{-1})_{1m} \\ 0 & (\mathbf{B}^{-1})_{21} & (\mathbf{B}^{-1})_{22} & \cdots & (\mathbf{B}^{-1})_{2m} \\ \cdot & \cdot & \cdot & & \cdot \\ \cdot & \cdot & \cdot & & \cdot \\ \cdot & \cdot & \cdot & & \cdot \\ 0 & (\mathbf{B}^{-1})_{m1} & (\mathbf{B}^{-1})_{m2} & \cdots & (\mathbf{B}^{-1})_{mm} \end{bmatrix}$$

$$= \begin{array}{c} \\ 1 \\ m \end{array} \begin{array}{c} 1 \quad\quad m \\ \left[\begin{array}{c|c} 1 & \mathbf{c}_B\mathbf{B}^{-1} \\ \hline \mathbf{0} & \mathbf{B}^{-1} \end{array}\right] \end{array}.$$

Hence,

$$\mathbf{B}_0^{-1}\begin{bmatrix} 1 & -\mathbf{c} & 0 \\ \mathbf{0} & \mathbf{A} & \mathbf{I} \end{bmatrix} = \begin{array}{c} \\ 1 \\ m \end{array} \begin{array}{c} 1 \quad\quad\quad n \quad\quad\quad m \\ \left[\begin{array}{c|c|c} 1 & \mathbf{c}_B\mathbf{B}^{-1}\mathbf{A} - \mathbf{c} & \mathbf{c}_B\mathbf{B}^{-1} \\ \hline \mathbf{0} & \mathbf{B}^{-1}\mathbf{A} & \mathbf{B}^{-1} \end{array}\right] \end{array},$$

so that *the complete set of equations is:*

$$\begin{array}{c} 1 \\ m \end{array}\left[\begin{array}{c|c|c} \overset{1}{1} & \overset{n}{\mathbf{c}_B\mathbf{B}^{-1}\mathbf{A} - \mathbf{c}} & \overset{m}{\mathbf{c}_B\mathbf{B}^{-1}} \\ \hline \mathbf{0} & \mathbf{B}^{-1}\mathbf{A} & \mathbf{B}^{-1} \end{array}\right]\left[\begin{array}{c} x_0 \\ \hline \mathbf{x} \\ \mathbf{x}_s \end{array}\right] = \begin{array}{c} 1 \\ m \end{array}\left[\begin{array}{c} \overset{1}{\mathbf{c}_B\mathbf{B}^{-1}\mathbf{b}} \\ \hline \mathbf{B}^{-1}\mathbf{b} \end{array}\right].$$

Therefore, any number in the current set of equations can be calculated directly by performing the indicated matrix manipulation in this expression. This is the key to the revised simplex method.

Postponing for the moment the question of how to obtain $\mathbf{B}^{-1}$ at each iteration, the stage is now set for summarizing the revised simplex method. It differs from the original simplex method only in the organization of the computations, the main steps at each iteration being the same as those summarized in Sec. 5.5.

The first step is to determine the new entering basic variable. The simplex method does this, simultaneously with testing whether the previous solution is optimal, by checking the $(z_j - c_j)$, the coefficients in equation (0), for the non-basic variables. The revised simplex method computes each of these coefficients by using the corresponding element in the above matrix. Thus,

$$z_j - c_j = \mathbf{c}_B\mathbf{B}^{-1}\mathbf{A}_j - c_j,$$

where the column vector $\mathbf{A}_j$ is the jth column of $\mathbf{A}$, so that

$$\mathbf{A}_j = \begin{bmatrix} a_{1j} \\ a_{2j} \\ \cdot \\ \cdot \\ \cdot \\ a_{mj} \end{bmatrix},$$

where a_{ij} is the coefficient of x_j in the original equation (i). If $n + 1 \leq j \leq n + m$, then $c_j = 0$, $a_{jj} = 1$, and $a_{ij} = 0$ for $i \neq j$, so the above expression reduces to $z_j = \mathbf{c}_B(\mathbf{B}^{-1})_{j-n}$, where the column vector $(\mathbf{B}^{-1})_i$ is

$$(\mathbf{B}^{-1})_i = \begin{bmatrix} (\mathbf{B}^{-1})_{1i} \\ (\mathbf{B}^{-1})_{2i} \\ \cdot \\ \cdot \\ \cdot \\ (\mathbf{B}^{-1})_{mi} \end{bmatrix}.$$

If this coefficient, $(z_j - c_j)$, is non-negative for all n non-basic variables, then an optimal solution has been found. Otherwise, select the variable with the largest negative coefficient as the entering basic variable. Let k be the subscript of this variable.

The second step is to determine the leaving basic variable. The simplex method does this by comparing b'_i, the right-hand side of the current equation (i), and a'_{ik}, the coefficient of x_k (the entering basic variable), in the current equation (i), for $i = 1, 2, \cdots, m$. Considering only positive a'_{ik}, the basic variable associated with the equation having the smallest value of b'_i/a'_{ik} is selected, since it reaches zero first as the entering basic variable is increased. The revised simplex method computes the a'_{ik} by the matrix manipulation,

$$\begin{bmatrix} a'_{1k} \\ a'_{2k} \\ \cdot \\ \cdot \\ \cdot \\ a'_{mk} \end{bmatrix} = \mathbf{B}^{-1}\mathbf{A}_k\,,$$

which reduces to $(\mathbf{B}^{-1})_{k-n}$ when $k > n$. The b'_i are computed by the matrix manipulation,

$$\begin{bmatrix} b'_1 \\ b'_2 \\ \cdot \\ \cdot \\ \cdot \\ b'_m \end{bmatrix} = \mathbf{B}^{-1}\mathbf{b}\,.$$

Let r be the number of the equation containing the leaving basic variable.

The only step remaining before again testing for optimality is to update the basic data required for executing the next iteration. (This also permits the identification of the new basic feasible solution, if desired.) In the original simplex method, this involves finding the new set of equations. The revised simplex method instead finds the new $\mathbf{B}^{-1}$. Since $\mathbf{B}^{-1}$ is known to be $\mathbf{I}$ at the first iteration, it is sufficient to obtain the new $\mathbf{B}^{-1}$ (denote it as $\mathbf{B}^{-1}_{\text{new}}$) from the $\mathbf{B}^{-1}$ at the previous iteration (denote it as $\mathbf{B}^{-1}_{\text{old}}$). The method for doing this is motivated readily by applying the previously discussed interpretation of the elements of $\mathbf{B}^{-1}$. Recall that the new set of equations [excluding equation (0)] can be obtained from the previous set by subtracting a'_{ik}/a'_{rk} times equation (r) from equation (i), for $i = 1, 2, \cdots, r-1, r+1, \cdots m$, and then dividing equation (r) by a'_{rk}. Therefore,

$$(\mathbf{B}^{-1}_{\text{new}})_{ij} = \begin{cases} (\mathbf{B}^{-1}_{\text{old}})_{ij} - \dfrac{a'_{ik}}{a'_{rk}}(\mathbf{B}^{-1}_{\text{old}})_{rj}\,, & \text{if } i \neq r \\[2ex] \dfrac{1}{a'_{rk}}(\mathbf{B}^{-1}_{\text{old}})_{rk}\,, & \text{if } i = r\,. \end{cases}$$

This is expressed in matrix notation as

$$\mathbf{B}_{\text{new}}^{-1} = \mathbf{E}\mathbf{B}_{\text{old}}^{-1},$$

where the matrix $\mathbf{E}$ is an identity matrix, except that its rth column is replaced by

$$\eta = \begin{bmatrix} -a'_{1k}/a'_{rk} \\ -a'_{2k}/a'_{rk} \\ \cdot \\ \cdot \\ \cdot \\ -a'_{(r-1)k}/a'_{rk} \\ 1/a'_{rk} \\ -a'_{(r+1)k}/a'_{rk} \\ \cdot \\ \cdot \\ \cdot \\ -a'_{mk}/a'_{rk} \end{bmatrix}.$$

Thus, $\mathbf{E} = [\mathbf{U}_1, \mathbf{U}_2, \cdots, \mathbf{U}_{r-1}, \eta, \mathbf{U}_{r+1}, \cdots, \mathbf{U}_m]$, where the m elements of each of the $\mathbf{U}_i$ column vectors are zeros except for a one in the ith position.

This procedure is now illustrated using the example of Sec. 5.5. For this problem, the linear programming formulation in matrix form is maximize

$$x_0 = [3, 5] \begin{bmatrix} x_1 \\ x_2 \end{bmatrix},$$

subject to

$$\begin{bmatrix} 1 & 0 \\ 0 & 1 \\ 3 & 2 \end{bmatrix} \begin{bmatrix} x_1 \\ x_2 \end{bmatrix} \leq \begin{bmatrix} 4 \\ 6 \\ 18 \end{bmatrix} \quad \text{and} \quad \begin{bmatrix} x_1 \\ x_2 \end{bmatrix} \geq \begin{bmatrix} 0 \\ 0 \end{bmatrix}.$$

After introducing slack variables, the constraints become

$$\begin{bmatrix} 1 & 0 & 1 & 0 & 0 \\ 0 & 1 & 0 & 1 & 0 \\ 3 & 2 & 0 & 0 & 1 \end{bmatrix} \begin{bmatrix} x_1 \\ x_2 \\ x_3 \\ x_4 \\ x_5 \end{bmatrix} = \begin{bmatrix} 4 \\ 6 \\ 18 \end{bmatrix} \quad \text{and} \quad \begin{bmatrix} x_1 \\ x_2 \\ x_3 \\ x_4 \\ x_5 \end{bmatrix} \geq \begin{bmatrix} 0 \\ 0 \\ 0 \\ 0 \\ 0 \end{bmatrix}.$$

The slack variables become the initial basic variables, so that

$$\mathbf{x}_B = \begin{bmatrix} x_3 \\ x_4 \\ x_5 \end{bmatrix}, \quad \mathbf{B} = \begin{bmatrix} 1 & 0 & 0 \\ 0 & 1 & 0 \\ 0 & 0 & 1 \end{bmatrix}, \quad \text{and} \quad \mathbf{B}^{-1} = \begin{bmatrix} 1 & 0 & 0 \\ 0 & 1 & 0 \\ 0 & 0 & 1 \end{bmatrix}.$$

Furthermore, $\mathbf{c}_B = [0, 0, 0]$, so that

$$\mathbf{B}_0 = \begin{bmatrix} 1 & 0 & 0 & 0 \\ 0 & 1 & 0 & 0 \\ 0 & 0 & 1 & 0 \\ 0 & 0 & 0 & 1 \end{bmatrix} \quad \text{and} \quad \mathbf{B}_0^{-1} = \begin{bmatrix} 1 & 0 & 0 & 0 \\ 0 & 1 & 0 & 0 \\ 0 & 0 & 1 & 0 \\ 0 & 0 & 0 & 1 \end{bmatrix}.$$

Given this $\mathbf{c}_B$, it follows that $z_1 = 0$ and $z_2 = 0$, so that $z_1 - c_1 = -3$ and $z_2 - c_2 = -5$, which indicates lack of optimality with x_2 as the entering basic variable. Since this is the first iteration, so that $\mathbf{B}^{-1} = \mathbf{I}$, then

$$\begin{bmatrix} a'_{12} \\ a'_{22} \\ a'_{32} \end{bmatrix} = \mathbf{A}_2 = \begin{bmatrix} 0 \\ 1 \\ 2 \end{bmatrix}, \quad \text{and} \quad \begin{bmatrix} b'_1 \\ b'_2 \\ b'_3 \end{bmatrix} = \mathbf{b} = \begin{bmatrix} 4 \\ 6 \\ 18 \end{bmatrix}.$$

Comparing $b'_2/a'_{22} = 6$ and $b'_3/a'_{32} = 9$, $x_{B2} = x_4$ is chosen as the leaving basic variable. The new $\mathbf{B}^{-1}$ is then

$$\mathbf{B}_{\text{new}}^{-1} = \begin{bmatrix} 1 & 0 & 0 \\ 0 & 1 & 0 \\ 0 & -2 & 1 \end{bmatrix} \begin{bmatrix} 1 & 0 & 0 \\ 0 & 1 & 0 \\ 0 & 0 & 1 \end{bmatrix} = \begin{bmatrix} 1 & 0 & 0 \\ 0 & 1 & 0 \\ 0 & -2 & 1 \end{bmatrix}.$$

At the second iteration, $\mathbf{c}_B = [0, 5, 0]$ since

$$\mathbf{x}_B = \begin{bmatrix} x_3 \\ x_2 \\ x_5 \end{bmatrix}.$$

Therefore,

$$z_1 - c_1 = [0, 5, 0] \begin{bmatrix} 1 & 0 & 0 \\ 0 & 1 & 0 \\ 0 & -2 & 1 \end{bmatrix} \begin{bmatrix} 1 \\ 0 \\ 3 \end{bmatrix} - 3 = -3$$

and

$$z_4 - c_4 = [0, 5, 0] \begin{bmatrix} 0 \\ 1 \\ -2 \end{bmatrix} = 5,$$

so that the current solution is not optimal, and x_1 becomes the new entering basic variable. The information required for determining the leaving basic variable is

$$\begin{bmatrix} a'_{11} \\ a'_{21} \\ a'_{31} \end{bmatrix} = \begin{bmatrix} 1 & 0 & 0 \\ 0 & 1 & 0 \\ 0 & -2 & 1 \end{bmatrix} \begin{bmatrix} 1 \\ 0 \\ 3 \end{bmatrix} = \begin{bmatrix} 1 \\ 0 \\ 3 \end{bmatrix}$$

and

$$\begin{bmatrix} b'_1 \\ b'_2 \\ b'_3 \end{bmatrix} = \begin{bmatrix} 1 & 0 & 0 \\ 0 & 1 & 0 \\ 0 & -2 & 1 \end{bmatrix} \begin{bmatrix} 4 \\ 6 \\ 18 \end{bmatrix} = \begin{bmatrix} 4 \\ 6 \\ 6 \end{bmatrix}.$$

Considering only positive a'_{i1}, $b'_1/a'_{11} = 4$ and $b'_3/a'_{31} = 2$ indicate that $x_{B3} = x_5$ is the leaving basic variable. Hence,

$$\mathbf{B}_{\text{new}}^{-1} = \begin{bmatrix} 1 & 0 & -\frac{1}{3} \\ 0 & 1 & 0 \\ 0 & 0 & \frac{1}{3} \end{bmatrix} \begin{bmatrix} 1 & 0 & 0 \\ 0 & 1 & 0 \\ 0 & -2 & 1 \end{bmatrix} = \begin{bmatrix} 1 & \frac{2}{3} & -\frac{1}{3} \\ 0 & 1 & 0 \\ 0 & -\frac{2}{3} & \frac{1}{3} \end{bmatrix}.$$

At the next iteration,

$$\mathbf{x}_B = \begin{bmatrix} x_3 \\ x_2 \\ x_1 \end{bmatrix},$$

so that $\mathbf{c}_B = [0, 5, 3]$. Therefore,

$$z_4 - c_4 = [0, 5, 3] \begin{bmatrix} \frac{2}{3} \\ 1 \\ -\frac{2}{3} \end{bmatrix} = 3$$

and

$$z_5 - c_5 = [0, 5, 3] \begin{bmatrix} -\frac{1}{3} \\ 0 \\ \frac{1}{3} \end{bmatrix} = 1.$$

Hence, the current solution is optimal and the procedure terminates. This solution is

$$\mathbf{x}_B = \begin{bmatrix} x_3 \\ x_2 \\ x_1 \end{bmatrix} = \begin{bmatrix} 1 & \frac{2}{3} & -\frac{1}{3} \\ 0 & 1 & 0 \\ 0 & -\frac{2}{3} & \frac{1}{3} \end{bmatrix} \begin{bmatrix} 4 \\ 6 \\ 18 \end{bmatrix} = \begin{bmatrix} 2 \\ 6 \\ 2 \end{bmatrix},$$

with the non-basic variables, x_4 and x_5, equal to zero.

While the above describes the essence of the revised simplex method, it should be pointed out that minor modifications may be made to improve the efficiency of execution on electronic computers. For example, $\mathbf{B}^{-1}$ may be obtained as the product of the previous E matrices. This only requires storing the η column of $\mathbf{E}$ and the number of the column, rather than the $\mathbf{B}^{-1}$ matrix at each iteration. If magnetic tape rather than core storage must be used, this "product form" of the basis inverse may be the most efficient.

It should also be noted that the preceding discussion was limited to the case of linear programming problems whose form is that given in Sec. 5.2. If artificial variables are introduced to obtain an initial basic feasible solution (and to thereby obtain an identity matrix as the initial basis matrix), minor modifications analogous to those given in Sec. 5.6 must be made. The details regarding the resulting changes in the preceding description of the revised simplex method are left to the reader as an exercise.[102]

It would now be useful to summarize the advantages of the revised simplex method over the original simplex method. One is that the number of arithmetic computations may be less. This is especially true when the **A** matrix contains a large number of zero elements. The amount of information that must be stored at each iteration is less, sometimes considerably so. The revised simplex method also permits the control of round-off errors inevitably generated by digital computers. This can be done by periodically obtaining the current $\mathbf{B}^{-1}$ by directly inverting **B**. Furthermore, some of the post-optimality problems discussed in Sec. 15.2 can be handled more conveniently when the revised simplex method is used. For all of these reasons, the revised simplex method is usually preferable to the original simplex method when using a digital computer.

15.3.5 The Primal-Dual Algorithm

It is sometimes necessary to introduce many artificial variables in order to conveniently obtain an initial basic feasible solution. Section 15.1.2 pointed out that, in such cases, it may be easier to begin with an infeasible better-than-optimal basic solution instead and use the dual simplex method. Unfortunately, it may also be inconvenient to obtain an initial infeasible solution that is also better-than-optimal [i.e., all of the $(z_j - c_j)$ are nonnegative]. In these situations, it would seem expedient to begin with an infeasible solution which also violates the optimality criterion, and then work simultaneously toward both feasibility and optimality. The primal-dual algorithm has been developed for this purpose.

The primal-dual algorithm received its name because it deals directly with both the primal and the dual problems. It begins with a feasible dual solution. It then finds the optimal solution to a revised form of the primal problem by the simplex method. This leads to a better feasible dual solution, after which another revised form of the primal problem is solved. This process is repeated successively until, in a finite number of steps, an optimal dual solution and a feasible primal solution are reached. Complementary slackness is maintained at each step (by the revision of the primal problem) so that, when this feasible primal solution is obtained, it must also be optimal. The effect of solving each revised primal problem is to reduce the in-

[102] For a description of one relatively efficient approach, see G. Hadley, *Linear Programming,* Addison-Wesley, Reading, Mass., 1962, pp. 205–215.

feasibility of the original primal problem in such a way that the eventual feasible solution would already be optimal.[103]

Although the primal-dual algorithm is a promising approach, there is not yet conclusive evidence that it is more efficient than the revised simplex method with artificial variables.

15.3.6 The Decomposition Principle

Consider the linear programming formulation in matrix form, maximize

$$x_0 = \mathbf{cx},$$

subject to

$$\mathbf{Ax} \leq \mathbf{b}^{104} \quad \text{and} \quad \mathbf{x} \geq \mathbf{0}.$$

It frequently occurs that the **A** matrix has the structure,

$$\mathbf{A} = \begin{bmatrix} \mathbf{A}_1 & \mathbf{A}_2 & \cdots & \mathbf{A}_N \\ \mathbf{A}_{N+1} & \mathbf{0} & \cdots & \mathbf{0} \\ \mathbf{0} & \mathbf{A}_{N+2} & \cdots & \mathbf{0} \\ \cdot & \cdot & & \cdot \\ \cdot & \cdot & & \cdot \\ \cdot & \cdot & & \cdot \\ \mathbf{0} & \mathbf{0} & \cdots & \mathbf{A}_{2N} \end{bmatrix},$$

where the $\mathbf{A}_i$ $(i = 1, 2, \cdots, 2N)$ are matrices, and the **0** are null matrices. To illustrate, this is the case for the problem, maximize

$$x_0 = 4x_1 + 6x_2 + 8x_3 + 5x_4,$$

subject to

$$\begin{aligned} x_1 + 3x_2 + 2x_3 + 4x_4 &\leq 20 \\ 2x_1 + 3x_2 + 6x_3 + 4x_4 &\leq 25 \\ x_1 + x_2 &\leq 5 \\ x_1 + 2x_2 &\leq 8 \\ 4x_3 + 3x_4 &\leq 12 \end{aligned}$$

and

$$x_j \geq 0, \qquad \text{for } j = 1, 2, 3, 4,$$

since its **A** matrix is

$$\mathbf{A} = \left[\begin{array}{cc|cc} 1 & 3 & 2 & 4 \\ 2 & 3 & 6 & 4 \\ \hline 1 & 1 & 0 & 0 \\ 1 & 2 & 0 & 0 \\ \hline 0 & 0 & 4 & 3 \end{array}\right],$$

[103] The interested reader is referred to the Dantzig and the Hadley books referenced at the end of the chapter for details of the procedure.

[104] The following discussion would not be changed substantially if $\mathbf{Ax} = \mathbf{b}$.

so that $N = 2$ and

$$\mathbf{A}_1 = \begin{bmatrix} 1 & 3 \\ 2 & 3 \end{bmatrix}, \quad \mathbf{A}_2 = \begin{bmatrix} 2 & 4 \\ 6 & 4 \end{bmatrix}, \quad \mathbf{A}_3 = \begin{bmatrix} 1 & 1 \\ 1 & 2 \end{bmatrix}, \quad \mathbf{A}_4 = [4, 3].$$

This kind of $\mathbf{A}$ matrix results whenever most of the scarce resources involved can be used by only one of the groups of activities. For example, a corporation with branch plants will have resources unique to each of the plants, plus common resources which may be pooled by the plants. Any linear programming problem encompassing all of these activities would then consist of several (say, N) almost independent subproblems tied together by a few common constraints. Expressing this mathematically, the over-all problem reduces to maximize

$$x_0 = \sum_{j=1}^{N} \mathbf{c}_j \mathbf{x}_j ,$$

subject to

$$[\mathbf{A}_1, \mathbf{A}_2, \cdots, \mathbf{A}_N, \mathbf{I}] \begin{bmatrix} \mathbf{x} \\ \mathbf{x}_s \end{bmatrix} = \mathbf{b}_0, \quad \begin{bmatrix} \mathbf{x} \\ \mathbf{x}_s \end{bmatrix} \geq \mathbf{0} ,$$

$$\mathbf{A}_{N+j}\mathbf{x}_j \leq \mathbf{b}_j \quad \text{and} \quad \mathbf{x}_j \geq \mathbf{0}, \qquad \text{for } j = 1, 2, \cdots, N ,$$

where $\mathbf{c}_j$, $\mathbf{x}_j$, $\mathbf{b}_0$, and $\mathbf{b}_j$ are vectors such that $\mathbf{c} = [\mathbf{c}_1, \mathbf{c}_2, \cdots, \mathbf{c}_N]$,

$$\mathbf{x} = \begin{bmatrix} \mathbf{x}_1 \\ \mathbf{x}_2 \\ \cdot \\ \cdot \\ \cdot \\ \mathbf{x}_N \end{bmatrix}, \quad \mathbf{b} = \begin{bmatrix} \mathbf{b}_0 \\ \mathbf{b}_1 \\ \cdot \\ \cdot \\ \cdot \\ \mathbf{b}_N \end{bmatrix},$$

and where $\mathbf{x}_s$ is the vector of slack variables for the first set of constraints. (Thus, in the above example, $\mathbf{c}_1 = [4, 6]$, $\mathbf{c}_2 = [8, 5]$,

$$\mathbf{x}_1 = \begin{bmatrix} x_1 \\ x_2 \end{bmatrix}, \quad \mathbf{x}_2 = \begin{bmatrix} x_3 \\ x_4 \end{bmatrix}, \quad \mathbf{b}_0 = \begin{bmatrix} 20 \\ 25 \end{bmatrix}, \quad \mathbf{b}_1 = \begin{bmatrix} 5 \\ 8 \end{bmatrix}, \quad \mathbf{b}_2 = [12] . \Bigg)$$

This structure suggests that it may be possible to solve the over-all problem by doing little more than solving the N subproblems of the form,

$$\text{maximize} \quad \mathbf{c}_j \mathbf{x}_j,$$

subject to

$$\mathbf{A}_{N+j}\mathbf{x}_j \leq \mathbf{b}_j \quad \text{and} \quad \mathbf{x}_j \geq 0 ,$$

thereby greatly reducing computational effort. After some modifications, this procedure can indeed be used efficiently. This approach has been named the *decomposition principle for linear programs.*

Assume that the set of feasible solutions for each subproblem is a bounded set (i.e., none of the variables can approach infinity). Although a more complicated version of the approach can still be used otherwise, this assumption will simplify the discussion.

The set of points, $\mathbf{x}_j$ such that $\mathbf{x}_j \geq \mathbf{0}$ and $\mathbf{A}_{N+j}\mathbf{x}_j \leq \mathbf{b}_j$, constitute a convex set with a finite number of extreme points. Therefore, under the assumption that the set is bounded, any point in the set can be represented as a weighted average of the extreme points. To express this mathematically, let n_j be the number of extreme points, and denote these points by $\mathbf{x}_{jk}^*$ for $k = 1, 2, \cdots, n_j$. Then any solution $\mathbf{x}_j$ to subproblem j which satisfies the constraints, $\mathbf{A}_{N+j}\mathbf{x}_j \leq \mathbf{b}_j$ and $\mathbf{x}_j \geq 0$, also satisfies the equation

$$\mathbf{x}_j = \sum_{k=1}^{n_j} \rho_{jk}\mathbf{x}_{jk}^*$$

for some combination of the ρ_{jk} such that

$$\sum_{k=1}^{n_j} \rho_{jk} = 1$$

and $\rho_{jk} \geq 0$ $(k = 1, 2, \cdots, n_j)$. Furthermore, this is not true for any $\mathbf{x}_j$ which is not a feasible solution for subproblem j. Therefore, this equation for $\mathbf{x}_j$ and the constraints on the ρ_{jk} provide a method for representing the feasible solutions to subproblem j without using any of the original constraints. Hence, the over-all problem can now be reformulated with far fewer constraints as maximize

$$x_0 = \sum_{j=1}^{N} \sum_{k=1}^{n_j} (\mathbf{c}_j\mathbf{x}_{jk}^*)\rho_{jk} ,$$

subject to

$$\sum_{j=1}^{N} \sum_{k=1}^{n_j} (\mathbf{A}_j\mathbf{x}_{jk}^*)\rho_{jk} + \mathbf{x}_s = \mathbf{b}_0 , \quad \mathbf{x}_s \geq \mathbf{0} ,$$

$$\sum_{k=1}^{n_j} \rho_{jk} = 1 \qquad \text{for } j = 1, 2, \cdots, N ,$$

and

$$\rho_{jk} \geq 0, \qquad \text{for } j = 1, 2, \cdots, N \quad \text{and} \quad k = 1, 2, \cdots, N_j .$$

This formulation is completely equivalent to the ones given earlier. However, since it has far fewer constraints, it should be solvable with much less computational effort. The fact that the number of variables (which are now the ρ_{jk} and the elements of $\mathbf{x}_s$) is much larger does not matter much computationally if the revised simplex method is used. The one apparent flaw is that it would be tedious to identify all of the $\mathbf{x}_{jk}^*$. Fortunately, it is not necessary to do this when using the revised simplex method. The procedure is outlined below.

Let $\mathbf{A}'$ be the matrix of constraint coefficients for the new formulation of the problem and let $\mathbf{c}'$ be the vector of objective function coefficients. (The individual elements of $\mathbf{A}'$ and $\mathbf{c}'$ are determined only when they are needed.) As usual, let $\mathbf{B}$ be the current basis matrix, and let $\mathbf{c}_B$ be the corresponding vector of basic variable coefficients in the objective function. Then the first step at each iteration of the revised simplex method is to find the minimum element of $(\mathbf{c}_B\mathbf{B}^{-1}\mathbf{A}' - \mathbf{c}')$, the vector of coefficients in the current equation (0). Let $(z_{jk} - c_{jk})$ denote the element in this vector corresponding to ρ_{jk}. Let m_0 denote the number of elements of $\mathbf{b}_0$. Let $(\mathbf{B}^{-1})_{1;m_0}$ be the matrix consisting of the first m_0 columns of $\mathbf{B}^{-1}$, and let $(\mathbf{B}^{-1})_i$ be the vector consisting of the ith column of $\mathbf{B}^{-1}$. Then $(z_{jk} - c_{jk})$ reduces to

$$\begin{aligned} z_{jk} - c_{jk} &= \mathbf{c}_B(\mathbf{B}^{-1})_{1;m_0}\mathbf{A}_j\mathbf{x}_{jk}^* + \mathbf{c}_B(\mathbf{B}^{-1})_{m_0+j} - \mathbf{c}_j\mathbf{x}_{jk}^* \\ &= (\mathbf{c}_B(\mathbf{B}^{-1})_{1;m_0}\mathbf{A}_j - \mathbf{c}_j)\mathbf{x}_{jk}^* + \mathbf{c}_B(\mathbf{B}^{-1})_{m_0+j} . \end{aligned}$$

Since $\mathbf{c}_B(\mathbf{B}^{-1})_{m_0+j}$ is independent of k, the minimum value of $(z_{jk} - c_{jk})$ over $k = 1, 2, \cdots, n_j$ can be found as follows. Recall that the $\mathbf{x}_{jk}^*$ are just the basic feasible solutions for the set of constraints, $\mathbf{x}_j \geq \mathbf{0}$ and $\mathbf{A}_{N+j}\mathbf{x}_j \leq \mathbf{b}_j$, and that the simplex method identifies the basic feasible solution which minimizes (or maximizes) a given objective function. Therefore, solve the linear programming problem, minimize

$$Z_j = (\mathbf{c}_B(\mathbf{B}^{-1})_{1;m_0}\mathbf{A}_j - \mathbf{c}_j)\mathbf{x}_j + \mathbf{c}_B(\mathbf{B}^{-1})_{m_0+j} ,$$

subject to

$$\mathbf{A}_{N+j}\mathbf{x}_j \leq \mathbf{b}_j \quad \text{and} \quad \mathbf{x}_j \geq \mathbf{0} .$$

The optimal value of Z_j, say, Z_j^*, is the desired minimum value of $(z_{jk} - c_{jk})$ over k. Furthermore, the optimal solution for $\mathbf{x}_j$ is the corresponding $\mathbf{x}_{jk}^*$.

Therefore, the first step at each iteration requires solving N linear programming problems of the above type to find Z_j^* for $j = 1, 2, \cdots, N$. In addition, the current equation (0) coefficients of the elements of $\mathbf{x}_s$ would be found in the usual way as the elements of $\mathbf{c}_B(\mathbf{B}^{-1})_{1;m_0}$. If all of these coefficients [the Z_j^* and the elements of $\mathbf{c}_B(\mathbf{B}^{-1})_{1;m_0}$] are non-negative, the current solution is optimal. Otherwise, the minimum of these coefficients is found, and the corresponding variable is selected as the new entering basic variable. If that variable is ρ_{jk}, then the solution to the linear programming problem involving Z_j has identified $\mathbf{x}_{jk}^*$, so that the original constraint coefficients of ρ_{jk} are now identified. Hence, the revised simplex method can complete the iteration in the usual way.

Some manipulations are required to obtain the initial basic feasible solution for the new form of the problem. The above procedure is then repeated for a succession of iterations until the optimal solution is reached. The optimal values of the ρ_{jk} are then substituted into the equations for the $\mathbf{x}_j$ in order for the optimal solution to conform to the original form of the problem.

To illustrate the above procedure, consider again the example introduced at the beginning of this section. Thus, subproblem 1 is maximize

$$[4, 6]\begin{bmatrix} x_1 \\ x_2 \end{bmatrix},$$

subject to

$$\begin{bmatrix} 1 & 1 \\ 1 & 2 \end{bmatrix}\begin{bmatrix} x_1 \\ x_2 \end{bmatrix} \leq \begin{bmatrix} 5 \\ 8 \end{bmatrix} \quad \text{and} \quad \begin{bmatrix} x_1 \\ x_2 \end{bmatrix} \geq \begin{bmatrix} 0 \\ 0 \end{bmatrix},$$

so that its set of feasible solutions is as shown in Figure 15.2.

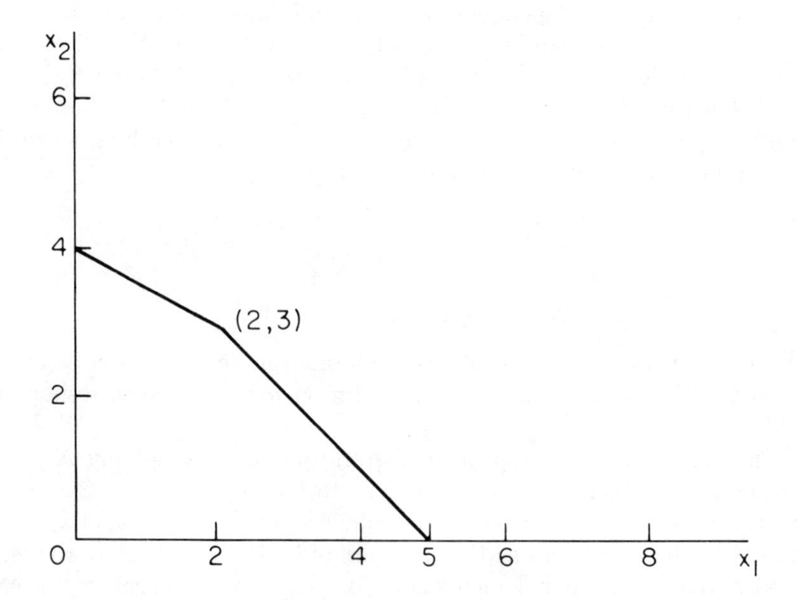

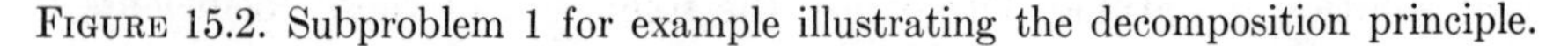
FIGURE 15.2. Subproblem 1 for example illustrating the decomposition principle.

It can be seen that this subproblem has four extreme points ($n_1 = 4$). One of these is the origin, considered the "first" of these extreme points, so

$$\mathbf{x}_{11}^* = \begin{bmatrix} 0 \\ 0 \end{bmatrix},$$

and ρ_{11} is the weight on this point.

Similarly, subproblem 2 is maximize

$$[8, 5] \begin{bmatrix} x_3 \\ x_4 \end{bmatrix},$$

subject to

$$[4, 3] \begin{bmatrix} x_3 \\ x_4 \end{bmatrix} \leq [12] \text{ and } \begin{bmatrix} x_3 \\ x_4 \end{bmatrix} \geq \begin{bmatrix} 0 \\ 0 \end{bmatrix},$$

and its set of feasible solutions is shown in Figure 15.3.

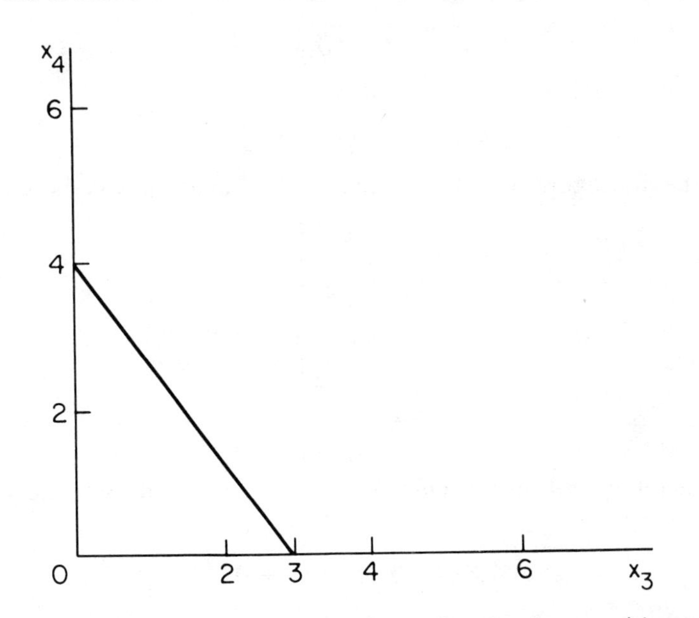

FIGURE 15.3. Subproblem 2 for example illustrating the decomposition principle.

One of the three extreme points is the origin, considered the "first" of these, so

$$\mathbf{x}_{21}^* = \begin{bmatrix} 0 \\ 0 \end{bmatrix},$$

and ρ_{21} is the weight on this point.

To initiate the procedure with the reformulated problem, let x_{s1}, x_{s2}, ρ_{11}, and ρ_{21} be the initial basic variables, so that (in the notation of the revised simplex method)

$$\mathbf{x}_B = \begin{bmatrix} x_{s1} \\ x_{s2} \\ \rho_{11} \\ \rho_{21} \end{bmatrix}.$$

Therefore, since $\mathbf{A}_1\mathbf{x}_{11}^* = \mathbf{0}$, $\mathbf{A}_2\mathbf{x}_{21}^* = \mathbf{0}$, $\mathbf{c}_1\mathbf{x}_{11}^* = \mathbf{0}$, and $\mathbf{c}_2\mathbf{x}_{21}^* = \mathbf{0}$, then

$$\mathbf{B} = \begin{bmatrix} 1 & 0 & 0 & 0 \\ 0 & 1 & 0 & 0 \\ 0 & 0 & 1 & 0 \\ 0 & 0 & 0 & 1 \end{bmatrix} = \mathbf{B}^{-1}, \quad \mathbf{x}_B = \mathbf{b}' = \begin{bmatrix} 20 \\ 25 \\ 1 \\ 1 \end{bmatrix}, \quad \mathbf{c}_B = [0, 0, 0, 0],$$

for the initial basic feasible solution.

To begin testing for optimality, let $j = 1$ and solve the linear programming problem, minimize

$$Z_1 = (\mathbf{0} - \mathbf{c}_1)\,\mathbf{x}_1 + 0,$$

subject to

$$\mathbf{A}_3\mathbf{x}_1 \leq \mathbf{b}_1 \quad \text{and} \quad \mathbf{x}_1 \geq \mathbf{0}.$$

Using the first figure to solve graphically, it is evident that the solution is

$$\mathbf{x}_1 = \begin{bmatrix} 2 \\ 3 \end{bmatrix},$$

so that $Z_1^* = -26$. (Let this extreme point be the "second" one, so that

$$\mathbf{x}_{12}^* = \begin{bmatrix} 2 \\ 3 \end{bmatrix},$$

and ρ_{12} is the weight on this point.) Next, let $j = 2$ and solve the problem, minimize

$$Z_2 = (\mathbf{0} - \mathbf{c}_2)\,\mathbf{x}_2 + 0,$$

subject to

$$\mathbf{A}_4\mathbf{x}_2 \leq \mathbf{b}_2 \quad \text{and} \quad \mathbf{x}_2 \geq \mathbf{0}.$$

Using the second figure, the solution is

$$\mathbf{x}_2 = \begin{bmatrix} 3 \\ 0 \end{bmatrix},$$

so $Z_2^* = -24$. Finally, calculate the current equation (0) coefficients of x_{s1} and x_{s2} as the elements of $\mathbf{c}_B(\mathbf{B}^{-1})_{1;m_0} = [0, 0]$. It can now be concluded that, since both $Z_1^* < 0$ and $Z_2^* < 0$, the current basic feasible solution is not optimal. Furthermore, since Z_1^* is the smaller of these, ρ_{12} is the new entering basic variable.

In order to perform the next iteration of the revised simplex method, it is now necessary to calculate the column of $\mathbf{A}'$ giving the coefficients of ρ_{12}. This column is

$$\mathbf{A}'_k = \begin{bmatrix} \mathbf{A}_1\mathbf{x}_{12}^* \\ 1 \\ 0 \end{bmatrix} = \begin{bmatrix} 11 \\ 13 \\ 1 \\ 0 \end{bmatrix}.$$

Proceeding in the usual way,

$$\mathbf{B}^{-1}\mathbf{A}'_k = \begin{bmatrix} 11 \\ 13 \\ 1 \\ 0 \end{bmatrix}, \quad \mathbf{B}^{-1}\mathbf{b}' = \begin{bmatrix} 20 \\ 25 \\ 1 \\ 1 \end{bmatrix},$$

so (in the notation of the revised simplex method)

$$\min_{a'_{ik}>0} \left\{ \frac{b'_i}{a'_{ik}} \right\} = 1,$$

which indicates that $r = 3$, i.e., ρ_{11} is the new leaving basic variable. Thus, the new values of $\mathbf{x}_B$ and $\mathbf{c}_B$ are

$$\mathbf{x}_B = \begin{bmatrix} x_{s1} \\ x_{s2} \\ \rho_{12} \\ \rho_{21} \end{bmatrix}, \quad \mathbf{c}_B = [0, 0, 26, 0].$$

To find the new value of $\mathbf{B}^{-1}$, set

$$\mathbf{E} = \begin{bmatrix} 1 & 0 & -11 & 0 \\ 0 & 1 & -13 & 0 \\ 0 & 0 & 1 & 0 \\ 0 & 0 & 0 & 1 \end{bmatrix},$$

so

$$\mathbf{B}_{\text{new}}^{-1} = \mathbf{E}\mathbf{B}_{\text{old}}^{-1} = \begin{bmatrix} 1 & 0 & -11 & 0 \\ 0 & 1 & -13 & 0 \\ 0 & 0 & 1 & 0 \\ 0 & 0 & 0 & 1 \end{bmatrix}.$$

The stage is now set for again testing whether the current basic feasible solution is optimal. In this case,

$$Z_1 = (\mathbf{0} - \mathbf{c}_1)\,\mathbf{x}_1 + 26\,,$$

so the minimum feasible solution is

$$\mathbf{x}_1 = \begin{bmatrix} 2 \\ 3 \end{bmatrix},$$

with $Z_1^* = 0$. Similarly,

$$Z_2 = (\mathbf{0} - \mathbf{c}_2)\,\mathbf{x}_2 + 0\,,$$

so the minimizing solution is

$$\mathbf{x}_2 = \begin{bmatrix} 3 \\ 0 \end{bmatrix},$$

with $Z_2^* = -24$. (Let this extreme point be the "second" one for subproblem 2, so

$$\mathbf{x}_{22}^* = \begin{bmatrix} 3 \\ 0 \end{bmatrix},$$

and ρ_{22} is the weight on this point.) Finally, $\mathbf{c}_B(\mathbf{B}^{-1})_{1;m_0} = [0, 0]$. Therefore, the current solution is not optimal, and ρ_{22} is the new entering basic variable.

Proceeding with the revised simplex method,

$$\mathbf{A}_k' = \begin{bmatrix} \mathbf{A}_2\mathbf{x}_{22}^* \\ 0 \\ 1 \end{bmatrix} = \begin{bmatrix} 6 \\ 18 \\ 0 \\ 1 \end{bmatrix},$$

so

$$\mathbf{B}^{-1}\mathbf{A}_k' = \begin{bmatrix} 6 \\ 18 \\ 0 \\ 1 \end{bmatrix}, \quad \mathbf{B}^{-1}\mathbf{b}' = \begin{bmatrix} 9 \\ 12 \\ 1 \\ 1 \end{bmatrix}.$$

Therefore,

$$\min_{a_{ik}'>0} \left\{\frac{b_i'}{a_{ik}'}\right\} = \frac{12}{18},$$

so $r = 2$, i.e., x_{s2} is the new leaving basic variable. Thus,

$$\mathbf{E} = \begin{bmatrix} 1 & -\frac{1}{3} & 0 & 0 \\ 0 & \frac{1}{18} & 0 & 0 \\ 0 & 0 & 1 & 0 \\ 0 & -\frac{1}{18} & 0 & 1 \end{bmatrix},$$

$$\mathbf{B}_{\text{new}}^{-1} = \mathbf{E}\mathbf{B}_{\text{old}}^{-1} = \begin{bmatrix} 1 & -\frac{1}{3} & -\frac{20}{3} & 0 \\ 0 & \frac{1}{18} & -\frac{13}{18} & 0 \\ 0 & 0 & 1 & 0 \\ 0 & -\frac{1}{18} & \frac{13}{18} & 1 \end{bmatrix}, \quad \mathbf{x}_B = \begin{bmatrix} x_{s1} \\ \rho_{22} \\ \rho_{12} \\ \rho_{21} \end{bmatrix},$$

and $\mathbf{c}_B = [0, 24, 26, 0]$.

Now test whether the new basic feasible solution is optimal. Since

$$Z_1 = \left([0, 24, 26, 0] \begin{bmatrix} 1 & -\frac{1}{3} \\ 0 & \frac{1}{18} \\ 0 & 0 \\ 0 & -\frac{1}{18} \end{bmatrix} \begin{bmatrix} 1 & 3 \\ 2 & 3 \end{bmatrix} - [4, 6]\right) \begin{bmatrix} x_1 \\ x_2 \end{bmatrix} + [0, 24, 26, 0] \begin{bmatrix} -\frac{20}{3} \\ -\frac{13}{18} \\ 1 \\ \frac{13}{18} \end{bmatrix}$$

$$= \left(\left[0, \frac{4}{3}\right] \begin{bmatrix} 1 & 3 \\ 2 & 3 \end{bmatrix} - [4, 6]\right) \begin{bmatrix} x_1 \\ x_2 \end{bmatrix} + \frac{26}{3}$$

$$= -\frac{4}{3}x_1 - 2x_2 + \frac{26}{3},$$

it is easily found graphically that the minimum feasible solution is

$$\begin{bmatrix} x_1 \\ x_2 \end{bmatrix} = \begin{bmatrix} 2 \\ 3 \end{bmatrix},$$

so $Z_1^* = 2/3$. Similarly,

$$Z_2 = \left(\left[0, \frac{4}{3}\right] \begin{bmatrix} 2 & 4 \\ 6 & 4 \end{bmatrix} - [8, 5]\right) \begin{bmatrix} x_3 \\ x_4 \end{bmatrix} + 0$$

$$= 0x_3 + \frac{1}{3}x_4,$$

so the minimizing solution is

$$\begin{bmatrix} x_3 \\ x_4 \end{bmatrix} = \begin{bmatrix} 0 \\ 0 \end{bmatrix},$$

and $Z_2^* = 0$.

Finally, $\mathbf{c}_B(\mathbf{B}^{-1})_{1;m_0} = [0,\ 4/3]$. Therefore, since $Z_1^* \geq 0$, $Z_2^* \geq 0$, and $\mathbf{c}_B(\mathbf{B}^{-1})_{1;m_0} \geq \mathbf{0}$, the current basic feasible solution is optimal. To identify this solution, set

$$\mathbf{x}_B = \begin{bmatrix} x_{s1} \\ \rho_{22} \\ \rho_{12} \\ \rho_{21} \end{bmatrix} = \mathbf{B}^{-1}\mathbf{b}' = \begin{bmatrix} 1 & -\frac{1}{3} & -\frac{20}{3} & 0 \\ 0 & \frac{1}{18} & -\frac{13}{18} & 0 \\ 0 & 0 & 1 & 0 \\ 0 & -\frac{1}{18} & \frac{13}{18} & 1 \end{bmatrix} \begin{bmatrix} 20 \\ 25 \\ 1 \\ 1 \end{bmatrix} = \begin{bmatrix} 5 \\ \frac{2}{3} \\ 1 \\ \frac{1}{3} \end{bmatrix}.$$

so

$$\mathbf{x}_1 = \begin{bmatrix} x_1 \\ x_2 \end{bmatrix} = \sum_{k=1}^{4} \rho_{1k}\mathbf{x}_{1k}^* = \mathbf{x}_{12}^* = \begin{bmatrix} 2 \\ 3 \end{bmatrix},$$

$$\mathbf{x}_2 = \begin{bmatrix} x_3 \\ x_4 \end{bmatrix} = \sum_{k=1}^{3} \rho_{2k}\mathbf{x}_{2k}^* = \frac{1}{3}\begin{bmatrix} 0 \\ 0 \end{bmatrix} + \frac{2}{3}\begin{bmatrix} 3 \\ 0 \end{bmatrix} = \begin{bmatrix} 2 \\ 0 \end{bmatrix}.$$

Thus, an optimal solution for this problem is $x_1 = 2$, $x_2 = 3$, $x_3 = 2$, $x_4 = 0$, with $x_0 = 42$.

15.4 LINEAR PROGRAMMING UNDER UNCERTAINTY

15.4.1 Introduction

One of the common problems in the practical application of linear programming is the difficulty of determining the proper values of the model parameters (the c_j, a_{ij}, and b_i). The true values of these parameters may not become known until after a solution has been chosen and implemented. This can sometimes be attributed solely to the inadequacy of the investigation. However, the values these parameters take on often are influenced by random events that are impossible to predict. In short, some or all of the model parameters may be random variables.

There are various ways of formulating the problem of linear programming under uncertainty.[105] These formulations can be classified into two types. The first is where the constraints are required to hold with probability one. The next section discusses how to cope with a certain problem of this type. The approach has been called stochastic programming since it is particularly applicable when the values of the decision variables are chosen at different points in time. The second type of formulation, called chance-constrained programming, is where feasible solutions are allowed to have a small probability of violating each constraint. A problem of this type is discussed in Sec. 15.4.3.

The general approach to the problems discussed here is to reduce them to ordinary linear programming problems that can be solved by the simplex method.

15.4.2 Stochastic Linear Programming

Consider the linear programming problem, maximize

$$x_0 = \sum_{j=1}^{n} c_j x_j ,$$

subject to

$$\sum_{j=1}^{n} a_{ij} x_j \leq b_i \text{[106]} \qquad \text{for } i = 1, 2, \cdots, m ,$$

$$\text{and} \quad x_j \geq 0, \qquad \text{for } j = 1, 2, \cdots, n ,$$

or, in matrix form,

$$\text{maximize} \quad x_0 = \mathbf{cx}, \qquad \text{subject to}$$
$$\mathbf{Ax} \leq \mathbf{b}$$
$$\text{and } \mathbf{x} \geq \mathbf{0} .$$

Now suppose that some or all of the parameters (the c_j, a_{ij}, and b_i) are random variables rather than constants. This necessitates a reformulation of the objective function. Since x_0 becomes a random variable if any of the c_j are random variables, and it is meaningless to maximize a random variable, x_0 must be replaced by some deterministic function. There are many possible choices for this function, each of which may be very reasonable under certain circumstances. Perhaps the most natural choice, and the one assumed here, is the expected value of x_0,

[105] The word "uncertainty" is being used here in a nontechnical way in order to conform with the common terminology for this problem. In general, a technical distinction is sometimes made between the terms "risk" and "uncertainty" to indicate that the probability distributions of the random variables involved are known and unknown, respectively. Technically speaking, only "risk" problems are considered throughout Sec. 15.4.

[106] Any constraint may also be expressed as an equation rather than an inequation.

$$E(x_0) = \sum_{j=1}^{n} E(c_j)x_j = E(\mathbf{cx}) .$$

Similarly, the constraints must be reinterpreted if any of the a_{ij} and b_i are random variables. One interpretation is that a solution is considered feasible only if it satisfies all of the constraints for all possible combinations of the parameter values. This is the interpretation assumed in this section, although it is soon modified to allow certain random variable parameters to become known before values are assigned to certain x_j. It should be noted that this interpretation may result in having no solutions that are considered feasible. If so, perhaps one should adopt some other interpretation, such as the one described in the next section.

No practical solution procedure has yet been developed for solving the general problem described above. However, a straightforward approach is available for solving the important special case where each random variable which is a model parameter can only take on any one of a finite number of known values. The reason it is solvable is that there is only a finite number of possible combinations of parameter values. To express this mathematically, let $\mathbf{M}$ be the matrix (or, more precisely, the array) such that

$$\mathbf{M} = \begin{bmatrix} c_1 & c_2 & \cdots & c_n & 0 \\ a_{11} & a_{12} & \cdots & a_{1n} & b_1 \\ a_{21} & a_{22} & \cdots & a_{2n} & b_2 \\ \cdot & \cdot & & \cdot & \cdot \\ \cdot & \cdot & & \cdot & \cdot \\ \cdot & \cdot & & \cdot & \cdot \\ a_{m1} & a_{m2} & \cdots & a_{mn} & b_m \end{bmatrix} = \begin{array}{c} \\ 1 \\ m \end{array} \begin{array}{c} \begin{array}{cc} n & 1 \end{array} \\ \left[\begin{array}{c|c} \mathbf{c} & 0 \\ \hline \mathbf{A} & \mathbf{b} \end{array}\right] \end{array} .$$

Since some of the elements of $\mathbf{M}$ are random variables, $\mathbf{M}$ can become any one of many different matrices when these random variables take on their various possible values. The special case being considered here is where $\mathbf{M}$ can only become any one of a finite number of different matrices, $\mathbf{M}^{(1)}$, $\mathbf{M}^{(2)}, \cdots, \mathbf{M}^{(N)}$, whose elements are numbers. Let p_k $(k = 1, 2, \cdots, N)$ be the probability that $\mathbf{M}$ will become $\mathbf{M}^{(k)}$, so that

$$\sum_{k=1}^{N} p_k = 1 .$$

Suppose that these probabilities are known or can be estimated. Now let $\mathbf{c}^{(k)}$, $\mathbf{A}^{(k)}$, and $\mathbf{b}^{(k)}$ denote the partitioned parts of $\mathbf{M}^{(k)}$ such that

$$\mathbf{M}^{(k)} = \begin{array}{c} \\ 1 \\ m \end{array} \begin{array}{c} \begin{array}{cc} n & 1 \end{array} \\ \left[\begin{array}{c|c} \mathbf{c}^{(k)} & 0 \\ \hline \mathbf{A}^{(k)} & \mathbf{b}^{(k)} \end{array}\right] \end{array}$$

Thus, $\mathbf{c}^{(k)}$, $\mathbf{A}^{(k)}$, and $\mathbf{b}^{(k)}$ are what **c**, **A**, and **b** become, respectively, when **M** becomes $\mathbf{M}^{(k)}$. For the moment, assume that all of the x_j $(j = 1, 2, \cdots, N)$ must be determined before any information becomes available regarding what **M** will become. The special case then easily reduces to an ordinary linear programming problem. In matrix form, the problem is to determine **x** so as to maximize

$$E(x_0) = \sum_{k=1}^{N} p_k \mathbf{c}^{(k)} \mathbf{x} \,,$$

subject to

$$\mathbf{A}^{(k)}\mathbf{x} \leq \mathbf{b}^{(k)}, \qquad \text{for } k = 1, 2, \cdots, N \,,$$
$$\text{and} \quad \mathbf{x} \geq \mathbf{0} \,.$$

Hence, the simplex method can be used to solve the problem (although the number of constraints may be prohibitively large if N is large).

The special case is now reformulated after dropping the above assumption that all of the x_j must be determined before observing the value taken on by any of the random variable elements of **M.** Frequently, when some of the model parameters are originally random variables, the final decision on the values of some of the x_j can be postponed until at least some of these parameters become known. This is typically true, for example, in dynamic situations where the final decisions on the x_j are made at different points in time. In such cases, the parameters associated with the earlier time periods considered become known before implementing the decisions involving the later time periods. A second example is where the final decisions on the x_j are made by different decision-makers in different parts of a decentralized organization. Since it may not be economical to obtain all relevant information, each decision-maker may only observe the values of the parameters which are directly related to his part of the organization before making his decision. To permit these possibilities, assume that, for each value of $j (j = 1, 2, \cdots, n)$, the value taken on by certain specified random variable elements of **M** will be known when the final decision on the value of x_j must be made. The known elements are generally not the same for all values of j. For $j = 1, 2, \cdots, n$, let $\mathbf{M}_j^{(k)} (k = 1, 2, \cdots, N)$ be the matrix obtained from $\mathbf{M}^{(k)}$ by replacing those elements which will not be known when x_j is chosen by *, where * denotes an unknown element. Thus, if **M** becomes $\mathbf{M}^{(k)}$, $\mathbf{M}_j^{(k)}$ includes the part of $\mathbf{M}^{(k)}$ that is known when the final decision on x_j must be made. Clearly, the decision made should be influenced by the new information that has become available. Therefore, the value assigned to x_j depends upon which one of the $\mathbf{M}_j^{(k)}$ matrices $(k = 1, 2, \cdots, N)$ is observed. Let $x_{jk} (k = 1, 2, \cdots, N)$ denote the value assigned to $x_j (j = 1, 2, \cdots, n)$ if $\mathbf{M}_j^{(k)}$ is observed. Thus, the x_{jk} become the new decision variables of the problem. Let the vector $\mathbf{x}^{(k)}$ be

$$\mathbf{x}^{(k)} = \begin{bmatrix} x_{1k} \\ x_{2k} \\ \cdot \\ \cdot \\ \cdot \\ x_{nk} \end{bmatrix}, \quad \text{for } k = 1, 2, \cdots, N.$$

Thus, the problem will be solved if the $\mathbf{x}^{(k)}$ can be determined, since this would determine in advance what the x_j should be for every possible situation that can arise.

The stage is now set for writing down the new formulation of the model. However, it should first be noted that there may be some duplication in the x_{jk} decision variables. The reason is that some of the $\mathbf{M}_j^{(k)}$ matrices may be identical. This occurs whenever some of the $\mathbf{M}^{(k)}$ matrices differ only in the elements that are not known when x_j is chosen. Since the decision should be the same whenever the known information is the same, $x_{jk_1} \equiv x_{jk_2}$ whenever $\mathbf{M}_j^{(k_1)} = \mathbf{M}_j^{(k_2)}$. Each such set of identical variables should be replaced by a single decision variable. This is necessary to insure that the solution procedure accurately differentiates between information that will and will not be known, and thereby assigns the same value to identical variables. It also decreases the computational effort.

The problem can now be formulated as an ordinary linear programming problem. Stated in matrix form, the problem is to determine the elements (as adjusted above) of $\mathbf{x}^{(1)}, \mathbf{x}^{(2)}, \cdots, \mathbf{x}^{(N)}$ so as to maximize

$$E(x_0) = \sum_{k=1}^{N} p_k \mathbf{c}^{(k)} \mathbf{x}^{(k)},$$

subject to

$$\begin{aligned} \mathbf{A}^{(k)}\mathbf{x}^{(k)} &\leq \mathbf{b}^{(k)}, && \text{for } k = 1, 2, \cdots, N, \\ \text{and } \mathbf{x}^{(k)} &\geq 0, && \text{for } k = 1, 2, \cdots, N. \end{aligned}$$

(Some of these constraints will be identical, so the extra ones can be deleted.) The optimal solution yielded by the simplex method provides a complete plan for assigning the values of the x_j as the available information becomes known. Furthermore, this plan yields the largest $E(x_0)$ from among those plans that guarantee the assigned values will turn out to constitute a feasible solution.

Notice that the earlier formulation is actually just the special case of this one such that all of the $\mathbf{x}^{(k)}$ vectors are identical. This is true because, if no new information will become available, all of the $\mathbf{M}_j^{(k)}$ are identical, so that the same decision variable is used for the jth element ($j = 1, 2, \cdots, n$) of all of the $\mathbf{x}^{(k)}$ ($k = 1, 2, \cdots, N$).

To illustrate this approach, consider the example of Sec. 5.5. Suppose that there is actually some uncertainty as to what the proper value of the coefficients in the objective function and in the third constraint will turn out to be. Therefore,

$$\mathbf{M} = \begin{bmatrix} c_1 & c_2 & 0 \\ a_{11} & a_{12} & b_1 \\ a_{21} & a_{22} & b_2 \\ a_{31} & a_{32} & b_3 \end{bmatrix} = \begin{bmatrix} c_1 & c_2 & 0 \\ 1 & 0 & 4 \\ 0 & 1 & 6 \\ a_{31} & a_{32} & 18 \end{bmatrix},$$

where c_1, c_2, a_{31}, and a_{32} are random variables. Suppose that the possible values of c_1 and a_{31} are $c_1 = 3$, $a_{31} = 3$, and $c_1 = 4$, $a_{31} = 2$. Suppose that the possible values of c_2 and a_{32} are $c_2 = 5$, $a_{32} = 2$, and $c_2 = 4$, $a_{32} = 3$. Therefore, $\mathbf{M}$ can become any one of the following four matrices.

$$\mathbf{M}^{(1)} = \begin{bmatrix} 3 & 5 & 0 \\ 1 & 0 & 4 \\ 0 & 1 & 6 \\ 3 & 2 & 18 \end{bmatrix}, \quad \mathbf{M}^{(2)} = \begin{bmatrix} 4 & 5 & 0 \\ 1 & 0 & 4 \\ 0 & 1 & 6 \\ 2 & 2 & 18 \end{bmatrix},$$

$$\mathbf{M}^{(3)} = \begin{bmatrix} 3 & 4 & 0 \\ 1 & 0 & 4 \\ 0 & 1 & 6 \\ 3 & 3 & 18 \end{bmatrix}, \quad \mathbf{M}^{(4)} = \begin{bmatrix} 4 & 4 & 0 \\ 1 & 0 & 4 \\ 0 & 1 & 6 \\ 2 & 3 & 18 \end{bmatrix}$$

Suppose it is known that these matrices are equally likely, so that $p_1 = p_2 = p_3 = p_4 = \frac{1}{4}$. Suppose that the values taken on by c_1 and a_{31} will become known before the final decision must be made regarding the value of x_1. Hence,

$$\mathbf{M}_1^{(1)} = \mathbf{M}_1^{(3)} = \begin{bmatrix} 3 & * & 0 \\ 1 & 0 & 4 \\ 0 & 1 & 6 \\ 3 & * & 18 \end{bmatrix}, \quad \text{and} \quad \mathbf{M}_1^{(2)} = \mathbf{M}_1^{(4)} = \begin{bmatrix} 4 & * & 0 \\ 1 & 0 & 4 \\ 0 & 1 & 6 \\ 2 & * & 18 \end{bmatrix}.$$

Similarly, suppose that c_2 and a_{32} become known before choosing x_2, so that

$$\mathbf{M}_2^{(1)} = \mathbf{M}_2^{(2)} = \begin{bmatrix} * & 5 & 0 \\ 1 & 0 & 4 \\ 0 & 1 & 6 \\ * & 2 & 18 \end{bmatrix}, \quad \text{and} \quad \mathbf{M}_2^{(3)} = \mathbf{M}_2^{(4)} = \begin{bmatrix} * & 4 & 0 \\ 1 & 0 & 4 \\ 0 & 1 & 6 \\ * & 3 & 18 \end{bmatrix}.$$

Let x_1' denote the value assigned to x_1 if $\mathbf{M}_1^{(1)}$ or $\mathbf{M}_1^{(3)}$ is observed, i.e., if it is learned that $c_1 = 3$, $a_{31} = 3$. Let x_1'' be the value of x_1 if $\mathbf{M}_1^{(2)}$ or $\mathbf{M}_1^{(4)}$ is observed. Let $x_2 = x_2'$ if $\mathbf{M}_2^{(1)}$ or $\mathbf{M}_2^{(2)}$ is observed, and let $x_2 = x_2''$ if $\mathbf{M}_2^{(3)}$ or $\mathbf{M}_2^{(4)}$ is observed. Then

$$\mathbf{x}^{(1)} = \begin{bmatrix} x_1' \\ x_2' \end{bmatrix}, \quad \mathbf{x}^{(2)} = \begin{bmatrix} x_1'' \\ x_2' \end{bmatrix}, \quad \mathbf{x}^{(3)} = \begin{bmatrix} x_1' \\ x_2'' \end{bmatrix}, \quad \mathbf{x}^{(4)} = \begin{bmatrix} x_1'' \\ x_2'' \end{bmatrix}.$$

Referring to the general formulation given earlier, it is seen that the ordinary linear programming formulation of this problem is, maximize

$$E(x_0) = \frac{1}{4}[(3x_1' + 5x_2') + (4x_1'' + 5x_2') + (3x_1' + 4x_2'') + (4x_1'' + 4x_2'')]$$
$$= \frac{3}{2}x_1' + 2x_1'' + \frac{5}{2}x_2' + 2x_2'',$$

subject to

$$\begin{array}{rlr}
(1) & x_1' & \leq 4 \\
(2) & x_2' & \leq 6 \\
(3) & 3x_1' + 2x_2' & \leq 18 \\
(4) & x_1'' & \leq 4 \\
(5) & x_2' & \leq 6 \\
(6) & 2x_1'' + 2x_2' & \leq 18 \\
(7) & x_1' & \leq 4 \\
(8) & x_2'' & \leq 6 \\
(9) & 3x_1' + 3x_2'' & \leq 18 \\
(10) & x_1'' & \leq 4 \\
(11) & x_2'' & \leq 6 \\
(12) & 2x_1'' + 3x_2'' & \leq 18
\end{array}$$

and

$$x_1' \geq 0, x_1'' \geq 0, x_2' \geq 0, x_2'' \geq 0.$$

Constraints (5), (7), (10), and (11) can be deleted from the model since they duplicate previous constraints. Nevertheless, this example illustrates that the stochastic programming approach to linear programming under uncertainty greatly increases the size of the model to be solved.

15.4.3 Chance-Constrained Programming

Abraham Charnes and William Cooper have developed an approach to linear programming under uncertainty which they have called chance-constrained programming.[107] This approach may be used when it is highly desirable, but not absolutely essential, that the constraints hold. The formulation in the preceding section required that all of the constraints must hold for all possible combinations of the parameter values. The chance-constrained programming formulation requires only that each constraint must hold for most of these combinations. More precisely, this formulation replaces the original linear programming constraints,

$$\sum_{j=1}^{n} a_{ij}x_j \leq b_i, \qquad (i = 1, 2, \cdots, m),$$

[107] A. Charnes and W. W. Cooper, "Chance-Constrained Programming," *Management Science*, **6,** 73–80 (1959).

by

$$P\left\{\sum_{j=1}^{n} a_{ij}x_j \leq b_i\right\} \geq \alpha_i, \qquad (i = 1, 2, \cdots, m),$$

where the α_i are specified constants between zero and one (although they are normally chosen to be reasonably close to one). Therefore, a non-negative solution, $(x_1, x_2, \cdots, x_n)$, is considered to be feasible if and only if

$$P\left\{\sum_{j=1}^{n} a_{ij}x_j \leq b_i\right\} \geq \alpha_i, \qquad \text{for } i = 1, 2, \cdots, m.$$

Each complementary probability, $1 - \alpha_i$, represents the allowable risk that the random variables will take on values such that

$$\sum_{j=1}^{n} a_{ij}x_j > b_i.$$

Thus, the objective is to select the "best" non-negative solution that "probably" will turn out to satisfy each of the original constraints when the random variables (the a_{ij}, b_i, and c_j) take on their values.

There are many possible expressions for the objective function when some of the c_j are random variables, and several of these have been explored elsewhere[108] in the context of chance-constrained programming. However, only the one assumed in the preceding section, viz., the expected value function, is considered here.

No procedure is now available for solving the general chance-constrained (linear) programming problem. However, certain important special cases are solvable. The one discussed here is where: (1) all of the a_{ij} parameters are constants, so that only some or all of the c_j and b_i are random variables, (2) the probability distribution of the b_i is a known multivariate normal distribution, and (3) c_j is statistically independent of b_i $(j = 1, 2, \cdots, n;\ i = 1, 2, \cdots, m)$.

As in the preceding section, it is initially assumed that all of the x_j must be determined before learning the value taken on by any of the random variables. Then, after the approach for this case is developed, the more general case where this assumption is dropped will be discussed.

The chance-constrained programming problem considered here fits the linear programming model format except for the constraints,

$$P\left\{\sum_{j=1}^{n} a_{ij}x_j \leq b_i\right\} \geq \alpha_i, \qquad (i = 1, 2, \cdots, m).$$

[108] A. Charnes and W. W. Cooper, "Deterministic Equivalents for Optimizing and Satisficing under Chance Constraints," *Operations Research*, **11**, 18–39 (1963).

Therefore, the goal is to convert these constraints into legitimate linear programming constraints, so that the simplex method can be used to solve the problem. This is easy to do under the stated assumptions. To begin, notice that

$$P\left\{\sum_{j=1}^{n} a_{ij}x_j \leq b_i\right\} = P\left\{\frac{\sum_{j=1}^{n} a_{ij}x_j - E(b_i)}{\sigma_{b_i}} \leq \frac{b_i - E(b_i)}{\sigma_{b_i}}\right\},$$

where $E(b_i)$ and σ_{b_i} are the mean and standard deviation of b_i, respectively. Since b_i is assumed to have a normal distribution, $[b_i - E(b_i)]/\sigma_{b_i}$ must also be normal with mean zero and standard deviation one. In Sec. 3.7.4, K_β is taken to be the constant such that

$$P\{Z \geq K_\beta\} = \beta,$$

where β is any given number between zero and one, and where Z is the random variable whose probability distribution is normal with mean zero and standard deviation one. Table A5.1 in Appendix 5 gives K_β for various values of β. For example,

$$K_{0.90} = -1.28,\ K_{0.95} = -1.645, \text{ and } K_{0.99} = -2.33\,.$$

Therefore, it now follows that

$$P\left\{K_{\alpha_i} \leq \frac{b_i - E(b_i)}{\sigma_{b_i}}\right\} = \alpha_i\,.$$

It is obvious that this probability would be increased if K_{α_i} were replaced by a smaller number, and that it would be decreased if K_{α_i} were replaced by a larger number. Hence,

$$P\left\{\frac{\sum_{j=1}^{n} a_{ij}x_j - E(b_i)}{\sigma_{b_i}} \leq \frac{b_i - E(b_i)}{\sigma_{b_i}}\right\} \geq \alpha_i$$

for a given solution if and only if

$$\frac{\sum_{j=1}^{n} a_{ij}x_j - E(b_i)}{\sigma_{b_i}} \leq K_{\alpha_i}\,.$$

Rewriting both expressions in an equivalent form, the conclusion is that

$$P\left\{\sum_{j=1}^{n} a_{ij}x_j \leq b_i\right\} \geq \alpha_i$$

if and only if

$$\sum_{j=1}^{n} a_{ij}x_j \leq E(b_i) + K_{\alpha_i}\sigma_{b_i},$$

so that the probability constraint can be replaced by this linear programming constraint. The fact that these constraints are equivalent is illustrated by Fig. 15.4.

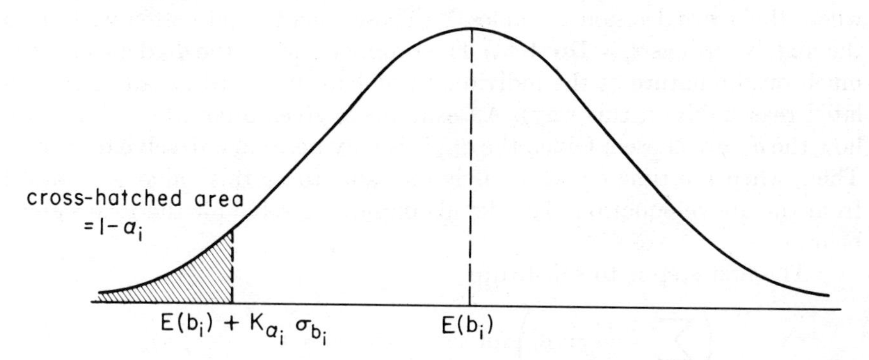

FIGURE 15.4. Probability density function of b_i.

To summarize, the chance-constrained programming problem considered above can be reduced to the following equivalent linear programming problem. Maximize

$$E(x_0) = \sum_{j=1}^{n} E(c_j)x_j,$$

subject to

$$\sum_{j=1}^{n} a_{ij}x_j \leq E(b_i) + K_{\alpha_i}\sigma_{b_i}, \qquad \text{for } i = 1, 2, \cdots, m,$$

and

$$x_j \geq 0, \qquad \text{for } j = 1, 2, \cdots, n.$$

Now consider the situation where some of the b_i become known before some of the x_j values must be chosen. This can occur in various ways as described in the preceding section. It is highly desirable to formulate and solve problems of this type in such a way that the final decision on the x_j is partially based on the new information that has become available. The chance-constrained programming approach to this situation is to solve for each x_j as an explicit function of the b_i whose values become known before a value must be assigned to x_j. From a computational standpoint, it is convenient to deal with linear functions of the b_i, thereby leading to what are called "linear decision rules" for the x_j. In particular, let

$$x_j = \sum_{k=1}^{m} d_{jk}b_k + y_j, \qquad \text{for } j = 1, 2, \cdots, n,$$

where the d_{jk} are specified constants (where $d_{jk} = 0$ whenever the value taken on by b_k is not known before a value must be assigned to x_j), and where the y_j are decision variables.[109] (These equations are often written in the matrix form as $\mathbf{x} = \mathbf{D}\mathbf{b} + \mathbf{y}$.) The proper choice of the d_{jk} depends very much on the nature of the individual problem (if indeed it can be formulated reasonably in this way). An example is given later which illustrates how the d_{jk} are chosen. Given the d_{jk}, it is only necessary to solve for the y_j. Then, when the time comes to assign a value to x_j, this value is obtained from the above equation. The details on how to solve for the y_j are given below.

The first step is to substitute

$$\left(\sum_{k=1}^{m} d_{jk}b_k + y_j\right) \text{for } x_j \qquad (\text{for } j = 1, 2, \cdots, n)$$

throughout the original chance-constrained programming model. The objective function becomes

$$\begin{aligned} E(x_0) &= E\left[\sum_{j=1}^{n} c_j \left(\sum_{k=1}^{m} d_{jk}b_k + y_j\right)\right] \\ &= \sum_{j=1}^{n} \sum_{k=1}^{m} d_{jk}E(c_j)E(b_k) + \sum_{j=1}^{n} E(c_j)y_j . \end{aligned}$$

Since

$$\sum_{j=1}^{n} \sum_{k=1}^{m} d_{jk}E(c_j)E(b_k)$$

is a constant, it can be dropped from the objective function, so that the new objective becomes, maximize

$$\sum_{j=1}^{n} E(c_j)y_j .$$

[109] Another common type of linear decision rule in chance-constrained programming is to let

$$x_j = \sum_{k=1}^{m} b_k d_{jk}, \quad \text{for} \quad j = 1, 2, \cdots, n,$$

where d_{jk} is a *decision variable* if b_k becomes known before a value must be assigned to x_j and is zero otherwise. This case is considered in Problem 21.

Since

$$\sum_{j=1}^{n} a_{ij}x_j = \sum_{j=1}^{n} a_{ij}\left(\sum_{k=1}^{m} d_{jk}b_k + y_j\right)$$
$$= \sum_{j=1}^{n} \sum_{k=1}^{m} a_{ij}\, d_{jk}b_k + \sum_{j=1}^{n} a_{ij}y_j\,,$$

the constraints,

$$P\left\{\sum_{j=1}^{n} a_{ij}x_j \le b_i\right\} \ge \alpha_i, \qquad (i = 1, 2, \cdots, m)\,,$$

become

$$P\left\{\sum_{j=1}^{n} a_{ij}y_j \le b_i - \sum_{j=1}^{n} \sum_{k=1}^{m} a_{ij}\, d_{jk}b_k\right\} \ge \alpha_i, \qquad (i = 1, 2, \cdots, m)\,.$$

The next step is to reduce these constraints to linear programming constraints. This is done just as before since the fundamental nature of the constraints has not been changed. Since

$$\left(b_i - \sum_{j=1}^{n} \sum_{k=1}^{m} a_{ij}\, d_{jk}b_k\right)$$

is a linear function of normal random variables, it must also be a normally distributed random variable. Let μ_i and σ_i denote the mean and standard deviations, respectively, of

$$\left(b_i - \sum_{j=1}^{n} \sum_{k=1}^{m} a_{ij}\, d_{jk}b_k\right).$$

(Thus,

$$\mu_i = E(b_i) - \sum_{j=1}^{n} \sum_{k=1}^{m} a_{ij}\, d_{jk}E(b_k)\,,$$

and, if the b_k are mutually independent,

$$\sigma_i^2 = \sum_{\substack{k=1\\k\neq i}}^{m}\left[\sum_{j=1}^{n} a_{ij}\, d_{jk}\right]^2 \sigma_{b_k}^2 + \left[1 - \sum_{j=1}^{n} a_{ij}\, d_{ji}\right]^2 \sigma_{b_i}^2\,.$$

Lacking independence, covariance terms would be included.) It then follows as before that these constraints are equivalent to the linear programming constraints,

$$\sum_{j=1}^{n} a_{ij}y_j \le \mu_i + K_{\alpha_i}\sigma_i, \qquad (i = 1, 2, \cdots, m)\,.$$

It usually makes sense for the individual problem to add the restriction that

$$y_j \geq 0, \qquad \text{for } j = 1, 2, \cdots, n\,.$$

The model consisting of the new objective function and these constraints can then be solved by the simplex method.

To illustrate the way in which linear decision rules may arise, consider the problem of scheduling the production output for a given product over the next n time periods. Let x_j ($j = 1, 2, \cdots, n$) be the total number of units produced in time periods 1 through j, so that $(x_j - x_{j-1})$ is the output in period j. Thus, the x_j are the decision variables. Let S_j ($j = 1, 2, \cdots, n$) be the total number of units sold in time periods 1 through j. Assuming sales cannot be predicted exactly in advance, the S_j are random variables such that the value taken on by S_j becomes known at the end of period j. Assume that the S_j are normally distributed. Suppose that the firm's management places a high priority on not alienating customers by a late delivery of their purchases. Hence, assuming no initial inventory, the x_j should be chosen such that it is almost certain that $x_j \geq S_j$. Therefore, one set of constraints that should be included in the mathematical model is

$$P\{x_j \geq S_j\} \geq \alpha_j, \qquad \text{for } j = 1, 2, \cdots, n\,,$$

where the α_j are selected numbers close to one. However, rather than solving for the x_j directly at the outset, the problem should be solved in such a way that the information on cumulative sales can be used as it becomes available. Suppose that the final decision on x_j need not be made until the beginning of period j. Then it is clear that it would be highly desirable to take into account the value taken on by S_{j-1} before assigning a value to x_j. Therefore, let $x_j = S_{j-1} + y_j$ for $j = 1, 2, \cdots, n$ (where $S_0 = 0$), and then solve only for the y_j at the outset. To express this in the notation used earlier, the constraints should be written as

$$P\{-x_j \leq -S_i\} \geq \alpha_i\,, \qquad \text{for } i = 1, 2, \cdots, m(m = n)\,,$$

so that $b_i = -S_i$. Hence,

$$x_j = \sum_{k=1}^{m} d_{jk} b_k + y_j = -b_{j-1} + y_j\,,$$

so that $d_{j(j-1)} = -1$ and $d_{jk} = 0$ for $k \neq j - 1$. Since y_j is just the number of units of the product that is available for immediate delivery in period j, it is natural to impose the additional restriction that $y_j \geq 0$ for $j = 1, 2, \cdots, n$. Therefore, assuming that the remainder of the model also fits the linear programming format, this particular problem can be formulated and solved by the general procedure described in this section.[110]

[110] For a complete formulation of a (more complicated) problem of this type, see A. Charnes, W. W. Cooper, and G. H. Symonds, "Cost Horizons and Certainty Equivalents: An Approach to Stochastic Programming of Heating Oil Production," *Management Science*, **4**, 235–263 (1958).

SELECTED REFERENCES

1. Dantzig, George B., *Linear Programming and Extensions*, Princeton University Press, Princeton, N.J., 1963.
2. Hadley, G., *Linear Programming*, Addison-Wesley, Reading, Mass., 1962.
3. Näslund, Bertil, "Mathematical Programming under Risk," *The Swedish Journal of Economics*, **18,** 240–255 (1965).
4. Simonnard, Michel, *Linear Programming*, translated by William Jewell, Prentice-Hall, Englewood Cliffs, N.J., 1966.
5. Graves, Robert L., and Wolfe, Philip, (eds.), *Recent Advances in Mathematical Programming*, McGraw-Hill, New York, 1963.

PROBLEMS

1. Consider the problem, maximize

$$Z_x = 4x_1 + 3x_2 ,$$

subject to

$$\begin{aligned} 2x_1 + \quad x_2 &\leq 10 \\ 2x_1 + \quad 5x_2 &\leq 20 \\ x_1 \geq 0,\ x_2 &\geq \ 0 . \end{aligned}$$

Write the dual model for this problem, and then graphically draw the constraints and set of feasible solutions for both problems. Identify the six basic solutions (both feasible and infeasible) for each problem. Then apply the simplex method (algebraically) to the primal problem. At each iteration, find the basic feasible solution for the primal problem and the complementary basic solution for the dual problem, and identify the corresponding points on the two drawings.

2. Consider the primal and dual problems in the form presented at the beginning of Sec. 5.7.1. Let $y_1^*, y_2^*, \cdots, y_m^*$ denote the optimal solution for this dual problem. Suppose that $b_1, b_2, \cdots, b_m$ are then replaced by $b_1', b_2', \cdots, b_m'$. Let $x_1', x_2', \cdots, x_n'$ denote the optimal solution for the new primal problem.

Prove that

$$\sum_{j=1}^{n} c_j x_j' \leq \sum_{i=1}^{m} b_i' y_i^* .$$

3. Suppose that the primary constraints for the primal problem are equations rather than inequations, so that the problem is, maximize

$$Z_x = \sum_{j=1}^{n} c_j x_j ,$$

subject to

$$\sum_{j=1}^{n} a_{ij}x_j = b_i, \qquad \text{for } i = 1, 2, \cdots, m,$$

and

$$x_j \geq 0, \qquad \text{for } j = 1, 2, \cdots, n.$$

Let $y_1, y_2, \cdots, y_m$ denote the corresponding dual variables, where y_i^* denotes the optimal value of y_i ($i = 1, 2, \cdots, m$).

Suppose that, in order to initiate the simplex method on the primal problem, artificial slack variables are introduced by the Big M method discussed in Sec. 5.6.4. Thus, *before* eliminating the basic variables from equation (0), the initial set of equations is:

$$\begin{aligned}
&(0) \quad Z_x - c_1x_1 - c_2x_2 - \cdots - c_nx_n + Mx_{n+1} + Mx_{n+2} + \cdots + Mx_{n+m} = 0\\
&(1) \quad a_{11}x_1 + a_{12}x_2 + \cdots + a_{1n}x_n + x_{n+1} = b_1\\
&(2) \quad a_{21}x_1 + a_{22}x_2 + \cdots + a_{2n}x_n + x_{n+2} = b_2\\
&\qquad \vdots\\
&(m) \quad a_{m1}x_1 + a_{m2}x_2 + \cdots + a_{mn}x_n + x_{n+m} = b_m.
\end{aligned}$$

Suppose that the simplex method is then used to obtain the optimal solution. Let z_j^* denote the net amount by which the coefficient of x_j in equation (0) has been increased in the process of obtaining the optimal solution, where $j = 1, 2, \cdots, n + m$. Thus, the final equation (0) is

$$Z_x + \sum_{j=1}^{n} (z_j^* - c_j)x_j + \sum_{i=1}^{m} (z_{n+i}^* + M)x_{n+i} = Z_x^*.$$

Prove that

$$y_i^* = z_{n+i}^*, \qquad \text{for } i = 1, 2, \cdots, m.$$

4. Apply the dual simplex method to the dual model obtained in Problem 1.

5. Consider the problem, minimize

$$Z = 4x_1 + 6x_2 + 3x_3,$$

subject to

$$\begin{aligned}
3x_1 + 4x_2 + x_3 &\geq 10\\
-2x_1 - 3x_2 + 2x_3 &\leq -5\\
x_1 - 2x_2 - 3x_3 &\leq -1\\
3x_1 + 2x_2 + 2x_3 &\geq 5
\end{aligned}$$

and

$$x_j \geq 0, \quad \text{for } j = 1, 2, 3 .$$

Solve this problem by the dual simplex method.

6. Consider the following linear programming problem. Maximize

$$Z = -x_1 + 3x_2 - 2x_3 ,$$

subject to

$$\begin{aligned} 3x_1 - x_2 + 2x_3 &\leq 7 \text{ (resource A)} \\ -2x_1 + 4x_2 &\leq 12 \text{ (resource B)} \\ -4x_1 + 3x_2 + 8x_3 &\leq 10 \text{ (resource C)} \end{aligned}$$

and

$$x_j \geq 0, \quad \text{for } j = 1, 2, 3 .$$

Let x_4, x_5, and x_6 be introduced as slack variables in the usual way. The corresponding *final* set of equations yielding the optimal solution is:

$$\begin{aligned} Z + \frac{12}{5} x_3 + \frac{1}{5} x_4 + \frac{4}{5} x_5 &= 11 \\ x_1 + \frac{4}{5} x_3 + \frac{2}{5} x_4 + \frac{1}{10} x_5 &= 4 \\ x_2 + \frac{2}{5} x_3 + \frac{1}{5} x_4 + \frac{3}{10} x_5 &= 5 \\ 10x_3 + x_4 - \frac{1}{2} x_5 + x_6 &= 11 . \end{aligned}$$

(a) What is the optimal solution (the optimal values for Z, x_1, x_2, x_3, x_4, x_5, x_6)?
(b) What is the corresponding dual model?
(c) What is the optimal solution for the dual model?
(d) Considering Z as profit in dollars, what would be the contribution to profit if one more unit of resource A were made available? Answer the same question for resources B and C.
(e) Suppose that more recent data have led to the following revision of the original objective function, $Z = -x_1 + 3x_2 + x_3$. Is the old solution [Part (a)] still optimal? If not, find the new optimal solution.
(f) Suppose that one instead wants to investigate the effect of revising the objective function to $Z = -x_1 + x_2 - 2x_3$. Is the old solution still optimal? If not, find the new optimal solution.
(g) If one finds that only 10 units of resource B are available, does the same basis at new values remain optimal? If so, what are the new values?
(h) If the constraint for resource C were really $-4x_1 + 3x_2 + 7x_3 \leq 10$,

would the old solution remain optimal? If not, find the new optimal solution.

(i) If the constraint for resource C were really $+4x_1 + 3x_2 + 8x_3 \leq 10$ instead, find the new optimal solution.

(j) Suppose it is discovered that a fourth activity (whose level is denoted by x_7) is relevant and that the appropriate model should be, maximize

$$Z = -x_1 + 3x_2 - 2x_3 + x_7,$$

subject to

$$\begin{aligned} 3x_1 - 1x_2 + 2x_3 + x_7 &\leq 7 \\ -2x_1 + 4x_2 \qquad\quad - 2x_7 &\leq 12 \\ -4x_1 + 3x_2 + 8x_3 - x_7 &\leq 10 \end{aligned}$$

and

$$x_j \geq 0, \qquad \text{for } j = 1, 2, 3, 7.$$

Is the old solution, plus $x_7 = 0$, still optimal? If not, find the new optimal solution.

(k) Would the additional constraint, $x_1 + x_2 + x_3 \leq 8$, change the optimal solution? If so, find the new optimal solution.

(*NOTE:* No extensive calculations are necessary or desired for any of these parts.)

7. Consider the following linear programming problem. Maximize

$$Z = 3x_1 + x_2 + 4x_3,$$

subject to

$$\begin{aligned} 6x_1 + 3x_2 + 5x_3 &\leq 25 \\ 3x_1 + 4x_2 + 5x_3 &\leq 20 \end{aligned}$$

and

$$x_1 \geq 0,\ x_2 \geq 0,\ x_3 \geq 0.$$

The corresponding *final* set of equations yielding the optimal solution is

$$\begin{aligned} &(0) \quad Z + 2x_2 + \frac{1}{5}x_4 + \frac{3}{5}x_5 = 17 \\ &(1) \quad x_1 - \frac{1}{3}x_2 + \frac{1}{3}x_4 - \frac{1}{3}x_5 = \frac{5}{3} \\ &(2) \quad x_2 + x_3 - \frac{1}{5}x_4 + \frac{2}{5}x_5 = 3. \end{aligned}$$

Suppose the original model is then changed to, maximize

$$Z = 3x_1 + 3x_2 + 4x_3,$$

subject to

$$\begin{aligned} 6x_1 + \ 2x_2 + \ 5x_3 &\leq 25 \\ 3x_1 + \ 3x_2 + \ 5x_3 &\leq 20 \end{aligned}$$

and

$$x_1 \geq 0, x_2 \geq 0, x_3 \geq 0 .$$

Use duality to determine if the previous optimal solution is still optimal. If it is not, adjust the final set of equations and determine the new optimal solution.

8. Consider the problem, maximize

$$Z = 4x_1 + 12x_2 ,$$

subject to

$$\begin{aligned} x_1 + \ 2x_2 &\leq 20 \\ x_1 + \ x_2 &\leq 13 \\ 3x_1 + \ 2x_2 &\leq 36 \end{aligned}$$

and

$$x_1 \geq 0, x_2 \geq 0 .$$

Suppose that Z represents profit, and that it is possible to modify the objective function somewhat by an appropriate shifting of key personnel between the two activities. In particular, suppose that the unit profit of activity 1 can be increased above 4 (to a maximum of 9) at the expense of decreasing the unit profit of activity 2 below 12 by twice the amount. Thus, Z can actually be represented as

$$Z = (4 + \theta)x_1 + (12 - 2\theta)x_2 ,$$

where θ is also a decision variable such that $0 \leq \theta \leq 5$.

(a) Find the optimal solution to the original form of the problem by the simplex method. Then use parametric linear programming to find the optimal solution, and the optimal value of Z, as a function of θ, for $0 \leq \theta \leq 5$. Also indicate graphically what this algebraic procedure is doing.

(b) Determine the optimal value of θ. Then indicate how this optimal value could have been identified directly by solving only two ordinary linear programming problems.

9. Consider the problem, maximize

$$Z = (7 + 2\theta)x_1 + (12 + \theta)x_2 + (10 - \theta)x_3 + (16 - \theta)x_4 ,$$

subject to

$$\begin{aligned} 5x_1 + 4x_2 + 4x_3 + 5x_4 &\leq 40 \\ 2x_1 + 4x_2 + 5x_3 + 3x_4 &\leq 30 \end{aligned}$$

and

$$x_j \geq 0, \qquad \text{for } j = 1, 2, 3, 4 .$$

(a) Find the optimal solution for this problem as a function of θ, for $\theta \geq 0$.
(b) Construct the dual model for this problem. Then find the optimal solution for this dual problem as a function of θ, for $\theta \geq 0$, by the method described in Sec. 15.2.3.2. Indicate graphically what this algebraic procedure is doing. Compare the solutions obtained with the complementary solutions obtained in Part (a).

10. Using the parametric linear programming procedure for making systematic changes in the b_i in order to find the optimal solution for the following problem as a function of θ, for $0 \leq \theta \leq 20$. Maximize

$$Z = 7x_1 + 4x_2 + 6x_3 + 5x_4 ,$$

subject to

$$\begin{aligned} 2x_1 + x_2 + 2x_3 + x_4 &\leq 10 + \theta \\ 2x_1 - x_2 + 4x_3 + 2x_4 &\leq 26 - \theta \\ 3x_1 + x_2 - 2x_3 + 3x_4 &\leq 45 - 2\theta \end{aligned}$$

and

$$x_j \geq 0, \qquad \text{for } j = 1, 2, 3, 4 .$$

Then identify the value of θ that gives the largest optimal value of Z.

11. Prove the Corollary to Theorem 15.4 by using Theorem 15.4 and duality theory.

12. Let $Z^* = \max \left\{ \sum_{j=1}^{n} c_j x_j \right\}$, subject to

$$\sum_{j=1}^{n} a_{ij} x_j \leq b_i, \qquad \text{for } i = 1, 2, \cdots, m ,$$

and

$$x_j \geq 0, \qquad \text{for } j = 1, 2, \cdots, n ,$$

(where the a_{ij}, b_i, and c_j are fixed constants), and let $(y_1^*, y_2^*, \cdots, y_m^*)$ be the corresponding optimal dual solution. Then let

$$Z^{**} = \max \left\{ \sum_{j=1}^{n} c_j x_j \right\}, \qquad \text{subject to}$$

$$\sum_{j=1}^{n} a_{ij} x_j \leq b_i + k_i, \qquad \text{for } i = 1, 2, \cdots, m ,$$

and

$$x_j \geq 0, \qquad \text{for } j = 1, 2, \cdots, n,$$

where $k_1, k_2, \cdots, k_m$ are given constants. Show that

$$Z^{**} \leq Z^* + \sum_{i=1}^{m} k_i y_i^* .$$

13. Consider the following linear programming problem. Maximize

$$Z = 2x_1 + 4x_2 + x_3 ,$$

subject to

$$\begin{aligned} x_2 + 2x_3 &\leq 2 \\ x_1 + x_2 + x_3 &\leq 3/2 \\ x_1 &\leq 1 \\ x_2 &\leq 1 \\ x_3 &\leq 1 \end{aligned}$$

and

$$x_1 \geq 0, \; x_2 \geq 0, \; x_3 \geq 0 .$$

Find the optimal solution to this problem by applying the modified version of the simplex method which uses the special technique for handling upper bound constraints on the variables.

14. Consider the following linear programming problem. Maximize

$$Z = 4x_1 - x_2 + 5x_3 ,$$

subject to

$$\begin{aligned} 4x_1 - 2x_2 + 3x_3 &\leq 145 \\ 2x_1 + x_2 + 3x_3 &\leq 150 \\ x_2 - 4x_3 &\leq 20 \\ 2x_1 + x_2 + 2x_3 &\geq 50 \\ 5 \leq x_1 &\leq 25 \\ 5 \leq x_2 &\leq 25 \\ 5 \leq x_3 &\leq 25 . \end{aligned}$$

(a) Make the necessary adjustments (introducing slack variables, artificial variables, etc.) in preparation for applying the simplex method to the problem as formulated above. Obtain the initial set of equations and the corresponding initial (artificial) basic feasible solution, but do not solve further.

(b) Solve the problem by using the technique discussed in Sec. 15.3 for handling lower bound constraints, secondary constraints, and upper bound constraints. Consider the third and fourth constraints to be the secondary constraints.

15. Use the revised simplex method to solve the linear programming problem given in Problem 4 at the end of Chapter 5.

16. Consider the linear programming problem, maximize

$$x_0 = 8x_1 + 2x_2 + 7x_3 + 12x_4 + 9x_5 + 3x_6 + 10x_7 ,$$

subject to

$$\begin{aligned} 3x_1 + x_2 + 5x_3 + 10x_4 + 2x_5 + 2x_6 + 7x_7 &\leq 10 \\ 3x_1 + 3x_2 + 6x_3 + 8x_4 + 5x_5 + 4x_6 + 6x_7 &\leq 25 \\ 2x_1 + 3x_2 + 4x_3 + 5x_4 + 4x_5 + x_6 + 2x_7 &\leq 16 \end{aligned}$$

and

$$x_j \geq 0, \quad \text{for } j = 1, 2, \cdots, 7 .$$

(a) Solve this problem by the revised simplex method.
(b) Given the solution in Part (a), identify the optimal dual solution.
(c) Given the solution in Part (a), study the sensitivity of this solution to changes in the original right-hand side of the three functional constraints (10, 25, and 16). In particular, indicate the rate at which the optimal value of Z and the x_j would change if a small change were made in each right-hand side individually. Also indicate how much each right-hand side could be changed individually before the current basis would no longer be optimal, and describe how the new optimal solution should then be obtained.

17. Use the decomposition principle to solve each of the following linear programming problems.

(a) The example introduced at the beginning of Sec. 5.5.
(b) Maximize

$$x_0 = 8x_1 + 6x_2 + 10x_3 + 8x_4 + 5x_5 + 4x_6 ,$$

subject to

$$\begin{aligned} x_1 + x_2 + x_3 + x_4 + x_5 + x_6 &\leq 10 \\ 5x_1 + 4x_2 + 2x_3 + 4x_4 + 8x_5 + 7x_6 &\leq 50 \\ x_1 + 3x_2 &\leq 9 \\ 2x_1 + x_2 &\leq 12 \\ x_3 + x_4 &\leq 5 \\ x_3 &\leq 4 \\ x_4 &\leq 3 \\ 2x_5 + 3x_6 &\leq 6 \end{aligned}$$

and

$$x_j \geq 0 , \quad \text{for } j = 1, 2, \cdots, 6 .$$

18. Consider the following linear programming problem. Maximize

$$Z = 4x_1 + x_2 + 2x_3 + 3x_4 - x_5 + 6x_6 ,$$

subject to

$$\begin{aligned} x_1 + 3x_2 + 2x_3 &\le 20 \\ 2x_5 - x_6 &\le 10 \\ 2x_1 - x_2 + 5x_3 + x_4 + 2x_5 + x_6 &\le 10 \\ 3 \le x_4 &\le 10 \\ x_5 + 3x_6 &\le 25 \\ 5x_1 - x_3 &\le 20 \\ 3x_1 + x_2 + 2x_4 + 3x_6 &\le 50 \\ -x_1 + 2x_2 + x_3 &\ge 10 \end{aligned}$$

and

$$x_j \ge 0, \qquad \text{for } j = 1, 2, \cdots, 6 .$$

Formulate this problem in a form that demonstrates it can be solved by using the decomposition principle. Use the form given at the beginning of Sec. 15.3.6, and exhibit all of the matrices involved, including the $\mathbf{A}_i (i = 1, 2, \cdots, 2N)$.

19. Consider the problem, maximize

$$x_0 = 20x_1 + 30x_2 + 25x_3 ,$$

subject to

$$\begin{aligned} 3x_1 + 2x_2 + x_3 &\le b_1 \\ 2x_1 + 4x_2 + 2x_3 &\le b_2 \\ x_1 + 3x_2 + 5x_3 &\le b_3 \end{aligned}$$

and

$$x_j \ge 0, \qquad \text{for } j = 1, 2, 3 ,$$

where b_1, b_2, and b_3 are random variables. Assume that the probability distribution of each of these random variables is such that it can take on any one of three possible values. These values are (29, 30, 31) for b_1, (48, 50, 52) for b_2, and (57, 60, 63) for b_3. In each case, the probability of the middle value is 1/2, whereas, each of the other two values has a probability of 1/4. The random variables are statistically independent. Suppose that the constraints are required to hold with probability one.

(a) Reformulate this problem as an equivalent ordinary linear programming problem.
(b) Suppose that the value taken on by b_1 will be known when a value must be assigned to x_2, and both b_1 and b_2 will be known when x_3 must be specified. Use the stochastic linear programming approach to for-

mulate an equivalent ordinary linear programming problem that maximizes $E(x_0)$ while taking this information into account.

20. Reconsider Problem 19. Suppose, after further analysis, it is decided that b_1, b_2, and b_3 each actually has a normal distribution, with a mean and standard deviation of (30, 1), (50, 2), and (60, 3), respectively. Therefore, a chance-constrained programming approach is to be used instead, where the first, second, and third constraints are required to hold with probability 0.975, 0.95, and 0.90, respectively.

(a) Consider the solution, $(x_1, x_2, x_3) = (2\frac{1}{3}, 7\frac{1}{3}, 6\frac{1}{3})$. What are the probabilities that the respective original constraints will be satisfied by this solution? Is this solution feasible? What is the probability that all of the original constraints will be satisfied by this solution?
(b) Reformulate this chance-constrained programming problem as an equivalent ordinary linear programming problem.
(c) Suppose that [as in Part (b) of Problem 19] the value taken on by b_1 will be known when a value must be assigned to x_2, and both b_1 and b_2 will be known when x_3 must be specified. Use the linear decision rules,

$$x_2 = \frac{1}{4} b_1 - y_2 ,$$

$$x_3 = \frac{1}{2} b_1 + \frac{1}{2} b_2 - y_3 ,$$

in order to formulate an equivalent ordinary linear programming problem that maximizes $E(x_0)$ while taking this information into account.

21. Consider the chance-constrained programming constraint,

$$P\left\{\sum_{j=1}^{n} a_{ij}x_j \leq b_i\right\} \geq \alpha_i .$$

(a) Suppose that, in addition to b_i, the a_{ij} also are (independent) random variables whose probability distributions are normal with known mean $E(a_{ij})$ and variance $\text{var}(a_{ij})$. Convert this constraint into an equivalent deterministic non-linear constraint.
(b) Suppose that the x_j are expressed as linear decision rules of the form,

$$x_j = \sum_{k=1}^{m} b_k\, d_{jk}, \qquad \text{for } j = 1, 2, \cdots, n ,$$

where each d_{jk} is a *decision variable* if the value taken on by b_k will be known when a value must be assigned to x_j, and is zero otherwise. Assume that the b_k are independent random variables with known normal distributions, and that the a_{ij} are constants. Convert this constraint into an equivalent constraint of the form obtained in Part (a).

CHAPTER 16

Integer Programming

16.1 INTRODUCTION

In many practical problems, the decision variables make sense only if they have integer values. For example, it is often necessary to assign men, machines, and vehicles to activities in integer quantities. This restriction is a difficult one to handle mathematically. However, some progress has been made in developing solution procedures for the case of linear programming problems subjected to this additional restriction that the decision variables must have integer values.

In practice, the usual approach to integer linear programming problems has been to use the simplex method (thereby ignoring the integer restriction) and then rounding off the non-integer values to integers in the resulting solution. Although this is often adequate, there are pitfalls in this approach. One is that the optimal non-integer solution is not necessarily feasible after it is rounded off. Often it is difficult to see in which way the rounding should be done in order to retain feasibility. It may even be necessary to change the value of some variables by one or more units after rounding off. To illustrate, suppose that some of the constraints are

$$-x_1 + x_2 \leq \ 3\frac{1}{2}$$

$$x_1 + x_2 \leq 16\frac{1}{2},$$

and that the simplex method has identified the optimal non-integer solution as $x_1 = 6\frac{1}{2}$, $x_2 = 10$. Notice that it is impossible to round off x_1 to 6 or 7 (or any other integer) and retain feasibility. This can only be done by also changing the integer value of x_2. It is easy to imagine how such difficulties can be compounded when there are tens or hundreds of constraints and variables.

Even if the optimal non-integer solution is rounded off successfully, there remains another pitfall. There is no guarantee that this rounded-off solution will be the optimal integer solution. In fact, it may even be far from optimal in terms of the value of the objective function. This is illustrated by the following problem: Maximize

$$x_0 = x_1 + 5x_2 ,$$

subject to the restrictions,

$$\begin{aligned} x_1 + 10x_2 &\leq 20 \\ x_1 \qquad &\leq 2 \end{aligned}$$

and

$$x_1 \text{ and } x_2 \text{ are non-negative integers.}$$

Since there are only two decision variables, this problem can be depicted graphically as given below.

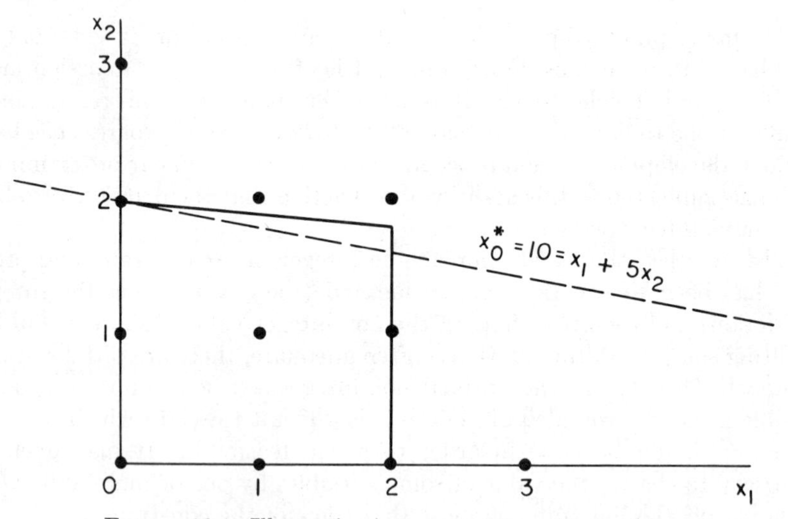

FIGURE 16.1. Illustrative integer programming problem.

Either the graph or the simplex method may be used to find that the optimal non-integer solution is $x_1 = 2$, $x_2 = 9/5$, with $x_0 = 11$. If a graphical solution were not available (which it would not be with more than three decision variables), then the variable with the non-integer value, $x_2 = 9/5$, would normally be rounded off in the feasible direction to $x_2 = 1$. The resulting integer solution is $x_1 = 2$, $x_2 = 1$, which yields $x_0 = 7$. Notice that this is far from the optimal solution, $(x_1, x_2) = (0, 2)$, where $x_0 = 10$.

For these reasons, it would be useful to have an efficient solution procedure for obtaining an optimal solution to integer linear programming problems. Some progress has been made in recent years, largely by Ralph Gomory, in developing solution procedures (commonly called algorithms[111]) for this purpose. Unfortunately, these algorithms have proven to be rather inefficient for most problems. In fact, they sometimes require a prohibitive amount of electronic computer time even to solve small problems involving only a few constraints and a few variables. The development of efficient integer programming algorithms appears to be inherently difficult. However, research continues and more progress is being made, largely by applying new combinatorial methods. Efficient suboptimal algorithms for finding at least a nearly optimal solution also are beginning to be developed.

The next section describes a slightly simplified version of an integer linear programming algorithm developed by Ralph Gomory. Although this algorithm requires that all of the variables must be integers, Gomory has also extended his procedure to cover the more difficult case of mixed integer linear programming, where only certain of the variables are required to be integers. Section 16.3 describes how the mixed integer programming techniques can be used to help solve certain non-integer programming problems. Section 16.4 then describes the branch-and-bound technique, which is a relatively new kind of combinatorial approach that is being applied (with variations) to integer programming and related problems.

16.2 AN INTEGER LINEAR PROGRAMMING ALGORITHM

How does one find the optimal solution to a linear programming problem where all[112] of the variables are required to be integers? Since the simplex method and its variants could be used except for the integer restriction, one approach is to attempt to modify the problem so that these efficient solution procedures can still be used. The key idea that enables this to be done is the following. Consider any new linear programming problem whose set of feasible integer solutions coincides with the set of feasible solutions for the integer linear programming problem of interest. If the best feasible solution to this linear programming problem is an integer solution, it must then be the best feasible solution to the integer linear programming problem. Therefore, what is required is to find such a linear programming problem whose optimal solution is an integer solution. A method for doing this is as follows.

[111] "Algorithm" is a name that is sometimes used for iterative solution procedures. One example is the simplex method, which is also called the simplex algorithm.

[112] The algorithm also requires that all new variables (such as slack variables and artificial variables) must also be integers. Therefore, any constraint requiring such a variable must have only integers for its coefficients and right-hand side. (Otherwise, introducing this integer-valued variable will change the constraint.) If only rational numbers are involved, this can always be achieved by multiplying both sides of the original constraint by a constant.

Begin with the original linear programming problem without the integer restriction. Find the optimal solution by the simplex method. If all of the variables have integer values, it is the optimal solution to the corresponding integer programming problem. If not, then modify the original linear programming problem by adding a new constraint which eliminates some non-integer solutions (including the previously optimal one), but which does not eliminate any feasible integer solutions. (The determination of this new constraint is the key step in the algorithm; it is discussed in detail subsequently.) Find the optimal solution to the modified problem. Since the new constraint has made the previous optimal solution infeasible, the dual simplex method (described in Sec. 15.1.2) can be applied to the last set of equations to obtain the new optimal solution efficiently. If this solution is an integer solution, it solves the integer linear programming problem. Otherwise, add another new constraint to the linear programming problem and repeat the procedure. The optimal integer solution will be reached eventually after enough new constraints have been added to pare away all of the superior non-integer solutions.

This entire procedure is illustrated later by a complete example. However, it is necessary now to elaborate on how to select the new constraint at each iteration. To illustrate how this is done, suppose that $x_1 = 4\frac{3}{5}$ is the only non-integer variable in the optimal solution for the current form of the linear programming problem. Suppose that

$$x_1 + 2\frac{3}{10}x_2 - \frac{1}{2}x_4 + 2x_5 - 3\frac{3}{4}x_7 + \frac{1}{4}x_8 - 3x_{10} = 4\frac{3}{5}$$

is the corresponding equation in the final set of equations. Now write each constant in the equation as the sum of (1) an integer, and (2) a non-negative fraction less than one.

$$(1+0)x_1 + \left(2 + \frac{3}{10}\right)x_2 + \left(-1 + \frac{1}{2}\right)x_4 + (2+0)x_5 + \left(-4 + \frac{1}{4}\right)x_7 + \left(0 + \frac{1}{4}\right)x_8 + (-3+0)x_{10} = 4 + \frac{3}{5}\cdot$$

Now rewrite the equation by transposing the integer coefficients to the right-hand side.

$$\frac{3}{10}x_2 + \frac{1}{2}x_4 + \frac{1}{4}x_7 + \frac{1}{4}x_8 = \frac{3}{5} + (4 - x_1 - 2x_2 + x_4 - 2x_5 + 4x_7 + 3x_{10})\,.$$

When all of the variables are non-negative integers, the left-hand side of the equation is clearly non-negative, and the right-hand side must equal $\frac{3}{5}$ plus some integer. Keep in mind that, regardless of the form in which one writes it, any feasible solution is still required to satisfy the equation. Therefore, since

$$\frac{3}{10}x_2 + \frac{1}{2}x_4 + \frac{1}{4}x_7 + \frac{1}{4}x_8 = \frac{3}{5} + \text{some integer}$$

and

$$\frac{3}{10}x_2 + \frac{1}{2}x_4 + \frac{1}{4}x_7 + \frac{1}{4}x_8 \geq 0$$

for non-negative integer-valued variables, it now follows that

$$\frac{3}{10}x_2 + \frac{1}{2}x_4 + \frac{1}{4}x_7 + \frac{1}{4}x_8 \geq \frac{3}{5}$$

for any feasible solution to the integer programming problem. Therefore, this is the desired new constraint to be added to the linear programming problem. Introducing a non-negative slack variable x_s, this constraint may be written as

$$-\frac{3}{10}x_2 - \frac{1}{2}x_4 - \frac{1}{4}x_7 - \frac{1}{4}x_8 + x_s = -\frac{3}{5}.\text{[113]}$$

To obtain the next optimal solution, this equation is appended to the last set of equations. Beginning with the previously optimal solution and $x_s = -3/5$, the dual simplex method is then applied with x_s as the initial leaving basic variable.

The above discussion about determining the new constraint assumed that only one variable in the current optimal solution had a non-integer value. Now suppose that more than one variable is not integer-valued, i.e., there is more than one equation whose right-hand side is not an integer. The only resulting difference is that a choice must be made as to which variable (and corresponding equation) will be used to derive the new constraint. The procedure is the same as described above after the selection is made. One method for making this choice that seems to have worked well in practice is to choose the non-integer variable (and its equation) with the largest fractional part. [It is permissible to choose x_0 and equation (0) if all of the c_j are integers so that x_0 must be an integer.] Although this method is assumed in the subsequent discussion, it should be noted that others may also be used. For example, Gomory uses a particular indexing system, under which he proves that the algorithm must reach an optimal solution in a finite number of iterations. The proof still holds if this method is mixed with the largest fractional part method. Another scheme is to select all of the non-integer variables, thereby adding a number of new constraints simultaneously.

[113] Notice that subsequently applying the restriction that (like all the other variables) x_s must also be an integer only reduces the constraint to

$$\frac{3}{10}x_2 + \frac{1}{2}x_4 + \frac{1}{4}x_7 + \frac{1}{4}x_8 = \frac{3}{5} + \text{some non-negative integer},$$

which is also satisfied by any feasible integer solution.

The algorithm may now be formalized after introducing some new notation. Consider any constant c. Let $[c]_I$ denote the integer part of c (the largest integer not exceeding c), and let $[c]_F$ denote the fractional part of c (the amount by which c exceeds $[c]_I$), so that

$$c = [c]_I + [c]_F .$$

Let

$$\sum_{j=0}^{n'} a'_{ij}x_j = b'_i, \qquad \text{for } i = 0, 1, \cdots, m'$$

be the set of equations corresponding to the optimal solution for the current form of the linear programming problem. Thus, n' is the current number of variables (excluding x_0), and m' is the current number of equations [excluding equation (0)].

The first iteration of the algorithm consists of finding the optimal solution for the original problem without the integer restriction. If it is an integer solution, it solves the integer problem and the algorithm stops. Otherwise, proceed to the next iteration. Each succeeding iteration has the following steps:

1. Find $[b'_{i*}]_F = \max_i [b'_i]_F$.

2. The new constraint is $\sum_{j=0}^{n'} [a'_{i*j}]_F x_j \geq [b'_{i*}]_F$.

   Therefore, append the equation,

$$-\sum_{j=0}^{n'} [a'_{i*j}]_F x_j + x_{n'+1} = -[b'_{i*}]_F ,$$

   to the current set of equations.

3. Beginning with this new set of equations, find the new optimal solution by the dual simplex method (so that $x_{n'+1}$ is the initial leaving basic variable).

4. If this new optimal solution for the modified linear programming problem is an integer solution, it is also feasible and optimal for the integer linear programming problem, so the algorithm terminates. Otherwise, return to step 1 for the next iteration.

The algorithm can now be illustrated by applying it to the problem discussed in the preceding section. Thus, the initial set of equations for this problem without the integer restriction is the following:

$$
\begin{aligned}
&(0) \quad x_0 - x_1 - 5x_2 &&= 0\\
&(1) \quad x_1 + 10x_2 + x_3 &&= 20\\
&(2) \quad x_1 + x_4 &&= 2\,.
\end{aligned}
$$

Applying the simplex method leads in two iterations to the optimal solution (for this non-integer problem) and its set of equations:

$$
\begin{aligned}
&(0) \quad x_0 + \frac{1}{2}x_3 + \frac{1}{2}x_4 = 11\\
&(1) \quad x_2 + \frac{1}{10}x_3 - \frac{1}{10}x_4 = \frac{9}{5}\\
&(2) \quad x_1 + x_4 = 2\,.
\end{aligned}
$$

This optimal solution, $(x_1, x_2, x_3, x_4) = (2, \frac{9}{5}, 0, 0)$, is not an integer solution. Therefore, equation (1) is selected for generating the new constraint,

$$\frac{1}{10}x_3 + \frac{9}{10}x_4 \geq \frac{4}{5},$$

so the equation,

$$(3) \quad -\frac{1}{10}x_3 - \frac{9}{10}x_4 + x_5 = -\frac{4}{5},$$

is appended to the set of equations. Applying the dual simplex method, x_5 is the initial leaving basic variable, and x_4 becomes the entering basic variable, which yields the following set of equations:

$$
\begin{aligned}
&(0) \quad x_0 + \frac{4}{9}x_3 + \frac{5}{9}x_5 = 10\frac{5}{9}\\
&(1) \quad x_2 + \frac{1}{9}x_3 - \frac{1}{9}x_5 = \frac{17}{9}\\
&(2) \quad x_1 - \frac{1}{9}x_3 + \frac{10}{9}x_5 = \frac{10}{9}\\
&(3) \quad \frac{1}{9}x_3 + x_4 - \frac{10}{9}x_5 = \frac{8}{9}\,.
\end{aligned}
$$

This single dual simplex method iteration happens to yield the optimal solution, $(x_1, x_2, x_3, x_4, x_5) = (\frac{10}{9}, \frac{17}{9}, 0, \frac{8}{9}, 0)$, for the current linear programming problem. However, it is not an integer solution, so a new variable and its equation must be selected for generating a new constraint. Equations (1) and (3) are tied with $[b_i']_F = \frac{8}{9}$, so either may be selected arbitrarily. Both choices happen to yield the same new constraint,

$$\frac{1}{9}x_3 + \frac{8}{9}x_5 \geq \frac{8}{9},$$

so the equation,

$$(4) \quad -\frac{1}{9}x_3 - \frac{8}{9}x_5 + x_6 = -\frac{8}{9},$$

is appended to the set of equations. The dual simplex method is now applied. The first basis change, with x_6 as the leaving basic variable and x_5 as the entering basic variable, yields the following:

$$
\begin{array}{llcl}
(0) & x_0 + \frac{3}{8}x_3 & + \frac{5}{8}x_6 = & 10 \\
(1) & x_2 + \frac{1}{8}x_3 & - \frac{1}{8}x_6 = & 2 \\
(2) & x_1 - \frac{1}{4}x_3 & + \frac{5}{4}x_6 = & 0 \\
(3) & + \frac{1}{4}x_3 + x_4 & - \frac{5}{4}x_6 = & 2 \\
(4) & \frac{1}{8}x_3 & + x_5 - \frac{9}{8}x_6 = & 1 .
\end{array}
$$

The corresponding solution, $(x_1, x_2, x_3, x_4, x_5, x_6) = (0, 2, 0, 2, 1, 0)$, is seen to be optimal for the current linear programming problem. Furthermore, it is an integer solution, so that $(x_1, x_2) = (0, 2)$ is feasible and optimal for the integer linear programming problem.

It is instructive to trace through the steps of the above example graphically. Referring to Fig. 16.1, the algorithm began by finding the optimal non-integer solution at the extreme point, $(x_1, x_2) = (2, \frac{9}{5})$. It then imposed a new constraint, $\frac{1}{10}x_3 + \frac{9}{10}x_4 \geq \frac{4}{5}$. Since $x_3 = 20 - x_1 - 10x_2$ and $x_4 = 2 - x_1$, so that $\frac{1}{10}x_3 + \frac{9}{10}x_4 = 2 - \frac{1}{10}x_1 - x_2 + \frac{9}{5} - \frac{9}{10}x_1$, this new constraint really is

$$x_1 + x_2 \leq 3$$

in terms of the original variables. Therefore, this constraint slices off a triangle in the upper right-hand corner of the graph. The optimal solution for the new linear programming problem was then found to be at the new extreme point, $(x_1, x_2) = (\frac{10}{9}, \frac{17}{9})$, lying at the intersection of $x_1 + 10x_2 = 20$ and $x_1 + x_2 = 3$. At the next iteration, the constraint, $\frac{1}{9}x_3 + \frac{8}{9}x_5 \geq \frac{8}{9}$, was added. Since $x_3 = 20 - x_1 - 10x_2$ and $x_5 = 3 - x_1 - x_2$, this constraint can also be written as

$$x_1 + 2x_2 \leq 4 .$$

This constraint pares off additional non-integer solutions without eliminating any feasible integer solution. The result was that the best remaining feasible linear programming solution was found to lie at the extreme point, $(x_1, x_2) = (0,2)$, which is the desired optimal integer solution. The sequence of changes that the algorithm imposed upon the original graph is shown in Fig. 16.2.

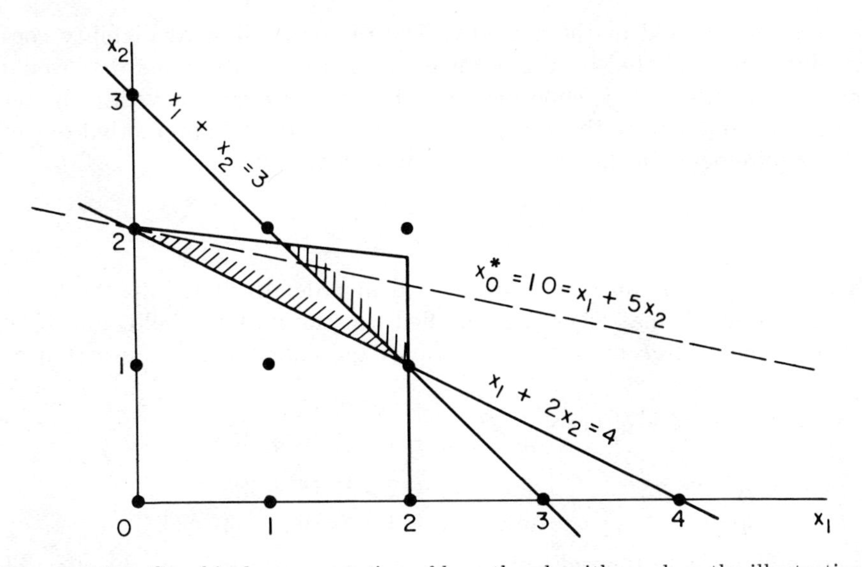

FIGURE 16.2. Graphical representation of how the algorithm solves the illustrative problem.

16.3 INDIRECT CONTRIBUTIONS OF MIXED INTEGER PROGRAMMING

16.3.1 Introduction

Problems are sometimes encountered that fit into the linear programming format (or a more general mathematical programming format) except for some minor disparity. Fortunately, certain tricks are available for circumventing some of these disparities. However, this can be done only at the expense of introducing one or more artificial variables which are restricted to be integers. This reduces the problem to a mixed integer problem (or to a fully integer problem if the original variables are also restricted to be integers) in the desired format. Therefore, if progress continues in the development of efficient mixed-integer and integer algorithms, this approach should eventually attain considerable practical importance.

Some of the cases that can be handled by this approach are discussed below.

16.3.2 Either–Or Constraints

Consider the important case where a choice can be made between two constraints, so that one must hold but not necessarily both. For example, there may be a choice as to which of two resources to use for a certain purpose, so that it is only necessary for one of the two resource availability constraints to hold mathematically. The resource whose availability constraint is not violated by the optimal solution is then the one that would actually be used, since choosing the other resource cannot yield a better solution. To illustrate the approach to such situations, suppose that one of the requirements in the over-all problem is that

$$\begin{aligned} \text{either} \quad & 3x_1 + 2x_2 \leq 18 \\ \text{or} \quad & x_1 + 4x_2 \leq 16 \, . \end{aligned}$$

This requirement must be reformulated in order to fit it into the linear programming format where all specified constraints must hold. Let M be an extremely large number. Then this requirement can be rewritten as

$$\text{either} \begin{cases} & 3x_1 + 2x_2 \leq 18 \\ \text{and} & x_1 + 4x_2 \leq 16 + M \end{cases}$$

$$\text{or} \begin{cases} & 3x_1 + 2x_2 \leq 18 + M \\ \text{and} & x_1 + 4x_2 \leq 16 \, , \end{cases}$$

since adding M to the right-hand side of such constraints has the effect of eliminating them. (This assumes that the set of feasible solutions for the over-all problem is a bounded set, and that M is sufficiently large that it will not eliminate any feasible solutions.) This formulation is equivalent to the set of constraints,

$$\begin{aligned} 3x_1 + 2x_2 &\leq 18 + y\,M \\ x_1 + 4x_2 &\leq 16 + (1 - y)\,M \\ y &= 0 \text{ or } 1 \, , \end{aligned}$$

which can be expressed in a mixed integer linear programming format as

$$\begin{aligned} 3x_1 + 2x_2 - My &\leq 18 \\ x_1 + 4x_2 + My &\leq 16 + M \\ y &\leq 1 \\ y &\geq 0 \\ \text{and } y \text{ is an integer} \, . \end{aligned}$$

Since the new artificial variable y must be either zero or one, this formulation guarantees that one of the original constraints must hold while the other one is eliminated in effect. This new set of constraints would then be appended to the other constraints in the over-all problem before attempting to solve it by a mixed integer algorithm.

A formal presentation of this approach is given in the next section for a more general case.

Until more efficient algorithms for mixed integer programming are available, it is likely that any problem with an either–or pair of constraints will be solved by solving it once with one constraint and once with the other, and then choosing the better solution.

16.3.3 K out of N Constraints Must Hold

Now consider the case where, given a set of N possible constraints, it is only required that some K of these constraints must hold. (Assume $K < N$.) Thus, this is a direct generalization of the case considered in the preceding section for which $K = 1$ and $N = 2$. Denote these N constraints by

$$\begin{aligned} f_1(x_1, x_2, \cdots, x_n) &\leq d_1 \\ f_2(x_1, x_2, \cdots, x_n) &\leq d_2 \\ &\cdot \\ &\cdot \\ &\cdot \\ f_N(x_1, x_2, \cdots, x_n) &\leq d_N . \end{aligned}$$

Then, applying the logic used in the preceding section, it is evident that an equivalent formulation of this requirement is

$$\begin{aligned} f_1(x_1, x_2, \cdots, x_n) &\leq d_1 + My_1 \\ f_2(x_1, x_2, \cdots, x_n) &\leq d_2 + My_2 \\ &\cdot \\ &\cdot \\ &\cdot \\ f_N(x_1, x_2, \cdots, x_n) &\leq d_N + My_N \end{aligned}$$

$$\sum_{i=1}^{N} y_i = N - K$$

$$\begin{aligned} y_i &\leq 1 \\ y_i &\geq 0 \end{aligned}$$

$$\text{and } y_i \text{ is an integer,} \qquad \text{for } i = 1, 2, \cdots, N ,$$

where M is an extremely large number as described in the preceding section. Since the constraints on the y_i guarantee that K of these artificial variables will equal zero and those remaining will equal one, K of the original constraints will be unchanged and the rest will, in effect, be eliminated.

16.3.4 Functions with N Possible Values

Consider the situation where a given function is required to take on any one of N given values. Denote this requirement by

$$f(x_1, x_2, \cdots, x_n) = d_1, \quad \text{or} \quad d_2, \cdots, \quad \text{or} \quad d_N .$$

One special case is where this function is

$$f(x_1, x_2, \cdots, x_n) = \sum_{j=1}^{n} a_j x_j ,$$

as on the left-hand side of a linear programming constraint. Another special case is where $f(x_1, x_2, \cdots, x_n) = x_j$ for a given value of j, so the requirement becomes that x_j must take on any one of N given values.

The equivalent mixed integer programming formulation of this requirement is the following:

$$f(x_1, x_2, \cdots, x_n) = \sum_{i=1}^{N} d_i y_i$$

$$\sum_{i=1}^{N} y_i = 1$$

$$y_i \leq 1$$
$$y_i \geq 0$$
$$\text{and } y_i \text{ is an integer,} \qquad \text{for } i = 1, 2, \cdots, N .$$

It is evident that this is an equivalent formulation since exactly one y_i must equal one, and the others must equal zero.

16.3.5 The Fixed-Charge Problem

It is quite common to incur a fixed charge or "setup cost" when undertaking an activity. In such cases, the total cost of the activity is the sum of a variable cost related to the level of the activity and this setup cost required to initiate the activity. Frequently, the variable cost will be at least approximately proportional to the level of the activity. In other words, if x_j denotes the level of activity j, the approximate total cost of activity j often will be $(k_j + c_j x_j)$ if $x_j > 0$, whereas the cost will be zero if $x_j = 0$. Were it not for the setup cost k_j, this cost structure would suggest the possibility of a linear programming formulation for determining the optimal levels of the competing activities. (This is amplified in Sec. 5.4.1.) Fortunately, even with the k_j, a trick involving mixed integer programming may still be used to obtain a legitimate linear programming objective function.

Let

$$x_0 = f_1(x_1) + f_2(x_2) + \cdots + f_n(x_n) ,$$

where

$$f_j(x_j) = \begin{cases} k_j + c_j x_j, & \text{if } x_j > 0 \\ 0, & \text{if } x_j = 0 , \end{cases}$$

and where x_j is constrained to be non-negative, for $j = 1, 2, \cdots, n$. Notice that x_0 would be a linear programming objective function if $k_j = 0$ for $j = 1, 2, \cdots, n$. Assume that $k_j \geq 0$ for $j = 1, 2, \cdots, n$. Suppose that the problem of interest is to

$$\text{minimize } x_0 ,$$

subject to

$$\text{given linear programming constraints} .$$

How can this problem be reformulated into the mixed integer linear programming format when some or all of the k_j are strictly positive?

Notice that

$$x_0 = \sum_{j=1}^{n} (c_j x_j + k_j y_j) ,$$

where

$$y_j = \begin{cases} 1, & \text{if } x_j > 0 \\ 0, & \text{if } x_j = 0 . \end{cases}$$

Hence, it is only necessary to find linear or integer constraints which insure that the y_j will take on the correct values. To begin, it is clear that necessary constraints include

$$\begin{aligned} &y_i \leq 1 \\ &y_j \geq 0 \\ &\text{and } y_j \text{ is an integer,} \qquad \text{for } j = 1, 2, \cdots, n . \end{aligned}$$

Next, let M be an extremely large number which exceeds the maximum feasible value of any x_j ($j = 1, 2, \cdots, n$). Then the constraints,

$$x_j \leq My_j, \qquad \text{for } j = 1, 2, \cdots, n ,$$

will insure that $y_j = 1$ rather than zero whenever $x_j > 0$. The one problem remaining is that these constraints leave y_j free to be either zero or one when $x_j = 0$. Fortunately, this problem is automatically taken care of because of the nature of the objective function. Recall that $k_j \geq 0$. The case where $k_j = 0$ can be ignored since y_j can then be deleted from the formulation. So consider the only other case, namely, where $k_j > 0$. When $x_j = 0$, so that the constraints permit a choice between $y_j = 0$ and $y_j = 1$, $y_j = 0$ must yield a smaller value of x_0 than $y_j = 1$. Therefore, since the objective is to minimize x_0, an algorithm yielding the optimal solution would always choose $y_j = 0$ when $x_j = 0$.

To summarize, it was shown above that an equivalent formulation of the problem is, minimize

$$x_0 = \sum_{j=1}^{n} (c_j x_j + k_j y_j) ,$$

subject to

$$\begin{aligned} &\text{the original constraints, plus} \\ &x_j - My_j \leq 0 \\ &y_j \leq 1 \\ &y_j \geq 0 \\ &\text{and } y_j \text{ is an integer,} \qquad \text{for } j = 1, 2, \cdots, n . \end{aligned}$$

16.4 THE BRANCH-AND-BOUND TECHNIQUE

Since any bounded integer programming problem has only a finite number of feasible solutions, it is natural to consider using some kind of enumeration procedure for finding an optimal solution. Unfortunately, this finite number can be, and usually is, very large. For example, if there are only ten variables, and each one has ten feasible values, then there can be as many as 10^{10} feasible solutions. Despite the fact that today's digital computers can perform as many as 1,000,000 elementary arithmetic operations (additions or subtractions) per second, exhaustive enumeration would be prohibitively time-consuming for problems as large as this. Therefore, it is imperative that any enumeration procedure be cleverly structured so that only a tiny fraction of the feasible solutions actually need be examined. For example, dynamic programming (see Chapter 8) provides one such kind of procedure for many problems having a finite number of feasible solutions (although it is not particularly efficient for most integer programming problems). Another such approach is provided by the *branch-and-bound technique*. This technique, and variations of it, have recently been applied with some success to a number of problems, including certain kinds of integer programming problems.

The basic idea of the branch-and-bound technique is the following. Suppose that the objective function is to be minimized. Assume that an upper bound on the optimal value of the objective function is available. (This usually is the value of the objective function for the best feasible solution identified thus far.) The first step is to partition the set of all feasible solutions into several subsets, and, for each one, a *lower bound* is obtained for the value of objective function of the solutions within that subset. Those subsets whose lower bounds exceeds the current upper bound on the objective function are then excluded from further consideration. One of the remaining subsets, say, the one with the smallest lower bound, is then partitioned further into several subsets. Their lower bounds are obtained in turn and used as before to exclude some of these subsets from further consideration. From *all* of the remaining subsets, another one is selected for further partitioning, etc. This process is repeated again and again until a feasible solution is found such that the corresponding value of the objective function is no greater than the lower bound for any subset.

To illustrate this approach, consider the assignment problem (see Sec. 6.4) whose cost matrix is the following

		Assignment			
		1	2	3	4
Assignee	A	94	1	54	68
	B	74	10	88	82
	C	62	88	8	76
	D	11	74	81	21

Thus, the objective is to assign each of the four assignees to its unique assignment in such a way as to minimize the sum of the four corresponding entries in the cost matrix. There are $4!(=24)$ feasible solutions. A natural way of partitioning these solutions into subsets is to specify one or more of the assignments. For example, if A were assigned to assignment 1, then there would be 3! possible solutions, corresponding to the six ways in which B, C, and D can be assigned uniquely to assignments 2, 3, and 4, respectively.

In order to apply the branch-and-bound technique to this problem, it is necessary to be able to efficiently establish a tight lower bound on the total cost for any of the solutions in a given subset of the feasible solutions. One way of doing this is to add the allowable cost of the respective assignments without worrying about whether or not this corresponds to a feasible solution (where each assignee is assigned *uniquely* to an assignment). Thus, such a lower bound over all feasible solutions is the sum of the minimum of the respective columns of the cost matrix, $11 + 1 + 8 + 21 = 41$. Similarly, if A were assigned to assignment 1, then the lower bound for the resulting subset of six feasible solutions would be the cost of this assignment plus the sum of the minimum costs (ignoring row A) for the last three columns, $94 + (10 + 8 + 21) = 133$. (This coincidentally happens to correspond to a feasible solution.)

To begin, the 24 feasible solutions would be partitioned into, say, the four subsets corresponding to the four possible ways in which assignment 1 can be made. The corresponding lower bounds are 133 (as obtained above) for the $A - 1$ subset, $74 + 1 + 8 + 21 = 104$ for the $B - 1$ subset, $62 + 1 + 54 + 21 = 138$ for the $C - 1$ subset, and $11 + 1 + 8 + 68 = 88$ for the $D - 1$ subset. Since this second lower bound (104) happens to correspond to a feasible solution, 104 also is an *upper bound* on the total cost for the optimal solution. These results are summarized by the following "tree" (as defined in Chapter 7).

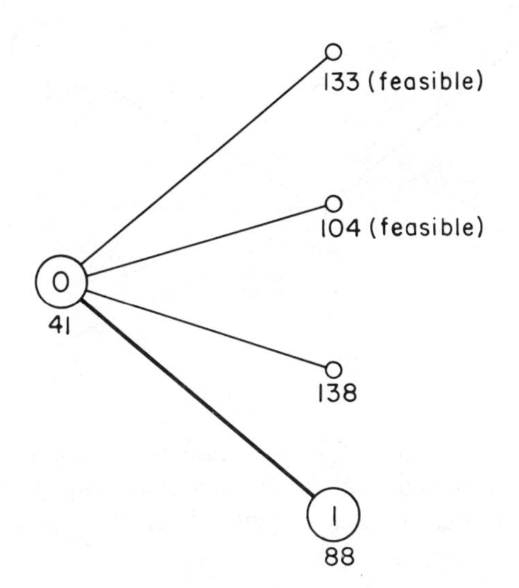

Since the lower bound for the first and third subsets (133 and 138) exceed the current upper bound for the problem (104), the twelve feasible solutions that include the corresponding assignments ($A - 1$ or $C - 1$) are excluded from further consideration. Since the fourth subset has the smallest lower bound (88), it is selected as the first subset to be partitioned further into smaller subsets (so the corresponding node is designated as node 1 in the above tree). This partitioning is done by designating both $D - 1$ and assignment 2 in the three possible ways. Thus, the first such subset is the set of (the two) feasible solutions that include $D - 1$ and $A - 2$, and its lower bound is $11 + 1 + (8 + 76) = 96$. Similarly, the lower bound for the subset whose solutions include $D - 1$ and $B - 2$ is $11 + 10 + (8 + 68) = 97$. Since this bound (97) corresponds to a feasible solution, and 97 is less than the current upper bound (104) for the problem, 97 becomes the new upper bound. (Thus, the $B - 1$ subset can now be excluded from further consideration, so $D - 1$ must be included in the optimal solution.) The lower bound for the third new subset is $11 + 88 + (54 + 68) = 221$, so it is ignored henceforth. The following tree has now been obtained.

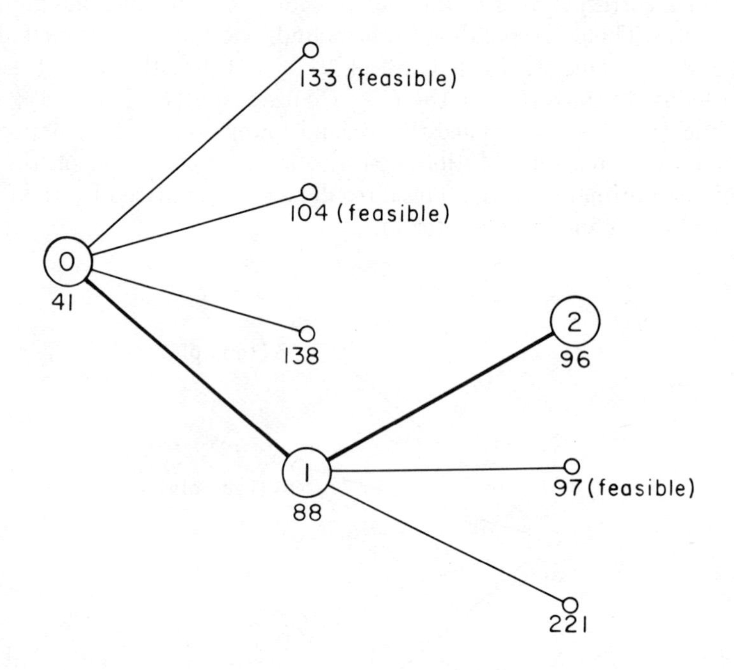

Since the first new subset has a smaller lower bound (96) than any other subset, it is selected next for further partitioning. This partitioning divides the subset into its two individual feasible solutions. Their total costs are $11 + 1 + 88 + 76 = 176$ and $11 + 1 + 8 + 82 = 102$, respectively, both of which exceed the current upper bound (97), so these two solutions are discarded. The smallest lower bound for any remaining subset is 97, which corresponds to a feasible solution. Therefore, this solution ($D - 1$, $B - 2$, $C - 3$, $A - 4$) is optimal, as indicated by the following tree.

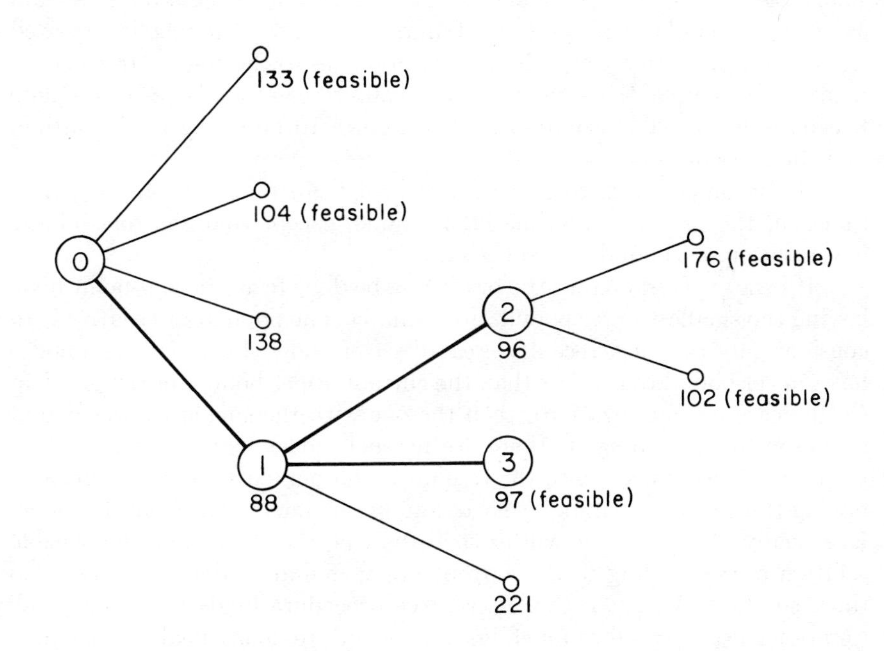

This sequence of steps can also be summarized by the following table.

Step	*Lower bound*	*Upper bound*
0	41	$+\infty$
1	88	104
2	96	97
3	97	97

At the last step, the current lower bound and upper bound are equal, so the feasible solution corresponding to this upper bound is the desired optimal solution.

The branch-and-bound technique in general can be described in terms of a tree such as that shown above. The origin corresponds to the set of all feasible solutions. This set is partitioned into several subsets, usually by designating the respective values of one of the decision variables. Each of these values corresponds to a node at the end of a branch out of the origin.

Associated with each node is a lower bound on the value of the objective function for the feasible solutions that can be reached from that node. One then branches out from the origin to the node with the smallest lower bound. The branches out of this node are constructed, and a lower bound obtained for the node at the end of each of these branches. From among all of the nodes that comprise the end points of the tree, the one with the smallest lower bound is chosen for constructing the next set of branches and associated bounds. This process of branching and bounding is repeated again and again, each time adding new branches to the tree, until the end-point node having the smallest lower bound corresponds to a complete feasible solution. This solution is then known to be an optimal solution, and the procedure is completed.

If the objective is to maximize, rather than minimize the objective function, the procedure is exactly the same, except that the roles of the lower and upper bounds are reversed.

It is not necessary that the branching be done from the end-point node having the smallest lower bound. For example, one popular alternative is to consider only the most recently created set of nodes. If any of these nodes has a lower bound that is less than the current upper bound for the problem (in the case of minimization), then the one with the smallest lower bound is chosen for branching. If there are no such nodes from among this set, then one "back-tracks" into the tree until another existing end-point node having this property can be reached, and branching is done from this node. Eventually, no such node will exist in the tree, at which time the feasible solution corresponding to the current upper bound is identified as an optimal solution. Although this alternative procedure tends to require more iterations, it also requires much less storage of previous calculations, which is sometimes an important consideration for computer execution.

Finally, it should be noted that, rather than finding an optimal solution, the branch-and-bound technique can also be used to find a nearly optimal solution, generally with much less computational effort. This is done merely by terminating the procedure the first time that the smallest lower bound is within a prespecified percentage (or quantity) of the current upper bound for the problem (in the case of minimization). The feasible solution corresponding to the upper bound is then the desired suboptimal solution such that the resulting value of the objective function is guaranteed to be within the prespecified amount of the optimal value.

SELECTED REFERENCES

1. Balinski, M. L., "Integer Programming: Methods, Uses, Computation," *Management Science*, **12,** No. 3, 253–313 (1965).

2. Beale, E. M. L., "Survey of Integer Programming," *Operational Research Quarterly*, **16,** No. 2, 219–228 (1965).
3. Dantzig, George B., *Linear Programming and Extensions*, Princeton University Press, Princeton, N.J., 1963, chap. 26.
4. Glover, Fred, "Truncated Enumeration Methods for Solving Pure and Mixed Integer Linear Programs," Working Paper No. 27, Operations Research Center, University of California, Berkeley, May, 1966. Pending publication in 1967.
5. Gomory, Ralph E., "An Algorithm for Integer Solutions to Linear Programs," in R. L. Graves and P. Wolfe (eds.), *Recent Advances in Mathematical Programming*, McGraw-Hill, New York, 1963, pp. 269–302. First issued in 1958.
6. Lawler, E. L., and Wood, D. E., "Branch-and-Bound Methods: A Survey," *Operations Research*, **14,** No. 4, 699–719 (1966).

PROBLEMS

1. Suppose that the integer linear programming algorithm described in Sec. 16.2 is being used, and the following equation has been selected for deriving the next new constraint:

$$2\frac{3}{4}x_1 + x_3 - \frac{2}{5}x_5 + 2x_6 + \frac{2}{3}x_8 - 1\frac{9}{10}x_9 + 4\frac{1}{4}x_{10} = 10\frac{4}{5}.$$

Use this equation to derive the new constraint, and then write the resulting new equation that is to be appended to the set of equations.

2. Consider the integer linear programming problem, maximize

$$x_0 = 11x_1 + 4x_2,$$

subject to

$$\begin{aligned} -x_1 + 2x_2 &\leq 4 \\ 5x_1 + 2x_2 &\leq 16 \\ 2x_1 - x_2 &\leq 4 \\ x_1 \geq 0,\ x_2 &\geq 0 \end{aligned}$$

and

$$x_1,\ x_2 \text{ are integers.}$$

(a) Solve this problem graphically. Compare the value of x_0 for the optimal solution with that obtained by rounding the optimal noninteger solution to the nearest integer solution.
(b) Solve this problem by the algorithm described in Sec. 16.2.

3. Consider the integer linear programming problem, maximize

$$x_0 = 4x_1 - 2x_2 + 7x_3,$$

subject to

$$\begin{aligned} x_1 \qquad\quad + 5x_3 &\le 10 \\ x_1 + x_2 - x_3 &\le 1 \\ 6x_1 - 5x_2 \qquad &\le 0 \\ x_1 \ge 0,\ x_2 \ge 0,\ x_3 &\ge 0 \end{aligned}$$

and

$$x_1,\ x_2,\ x_3 \text{ are integers.}$$

Suppose that the simplex method has been applied to this problem to initially obtain the optimal non-integer solution. The resulting final set of equations is the following:

$$\begin{aligned} &(0) \quad x_0 \qquad\qquad + \frac{17}{12}x_4 + \frac{1}{12}x_5 + \frac{5}{12}x_6 = 14\frac{1}{4} \\ &(1) \qquad\qquad x_3 + \frac{11}{60}x_4 - \frac{1}{12}x_5 - \frac{1}{60}x_6 = 1\frac{3}{4} \\ &(2) \qquad\quad x_2 \qquad + \frac{1}{10}x_4 + \frac{1}{2}x_5 - \frac{1}{10}x_6 = 1\frac{1}{2} \\ &(3) \qquad x_1 \qquad\quad + \frac{1}{12}x_4 + \frac{5}{12}x_5 + \frac{1}{12}x_6 = 1\frac{1}{4}. \end{aligned}$$

Thus, the optimal non-integer solution is $(x_1, x_2, x_3) = (1\frac{1}{4}, 1\frac{1}{2}, 1\frac{3}{4})$.

(a) Demonstrate by trial and error that a feasible (integer) solution cannot be obtained by rounding off the optimal non-integer solution in any way.

(b) Solve this problem by the algorithm described in Sec. 16.2.

4. Consider the following mathematical model. Maximize

$$x_0 = 3x_1 + f(x_2) + 4x_3 + g(x_4)\ ,$$

subject to the restrictions,

(1) $2x_1 - x_2 + x_3 + 3x_4 \le 15$,

(2) At least one of the following two inequalities hold:

$$\begin{aligned} x_1 + x_2 + x_3 + x_4 &\le 10 \\ 3x_1 - x_2 - x_3 + x_4 &\le 20\ , \end{aligned}$$

(3) At least two of the following four inequalities hold:

$$\begin{aligned} 5x_1 + 3x_2 + 3x_3 - x_4 &\le 30 \\ 2x_1 + 5x_2 - x_3 + 3x_4 &\le 30 \\ -x_1 + 3x_2 + 5x_3 + 3x_4 &\le 30 \\ 3x_1 - x_2 + 3x_3 + 5x_4 &\le 30\ , \end{aligned}$$

(4) $x_3 = 2$, or 3, or 4,

(5) $x_j \ge 0\ (j = 1, 2, \cdots, 4)$,

where

$$f(x_2) = \begin{cases} 10 + 2x_2, & \text{if } x_2 > 0 \\ 0, & \text{if } x_2 = 0 \end{cases}$$

and

$$g(x_4) = \begin{cases} 5 + 3x_4, & \text{if } x_4 > 0 \\ 0, & \text{if } x_4 = 0\,. \end{cases}$$

Formulate this problem as a mixed integer linear programming problem.

5. Consider the assignment problem with the following cost matrix.

		Assignment				
		1	2	3	4	5
Assignee	1	7	83	38	52	21
	2	26	57	93	10	56
	3	55	40	14	48	49
	4	43	77	29	61	48
	5	28	61	86	73	33

Use the branch-and-bound technique to find the set of assignments that minimizes total cost.

6. Consider the integer programming problem, maximize

$$x_0 = 60x_1 + 40x_2 + 30x_3 + 20x_4 - (6x_1 + 4x_2 + 3x_3 + 2x_4)^2\,,$$

subject to

$$x_j \leq 1$$
$$x_j \geq 0$$
$$\text{and } x_j \text{ is an integer,} \qquad \text{for } j = 1, 2, 3, 4\,.$$

Given the values of the first k variables $(x_1, \cdots, x_k)$, where $k = 0, 1, 2,$ or 3, an upper bound on the value of x_0 that can be achieved by the corresponding feasible solutions is

$$\sum_{j=1}^{k} c_j x_j - \left(\sum_{j=1}^{k} d_j x_j\right)^2 + \sum_{j=k+1}^{4} \max\left\{0,\, c_j - \left[\left(\sum_{i=1}^{k} d_i x_i + d_j\right)^2 - \left(\sum_{i=1}^{k} d_i x_i\right)^2\right]\right\},$$

where $c_1 = 60$, $c_2 = 40$, $c_3 = 30$, $c_4 = 20$, $d_1 = 6$, $d_2 = 4$, $d_3 = 3$, $d_4 = 2$. Use this bound to solve the problem by the branch-and-bound technique.

CHAPTER 17

Non-Linear Programming

17.1 INTRODUCTION

The general non-linear programming problem is to find $x_1, x_2, \cdots, x_n$ so as to

maximize

$$f(x_1, x_2, \cdots, x_n),$$

subject to

$$\begin{aligned} g_1(x_1, x_2 \cdots, x_n) &\leq b_1 \\ g_2(x_1, x_2, \cdots, x_n) &\leq b_2 \\ &\vdots \\ g_m(x_1, x_2, \cdots, x_n) &\leq b_m \end{aligned}$$

and

$$x_j \geq 0, \qquad \text{for } j = 1, 2, \cdots, n,$$

where $f(x_1, x_2, \cdots, x_n)$ and the $g_i(x_1, x_2, \cdots, x_n)$ are given functions of the n decision variables. Chapters 5, 6, and 15 were devoted to one special case, the linear programming problem, where all of these functions are linear. This reflected the fact that a great deal has been learned about this case from the pioneering research of the 1940's and 1950's. However, it has long been recognized that many practical problems can be described with sufficient accuracy by a mathematical model only if that model contains functions which are not linear. Therefore, in recent years, research attention has been turning from linear to non-linear programming. Although no efficient solution procedure is in sight for the general non-linear problem, substantial progress is being made for important special cases. The following sections briefly describe the primary types of results that are now available.

17.2 THE KUHN–TUCKER CONDITIONS

Before exploring solution procedures, it is useful to learn how to recognize an optimal solution to a non-linear programming problem. This section gives the so-called Kuhn–Tucker conditions, which describe such optimal solutions.

What are the characteristics of optimal solutions to non-linear programming problems? Classical calculus provides some motivation for the answer to this question. To begin, consider the case where there are no constraints (not even non-negativity constraints), and the objective function is differentiable. If the objective function contains only one variable, it is well known (see Appendix 2) that $x_1 = x_1^*$ can maximize $f(x_1)$ only if $df/dx_1 = 0$ at $x_1 = x_1^*$, where this is also a sufficient condition if $f(x_1)$ is a concave function (as defined in Appendix 1). Similarly, Appendix 2 indicates that, if the function contains several variables, then $(x_1^*, x_2^*, \cdots, x_n^*)$ can maximize $f(x_1, x_2, \cdots, x_n)$ only if $\partial f/\partial x_j = 0$ at $x_j = x_j^*$ for $j = 1, 2, \cdots, n$. This becomes a sufficient condition if $f(x_1, x_2, \cdots, x_n)$ is a concave function. Now suppose that the non-negativity constraints, $x_j \geq 0$ $(j = 1, 2, \cdots, n)$, are introduced. The only revision that must be made in the above statement is that, if $x_j^* = 0$, then the condition, $\partial f/\partial x_j = 0$ at $x_j = x_j^*$, is replaced by the condition, $\partial f/\partial x_j \leq 0$ at $x_j = x_j^*$.

Unfortunately, it becomes much more difficult to characterize an optimal solution if the other constraints involving the $g_i(x_1, x_2, \cdots, x_n)$ functions are also introduced. The difficulty is that increasing x_i may require changing other variables to avoid violating the constraints, so it is no longer sufficient to just look at the $\partial f/\partial x_j$ $(j = 1, 2, \cdots, n)$. However, Kuhn and Tucker derived the results[114] for this case that are analogous to those given above for simpler cases. Their basic result is embodied in the following theorem.

Theorem 17.1: Assume that $f(x_1, x_2, \cdots, x_n)$, $g_1(x_1, x_2, \cdots, x_n), \cdots, g_m(x_1, x_2, \cdots, x_n)$ are differentiable functions satisfying certain regularity conditions.[115] Then $(x_1^*, x_2^* \cdots, x_n^*)$ can be an optimal solution to the non-

[114] H. W. Kuhn and A. W. Tucker, "Nonlinear Programming," in Jerzy Neyman (ed.), *Proceedings of the Second Berkeley Symposium on Mathematical Statistics and Probability*, University of California Press, Berkeley, 1951, pp. 481–492.

[115] Ibid, p. 483. These regularity conditions are designed only to rule out singularities on the boundary of the set of feasible solutions, such as an outward pointing "cusp."

linear programming problem only if there exist m numbers, $u_1, u_2, \cdots, u_m$, such that all of the following conditions are satisfied:

(1) If $x_j^* > 0$, then $\frac{\partial f}{\partial x_j} - \sum_{i=1}^{m} u_i \frac{\partial g_i}{\partial x_j} = 0$ at $x_j = x_j^*$,
for $j = 1, 2, \cdots, n$.

(2) If $x_j^* = 0$, then $\frac{\partial f}{\partial x_j} - \sum_{i=1}^{m} u_i \frac{\partial g_i}{\partial x_j} \leq 0$ at $x_j = x_j^*$,
for $j = 1, 2, \cdots, n$.

(3) If $u_i > 0$, then $g_i(x_1^*, x_2^*, \cdots, x_n^*) - b_i = 0$,
for $i = 1, 2, \cdots, m$.

(4) If $u_i = 0$, then $g_i(x_1^*, x_2^*, \cdots, x_n^*) - b_i \leq 0$,
for $i = 1, 2, \cdots, m$.

(5) $x_j^* \geq 0$, for $j = 1, 2, \cdots, n$.

(6) $u_i \geq 0$, for $i = 1, 2, \cdots, m$.

These conditions are commonly referred to as the Kuhn–Tucker conditions. The u_i are somewhat analogous to the dual variables of linear programming, and they have a comparable economic interpretation. (However, the u_i actually arose in the mathematical derivation as generalized Lagrange multipliers.) Conditions (4) and (5) do nothing more than help insure the feasibility of the solution. The other conditions eliminate most of the feasible solutions as possible candidates for the optimal solution. However, it should be noted that satisfying these conditions does not guarantee that the solution is optimal. Just like the analogous condition for an unconstrained function that its partial derivatives be zero, these conditions are only necessary, and not sufficient, for optimality. However, just as before, if certain additional convexity assumptions are satisfied, these conditions do become sufficient to guarantee optimality. Kuhn and Tucker proved the following extension of the theorem.

Corollary: Assume that $f(x_1, x_2, \cdots, x_n)$ is a concave function and that $g_1(x_1, x_2, \cdots, x_n), g_2(x_1, x_2, \cdots, x_n), \cdots, g_m(x_1, x_2, \cdots, x_n)$ are convex functions satisfying the regularity conditions. Then $(x_1^*, x_2^*, \cdots, x_n^*)$ is an optimal solution if and only if all of the conditions of the theorem are satisfied.

To illustrate the formulation of the Kuhn–Tucker conditions, consider the following problem.

$$\text{Maximize } \{8x_1 + 10x_2 - 2x_1^2 - x_2^4\},$$

subject to

$$2e^{x_1} + x_1x_2 + x_2^2 \leq 10$$

and

$$x_1 \geq 0,\ x_2 \geq 0\,.$$

Thus, $f(x_1, x_2) = 8x_1 + 10x_2 + 2x_1^2 - x_2^4$ and $g_1(x_1, x_2) = 2e^{x_1} + x_1x_2 + x_2^2$. Note that $f(x_1, x_2)$ is concave since

$$\frac{\partial^2 f}{\partial x_1^2} = -4 < 0 \quad \text{and} \quad \frac{\partial^2 f}{\partial x_1^2}\frac{\partial^2 f}{\partial x_2^2} - \frac{\partial^2 f}{\partial x_1\,\partial x_2}\frac{\partial^2 f}{\partial x_2\,\partial x_1} = 48x_2^2 - 0 \geq 0$$

for all non-negative x_1 and x_2 (see Appendix 1). Furthermore, $g_1(x_1, x_2)$ is convex in the feasible region since

$$\frac{\partial^2 g_1}{\partial x_1^2} = 2e^{x_1} > 0 \quad \text{and} \quad \frac{\partial^2 g_1}{\partial x_1^2}\frac{\partial^2 g_1}{\partial x_2^2} - \frac{\partial^2 g_1}{\partial x_1\,\partial x_2}\frac{\partial^2 g_1}{\partial x_2\,\partial x_1} = 4e^{x_1} - 1 > 0$$

for $x_1 \geq 0$. Hence, the Corollary to Theorem 17.1 applies. The Kuhn–Tucker conditions for this problem are the following:

(1a) If $x_1 > 0$, then $8 - 4x_1 - u_1(2e^{x_1} + x_2) = 0$.
(1b) If $x_2 > 0$, then $10 - 4x_2^3 - u_1(x_1 + 2x_2) = 0$.
(2a) If $x_1 = 0$, then $8 - 4x_1 - u_1(2e^{x_1} + x_2) \leq 0$.
(2b) If $x_2 = 0$, then $10 - 4x_2^3 - u_1(x_1 + 2x_2) \leq 0$.
(3) If $u_1 > 0$, then $2e^{x_1} + x_1x_2 + x_2^2 = 10$.
(4) If $u_1 = 0$, then $2e^{x_1} + x_1x_2 + x_2^2 \leq 10$.
(5) $x_1 \geq 0,\ x_2 \geq 0$.
(6) $u_1 \geq 0$.

Therefore, if one were able to solve for the value of x_1, x_2, u_1 that satisfies these conditions, this value of x_1, x_2 would be the optimal solution. To begin, $u_1 = 0$ implies that $x_1 = 2$ [from conditions (1a) and (2a)], which must violate condition (4) or (5). Therefore, $u_1 > 0$, so condition (3) implies that $2e^{x_1} + x_1x_2 + x_2^2 = 10$. This rules out $x_1 = 0$ since then $x_2 = 2\sqrt{2}$, which must violate condition (1b). It also rules out $x_2 = 0$ since then $x_1 = \ln 5$, and the corresponding solution for u_1 from condition (1a) would violate condition (2b). Since $x_1 > 0$, $x_2 > 0$, $u_1 > 0$ for optimality, the problem is now reduced to solving the three equations, $8 - 4x_1 - u_1(2e^{x_1} + x_2) = 0$, $10 - 4x_2^3 - u_1(x_1 + 2x_2) = 0$, and $2e^{x_1} + x_1x_2 + x_2^2 = 10$, for these three positive unknowns. Unfortunately, these equations are not linear, so that the exact solution is not obtainable by elementary means. However, upper and lower bounds can now be established on x_1 and x_2, and one can even converge upon the solution by trial and error methods.

As the above example illustrates, it is usually difficult, if not essentially impossible, to derive the optimal solution directly from the Kuhn–Tucker conditions. However, they do provide valuable clues as to the identity of the optimal solution, and they also permit checking whether a proposed solution may be optimal. Furthermore, there are many valuable indirect applications of the Kuhn–Tucker conditions. One example of them arises in the next section.

17.3 QUADRATIC PROGRAMMING

The name, "quadratic programming," now conventionally refers to the problem of maximizing (or minimizing) a quadratic objective function subject to linear constraints. Thus, the quadratic programming problem differs from the linear programming problem only in that the objective function also includes x_j^2 and $x_j x_k (j \neq k)$ terms. In short, the problem is to find $x_1, x_2, \cdots, x_n$ so as to

$$\text{maximize} \left\{ \sum_{j=1}^{n} c_j x_j - \frac{1}{2} \sum_{j=1}^{n} \sum_{k=1}^{n} q_{jk} x_j x_k \right\},$$

subject to

$$\sum_{j=1}^{n} a_{ij} x_j \leq b_i, \qquad \text{for } i = 1, 2, \cdots, m,$$

and

$$x_j \geq 0, \qquad \text{for } j = 1, 2, \cdots, n,$$

where the q_{jk} are given constants such that $q_{jk} = q_{kj}$.

Several solution procedures have been developed for the special case of the quadratic programming problem where the objective function is a concave function. (One way of verifying that it is indeed a concave function is to verify the equivalent condition that

$$\sum_{j=1}^{n} \sum_{k=1}^{n} q_{jk} x_j x_k \geq 0$$

for all values of $x_1, x_2, \cdots, x_n$. Mathematically speaking, this equivalent condition is that the q_{jk} are the elements of a "positive semi-definite" matrix.) The relative merits of these procedures will become apparent only after more computational experience. The one described below has had considerable use since its development by Wolfe[116] in 1959.

The first step is to formulate the Kuhn–Tucker conditions for this problem. A convenient form for expressing them for this case is the following:

[116] Philip Wolfe, "The Simplex Method for Quadratic Programming," *Econometrica*, **27**, 382–398 (1959).

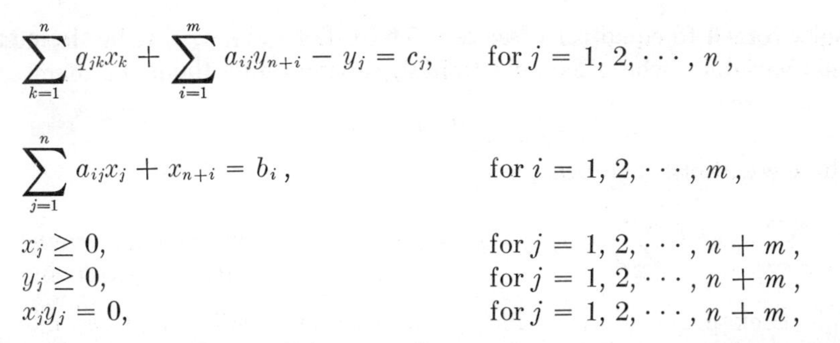

$$\sum_{k=1}^{n} q_{jk}x_k + \sum_{i=1}^{m} a_{ij}y_{n+i} - y_j = c_j, \qquad \text{for } j = 1, 2, \cdots, n,$$

$$\sum_{j=1}^{n} a_{ij}x_j + x_{n+i} = b_i, \qquad \text{for } i = 1, 2, \cdots, m,$$

$$x_j \geq 0, \qquad \text{for } j = 1, 2, \cdots, n+m,$$
$$y_j \geq 0, \qquad \text{for } j = 1, 2, \cdots, n+m,$$
$$x_jy_j = 0, \qquad \text{for } j = 1, 2, \cdots, n+m,$$

where the y_{n+i} are the u_i of the preceding section, and where the y_j ($j = 1, 2, \cdots, n$) and the x_j ($j = n+1, \cdots, n+m$) are slack variables. (The reader is asked in Problem 2 to verify that these indeed are one form of the Kuhn–Tucker conditions.) Since the objective function is assumed to be concave and the constraint functions are linear and therefore convex, the Corollary to Theorem 17.1 applies. Thus, $(x_1, x_2, \cdots, x_n)$ is optimal if and only if there exist values of $x_{n+1}, \cdots, x_{n+m}, y_1, \cdots, y_{n+m}$ such that $(x_1, \cdots, x_{n+m}, y_1, \cdots, y_{n+m})$ satisfies all of these conditions. The problem is thereby reduced to finding a feasible solution to these conditions.

Now notice the key fact that, with the exception of the last restriction ($x_jy_j = 0$ for $j = 1, 2, \cdots, n+m$), these Kuhn–Tucker conditions are nothing more than linear programming constraints involving $2(n+m)$ variables. Furthermore, this $x_jy_j = 0$ restriction simply says that it is not permissible for both x_j and y_j to be basic variables when considering (nondegenerate) basic feasible solutions. Therefore, the problem reduces to finding an initial basic feasible solution to any linear programming problem having these constraints, subject to this additional restriction on the identity of the basic variables. (This "initial" basic feasible solution may be the only feasible solution in this case.) The obvious initial basic variables for the second group of equations,

$$\sum_{j=1}^{n} a_{ij}x_j + x_{n+i} = b_i \qquad (i = 1, 2, \cdots, m),$$

are the x_{n+i} (assuming the b_i are positive). However, since most or all of the c_j normally are positive, it is not obvious what the initial basic variables should be for the other equations,

$$\sum_{k=1}^{n} q_{jk}x_k + \sum_{i=1}^{m} a_{ij}y_{n+i} - y_j = c_j \qquad (j = 1, 2, \cdots, n).$$

The standard linear programming trick when there is not an obvious initial basic feasible solution is to introduce artificial variables which are eventually forced to equal zero (see Sec. 5.6.3). Let $z_1, z_2, \cdots, z_n$ be these artificial variables, where the only (initial) restriction on them is

$$z_j \geq 0, \qquad \text{for } j = 1, 2, \cdots, n\,.$$

These equations then become

$$\sum_{k=1}^{n} q_{jk}x_k + \sum_{i=1}^{m} a_{ij}y_{n+i} - y_j + c_jz_j = c_j, \qquad \text{for } j = 1, 2, \cdots, n\,.$$

This trick provides an artificial initial basic feasible solution, namely, $z_j = 1$ (for $j = 1, 2, \cdots, n$), $x_{n+i} = b_i$ (for $i = 1, 2, \cdots, m$), $x_j = 0$ (for $j = 1, 2, \cdots, n$), and $y_j = 0$ (for $j = 1, 2, \cdots, n + m$). However, a feasible solution to this artificial problem is feasible for the real problem if and only if $z_j = 0$ for $j = 1, 2, \cdots, n$. Therefore,

$$\sum_{j=1}^{n} z_j$$

must be decreased to zero in order to obtain the desired feasible solution. This suggests the following final steps in the solution procedure. Starting with the initial basic feasible solution given above, apply a modification of the simplex method to the following problem.

$$\text{Minimize} \sum_{j=1}^{n} z_j\,,$$

subject to

$$\begin{aligned}
&\sum_{k=1}^{n} q_{jk}x_k + \sum_{i=1}^{m} a_{ij}y_{n+i} - y_j + c_jz_j = c_j, && \text{for } j = 1, 2, \cdots, n\\
&\sum_{j=1}^{n} a_{ij}x_j + x_{n+i} = b_i, && \text{for } i = 1, 2, \cdots, m\\
&x_j \geq 0, && \text{for } j = 1, 2, \cdots, n + m\\
&y_j \geq 0, && \text{for } j = 1, 2, \cdots, n + m\\
&z_j \geq 0, && \text{for } j = 1, 2, \cdots, n\,.
\end{aligned}$$

The modification is that y_j is not permitted to become a basic variable whenever x_j is already a basic variable, and vice-versa, for $j = 1, 2, \cdots, n + m$. This insures that $x_jy_j = 0$ for each value of j. When the optimal solution, $(x_1^*, \cdots, x_{n+m}^*, y_1^*, \cdots, y_{n+m}^*, z_1 = 0, \cdots, z_n = 0)$, is obtained to this problem, $(x_1^*, \cdots, x_n^*)$ is the desired optimal solution to the original quadratic programming problem.

17.4 SEPARABLE CONVEX PROGRAMMING

Consider the case where the objective function can be written in the form,

$$f(x_1, x_2, \cdots, x_n) = f_1(x_1) + f_2(x_2) + \cdots + f_n(x_n) \,,$$

where $f_j(x_j)$ is a specified function of x_j only, for $j = 1, 2, \cdots, n$. Thus, $f(x_1, x_2, \cdots, x_n)$ is what is called a "separable" function, since it can be written as a finite sum of separate terms, each of which involves only a single variable. In other words, $f(x_1, x_2, \cdots, x_n)$ has the additivity property discussed in Sec. 5.4.2. One example of a separable function is the linear programming objective function, where $f_j(x_j) = c_j x_j$. On the other hand, the general quadratic programming problem objective function is not separable since it contains $x_j x_k$ terms $(j \neq k)$.

A special technique is widely used for obtaining an approximate solution to certain non-linear programming problems having a separable objective function. This technique involves reducing the problem to a linear programming problem by approximating each $f_j(x_j)$ by a piecewise linear function. However, it guarantees a valid result only if all of the $f_j(x_j)$ are concave functions[117] and the objective is to maximize $f(x_1, x_2, \cdots, x_n)$, or if all of the $f_j(x_j)$ are convex functions[117] and the objective is to minimize $f(x_1, x_2, \cdots, x_n)$. The maximizing objective is assumed here, although the approach to both cases is the same. The discussion is also limited to the case where the constraints are linear programming constraints [although the technique can also be extended to the case where each $g_i(x_1, x_2, \cdots, x_n)$ is a non-linear separable function whose component functions are all convex]. In summary, the problem being considered here is

$$\text{maximize} \sum_{j=1}^{n} f_j(x_j) \,,$$

subject to

$$\sum_{j=1}^{n} a_{ij} x_j \leq b_i, \qquad \text{for } i = 1, 2, \cdots, m \,,$$

and

$$x_j \geq 0, \qquad \text{for } j = 1, 2, \cdots, n \,,$$

where $f_j(x_j)$ is a concave function, for $j = 1, 2, \cdots, n$.

The key to the technique is the fact that a concave function of a single

[117] See Appendix 1 for a definition of convex function and concave function.

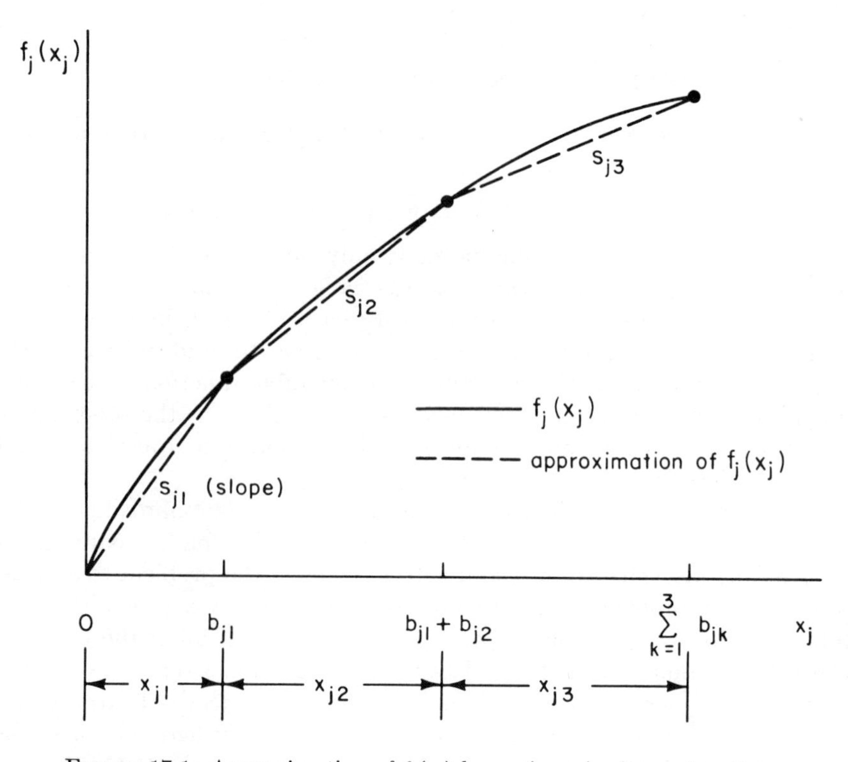

FIGURE 17.1. Approximation of $f_j(x_j)$ by a piecewise linear function.

variable can be approximated as closely as desired by a piecewise linear function (i.e., a continuous function with linear segments so that its graph comprises part of a polygon). This is illustrated by Fig. 17.1. Thus, the first step in the technique is to select a piecewise linear function to approximate each $f_j(x_j)$, for $j = 1, 2, \cdots, n$. This is done by judiciously selecting points lying on $f_j(x_j)$ as break points (points at which the slope changes) of the piecewise linear function. Let m_j be the number of break points for this function approximating $f_j(x_j)$. (Thus, $m_j = 3$ in Fig. 17.1.)

Let

$$b_{j1},\ b_{j1},+b_{j2},\cdots,\ \sum_{k=1}^{m_j} b_{jk}$$

be the (ascending) values of x_j at which the break points occur. (If x_j does not have an upper bound, $b_{jm_j} = \infty$.) Let s_{jk} $(k = 1, 2, \cdots, m_j)$ be the slope (derivative) of this piecewise linear function when

$$\sum_{l=1}^{k-1} b_{jl} < x_j < \sum_{l=1}^{k} b_{jl}\,.$$

The next step is to decompose x_j into auxiliary variables, $x_{j1}, x_{j2}, \cdots, x_{jm_j}$, so that this piecewise linear function can be written as an ordinary linear function of these variables. Define x_{jk} as

$$x_{jk} \equiv \begin{cases} 0, & \text{if } x_j \le \sum_{l=1}^{k-1} b_{jl} \\ x_j - \sum_{l=1}^{k-1} b_{jl}, & \text{if } \sum_{l=1}^{k-1} b_{jl} \le x_j \le \sum_{l=1}^{k} b_{jl} \\ \sum_{l=1}^{k} b_{jl} - \sum_{l=1}^{k-1} b_{jl}, & \text{if } x_j \ge \sum_{l=1}^{k} b_{jl}, \end{cases}$$

for $k = 1, 2, \cdots, m_j$ and $j = 1, 2, \cdots, n$. Notice this definition implies that

$$0 \le x_{jk} \le b_{jk} .$$

Furthermore, if k^* is the value of k such that

$$\sum_{l=1}^{k^*-1} b_{jl} \le x_j \le \sum_{l=1}^{k^*} b_{jl} ,$$

then

$$x_{jk} = \begin{cases} b_{jk}, & \text{for } k = 1, 2, \cdots, k^* - 1 \\ x_j - \sum_{l=1}^{k^*-1} b_{jl}, & \text{for } k = k^* \\ 0, & \text{for } k = k^* + 1, \cdots, m_j . \end{cases}$$

Therefore,

$$x_j \equiv x_{j1} + x_{j2} + \cdots + x_{jm_j} ,$$

and the linear piecewise function approximating $f_j(x_j)$ is

$$f_j(x_j) \approx s_{j1}x_{j1} + s_{j2}x_{j2} + \cdots + s_{jm_j}x_{jm_j} ,$$

for $j = 1, 2, \cdots, n$.

The final part of the technique is to reformulate the problem in terms of the x_{jk} instead of the x_j. To begin, substitute

$$\sum_{k=1}^{m_j} x_{jk} \quad \text{for } x_j \quad \text{and} \quad \sum_{k=1}^{m_j} s_{jk}x_{jk} \quad \text{for } f_j(x_j)$$

throughout the original model, for $j = 1, 2, \cdots, n$. This yields the following:

$$\text{maximize} \sum_{j=1}^{n} \left(\sum_{k=1}^{m_j} s_{jk} x_{jk} \right),$$

subject to

$$\sum_{j=1}^{n} a_{ij} \left(\sum_{k=1}^{m_j} x_{jk} \right) \leq b_i, \qquad \text{for } i = 1, 2, \cdots, m,$$

and

$$\sum_{k=1}^{m_j} x_{jk} \geq 0, \qquad \text{for } j = 1, 2, \cdots, n.$$

However, this is not sufficient since it does not insure that the x_{jk} will be assigned values consistent with their definition. The restrictions imposed on the x_{jk} by their definition may be summarized as:

$$(1) \quad 0 \leq x_{jk} \leq b_{jk}, \text{ and } (2) \quad x_{jk} = 0 \text{ whenever } x_{j(k-1)} < b_{j(k-1)}.$$

Restriction (1) is in the proper format to be added to the model, so this should be done. (This also insures that

$$\sum_{k=1}^{m_j} x_{jk} \geq 0,$$

which may therefore be deleted from the model.) However, restriction (2) does not fit the linear programming format. Fortunately, it is not necessary to add this restriction to the model. It is satisfied automatically! This is where the assumption that all of the $f_j(x_j)$ are concave functions plays its role. This assumption implies that

$$s_{j1} > s_{j2} > \cdots > s_{jm_j}, \qquad \text{for } j = 1, 2, \cdots, n.$$

This fact makes it easy to see that any solution violating restriction (2) cannot be the optimal solution to the current model. To show this, consider any feasible solution for the current model such that $x_{j,k-1} < b_{j,k-1}$ and $x_{jk} > 0$. Let ϵ equal x_{jk} or $(b_{j,k-1} - x_{j,k-1})$, whichever is smaller. Notice that the constraints are such that it must be feasible to subtract ϵ from x_{jk} and add it to $x_{j,k-1}$. Furthermore, this change increases the objective function by $\epsilon(s_{j,k-1} - s_{jk}) > 0$, so that this new solution is better than the original solution. Hence, the original solution cannot be optimal. The conclusion is that it is sufficient to apply the simplex method to find the optimal solution for the linear programming problem,

$$\text{maximize} \sum_{j=1}^{n} \left(\sum_{k=1}^{m_j} s_{jk} x_{jk} \right),$$

subject to

$$\sum_{j=1}^{n} a_{ij}\left(\sum_{k=1}^{m_j} x_{jk}\right) \leq b_i, \qquad \text{for } i = 1, 2, \cdots, m\,,$$

$$x_{jk} \leq b_{jk}, \qquad \text{for } j = 1, 2, \cdots, n\,, \quad k = 1, 2, \cdots, m_j\,,$$

and

$$x_{jk} \geq 0, \qquad \text{for } j = 1, 2, \cdots, n\,, \quad k = 1, 2, \cdots, m_j\,.$$

If $(x_{11}^*, x_{12}^*, \cdots, x_{nm_n}^*)$ is the optimal solution to this problem, then

$$\left(x_1 = \sum_{k=1}^{m_1} x_{1k}^*,\ x_2 = \sum_{k=1}^{m_2} x_{jk}^*,\ \cdots,\ x_n = \sum_{k=1}^{m_n} x_{nk}^*\right)$$

must be the optimal solution to the approximate form of the original problem.

Although there is a large number of $x_{jk} \leq b_{jk}$ constraints in the above model, they do not need to be handled like ordinary constraints by the simplex method. The special technique for handling upper bounds described in Sec. 15.3.2 provides a much more efficient approach.

To illustrate the procedure described above, consider the example used in Sec. 5.5, viz., maximize $\{3x_1 + 5x_2\}$, subject to $x_1 \leq 4$, $x_2 \leq 6$, $3x_1 + 2x_2 \leq 18$, and $x_1 \geq 0$, $x_2 \geq 0$. Suppose that x_1 and x_2 represent the levels of activities 1 and 2, respectively. Suppose that it has been found that $3 < x_1 \leq 4$ and $3 < x_2 \leq 6$ is possible only by using overtime work, which reduces the net unit profit from 3 to 2 for activity 1 and from 5 to 1 for activity 2. Thus, the objective function becomes $\{f_1(x_1) + f_2(x_2)\}$, where $f_j(x_j)$ is the total net profit from activity j ($j = 1, 2$) as plotted in Fig. 17.2. Since the $f_j(x_j)$ are already piecewise linear functions, it is not necessary to use approximations in this situation. The auxiliary variables are x_{j1} and x_{j2}, which represent the level of activity j on regular time and on overtime, respectively, for $j = 1, 2$. Therefore, the linear programming problem to be solved is

$$\text{maximize } \{3x_{11} + 2x_{12} + 5x_{21} + x_{22}\}\,,$$

subject to

$$\begin{aligned} 3(x_{11} + x_{12}) + 2(x_{21} + x_{22}) &\leq 18 \\ x_{11} &\leq 3 \\ x_{12} &\leq 1 \\ x_{21} &\leq 3 \\ x_{22} &\leq 3 \end{aligned}$$

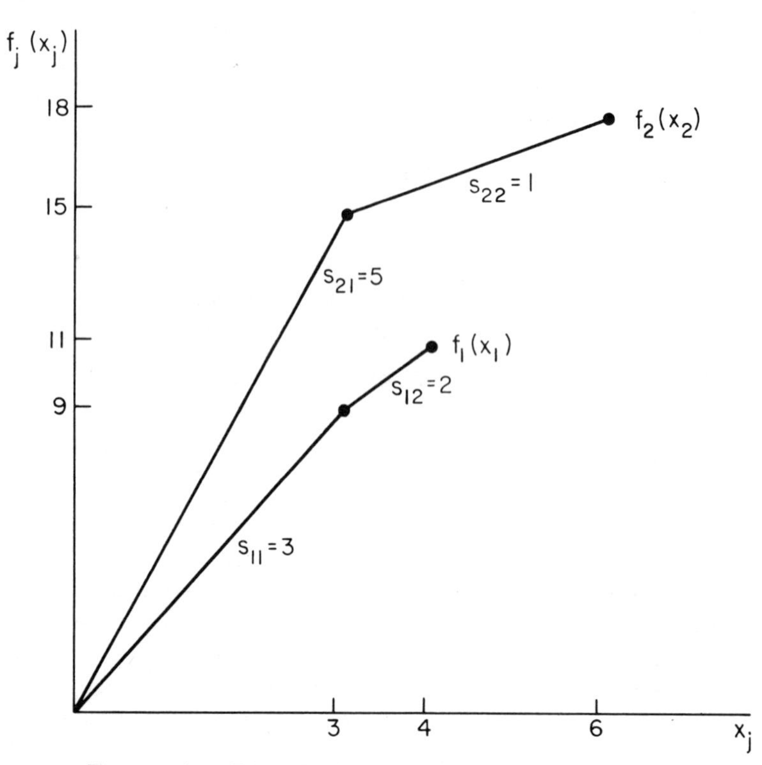

FIGURE 17.2. Piecewise linear functions for the example.

and

$$x_{jk} \geq 0, \qquad \text{for } j = 1, 2\,, \quad k = 1, 2\,.$$

After obtaining the optimal solution, $(x_{11}^*, x_{12}^*, x_{21}^*, x_{22}^*)$, for this problem, $x_1 = x_{11}^* + x_{12}^*$ and $x_2 = x_{21}^* + x_{22}^*$ will be the optimal total levels of activities 1 and 2, respectively.

As the above example illustrates, one important special case of separable convex programming is where the $f_j(x_j)$ are already piecewise linear functions. Another case of practical importance is where the $f_j(x_j)$ functions are not known exactly, but must be estimated instead. In this case, it is often reasonable, and helpful, to construct these estimates of the $f_j(x_j)$ as piecewise linear functions at the outset. These cases, plus the general cases alluded to previously, have given considerable practical importance to the separable convex programming technique.

17.5 GENERAL CONVEX PROGRAMMING

The general convex programming problem is the special case of the general non-linear programming problem where $f(x_1, x_2, \cdots, x_n)$ is a concave function, and all of the $g_i(x_1, x_2, \cdots, x_n)$ are convex functions. Thus far, very little progress has been made in developing general solution procedures for other non-linear programming problems which do not make these assumptions. However, these assumptions greatly simplify the problem. The convexity of the $g_i(x_1, x_2, \cdots, x_n)$ functions implies that the set of feasible solutions is a convex set. This property and the concavity of $f(x_1, x_2, \cdots, x_n)$ imply that any local optimum is also a global optimum, i.e., any feasible solution which maximizes $f(x_1, x_2, \cdots, x_n)$ over the feasible solutions in its immediate neighborhood also maximizes $f(x_1, x_2, \cdots, x_n)$ over the entire set of feasible solutions. Therefore, rather than having to find and compare a large (possibly infinite) number of local optima, it is only necessary to find one local, and therefore global, optimum. A large number of promising procedures for doing this are being developed and tested. Some of these approaches are briefly mentioned here to indicate the direction of current research on the general convex programming problem.[118]

Almost all of the approaches to this problem involve an iterative solution procedure. Thus, like the simplex method for linear programming, these procedures advance from one solution to the next in a pilgrimage toward the optimal solution. The basic difference between these procedures is in the way in which the successive solutions are selected.

Some of the approaches place their primary emphasis upon the objective function, particularly the "gradient" of the objective function, when selecting the successive solutions. The gradient of $f(x_1', x_2', \cdots, x_n')$, denoted by $\nabla f(x_1', x_2', \cdots, x_n')$, is the vector whose elements are the respective partial derivatives evaluated at $(x_1', x_2', \cdots, x_n')$,

$$\nabla f(x_1', x_2', \cdots, x_n') = \left(\frac{\partial f}{\partial x_1}, \frac{\partial f}{\partial x_2}, \cdots, \frac{\partial f}{\partial x_n}\right) \text{ at } (x_1, x_2, \cdots, x_n) = (x_1', x_2', \cdots, x_n') .$$

The significance of the gradient is that the (infinitesimal) change in $(x_1, x_2, \cdots, x_n)$ which maximizes the rate at which $f(x_1, x_2, \cdots, x_n)$ increases is the change which is proportional to $\nabla f(x_1, x_2, \cdots, x_n)$. To express this idea geometrically, the "direction" of the gradient, $\nabla f(x_1', x_2', \cdots, x_n')$, is interpreted as the direction of the directed line segment (arrow) from the origin $(0, 0, \cdots, 0)$ to the point $(\partial f/\partial x_1, \partial f/\partial x_2, \cdots, \partial f/\partial x_n)$, where $\partial f/\partial x_j$ is evaluated at $x_j = x_j'$. Therefore, it may be said that the rate at which $f(x_1, x_2, \cdots, x_n)$ increases is maximized if (infinitesimal) changes in $(x_1, x_2, \cdots, x_n)$ are in the direction of the gradient, $\nabla f(x_1, x_2, \cdots, x_n)$. Since the objective is to find the feasible solution maximizing $f(x_1, x_2, \cdots, x_n)$, it would seem expedient to attempt to move in the direction of the gradient as much as possible.

[118] A more complete description for relatively advanced readers is available in the survey articles cited at the end of this chapter.

One of the procedures based on the gradient is Rosen's "gradient projection method."[119] This method requires each successive point to be a feasible point that yields a larger value of $f(x_1, x_2, \cdots, x_n)$ than the preceding point. Given a feasible point, $(x_1', x_2', \cdots, x_n')$, the next point is selected in the following way. The first step is to determine the direction in which to move. Visualize a straight line extended from $(x_1', x_2', \cdots, x_n')$ in the direction of the gradient $\nabla f(x_1', x_2', \cdots, x_n')$. If it is possible to move a positive distance along this line without becoming infeasible, then this is the desired direction. On the other hand, if $(x_1', x_2', \cdots, x_n')$ is on the boundary of the set of feasible solutions and the direction of the gradient is away from the set, then some other direction must be selected. In this case, proceed as follows. Assume for the moment that the constraints are all linear constraints, so that the boundary of the set of feasible solutions consists of planes (or, more precisely, hyperplanes) of the form,

$$\sum_{j=1}^{n} a_{ij}x_j = b_i .$$

Consider the plane passing through $(x_1', x_2', \cdots, x_n')$. (If there is more than one such plane, consider instead the intersection of certain of these planes.) Find the projection of the straight line described above onto this plane. (The projection of a line onto a plane is the locus of points on the plane lying at the foot of a perpendicular from the plane to some point on the line.) Thus, this projection is a straight line on this plane extending from $(x_1', x_2', \cdots, x_n')$. The direction to move is along this line. Having selected the direction, it remains to determine how far to move. Try moving to the farthest feasible point in this direction. However, if this does not increase $f(x_1, x_2, \cdots, x_n)$, then find the feasible point in this direction which yields the largest increase in $f(x_1, x_2, \cdots, x_n)$. Either way, this determines the next point. This procedure is then repeated for succeeding points until the optimal solution is reached. For the case of non-linear constraints, the projection is made instead onto the plane passing through $(x_1', x_2', \cdots, x_n')$ which is tangent to the boundary of the set of feasible solutions. After selecting a point on this projection, a nearby point on the boundary of the set of feasible solutions is then chosen to be the next feasible solution.

Another approach which uses the gradient is Zoutendijk's "methods of feasible directions."[120] Given a feasible solution, $(x_1', x_2', \cdots, x_n')$, these methods find the next solution by variants of the following procedure. As an approximation, suppose that the gradient $\nabla f(x_1, x_2, \cdots, x_n)$ at all other solutions is the same as at $(x_1', x_2', \cdots, x_n')$. This would imply that each

[119] J. B. Rosen, "The Gradient Projection Method for Nonlinear Programming—Part I: Linear Constraints," *Journal of the Society for Industrial and Applied Mathematics*, **8,** 181–217 (1960); "Part II: Nonlinear Constraints," *ibid.*, **9,** 514–532 (1961).

[120] G. Zoutendijk, *Methods of Feasible Directions*, Elsevier, Amsterdam, 1960.

$\partial f/\partial x_j$ is a constant, so that $f(x_1, x_2, \cdots, x_n)$ would be a linear function whose coefficients are these constants. In short, approximate the objective function $f(x_1, x_2, \cdots, x_n)$ by a linear function,

$$\sum_{j=1}^{n} c_j x_j, \quad \text{where} \quad c_j = \frac{\partial f}{\partial x_j} \quad \text{at} \quad (x_1, x_2, \cdots, x_n) = (x_1', x_2', \cdots, x_n').$$

Assuming linear constraints, the simplex method is then used to maximize this new objective function, subject to the constraints of the original problem. Let $(x_1^*, x_2^*, \cdots, x_n^*)$ denote the solution yielded by the simplex method. Since this is a feasible solution to the original problem, and the set of feasible solutions is a convex set, it must be feasible to move from $(x_1', x_2', \cdots, x_n')$ toward $(x_1^*, x_2^*, \cdots, x_n^*)$. In other words, the direction from $(x_1', x_2', \cdots, x_n')$ to $(x_1^*, x_2^*, \cdots, x_n^*)$ is a "feasible direction." Next, find the feasible point in this direction which maximizes $f(x_1, x_2, \cdots, x_n)$. This is the desired next solution. Zoutendijk has also extended the procedure so that it will handle the case of non-linear constraints.

An approach which deals primarily with the constraints is Kelley's "cutting-plane method."[121] Rather than selecting a sequence of feasible points that are moving toward optimality, this method obtains infeasible "better-than-optimal" points that move toward feasibility. It is designed primarily for the case where some or all of the $g_i(x_1, x_2, \cdots, x_n)$ functions are not linear. The objective function $f(x_1, x_2, \cdots, x_n)$ may be assumed to be linear. [If $f(x_1, x_2, \cdots, x_n)$ is not linear, then maximize x_0 instead and introduce $x_0 - f(x_1, x_2, \cdots, x_n) = 0$ as a constraint.] The basic fact upon which this method is based is that any convex set of feasible solutions may be enclosed within, but approximated as closely as desired, by a set constructed entirely from linear constraints. This fact is intuitively plausible since, by definition of convex set (see Appendix 1), no plane (or hyperplane) can penetrate the boundary of a convex set if it is tangent to the boundary at some point. Therefore, by constructing enough of these tangent planes, it is possible to fully enclose the set in such a way that the maximum distance between the boundary and the nearest plane is as small as desired. As a result of this fact, it is possible to construct a linear programming problem which differs from the original problem only in that a small proportion of its feasible solutions are not feasible for the original problem. The method then proceeds to use the simplex method to find the optimal solution to this linear programming problem. If this solution happens to be feasible for the original problem, it must also be optimal (since it is the best solution from among all of the solutions that are feasible, plus some that are not). If this solution is not feasible, a new linear programming problem must be con-

[121] J. E. Kelley, Jr., "The Cutting-Plane Method for Solving Convex Programs," *Journal of the Society for Industrial and Applied Mathematics*, **8,** 703–712 (1960).

structed in order to try again. This may be done by appending a new linear constraint to the old linear programming problem, where this new constraint eliminates the previous solution but does not eliminate any feasible solutions for the original problem. Geometrically, this constraint creates a "cutting-plane" which passes between the last point obtained by the simplex method and the set of feasible solutions for the original problem. The simplex method is then used to solve the new linear programming problem. This procedure is repeated until a solution is obtained that is feasible, and therefore optimal, for the original problem.

Another promising approach is the "sequential unconstrained minimization technique" developed by Fiacco and McCormick.[122] This technique deals simultaneously with the objective function and constraints by combining them into a single function. By minimizing this function for different values of an auxiliary parameter, a sequence of feasible solutions is obtained that converges to the optimal solution. In order to motivate the relevance of this function, it is useful to reformulate the problem in an equivalent way. Write the objective as minimize $-f(x_1, x_2, \cdots, x_n)$, rather than maximize $f(x_1, x_2, \cdots, x_n)$. Also, let

$$h_i(x_1, x_2, \cdots, x_n) = \begin{cases} b_i - g_i(x_1, x_2, \cdots, x_n), & \text{if } i = 1, 2, \cdots, m \\ x_{i-m}, & \text{if } i = m+1, m+2, \cdots, m+n\,. \end{cases}$$

[If x_{i-m} is not required to be non-negative, then delete $h_i(x_1, x_2, \cdots, x_m)$ from the analysis.] The problem is then written as

$$\text{minimize } \{-f(x_1, x_2, \cdots, x_n)\},$$

subject to

$$h_i(x_1, x_2, \cdots, x_n) \geq 0, \qquad \text{for } i = 1, 2, \cdots, m+n\,.$$

Now consider the function,

$$P(x_1, x_2, \cdots, x_n; r) = -f(x_1, x_2, \cdots, x_n) + r \sum_{i=1}^{m+n} \left[\frac{1}{h_i(x_1, x_2, \cdots, x_n)}\right].$$

$P(x_1, x_2, \cdots, x_n; r)$ is the function that is to be minimized for different values of r, subject to $h_i(x_1, x_2, \cdots, x_n) \geq 0$ for $i = 1, 2, \cdots, m+n$. Notice that $1/h_i(x_1, x_2, \cdots, x_n)$ approaches infinity as $h_i(x_1, x_2, \cdots, x_n)$

[122] Anthony V. Fiacco and Garth P. McCormick, "The Sequential Unconstrained Minimization Technique for Nonlinear Programming, A Primal-Dual Method," *Management Science*, **10,** 360–366 (1964); also "Computational Algorithm for the Sequential Unconstrained Minimization Technique for Nonlinear Programming," *Management Science*, **10,** 601–617 (1964).

approaches zero. Therefore, the $(x_1, x_2, \cdots, x_n)$ that minimizes $P(x_1, x_2, \cdots, x_n; r)$ necessarily yields $h_i(x_1, x_2, \cdots, x_n) > 0$ for all i. Thus,

$$r \sum_{i=1}^{m+n} \left[\frac{1}{h_i(x_1, x_2, \cdots, x_n)} \right]$$

is a boundary repulsion term that drives the minimizing solution away from the boundary of the set of feasible solutions, where $h_i(x_1, x_2, \cdots, x_n) = 0$ for some $i = 1, 2, \cdots, n + m$. This is a key fact because it reduces the problem to a well-behaved minimization problem of calculus by obviating the very difficult task of investigating the boundary. (It may still be difficult to solve this problem, and it usually is necessary to use a method of successive approximations, but at least the problem can be solved by classical methods.) Furthermore, this fact greatly facilitates satisfying the requirement that only feasible solutions be considered.

The ultimate objective of the sequential unconstrained minimization technique is to find the feasible solution that minimizes $-f(x_1, x_2, \cdots, x_n)$. Therefore, another key to the technique is the fact that, if the boundary repulsion term,

$$r \sum_{i=1}^{m+n} \left[\frac{1}{h_i(x_1, x_2, \cdots, x_n)} \right],$$

were eliminated from $P(x_1, x_2, \cdots, x_n; r)$, then the feasible solution that minimizes $P(x_1, x_2, \cdots, x_n; r)$ would be the desired optimal solution. Although it is not convenient to eliminate the boundary repulsion term completely, it can be made negligibly small relative to $-f(x_1, x_2, \cdots, x_n)$ by making r sufficiently small. The feasible solution that minimizes $P(x_1, x_2, \cdots, x_n)$ would then be close to the optimal solution.

Thus, the procedure begins by finding the $(x_1, x_2, \cdots, x_n)$ that minimizes $P(x_1, x_2, \cdots, x_n; r)$ for a selected small value of r.[123] This reveals that the optimal solution probably lies somewhere near this $(x_1, x_2, \cdots, x_n)$. Then, to indicate the direction in which to move to reach the optimal solution, find the point that minimizes $P(x_1, x_2, \cdots, x_n; r)$ for a selected smaller value of r. Repeat this with successively smaller values of r until enough points have been obtained to justify extrapolating to the optimal solution at $r = 0$.

Useful information is available for guiding the decision on when this

[123] As described in Appendix 2, this is done by setting $\partial P/\partial x = 0$ for $j = 1, 2, \cdots, n$, and solving the resulting set of equations. Since these equations generally are not linear, finding this simultaneous solution usually requires the use of numerical methods (namely, first- and second-order gradient methods) which converge to the solution by successive approximations.

extrapolating should be done. In particular, if $(x_1', x_2', \cdots, x_n')$ is the minimizing point obtained for $r = r'$, it is then known that

$$-f(x_1', x_2', \cdots, x_n') - r\sum_{i=1}^{m+n}\left[\frac{1}{h_i(x_1', x_2', \cdots, x_n')}\right] \leq -f(x_1^*, x_2^*, \cdots, x_n^*)$$
$$\leq -f(x_1', x_2', \cdots, x_n'),$$

where $(x_1^*, x_2^*, \cdots, x_n^*)$ is the unknown optimal solution. Thus, $[-f(x_1', x_2', \cdots, x_n')]$ cannot exceed the optimal value of $[-f(x_1, x_2, \cdots, x_n)]$ by more than

$$r\sum_{i=1}^{m+n}\left[\frac{1}{h_i(x_1', x_2', \cdots, x_n')}\right].$$

Therefore, it would be reasonable to have the procedure extrapolate to the optimal solution at $r = 0$ whenever the resulting maximum error is considered to be sufficiently small.

Fiacco and McCormick[124] have developed the theoretical validation of this procedure. They also have developed detailed methods for its implementation, based on their computational experience.

In conclusion, it should be re-emphasized that the objective in this section was only to suggest the direction of current research on the general convex programming problem by conveying the main ideas in certain promising approaches. All of the procedures described here are relatively sophisticated algorithms that (except for particularly trivial problems) require the use of a digital computer. Therefore, no attempt has been made to give the details required to implement these procedures.

Research continues in this area, as well as on non-convex programming problems, and it is anticipated that much progress will be made during the next decade.

SELECTED REFERENCES

1. Dantzig, George B., *Linear Programming and Extensions*, Princeton University Press, Princeton, N.J., 1963, chap. 24.
2. Dorn, W. S., "Non-Linear Programming—A Survey," *Management Science*, **9,** 171–208 (1963).
3. Hadley, G., *Nonlinear Programming and Dynamic Programming*, Addison-Wesley, Reading, Mass., 1964.
4. Wolfe, Philip, "Methods of Nonlinear Programming," in Robert L. Graves and Philip Wolfe (eds.), *Recent Advances in Mathematical Programming*, McGraw-Hill, New York, 1963.

[124] *Ibid.*

PROBLEMS

1. Consider the non-linear programming problem given in Problem 7 at the end of Chapter 8. Verify whether $(x_1, x_2) = (1, 1)$ is or is not an optimal solution for this problem by applying the Kuhn–Tucker conditions.

2. Derive the Kuhn–Tucker conditions for the quadratic programming problem. Show that they can be expressed as given in Sec. 17.3.

3. Consider the quadratic programming problem,

$$\text{maximize } \{6x_1 + 3x_2 - x_1^2 + 4x_1x_2 - 4x_2^2\},$$

subject to

$$\begin{aligned} x_1 + x_2 &\leq 3 \\ 4x_1 + x_2 &\leq 9 \end{aligned}$$

and

$$x_1 \geq 0,\ x_2 \geq 0.$$

Suppose this problem is to be solved by the procedure described in Sec. 17.3.

(a) Formulate the equivalent problem that is to be solved by a modification of the simplex method.
(b) Solve the problem as formulated in Part (a).

4. A certain corporation is planning to produce and market three different products. Let x_1, x_2, and x_3 denote the number of units to be produced of the three respective products. The preliminary estimates of their potential profitability are as follows.

For the first 15 units produced of product 1, the unit profit would be approximately \$12. The unit profit would only be \$1 for any additional units of product 1. For the first 20 units produced of product 2, the unit profit is estimated at \$8. The unit profit would be \$4 for each of the next 20 units, and \$3 for any additional units. For the first 10 units of product 3, the unit profit would be \$15. The unit profit would be \$10 for each of the next 5 units, and \$6 for any additional units.

Certain limitations on the use of needed resources impose the following constraints on the production of the three products:

$$\begin{aligned} x_1 + x_2 + x_3 &\leq 60 \\ 3x_1 + 2x_2 &\leq 200 \\ x_1 + 2x_3 &\leq 70. \end{aligned}$$

Management wants to know what values of x_1, x_2, and x_3 should be chosen so as to maximize total profit.

(a) Treat this problem as a separable convex programming problem by formulating a mathematical model that could be solved by the simplex method. Show the appropriate linear objective function and constraints, but do not solve numerically.
(b) Solve the problem as formulated in Part (a).

5. Consider the convex programming problem,

$$\text{maximize } \{4x_1 + 6x_2 - x_1^3 - 2x_2^2\},$$

subject to

$$x_1 + 3x_2 \leq 8$$
$$5x_1 + 2x_2 \leq 14$$

and

$$x_1 \geq 0, x_2 \geq 0.$$

(a) Treat this problem as a separable convex programming problem by formulating an approximate mathematical model that could be solved by the simplex method. Use the integers as the break points of the piecewise linear functions.
(b) Solve the problem as formulated in Part (a).
(c) Derive the optimal solution from the Kuhn–Tucker conditions for this problem.

6. Consider the non-linear programming problem, minimize

$$f(x_1, x_2) = \frac{(x_1 + 1)^3}{3} + x_2,$$

subject to

$$x_1 \geq 1$$
$$x_2 \geq 0,$$

where $f(x_1, x_2)$ is a convex function over the set of feasible solutions.

(a) Derive the optimal solution from the Kuhn–Tucker conditions for this problem.
(b) Treat this problem as a separable convex programming problem by formulating an approximate mathematical model that could be solved by the simplex method. Use $x_1 = 1$, $x_1 = 2$, $x_1 = 3$, $x_1 = 4$, $x_1 = 6$, and $x_1 = 9$ as the break points of the piecewise linear function approximating the function of x_1 in the objective function. Assume that the possibility of x_1 exceeding nine can be ignored. Do not solve numerically.
(c) Obtain the optimal solution by using the sequential unconstrained minimization technique. Do this by finding the solution minimizing $P(x_1, x_2, \cdots, x_n; r)$ for $r = 1$, for $r = 0.01$, and for $r = 0.0001$, and then deducing the limit of the minimizing solution as r converges to zero.

Appendices

APPENDIX 1

Convexity

The concept of convexity is frequently used in operations research work. Therefore, the properties of convex (or concave) functions and convex sets are introduced in turn below.

Definition: A function of a single variable, say, $f(x)$, is a *convex function* if, for each pair of values of x, say, x' and x'',

$$f[\lambda x'' + (1 - \lambda)x'] \leq \lambda f(x'') + (1 - \lambda)f(x')$$

for all values of λ such that $0 \leq \lambda \leq 1$. It is a *strictly convex function* if $\leq$ can be replaced by $<$. It is a *concave function* (or a *strictly concave function*) if this statement holds when $\leq$ is replaced by $\geq$ (or by $>$).

This definition also has an enlightening geometrical interpretation. Consider the graph of the function $f(x)$ drawn as a function of x. Then $[x', f(x')]$ and $[x'', f(x'')]$ are two points on the graph of $f(x)$, and $[\lambda x'' + (1 - \lambda)x', \lambda f(x'') + (1 - \lambda)f(x')]$ represents the various points on the line segment between these two points when $0 \leq \lambda \leq 1$. Thus, the original inequality in the definition indicates that this line segment lies entirely above or on the graph of the function. Therefore, $f(x)$ is convex if, for each pair of points on the graph of $f(x)$, the line segment joining these two points lies entirely above or on the graph of $f(x)$. In other words, $f(x)$ is convex if it is "always bending upward." To be more precise, if $f(x)$ possesses a second derivative everywhere, then $f(x)$ is convex if and only if $d^2f(x)/dx^2 \geq 0$ for all values of x [for which $f(x)$ is defined]. Similarly, $f(x)$ is strictly convex when $d^2f(x)/dx^2 > 0$, concave when $d^2f(x)/dx^2 \leq 0$, and strictly concave when $d^2f(x)/dx^2 < 0$. Some examples are given in Figs. A1.1, A1.2, A1.3, and A1.4.

The concept of a convex function also generalizes to functions of more than one variable. Thus, if $f(x)$ is replaced by $f(x_1, x_2, \cdots, x_n)$, the definition

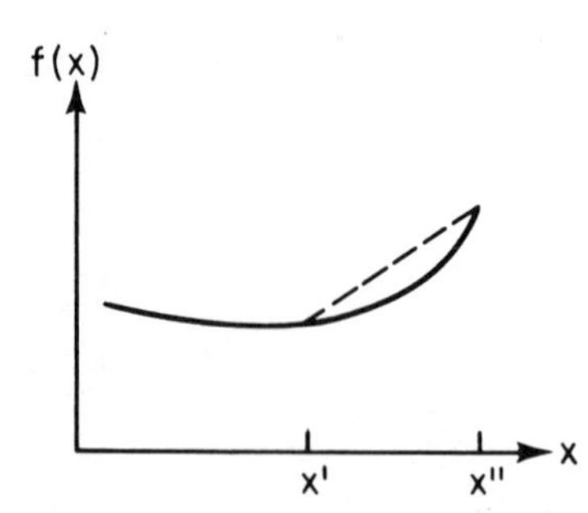

FIGURE A1.1. A convex function.

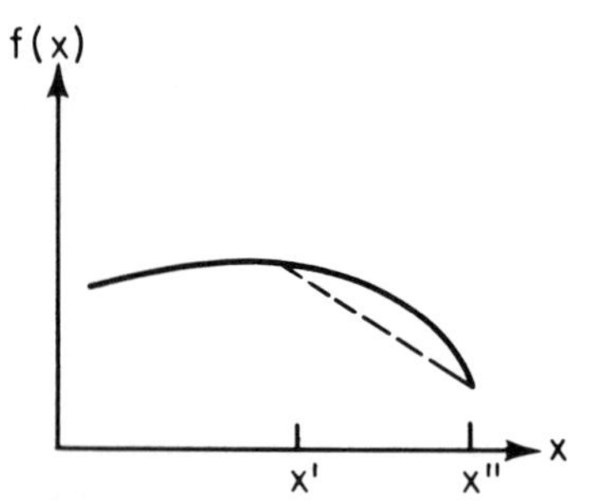

FIGURE A1.2. A concave function.

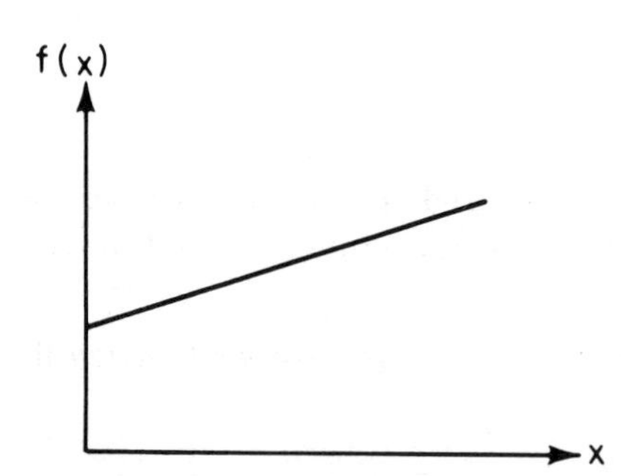

FIGURE A1.3. A function that is both convex and concave.

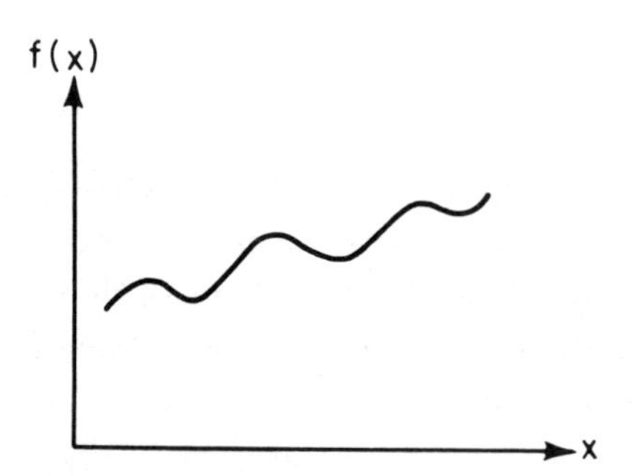

FIGURE A1.4. A function that is neither convex nor concave.

given above still applies if x is replaced everywhere by $(x_1, x_2, \cdots, x_n)$. Similarly, the corresponding geometrical interpretation is still valid after generalizing the concepts of "points" and "line segments." Thus, just as a particular value of (x, y) is interpreted as a point in two-dimensional space, each possible value of $(x_1, x_2, \cdots, x_m)$ may be thought of as a point in m-dimensional (Euclidean) space. By letting $m = n + 1$, the "points on the graph of $f(x_1, x_2, \cdots, x_n)$" become the possible values of $(x_1, x_2, \cdots, x_n, f(x_1, x_2, \cdots, x_n))$. Another point, $(x_1, x_2, \cdots, x_n, x_{n+1})$, is said to lie above, or on, or below the graph of $f(x_1, x_2, \cdots, x_n)$, according to whether x_{n+1} is larger, equal to, or smaller than $f(x_1, x_2, \cdots, x_n)$, respectively.

Definition: The *line segment* joining any two points, $(x', x_2', \cdots, x_m')$ and $(x_1'', x_2'', \cdots, x_m'')$, is the collection of points,

$$(x_1, x_2, \cdots, x_m) = [\lambda x_1'' + (1 - \lambda)x_1', \lambda x_2'' + (1 - \lambda)x_2', \cdots, \lambda x_m'' + (1 - \lambda)x_m'],$$

such that $0 \leq \lambda \leq 1$.

Thus, a line segment in m-dimensional space is a direct generalization of a line segment in two-dimensional space. For example, if

$$(x_1', x_2') = (2, 6), (x_1'', x_2'') = (3, 4),$$

then the line segment joining them is the collection of points,

$$(x_1, x_2) = [3\lambda + 2(1 - \lambda), 4\lambda + 6(1 - \lambda)],$$

where $0 \leq \lambda \leq 1$.

Definition: $f(x_1, x_2, \cdots, x_n)$ is a *convex function* if, for each pair of points on the graph of $f(x_1, x_2, \cdots, x_n)$, the line segment joining these two points lies entirely above or on the graph of $f(x_1, x_2, \cdots, x_n)$. It is a *strictly convex function* if this line segment actually lies entirely above this graph except at the end points of the line segment. *Concave* and *strictly concave* functions are defined in exactly the same way, except that "above" would be replaced by "below."

Just as the second derivative can be used (when it exists everywhere) to check whether a function of a single variable is convex or not, so second partial derivatives can be used to check functions of several variables, although in a more complicated way. For example, if there are two variables, then $f(x_1, x_2)$ is convex if and only if

$$(1) \quad \frac{\partial^2 f(x_1, x_2)}{\partial x_1^2} \frac{\partial^2 f(x_1, x_2)}{\partial x_2^2} - \left[\frac{\partial^2 f(x_1, x_2)}{\partial x_1 \, \partial x_2}\right]^2 \geq 0,$$

$$(2) \quad \frac{\partial^2 f(x_1, x_2)}{\partial x_1^2} \geq 0,$$

and

$$(3) \quad \frac{\partial^2 f(x_1, x_2)}{\partial x_2^2} \geq 0$$

for all possible values of (x_1, x_2), assuming that these partial derivatives exist everywhere. [Actually, condition (3) is superfluous and can be omitted, since it is implied by the other two conditions.] It is strictly convex if $\geq$ can be replaced by $>$ in all three conditions, whereas, $f(x_1, x_2)$ is concave if $\geq$ can be replaced by $\leq$ in conditions (2) and (3). When there are more than two variables, the conditions for convexity are a generalization of them. In mathematical terminology, $f(x_1, x_2, \cdots, x_n)$ is convex if and only if its "$n \times n$ Hessian matrix is positive semi-definite" for all possible values of $(x_1, x_2, \cdots, x_n)$.

Thus far, convexity has been treated as a general property of a function. However, many non-convex functions do satisfy the conditions for convexity over certain intervals for the respective variables. Therefore, it is meaningful to talk about a function being "convex over a certain region." For example, a function is said to be convex within a neighborhood of a specified point if its second derivative (or partial derivatives) satisfy the conditions for convexity at that point. This concept is useful in Appendix 2.

Finally, two particularly important properties of convex functions should be mentioned. First, if $f(x_1, x_2, \cdots, x_n)$ is a convex function, then $g(x_1, x_2, \cdots, x_n) \equiv -f(x_1, x_2, \cdots, x_n)$ is a concave function, and vice versa. Second, the sum of convex functions is a convex function. To illustrate,

$$f_1(x_1) = x_1^4 + 2x_1^2 - 5x_1$$

and

$$f_2(x_1, x_2) = x_1^2 + 2x_1x_2 + x_2^2$$

are both convex functions, as the reader can verify by calculating their second derivatives. Therefore, the sum of these functions,

$$f(x_1, x_2) = x_1^4 + 3x_1^2 - 5x_1 + 2x_1x_2 + x_2^2\,,$$

is a convex function, whereas its negative,

$$g(x_1, x_2) = -x_1^4 - 3x_1^2 + 5x_1 - 2x_1x_2 - x_2^2\,,$$

is a concave function.

The concept of a convex function leads quite naturally to the related concept of a *convex set*. Thus, if $f(x_1, x_2, \cdots, x_n)$ is a convex function, then the collection of points that lie above or on the graph of $f(x_1, x_2, \cdots, x_n)$ comprises a convex set. Similarly, the collection of points that lie below or on the graph of a concave function is a convex set. These cases are illustrated in Figs. A1.5 and A1.6 for the case of a single independent variable.

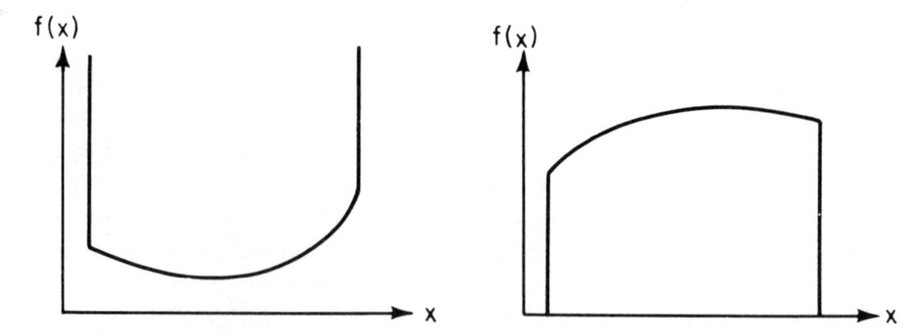

FIGURE A1.5. Example of a convex set determined by a convex function.

FIGURE A1.6. Example of a convex set determined by a concave function.

Furthermore, convex sets have the important property that, for any given group of convex sets, the collection of points that lie in all of them is also a convex set. Therefore, the collection of points that lie both above or on a convex function and below or on a concave function is a convex set, as illustrated in Fig. A1.7.

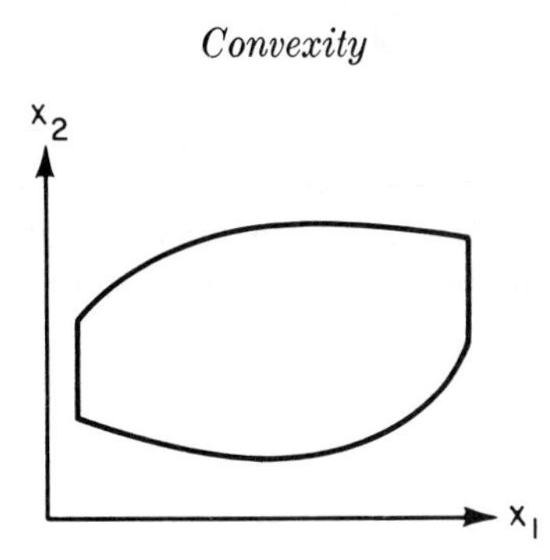

FIGURE A1.7. Example of a convex set determined by both convex and concave functions.

Thus, convex sets may be viewed intuitively as a collection of points whose "bottom boundary" is a convex function and whose "top boundary" is a concave function. To be a bit more precise, convex set may be defined as follows.

Definition: A *convex set* is a collection of points such that, for each pair of points in the collection, the entire line segment joining these two points is also in the collection.

The distinction between nonconvex sets and convex sets is illustrated in Figs. A1.8 and A1.9.

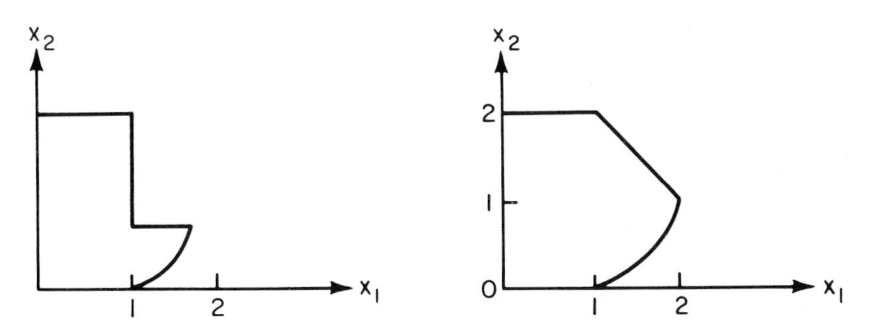

FIGURE A1.8. Example of a set which is not convex.

FIGURE A1.9. Example of a convex set.

Thus, the set of points shown in Fig. A1.8 is not a convex set since there exist many pairs of these points, e.g., (1, 2) and (2, 1), such that the line segment between them does not lie entirely within the set. This is not the case for the set in Fig. A1.9, which is convex.

In conclusion, the useful concept of an *extreme point* of a convex set needs to be introduced.

Definition: An *extreme point* of a convex set is a point in the set which does not lie on any line segment that joins two other points in the set.

Thus, the extreme points of the convex set in Fig. A1.9 are (0, 0), (0, 2), (1, 2), (2, 1), (1, 0), and all of the infinite number of points on the boundary between (2, 1) and (1, 0). If this particular boundary were a straight line instead, then the set would have only the five listed extreme points.

Classical Optimization Methods

This appendix briefly reviews the classical methods of calculus for finding a solution that maximizes or minimizes: (1) a function of a single variable, (2) a function of several variables, and (3) a function of several variables subject to constraints on the values of these variables. It is assumed that the functions considered possess continuous first and second derivatives and partial derivatives everywhere.

Consider a function of a single variable, such as that shown in Fig. A2.1. A necessary condition for a particular solution, $x = x^*$, to be either a minimum or a maximum is that

$$\frac{df(x)}{dx} = 0 \quad \text{at} \quad x = x^* .$$

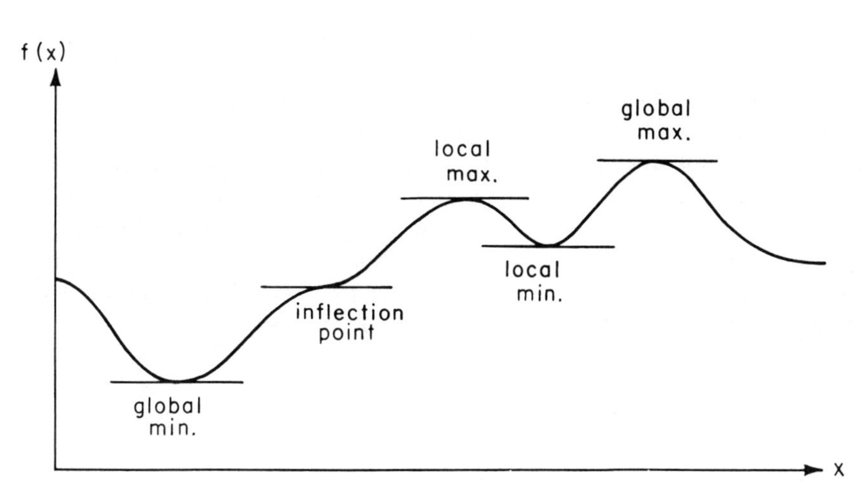

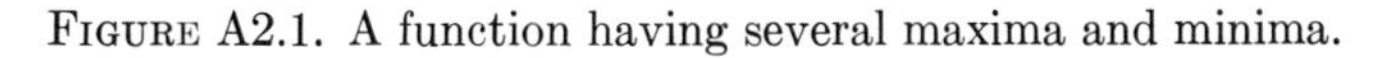

FIGURE A2.1. A function having several maxima and minima.

Thus, in Fig. A2.1, there are five solutions satisfying these conditions. To obtain more information about these five so-called *critical points*, it is necessary to examine the second derivative. Thus, if

$$\frac{d^2f(x)}{dx^2} > 0 \quad \text{at} \quad x = x^*,$$

then x^* must be at least a *local minimum* [i.e., $f(x^*) \leq f(x)$ for all x sufficiently close to x^*]. Using the language introduced in Appendix 1, this says that x^* must be a local minimum if $f(x)$ is strictly convex within a neighborhood of x^*. Similarly, a sufficient condition for x^* to be a *local maximum* (given that it satisfies the necessary condition) is that $f(x)$ is strictly concave within a neighborhood of x^* (i.e., the second derivative is negative at x^*). If the second derivative is zero, the issue is not resolved (the point may even be an inflection point), and it is necessary to examine higher derivatives.

To find a global minimum [i.e., a solution x^* such that $f(x^*) \leq f(x)$ for all x], it is necessary to compare the local minima and identify the one which yields the smallest value of $f(x)$. If this value is less than $f(x)$ as $x \to -\infty$ and as $x \to +\infty$ (or at the end points of the function, if it is only defined over a finite interval), then this point is a global minimum. Such a point is shown in Fig. A2.1, along with the global maximum identified in an analogous way.

However, if $f(x)$ is known to be either a convex or concave function (see Appendix 1 for a description of such functions), the analysis becomes much simpler. In particular, if $f(x)$ is a convex function, such as shown in Fig. A1.1, then any solution x^*, such that

$$\frac{df(x)}{dx} = 0 \quad \text{at} \quad x = x^*,$$

is known automatically to be a global minimum. In other words, this condition is not only a necessary, but also a sufficient, condition for a global minimum of a convex function. If this function actually is strictly convex, then this solution must be the only global minimum. (However, if the function is either always decreasing or always increasing, so the derivative is non-zero for all values of x, then there will be no global minimum at a finite value of x.) Otherwise, there could be a tie for the global minimum over a single interval where the derivative is zero. Similarly, if $f(x)$ is a concave function, then having

$$\frac{df(x)}{dx} = 0 \quad \text{at} \quad x = x^*$$

becomes both a necessary and sufficient condition for x^* to be a global maximum.

The analysis for an unconstrained function of several variables, $f(x_1, x_2, \cdots, x_n)$, is similar. Thus, a necessary condition for a solution, $(x_1, x_2, \cdots, x_n) = (x_1^*, x_2^*, \cdots, x_n^*)$, to be either a minimum or a maximum is that

$$\frac{\partial f(x_1, \cdots, x_n)}{\partial x_j} = 0 \text{ at } (x_1, \cdots, x_n) = (x_1^*, \cdots, x_n^*), \qquad \text{for } j = 1, 2, \cdots, n .$$

After identifying the critical points which satisfy this condition, each such point would then be classified as a local minimum or a local maximum if the function is strictly convex or strictly concave, respectively, within a neighborhood of the point. (Additional analysis is required if the function is neither one.) The global minimum and maximum would be found by comparing the relative minima and maxima and then checking the value of the function as some of the variables approach $-\infty$ or $+\infty$. However, if the function is known to be convex or concave, then a critical point must be a global minimum or a global maximum, respectively.

Now consider the problem of finding the minimum or maximum of the function,

$$f(x_1, x_2, \cdots, x_n) ,$$

subject to the restriction that $(x_1, x_2, \cdots, x_n)$ must satisfy all of the equations,

$$\begin{aligned} g_1(x_1, x_2, \cdots, x_n) &= b_1 \\ g_2(x_1, x_2, \cdots, x_n) &= b_2 \\ &\vdots \\ g_m(x_1, x_2, \cdots, x_n) &= b_m , \end{aligned}$$

where $m < n$. For example, if $n = 2$ and $m = 1$, the problem might be to

$$\begin{aligned} \text{maximize } f(x_1, x_2) &= x_1^2 + 2x_2, \quad \text{subject to} \\ g(x_1, x_2) &= x_1^2 + x_2^2 = 1 . \end{aligned}$$

In this case, (x_1, x_2) is restricted to be on the circle of radius one whose center is at the origin, so that the goal is to find the point on this circle which yields the largest value of $f(x_1, x_2)$. This example is soon solved, after outlining a general approach to the problem.

A classical method of dealing with this problem is the *method of Lagrange multipliers*. This procedure begins by formulating the composite function,

$$h(x_1, x_2, \cdots, x_n, \lambda_1, \lambda_2, \cdots, \lambda_m) = f(x_1, x_2, \cdots, x_n) - \sum_{i=1}^{m} \lambda_i[g_i(x_1, x_2, \cdots, x_n) - b_i] ,$$

where the new variables, $\lambda_1, \lambda_2, \cdots, \lambda_m$, are called *Lagrange multipliers.* Notice the key fact that, for the permissible values of $(x_1, x_2, \cdots, x_n)$, $g_i(x_1, x_2, \cdots, x_n) - b_i = 0$ for all i. Thus $h(x_1, x_2, \cdots, x_n, \lambda_1, \lambda_2, \cdots, \lambda_m) = f(x_1, x_2, \cdots, x_n)$. Therefore, it can be shown that, if $(x_1, x_2, \cdots, x_n, \lambda_1, \lambda_2, \cdots, \lambda_m) = (x_1^*, x_2^*, \cdots, x_n^*, \lambda_1^*, \lambda_2^*, \cdots, \lambda_m^*)$ is a local or global minimum or maximum for the unconstrained function, $h(x_1, x_2, \cdots, x_n, \lambda_1, \lambda_2, \cdots, \lambda_m)$, then $(x_1^*, x_2^*, \cdots, x_n^*)$ is a corresponding critical point for the original problem. As a result, the method now reduces to analyzing $h(x_1, x_2, \cdots, x_n, \lambda_1, \lambda_2, \cdots, \lambda_m)$ by the procedure described above for unconstrained functions. Thus, the $(n + m)$ partial derivatives would be set equal to zero, i.e.,

$$\frac{\partial h}{\partial x_j} = \frac{\partial f}{\partial x_j} - \sum_{i=1}^{m} \lambda_i \frac{\partial g_i}{\partial x_j} = 0, \qquad \text{for } j = 1, 2, \cdots, n,$$

$$\frac{\partial h}{\partial \lambda_i} = -g_i(x_1, x_2, \cdots, x_n) + b_i = 0, \qquad \text{for } i = 1, 2, \cdots, m,$$

and then the critical points would be obtained by solving these equations for $(x_1, x_2, \cdots, x_n, \lambda_1, \lambda_2, \cdots, \lambda_m)$. Notice that the last m equations are equivalent to the constraints in the original problem, so only permissible solutions are considered. After further analysis to identify the global minimum or maximum of $h(\cdot)$, the resulting value of $(x_1, x_2, \cdots, x_n)$ is then the desired solution to the original problem.

It should be pointed out that, from a practical computational viewpoint, the method of Lagrange multipliers is not a particularly powerful procedure. It is often essentially impossible to solve the equations to obtain the critical points. Furthermore, even when they can be obtained, the number of critical points may be so large (often infinite) that it is impractical to attempt to identify a global minimum or maximum. However, for certain types of small problems, this method can sometimes be used successfully. To illustrate, consider the example introduced above. In this case,

$$h(x_1, x_2) = x_1^2 + 2x_2 - \lambda[x_1^2 + x_2^2 - 1],$$

so that

$$\frac{\partial h}{\partial x_1} = 2x_1 - 2\lambda x_1 = 0.$$

$$\frac{\partial h}{\partial x_2} = 2 - 2\lambda x_2 = 0,$$

$$\frac{\partial h}{\partial \lambda} = -[x_1^2 + x_2^2 - 1] = 0.$$

The first equation implies that either $\lambda = 1$ or $x_1 = 0$. If $\lambda = 1$, then the other two equations imply that $x_2 = 1$ and $x_1 = 0$. If $x_1 = 0$, then the third equation implies that $x_2 = \pm 1$. Therefore, the two critical points for the original problem are $(x_1, x_2) = (0, 1)$ and $(0, -1)$. Thus, it is apparent that these points are the global maximum and minimum, respectively.

In presenting the classical optimization methods described above, it has been assumed that the reader already is familiar with derivatives and how to obtain them. However, there is a special case of importance in operations research work that warrants additional explanation, namely, the derivative of an integral. In particular, consider how to find the derivative of the function,

$$F(y) = \int_{g(y)}^{h(y)} f(x, y)dx .$$

where $g(y)$ and $h(y)$ are the limits of integration expressed as functions of y. To begin, suppose that these limits of integration are constants, so that $g(y) = a$ and $h(y) = b$, respectively. For this special case, it can be shown that, given the regularity conditions assumed at the beginning of this appendix, the derivative is simply

$$\frac{d}{dy}\int_{a}^{b} f(x, y)dx = \int_{a}^{b} \frac{\partial f(x, y)}{\partial y}\, dx .$$

For example, if $f(x, y) = e^{-xy}$, $a = 0$, and $b = \infty$, then

$$\frac{d}{dy}\int_{0}^{\infty} e^{-xy}\, dx = \int_{0}^{\infty} (-x)\, e^{-xy}\, dx = -\frac{1}{y^2}$$

at any positive value of y. Thus, the intuitive procedure of interchanging the order of differentiation and integration is valid for this case. However, finding the derivative becomes a little more complicated than this when the limits of integration are functions. In particular,

$$\frac{d}{dy}\int_{g(y)}^{h(y)} f(x, y)dx = \int_{g(y)}^{h(y)} \frac{\partial f(x, y)}{\partial y}\, dx + f(h(y), y)\, \frac{dh(y)}{dy} - f(g(y), y)\, \frac{dg(y)}{dy} ,$$

where $f(h(y), y)$ is obtained by writing out $f(x, y)$ and then replacing x wherever it appears by $h(y)$, and similarly for $f(g(y), y)$. To illustrate, if $f(x, y) = x^2y^3$, $g(y) = y$, and $h(y) = 2y$, then

$$\frac{d}{dy}\int_{y}^{2y} x^2y^3\, dx = \int_{y}^{2y} 3x^2y^2\, dx + (2y)^2y^3(2) - y^2y^3(1) = 14y^5$$

at any positive value of y.

SELECTED REFERENCES

1. Hadley, G., *Nonlinear and Dynamic Programming*, Addison-Wesley, Reading, Mass., 1964, chap. 3.
2. Kaplan, Wilfred, *Advanced Calculus*, Addison-Wesley, Reading, Mass., 1952.

PROBLEMS

1. Find the critical points of the following functions, and determine the nature of each of these points:

(a) $f(x) = 2x^3 + 3x^2 - 12x + 10$.
(b) $f(x_1, x_2) = x_1x_2 + 8/x_1 + 8/x_2$.

2. Find the critical points of the following constrained functions by the method of Lagrange multipliers:

(a) $f(x_1, x_2) = x_1 - x_2^2$, subject to $x_1^2 + x_2^2 = 1$.
(b) $f(x_1, x_2, x_3) = x_1 + 2x_2$, subject to $2x_1^2 + x_2^2 + 2x_3^2 = 18$.
(c) $f(x_1, x_2, x_3) = x_1x_2x_3$, subject to $x_1^2 + x_3^2 = 3$ and $x_1 - x_2 = 0$.

3. Evaluate the following derivatives:

(a) $$\frac{d}{dy}\int_1^2 [xy^2 + x^2y]\,dx.$$

$$\frac{d}{dy}\int_{y^2}^{y^3} \log_e (xy^2)\,dx, \qquad \text{for } y > 1.$$

APPENDIX 3

Matrices and Matrix Manipulations

A matrix is defined to be a rectangular array of numbers. For example,

$$\mathbf{A} = \begin{bmatrix} 2 & 5 \\ 3 & 0 \\ 1 & 1 \end{bmatrix}$$

is a 3×2 matrix (where 3×2 denotes "3 by 2"), since it is a rectangular array of numbers with 3 rows and 2 columns. The numbers in the rectangular array are called the "elements" of the matrix. For example,

$$\mathbf{B} = \begin{bmatrix} 1 & 2.4 & 0 & \sqrt{3} \\ -4 & 2 & -1 & 15 \end{bmatrix}$$

is a 2×4 matrix whose elements are 1, 2.4, 0, $\sqrt{3}$, -4, 2, -1, and 15. Thus, in more general terms,

$$\mathbf{A} = \begin{bmatrix} a_{11} & a_{12} & \cdots & a_{1n} \\ a_{21} & a_{22} & \cdots & a_{2n} \\ \cdot & \cdot & & \cdot \\ \cdot & \cdot & & \cdot \\ \cdot & \cdot & & \cdot \\ a_{m1} & a_{m2} & & a_{mn} \end{bmatrix} = ||a_{ij}||$$

is an $m \times n$ matrix, where $a_{11}, \cdots, a_{mn}$ represent the numbers that are the elements of this matrix; $||a_{ij}||$ is short-hand notation for identifying the matrix whose element in row i and column j is a_{ij} for every $i = 1, 2, \cdots, m$ and $j = 1, 2, \cdots, n$.

Since matrices do not possess a numerical value, they cannot be added, multiplied, etc., as if they were individual numbers. However, it is sometimes desirable to perform certain manipulations on arrays of numbers.

Therefore, rules have been developed for performing operations on matrices that are analogous to arithmetic operations. To describe these, let $\mathbf{A} = ||a_{ij}||$ and $\mathbf{B} = ||b_{ij}||$ be two matrices having the same number of rows and the same number of columns. Then **A** and **B** are said to be "equal," i.e., $\mathbf{A} = \mathbf{B}$, if and only if all of the corresponding elements are equal, i.e., $a_{ij} = b_{ij}$ for all i and j. The operation of multiplying a matrix by a number (denote this number by k) is performed by multiplying each element of the matrix by k, so that

$$k\mathbf{A} = ||ka_{ij}|| .$$

For example,

$$3\begin{bmatrix} 1 & \frac{1}{3} & 2 \\ 5 & 0 & -3 \end{bmatrix} = \begin{bmatrix} 3 & 1 & 6 \\ 15 & 0 & -9 \end{bmatrix}.$$

To "add" **A** and **B**, simply add the corresponding elements, so that

$$\mathbf{A} + \mathbf{B} = ||a_{ij} + b_{ij}|| .$$

To illustrate,

$$\begin{bmatrix} 5 & 3 \\ 1 & 6 \end{bmatrix} + \begin{bmatrix} 2 & 0 \\ 3 & 1 \end{bmatrix} = \begin{bmatrix} 7 & 3 \\ 4 & 7 \end{bmatrix}.$$

Similarly, "subtraction" is done as

$$\mathbf{A} - \mathbf{B} = \mathbf{A} + (-1)\mathbf{B} ,$$

so that

$$\mathbf{A} - \mathbf{B} = ||a_{ij} - b_{ij}|| .$$

For example,

$$\begin{bmatrix} 5 & 3 \\ 1 & 6 \end{bmatrix} - \begin{bmatrix} 2 & 0 \\ 3 & 1 \end{bmatrix} = \begin{bmatrix} 3 & 3 \\ -2 & 5 \end{bmatrix}.$$

Note that, with the exception of multiplication by a number, all of the above operations are defined only when the two matrices involved are of the same size. However, all of them are straightforward, since they only involve performing the same comparison or arithmetic operation on the corresponding elements of the matrices.

There exists one additional elementary operation that has not been defined, multiplication, but it is considerably more complicated. To find the element in row i, column j of the matrix resulting from "multiplying" **A** times **B**, it is necessary to multiply each element in row i of **A** by the corresponding element in column j of **B** and then to add these products. Therefore, this matrix multiplication is defined if and only if the number of columns of **A** equals the number of rows of **B**, since this is required to perform the specified element-by-element multiplication. Thus, if **A** is an $m \times n$ matrix and **B** is an $n \times r$ matrix, then their product is

$$\mathbf{AB} = \left\| \sum_{k=1}^{n} a_{ik} b_{kj} \right\| .$$

To illustrate,

$$\begin{bmatrix} 1 & 2 \\ 4 & 0 \\ 2 & 3 \end{bmatrix} \begin{bmatrix} 3 & 1 \\ 2 & 5 \end{bmatrix} = \begin{bmatrix} 1(3) + 2(2) & 1(1) + 2(5) \\ 4(3) + 0(2) & 4(1) + 0(5) \\ 2(3) + 3(2) & 2(1) + 3(5) \end{bmatrix} = \begin{bmatrix} 7 & 11 \\ 12 & 4 \\ 12 & 17 \end{bmatrix} .$$

On the other hand, if one attempts to multiply these matrices in the reverse order, the resulting product,

$$\begin{bmatrix} 3 & 1 \\ 2 & 5 \end{bmatrix} \begin{bmatrix} 1 & 2 \\ 4 & 0 \\ 2 & 3 \end{bmatrix} ,$$

is not even defined. Even when both **AB** and **BA** are defined,

$$\mathbf{AB} \neq \mathbf{BA} ,$$

in general. Thus, matrix multiplication should be viewed as a specially designed operation whose properties are quite different from those of arithmetic multiplication. To motivate why this special definition was adopted, consider the following system of equations:

$$\begin{aligned} 2x_1 - x_2 + 5x_3 + x_4 &= 20 \\ x_1 + 5x_2 + 4x_3 + 5x_4 &= 30 \\ 3x_1 + x_2 - 6x_3 + 2x_4 &= 20 . \end{aligned}$$

Rather than writing these equations "longhand" as shown here, they can be written much more concisely in matrix form as

$$\mathbf{Ax} = \mathbf{b} ,$$

where

$$\mathbf{A} = \begin{bmatrix} 2 & -1 & 5 & 1 \\ 1 & 5 & 4 & 5 \\ 3 & 1 & -6 & 2 \end{bmatrix} , \quad \mathbf{x} = \begin{bmatrix} x_1 \\ x_2 \\ x_3 \\ x_4 \end{bmatrix} , \quad \mathbf{b} = \begin{bmatrix} 20 \\ 30 \\ 20 \end{bmatrix} .$$

It is this kind of "multiplication" for which matrix multiplication is designed.

Carefully note that matrix division is not defined.

Although the matrix operations described above do not possess certain of the properties of arithmetic operations, they do satisfy the following laws:

$$\begin{aligned} \mathbf{A} + \mathbf{B} &= \mathbf{B} + \mathbf{A} , \\ (\mathbf{A} + \mathbf{B}) + \mathbf{C} &= \mathbf{A} + (\mathbf{B} + \mathbf{C}) , \\ \mathbf{A}(\mathbf{B} + \mathbf{C}) &= \mathbf{AB} + \mathbf{AC} , \\ \mathbf{A}(\mathbf{BC}) &= (\mathbf{AB})\mathbf{C} \end{aligned}$$

when the relative sizes of these matrices are such that the indicated operations are defined.

Another type of matrix operation, which has no arithmetic analogue, is the transpose operation. This operation involves nothing more than interchanging the rows and columns of the matrix, which is frequently useful for performing the multiplication operation in the desired way. Thus, for any matrix $\mathbf{A} = ||a_{ij}||$, its transpose $\mathbf{A}^T$ is

$$\mathbf{A}^T = ||a_{ji}|| .$$

For example, if

$$\mathbf{A} = \begin{bmatrix} 2 & 5 \\ 1 & 3 \\ 4 & 0 \end{bmatrix},$$

then

$$\mathbf{A}^T = \begin{bmatrix} 2 & 1 & 4 \\ 5 & 3 & 0 \end{bmatrix}.$$

Zero and one are numbers that play a special role in arithmetic. There also exist special matrices that play a similar role in matrix theory. In particular, the matrix "one" is the "identity matrix" **I**, which is a square matrix whose elements are zeros except for ones along the main diagonal. Thus,

$$\mathbf{I} = \begin{bmatrix} 1 & 0 & 0 & \cdots & 0 \\ 0 & 1 & 0 & \cdots & 0 \\ 0 & 0 & 1 & \cdots & 0 \\ \cdot & & & & \\ \cdot & & & & \\ \cdot & & & & \\ 0 & 0 & 0 & \cdots & 1 \end{bmatrix}$$

The number of rows or columns of **I** can be specified as desired. The analogy of **I** to "one" follows from the fact that, for any matrix **A**,

$$\mathbf{IA} = \mathbf{A} = \mathbf{AI} ,$$

where **I** is assigned the appropriate number of rows and columns in each case for the multiplication operation to be defined. Similarly, the matrix "zero" is the so-called "null matrix" **0**, which is a matrix of any size whose elements are all zeros. Thus,

$$\mathbf{0} = \begin{bmatrix} 0 & 0 & \cdots & 0 \\ 0 & 0 & \cdots & 0 \\ \cdot & \cdot & & \cdot \\ \cdot & \cdot & & \cdot \\ \cdot & \cdot & & \cdot \\ 0 & 0 & \cdots & 0 \end{bmatrix}$$

Therefore, for any matrix **A**,

$$\mathbf{A} + \mathbf{0} = \mathbf{A},\ \mathbf{A} - \mathbf{A} = \mathbf{0}, \quad \text{and} \quad \mathbf{0A} = \mathbf{0} = \mathbf{A0}\,,$$

where **0** is the appropriate size in each case for the operations to be defined.

On certain occasions, it is useful to partition a matrix into several smaller matrices called "submatrices." For example, one possible way of partitioning a 3×4 matrix would be

$$\mathbf{A} = \left[\begin{array}{c|ccc} a_{11} & a_{12} & a_{13} & a_{14} \\ \hline a_{21} & a_{22} & a_{23} & a_{24} \\ a_{31} & a_{32} & a_{33} & a_{34} \end{array}\right] = \begin{bmatrix} a_{11} & \mathbf{A}_{12} \\ \mathbf{A}_{21} & \mathbf{A}_{22} \end{bmatrix},$$

where

$$\mathbf{A}_{12} = [a_{12} \quad a_{13} \quad a_{14}], \quad \mathbf{A}_{21} = \begin{bmatrix} a_{21} \\ a_{31} \end{bmatrix}, \quad \mathbf{A}_{22} = \begin{bmatrix} a_{22} & a_{23} & a_{24} \\ a_{32} & a_{33} & a_{34} \end{bmatrix}.$$

Rather than perform operations element-by-element on such partitioned matrices, they can instead be done in terms of the submatrices, provided the partitionings are such that the operations are defined. For example, if **B** is a partitioned 4×1 matrix such that

$$\mathbf{B} = \begin{bmatrix} b_1 \\ b_2 \\ b_3 \\ b_4 \end{bmatrix} = \begin{bmatrix} b_1 \\ \mathbf{B}_2 \end{bmatrix},$$

$$\mathbf{AB} = \left[\begin{array}{c} a_{11} \quad b_1 \quad + \quad \mathbf{A}_{12} \quad \mathbf{B}_2 \\ \hline A_{21} \quad b_1 \quad + \quad \mathbf{A}_{22} \quad \mathbf{B}_2 \end{array}\right].$$

A special kind of matrix that plays an important role in matrix theory is that having either a single row or a column. Such matrices are often referred to as "vectors." Thus,

$$\mathbf{x} = [x_1, x_2, \cdots, x_n]$$

is a "row" vector, and

$$\mathbf{x} = \begin{bmatrix} x_1 \\ x_2 \\ \cdot \\ \cdot \\ \cdot \\ x_n \end{bmatrix}$$

is a "column" vector. These vectors also would sometimes be called "n-vectors" to indicate that they have n elements. For example,

$$\mathbf{x} = [1, 4, -2, \tfrac{1}{3}, 7]$$

is a "5-vector."

One reason that vectors play an important role in matrix theory is that any $m \times n$ matrix can be partitioned into either m row vectors or n column vectors, and important properties of the matrix can be analyzed in terms of these vectors. To amplify, consider a set of n-vectors, $\mathbf{x}_1, \mathbf{x}_2, \cdots, \mathbf{x}_m$, of the same type (i.e., they are either all row vectors or all column vectors).

Definition: A set of vectors, $\mathbf{x}_1, \mathbf{x}_2, \cdots, \mathbf{x}_m$ is said to be *linearly dependent* if there exist m numbers (denoted by $c_1, c_2, \cdots, c_m$), some of which are not zero, such that

$$c_1\mathbf{x}_1 + c_2\mathbf{x}_2 + \cdots + c_m\mathbf{x}_m = 0 .$$

Otherwise, the set is said to be *linearly independent.*

To illustrate, if $m = 3$ and

$$\begin{aligned} \mathbf{x}_1 &= [1, 1, 1] \\ \mathbf{x}_2 &= [0, 1, 1] \\ \mathbf{x}_3 &= [2, 5, 5] , \end{aligned}$$

then

$$2\mathbf{x}_1 + 3\mathbf{x}_2 - \mathbf{x}_3 = 0 ,$$

so that

$$\mathbf{x}_3 = 2\mathbf{x}_1 + 3\mathbf{x}_2 .$$

Thus, $\mathbf{x}_1, \mathbf{x}_2, \mathbf{x}_3$ would be linearly dependent since one of them is a linear combination of the others. However, if $\mathbf{x}_3$ were changed to

$$\mathbf{x}_3 = [2, 5, 6]$$

instead, then $\mathbf{x}_1, \mathbf{x}_2, \mathbf{x}_3$ would be linearly independent.

Definition: The *rank* of a set of vectors is the largest number of linearly independent vectors that can be chosen from the set.

Continuing the above example, the rank of the set of vectors, $\mathbf{x}_1, \mathbf{x}_2, \mathbf{x}_3$, was 2, but it became 3 after changing $\mathbf{x}_3$.

Definition: A *basis* for a set of vectors is a collection of linearly independent vectors taken from the set such that every vector in the set is a linear combination of the vectors in the collection (i.e., every vector in the set equals the sum of certain multiples of the vectors in the collection).

To illustrate, $\mathbf{x}_1$ and $\mathbf{x}_2$ constituted a basis for $\mathbf{x}_1, \mathbf{x}_2, \mathbf{x}_3$ in the above example before $\mathbf{x}_3$ was changed.

Theorem A3.1: A collection of r linearly independent vectors chosen from a set of vectors is a basis for the set if and only if the set has rank r.

Given the above results regarding vectors, it is now possible to present certain important concepts regarding matrices.

Definition: The *row rank* of a matrix is the rank of its set of row vectors. The *column rank* of a matrix is the rank of its set of column vectors.

For example, if the matrix **A** is

$$\mathbf{A} = \begin{bmatrix} 1 & 1 & 1 \\ 0 & 1 & 1 \\ 2 & 5 & 5 \end{bmatrix},$$

then its row rank was shown above to be 2. Note that the column rank of **A** is also 2. This is no coincidence, as the following general theorem indicates.

Theorem A3.2: The row rank and column rank of a matrix are the same.

Thus, it is only necessary to speak of "the rank" of a matrix.

The final concept to be discussed is that of the "inverse" of a matrix. For any non-zero number k, there exists a reciprocal or inverse, $k^{-1}=1/k$, such that

$$kk^{-1} = k^{-1}k = 1 .$$

Is there an analogous concept that is valid in matrix theory? In other words for a given matrix **A** other than the null matrix, does there exist a matrix $\mathbf{A}^{-1}$ such that

$$\mathbf{A}\,\mathbf{A}^{-1} = \mathbf{A}^{-1}\mathbf{A} = \mathbf{I}\ ?$$

If **A** is not a square matrix (i.e., if the number of rows and columns of **A** differ), the answer is "never," since these matrix products would necessarily have a different number of rows in order for the multiplication to be defined (so that the "equality" operation would not be defined). However, if **A** is square, then the answer is "under certain circumstances," as indicated in Theorem A3.3.

Definition: A matrix is called *nonsingular* if its rank equals both the number of rows and the number of columns. Otherwise, it is called *singular*.

Thus, only square matrices can be nonsingular. A useful way of testing for nonsingularity is provided by the fact that a square matrix is nonsingular if and only if its determinant is non-zero.

Theorem A3.3: (a) If **A** is nonsingular, there is a unique nonsingular matrix $\mathbf{A}^{-1}$, called the inverse of **A**, such that $\mathbf{A}\,\mathbf{A}^{-1} = \mathbf{I} = \mathbf{A}^{-1}\mathbf{A}$.

(b) If **A** is nonsingular and **B** is a matrix for which either $\mathbf{AB} = \mathbf{I}$ or $\mathbf{BA} = \mathbf{I}$, then $\mathbf{B} = \mathbf{A}^{-1}$.

(c) Only nonsingular matrices have inverses.

To illustrate, consider the matrix

$$\mathbf{A} = \begin{bmatrix} 5 & -4 \\ 1 & -1 \end{bmatrix}.$$

Notice that the rank of **A** is 2, so it is nonsingular. Therefore, **A** must have an inverse, which happens to be

$$\mathbf{A}^{-1} = \begin{bmatrix} 1 & -4 \\ 1 & -5 \end{bmatrix}.$$

Hence,

$$\mathbf{A}\mathbf{A}^{-1} = \begin{bmatrix} 5 & -4 \\ 1 & -1 \end{bmatrix} \begin{bmatrix} 1 & -4 \\ 1 & -5 \end{bmatrix} = \begin{bmatrix} 1 & 0 \\ 0 & 1 \end{bmatrix}$$

and

$$\mathbf{A}^{-1}A = \begin{bmatrix} 1 & -4 \\ 1 & -5 \end{bmatrix} \begin{bmatrix} 5 & -4 \\ 1 & -1 \end{bmatrix} = \begin{bmatrix} 1 & 0 \\ 0 & 1 \end{bmatrix}.$$

SELECTED REFERENCES

Hadley, G., *Linear Algebra*, Addison-Wesley, Reading, Mass., 1961.

PROBLEMS

1. Consider the matrices,

$$\mathbf{A} = \begin{bmatrix} 4 & 1 & 2 \\ -3 & 0 & 3 \\ -1 & 5 & 2 \end{bmatrix}, \quad \mathbf{B} = \begin{bmatrix} 1 & 5 & 4 \\ -2 & 2 & 0 \\ 1 & 0 & 1 \end{bmatrix},$$

$$\mathbf{C} = \begin{bmatrix} 1 & 1 & 1 \\ 2 & 0 & 2 \\ 1 & 4 & 1 \end{bmatrix}, \quad \mathbf{I} = \begin{bmatrix} 1 & 0 & 0 \\ 0 & 1 & 0 \\ 0 & 0 & 1 \end{bmatrix}.$$

Demonstrate that the following statements are true for these matrices:

(a) $\mathbf{A} + \mathbf{B} = \mathbf{B} + \mathbf{A}$.
(b) $(\mathbf{A} + \mathbf{B}) + \mathbf{C} = \mathbf{A} + (\mathbf{B} + \mathbf{C})$.
(c) $\mathbf{A} = \mathbf{IA} = \mathbf{AI}$.
(d) $\mathbf{AB} \neq \mathbf{BA}$.
(e) $\mathbf{A}(\mathbf{B} + \mathbf{C}) = \mathbf{AB} + \mathbf{AC}$.
(f) $\mathbf{A}(\mathbf{BC}) = (\mathbf{AB})\mathbf{C}$.

2. Consider the partitioned matrices,

$$\mathbf{A} = \left[\begin{array}{cc|cc} 2 & 3 & 0 & 1 \\ 1 & 0 & 4 & 2 \\ \hline -2 & 1 & 1 & 3 \\ 0 & 2 & 0 & 1 \end{array}\right] = \left[\begin{array}{c|c} \mathbf{A}_{11} & \mathbf{A}_{12} \\ \hline \mathbf{A}_{21} & \mathbf{A}_{22} \end{array}\right],$$

$$\mathbf{B} = \left[\begin{array}{cc} 0 & 2 \\ 5 & 1 \\ \hline 3 & 1 \\ 7 & 3 \end{array}\right] = \left[\begin{array}{c} \mathbf{B}_1 \\ \hline \mathbf{B}_2 \end{array}\right],$$

where $\mathbf{A}_{11}$, $\mathbf{A}_{12}$, $\mathbf{A}_{21}$, $\mathbf{A}_{22}$, $\mathbf{B}_1$, and $\mathbf{B}_2$ are the corresponding 2×2 submatrices. Demonstrate that

$$\mathbf{AB} = \left[\begin{array}{c} \mathbf{A}_{11}\mathbf{B}_1 + \mathbf{A}_{12}\mathbf{B}_2 \\ \hline \mathbf{A}_{21}\mathbf{B}_1 + \mathbf{A}_{22}\mathbf{B}_2 \end{array}\right].$$

3. Show that the rank of the matrix,

$$\mathbf{A} = \begin{bmatrix} -25 & 25 & 2 \\ 1 & 6 & 3 \\ -2 & 13 & 5 \end{bmatrix},$$

is 2. (Hint: Construct and solve a set of simultaneous linear equations in order to show that the row vectors are linearly dependent.)

4. Prove Theorem A3.1.

5. Prove Theorem A3.2.

6. (a) Prove Part (a) of Theorem A3.3.
(b) Prove Part (b) of Theorem A3.3.
(c) Prove Part (c) of Theorem A3.3.

7. If $\mathbf{A}$ is a nonsingular matrix, and $\mathbf{A}^{-1}$ is the inverse of $\mathbf{A}$, what is the inverse of $\mathbf{A}^{-1}$?

8. Determine the inverse of the matrix,

$$\mathbf{A} = \begin{bmatrix} 2 & 1 \\ -1 & 0 \end{bmatrix}$$

(*Hint:* Construct and solve a set of four simultaneous linear equations.)

APPENDIX 4

Simultaneous Linear Equations

Consider the system of simultaneous linear equations,

$$
\begin{aligned}
a_{11}x_1 + a_{12}x_2 + \cdots + a_{1n}x_n &= b_1 , \\
a_{21}x_1 + a_{22}x_2 + \cdots + a_{2n}x_n &= b_2 , \\
&\vdots \\
a_{m1}x_1 + a_{m2}x_2 + \cdots + a_{mn}x_n &= b_m .
\end{aligned}
$$

It is commonly assumed that this system has a solution, and a unique solution, if and only if $m = n$. However, this is an oversimplification. This raises the question, under what conditions will these equations have a simultaneous solution? Given that they do, when will there be only one such solution? If there is a unique solution, how can it be identified in a systematic way? These are the questions to be explored in this appendix. The discussion of the first two questions assumes that the reader is familiar with the basic information about matrices reviewed in Appendix 3.

The above system of equations can also be written in matrix form as

$$\mathbf{Ax} = \mathbf{b} ,$$

where

$$
\mathbf{A} = \begin{bmatrix} a_{11} & a_{12} & \cdots & a_{1n} \\ a_{21} & a_{22} & \cdots & a_{2n} \\ & & \vdots & \\ a_{m1} & a_{m2} & \cdots & a_{mn} \end{bmatrix}, \quad \mathbf{x} = \begin{bmatrix} x_1 \\ x_2 \\ \vdots \\ x_n \end{bmatrix}, \quad \mathbf{b} = \begin{bmatrix} b_1 \\ b_2 \\ \vdots \\ b_m \end{bmatrix}.
$$

The first two questions can be answered immediately in terms of the properties of these matrices. First, the system of equations possesses at least one solution if and only if the rank of **A** equals the rank of [**A, b**]. (Notice that this is guaranteed if the rank of **A** equals m.) This follows immediately from the definitions of rank and linear independence since, if the rank of [**A, b**] exceeds the rank of **A** by one (the only other possibility), then **b** is linearly independent of the column vectors of **A** (i.e., **b** cannot equal any linear combination, **Ax,** of these vectors). Second, given that these ranks are equal, there are then two possibilities. If the rank of **A** is n (its maximum possible value), then the system of equations will possess exactly one solution. [This follows from Theorem A3.1, the definition of a basis, and Part (b) of Theorem A3.3.] If the rank of **A** is less than n, then there will exist an infinite number of solutions. (This follows from the fact that, for any basis of the column vectors of **A,** the x_j corresponding to column vectors not in this basis can be assigned any value, and there will still exist a solution for the other variables as before.) Finally, it should be noted that, if **A** and [**A, b**] have a common rank r such that $r < m$, then $(m - r)$ of the equations must be linear combinations of the other ones, so that these $(m - r)$ redundant equations can be deleted without affecting the solution(s).

Now consider how to find a solution to the system of equations. Assume for the moment that $m = n$ and **A** is nonsingular, so that a unique solution exists. This solution can be obtained by the *Gauss–Jordan method of elimination,* which proceeds as follows. To begin, eliminate the first variable from all but one (say, the first) of the equations by adding an appropriate multiple of this equation to each of the others. (For convenience, this one equation would be divided by the coefficient of this variable, so that the final value of this coefficient is one.) Next, proceed in the same way to eliminate the second variable from all equations except one new one (say, the second). Then repeat this for the third variable, the fourth variable, etc., until each of the n variables remains in only one of the equations, and each of the n equations contains exactly one of these variables. The desired solution can then be read from the equations directly.

To illustrate the Gauss–Jordan method of elimination, consider the following system of linear equations:

$$
\begin{array}{lrcl}
(1) & x_1 - x_2 + 4x_3 & = & 10 \\
(2) & -x_1 + 3x_2 \qquad & = & 10 \\
(3) & 2x_2 + 5x_3 & = & 22\,.
\end{array}
$$

The method begins by eliminating x_1 from all but the first equation. This is done simply by adding equation (1) to equation (2), which yields:

$$
\begin{aligned}
&(1)\quad x_1 - x_2 + 4x_3 = 10\\
&(2)\quad \phantom{x_1 -{}} 2x_2 + 4x_3 = 20\\
&(3)\quad \phantom{x_1 -{}} 2x_2 + 5x_3 = 22\,.
\end{aligned}
$$

The next step is to eliminate x_2 from all but the second equation. Begin this by dividing equation (2) by 2, so that x_2 will have a coefficient of $+1$, as shown below:

$$
\begin{aligned}
&(1)\quad x_1 - x_2 + 4x_3 = 10\\
&(2)\quad \phantom{x_1 -{}} x_2 + 2x_3 = 10\\
&(3)\quad \phantom{x_1 -{}} 2x_2 + 5x_3 = 22\,.
\end{aligned}
$$

Then add equation (2) to equation (1), and subtract two times equation (2) from equation (3), which yields:

$$
\begin{aligned}
&(1)\quad x_1 \phantom{{}+x_2} + 6x_3 = 20\\
&(2)\quad \phantom{x_1 -{}} x_2 + 2x_3 = 10\\
&(3)\quad \phantom{x_1 - x_2 + 2{}} x_3 = 2\,.
\end{aligned}
$$

The final step is to eliminate x_3 from all but the third equation. This requires subtracting six times equation (3) from equation (1), and subtracting two times equation (3) from equation (2), which yields:

$$
\begin{aligned}
&(1)\quad x_1 \phantom{{}+x_2+x_3} = 8\\
&(2)\quad \phantom{x_1 -{}} x_2 \phantom{{}+x_3} = 6\\
&(3)\quad \phantom{x_1 - x_2 +{}} x_3 = 2\,.
\end{aligned}
$$

Thus, the desired solution is $(x_1, x_2, x_3) = (8, 6, 2)$, and the procedure is completed.

Now consider briefly what happens if the Gauss–Jordan method of elimination is applied when $m \neq n$ and/or $\mathbf{A}$ is singular. As discussed earlier, there are three possible cases to consider. First, if the rank of $[\mathbf{A}, \mathbf{b}]$ exceeds the rank of $\mathbf{A}$ by one, then there will not exist any solution to the system of equations. In this case, the Gauss–Jordan method would obtain an equation such that the left-hand side has vanished (i.e., all of the coefficients of the variables are zero), whereas, the right-hand side is nonzero. This is the signpost indicating that no solution exists, so there is no reason to proceed further. The second case is where both of these ranks are equal to n, so that a unique solution exists. This implies that $m \geq n$. If $m = n$, then the previous assumptions must hold and no difficulty arises. Therefore, suppose that $m > n$, so that there are $(m - n)$ redundant equations. In this case, all of these redundant equations would be eliminated (i.e., both the left-hand side and right-hand side would become zero) during the process of executing the Gauss–Jordan method, so the unique solution would be identified just as before. The final case is where both of these ranks are equal to r, where $r < n$, so that the system of equations possesses an infinite number of solutions. In this case, at the completion of the Gauss–Jordan method, each of r variables would remain in only one of the equations, and each of the r equations (any additional equations would have vanished) would contain exactly one of these variables. However, each of the other $(n - r)$ variables would either have vanished or would remain in some of the equations. Therefore, any solution obtained by assigning arbitrary values to the $(n - r)$ variables, and then identifying the respective values of the r variables in the usual way, would be a solution to the system of simultaneous equations. Equivalently, the transfer of these $(n - r)$ variables to the right-hand side of the equations (either before or after the method is executed) would identify the solution for the r variables as a function of these "extra" variables.

APPENDIX 5

Tables

TABLE A.5.1.* Areas under the Normal Curve from K_α to ∞

$$P\{\text{normal} \geq K_\alpha\} = \int_{K_\alpha}^{\infty} \frac{1}{\sqrt{2\pi}} e^{-\frac{x^2}{2}} dx = \alpha$$

$K\alpha$	.00	.01	.02	.03	.04	.05	.06	.07	.08	.09
0.0	.5000	.4960	.4920	.4880	.4840	.4801	.4761	.4721	.4681	.4641
0.1	.4602	.4562	.4522	.4483	.4443	.4404	.4364	.4325	.4286	.4247
0.2	.4207	.4168	.4129	.4090	.4052	.4013	.3974	.3936	.3897	.3859
0.3	.3821	.3783	.3745	.3707	.3669	.3632	.3594	.3557	.3520	.3483
0.4	.3446	.3409	.3372	.3336	.3300	.3264	.3228	.3192	.3156	.3121
0.5	.3085	.3050	.3015	.2981	.2946	.2912	.2877	.2843	.2810	.2776
0.6	.2743	.2709	.2676	.2643	.2611	.2578	.2546	.2514	.2483	.2451
0.7	.2420	.2389	.2358	.2327	.2296	.2266	.2236	.2206	.2177	.2148
0.8	.2119	.2090	.2061	.2033	.2005	.1977	.1949	.1922	.1894	.1867
0.9	.1841	.1814	.1788	.1762	.1736	.1711	.1685	.1660	.1635	.1611
1.0	.1587	.1562	.1539	.1515	.1492	.1469	.1446	.1423	.1401	.1379
1.1	.1357	.1335	.1314	.1292	.1271	.1251	.1230	.1210	.1190	.1170
1.2	.1151	.1131	.1112	.1093	.1075	.1056	.1038	.1020	.1003	.0985
1.3	.0968	.0951	.0934	.0918	.0901	.0885	.0869	.0853	.0838	.0823
1.4	.0808	.0793	.0778	.0764	.0749	.0735	.0721	.0708	.0694	.0681
1.5	.0668	.0655	.0643	.0630	.0618	.0606	.0594	.0582	.0571	.0559
1.6	.0548	.0537	.0526	.0516	.0505	.0495	.0485	.0475	.0465	.0455
1.7	.0446	.0436	.0427	.0418	.0409	.0401	.0392	.0384	.0375	.0367
1.8	.0359	.0351	.0344	.0336	.0329	.0322	.0314	.0307	.0301	.0294
1.9	.0287	.0281	.0274	.0268	.0262	.0256	.0250	.0244	.0239	.0233
2.0	.0228	.0222	.0217	.0212	.0207	.0202	.0197	.0192	.0188	.0183
2.1	.0179	.0174	.0170	.0166	.0162	.0158	.0154	.0150	.0146	.0143
2.2	.0139	.0136	.0132	.0129	.0125	.0122	.0119	.0116	.0113	.0110
2.3	.0107	.0104	.0102	.00990	.00964	.00939	.00914	.00889	.00866	.00842
2.4	.00820	.00798	.00776	.00755	.00734	.00714	.00695	.00676	.00657	.00639
2.5	.00621	.00604	.00587	.00570	.00554	.00539	.00523	.00508	.00494	.00480
2.6	.00466	.00453	.00440	.00427	.00415	.00402	.00391	.00379	.00368	.00357
2.7	.00347	.00336	.00326	.00317	.00307	.00298	.00289	.00280	.00272	.00264
2.8	.00256	.00248	.00240	.00233	.00226	.00219	.00212	.00205	.00199	.00193
2.9	.00187	.00181	.00175	.00169	.00164	.00159	.00154	.00149	.00144	.00139

$K\alpha$	.0	.1	.2	.3	.4	.5	.6	.7	.8	.9
3	.00135	$.0^{3}968$	$.0^{3}687$	$.0^{3}483$	$.0^{3}337$	$.0^{3}233$	$.0^{3}159$	$.0^{3}108$	$.0^{4}723$	$.0^{4}481$
4	$.0^{4}317$	$.0^{4}207$	$.0^{4}133$	$.0^{5}854$	$.0^{5}541$	$.0^{5}340$	$.0^{5}211$	$.0^{5}130$	$.0^{6}793$	$.0^{6}479$
5	$.0^{6}287$	$.0^{6}170$	$.0^{7}996$	$.0^{7}579$	$.0^{7}333$	$.0^{7}190$	$.0^{7}107$	$.0^{8}599$	$.0^{8}332$	$.0^{8}182$
6	$.0^{9}987$	$.0^{9}530$	$.0^{9}282$	$.0^{9}149$	$.0^{10}777$	$.0^{10}402$	$.0^{10}206$	$.0^{10}104$	$.0^{11}523$	$.0^{11}260$

* Reprinted by permission from Frederick E. Croxton, *Elementary Statistics with Applications in Medicine*, Prentice-Hall, Englewood Cliffs, N.J., 1953, p. 323.

TABLE A.5.2.* 100 α Percentage Points of Student's t-Distribution

P {Student's t with ν degrees of freedom $\geq$ tabled value} $= \alpha$

ν \ α	0.25	0.10	0.05	0.025	0.01	0.005
1	1.0000	3.0777	6.3138	12.7062	31.8205	63.6567
2	0.8165	1.8856	2.9200	4.3027	6.9646	9.9248
3	0.7649	1.6377	2.3534	3.1824	4.5407	5.8409
4	0.7407	1.5332	2.1318	2.7764	3.7469	4.6041
5	0.7267	1.4759	2.0150	2.5706	3.3649	4.0322
6	0.7176	1.4398	1.9432	2.4469	3.1427	3.7074
7	0.7111	1.4149	1.8946	2.3646	2.9980	3.4995
8	0.7064	1.3968	1.8595	2.3060	2.8965	3.3554
9	0.7027	1.3830	1.8331	2.2622	2.8214	3.2498
10	0.6998	1.3722	1.8125	2.2281	2.7638	3.1693
11	0.6974	1.3634	1.7959	2.2010	2.7181	3.1058
12	0.6955	1.3562	1.7823	2.1788	2.6810	3.0545
13	0.6938	1.3502	1.7709	2.1604	2.6503	3.0123
14	0.6924	1.3450	1.7613	2.1448	2.6245	2.9768
15	0.6912	1.3406	1.7531	2.1315	2.6025	2.9467
16	0.6901	1.3368	1.7459	2.1199	2.5835	2.9208
17	0.6892	1.3334	1.7396	2.1098	2.5669	2.8982
18	0.6884	1.3304	1.7341	2.1009	2.5524	2.8784
19	0.6876	1.3277	1.7291	2.0930	2.5395	2.8609
20	0.6870	1.3253	1.7247	2.0860	2.5280	2.8453
21	0.6864	1.3232	1.7207	2.0796	2.5177	2.8314
22	0.6858	1.3212	1.7171	2.0739	2.5083	2.8188
23	0.6853	1.3195	1.7139	2.0687	2.4999	2.8073
24	0.6848	1.3178	1.7109	2.0639	2.4922	2.7969
25	0.6844	1.3163	1.7081	2.0595	2.4851	2.7874
26	0.6840	1.3150	1.7056	2.0555	2.4786	2.7787
27	0.6837	1.3137	1.7033	2.0518	2.4727	2.7707
28	0.6834	1.3125	1.7011	2.0484	2.4671	2.7633
29	0.6830	1.3114	1.6991	2.0452	2.4620	2.7564
30	0.6828	1.3104	1.6973	2.0423	2.4573	2.7500
31	0.6825	1.3095	1.6955	2.0395	2.4528	2.7440
32	0.6822	1.3086	1.6939	2.0369	2.4487	2.7385
33	0.6820	1.3077	1.6924	2.0345	2.4448	2.7333
34	0.6818	1.3070	1.6909	2.0322	2.4411	2.7284
35	0.6816	1.3062	1.6896	2.0301	2.4377	2.7238
36	0.6814	1.3055	1.6883	2.0281	2.4345	2.7195
37	0.6812	1.3049	1.6871	2.0262	2.4314	2.7154
38	0.6810	1.3042	1.6860	2.0244	2.4286	2.7116
39	0.6808	1.3036	1.6849	2.0227	2.4258	2.7079
40	0.6807	1.3031	1.6839	2.0211	2.4233	2.7045
41	0.6805	1.3025	1.6829	2.0195	2.4208	2.7012
42	0.6804	1.3020	1.6820	2.0181	2.4185	2.6981
43	0.6802	1.3016	1.6811	2.0167	2.4163	2.6951
44	0.6801	1.3011	1.6802	2.0154	2.4141	2.6923
45	0.6800	1.3006	1.6794	2.0141	2.4121	2.6896
46	0.6799	1.3002	1.6787	2.0129	2.4102	2.6870
47	0.6797	1.2998	1.6779	2.0117	2.4083	2.6846

TABLE A.5.2 (Continued)

$P\{\text{Student's } t \text{ with } \nu \text{ degrees of freedom} \geq \text{tabled value}\} = \alpha$

ν \ α	0.25	0.10	0.05	0.025	0.01	0.005
48	0.6796	1.2994	1.6772	2.0106	2.4066	2.6822
49	0.6795	1.2991	1.6766	2.0096	2.4049	2.6800
50	0.6794	1.2987	1.6759	2.0086	2.4033	2.6778
51	0.6793	1.2984	1.6753	2.0076	2.4017	2.6757
52	0.6792	1.2980	1.6747	2.0066	2.4002	2.6737
53	0.6791	1.2977	1.6741	2.0057	2.3988	2.6718
54	0.6791	1.2974	1.6736	2.0049	2.3974	2.6700
55	0.6790	1.2971	1.6730	2.0040	2.3961	2.6682
56	0.6789	1.2969	1.6725	2.0032	2.3948	2.6665
57	0.6788	1.2966	1.6720	2.0025	2.3936	2.6649
58	0.6787	1.2963	1.6716	2.0017	2.3924	2.6633
59	0.6787	1.2961	1.6711	2.0010	2.3912	2.6618
60	0.6786	1.2958	1.6706	2.0003	2.3901	2.6603
61	0.6785	1.2956	1.6702	1.9996	2.3890	2.6589
62	0.6785	1.2954	1.6698	1.9990	2.3880	2.6575
63	0.6784	1.2951	1.6694	1.9983	2.3870	2.6561
64	0.6783	1.2949	1.6690	1.9977	2.3860	2.6549
65	0.6783	1.2947	1.6686	1.9971	2.3851	2.6536
66	0.6782	1.2945	1.6683	1.9966	2.3842	2.6524
67	0.6782	1.2943	1.6679	1.9960	2.3833	2.6512
68	0.6781	1.2941	1.6676	1.9955	2.3824	2.6501
69	0.6781	1.2939	1.6672	1.9949	2.3816	2.6490
70	0.6780	1.2938	1.6669	1.9944	2.3808	2.6479
71	0.6780	1.2936	1.6666	1.9939	2.3800	2.6469
72	0.6779	1.2934	1.6663	1.9935	2.3793	2.6459
73	0.6779	1.2933	1.6660	1.9930	2.3785	2.6449
74	0.6778	1.2931	1.6657	1.9925	2.3778	2.6439
75	0.6778	1.2929	1.6654	1.9921	2.3771	2.6430
76	0.6777	1.2928	1.6652	1.9917	2.3764	2.6421
77	0.6777	1.2926	1.6649	1.9913	2.3758	2.6412
78	0.6776	1.2925	1.6646	1.9908	2.3751	2.6403
79	0.6776	1.2924	1.6644	1.9905	2.3745	2.6395
80	0.6776	1.2922	1.6641	1.9901	2.3739	2.6387
81	0.6775	1.2921	1.6639	1.9897	2.3733	2.6379
82	0.6775	1.2920	1.6636	1.9893	2.3727	2.6371
83	0.6775	1.2918	1.6634	1.9890	2.3721	2.6364
84	0.6774	1.2917	1.6632	1.9886	2.3716	2.6356
85	0.6774	1.2916	1.6630	1.9883	2.3710	2.6349
86	0.6774	1.2915	1.6628	1.9879	2.3705	2.6342
87	0.6773	1.2914	1.6626	1.9876	2.3700	2.6335
88	0.6773	1.2912	1.6624	1.9873	2.3695	2.6329
89	0.6773	1.2911	1.6622	1.9870	2.3690	2.6322
90	0.6772	1.2910	1.6620	1.9867	2.3685	2.6316

* Reprinted by permission from D. B. Owen, *Handbook of Statistical Tables*, Addison-Wesley, Reading, Mass., 1962. (Courtesy of Atomic Energy Commission, Washington, D.C.)

TABLE A.5.3.* 100 α Percentage Points of the Chi-Square Distribution

$P\{\text{chi square with } \nu \text{ degrees of freedom} \geq \text{tabled value}\} = \alpha$

ν \ α	0.995	0.99	0.975	0.95	0.90	0.75
1	—	—	0.001	0.004	0.016	0.102
2	0.010	0.020	0.051	0.103	0.211	0.575
3	0.072	0.115	0.216	0.352	0.584	1.213
4	0.207	0.297	0.484	0.711	1.064	1.923
5	0.412	0.554	0.831	1.145	1.610	2.675
6	0.676	0.872	1.237	1.635	2.204	3.455
7	0.989	1.239	1.690	2.167	2.833	4.255
8	1.344	1.646	2.180	2.733	3.490	5.071
9	1.735	2.088	2.700	3.325	4.168	5.899
10	2.156	2.558	3.247	3.940	4.865	6.737
11	2.603	3.053	3.816	4.575	5.578	7.584
12	3.074	3.571	4.404	5.226	6.304	8.438
13	3.565	4.107	5.009	5.892	7.042	9.299
14	4.075	4.660	5.629	6.571	7.790	10.165
15	4.601	5.229	6.262	7.261	8.547	11.037
16	5.142	5.812	6.908	7.962	9.312	11.912
17	5.697	6.408	7.564	8.672	10.085	12.792
18	6.265	7.015	8.231	9.390	10.865	13.675
19	6.844	7.633	8.907	10.117	11.651	14.562
20	7.434	8.260	9.591	10.851	12.443	15.452
21	8.034	8.897	10.283	11.591	13.240	16.344
22	8.643	9.542	10.982	12.338	14.042	17.240
23	9.260	10.196	11.689	13.091	14.848	18.137
24	9.886	10.856	12.401	13.848	15.659	19.037
25	10.520	11.524	13.120	14.611	16.473	19.939
26	11.160	12.198	13.844	15.379	17.292	20.843
27	11.808	12.879	14.573	16.151	18.114	21.749
28	12.461	13.565	15.308	16.928	18.939	22.657
29	13.121	14.256	16.047	17.708	19.768	23.567
30	13.787	14.953	16.791	18.493	20.599	24.478
31	14.458	15.655	17.539	19.281	21.434	25.390
32	15.134	16.362	18.291	20.072	22.271	26.304
33	15.815	17.074	19.047	20.867	23.110	27.219
34	16.501	17.789	19.806	21.664	23.952	28.136
35	17.192	18.509	20.569	22.465	24.797	29.054
36	17.887	19.233	21.336	23.269	25.643	29.973
37	18.586	19.960	22.106	24.075	26.492	30.893
38	19.289	20.691	22.878	24.884	27.343	31.815
39	19.996	21.426	23.654	25.695	28.196	32.737
40	20.707	22.164	24.433	26.509	29.051	33.660
41	21.421	22.906	25.215	27.326	29.907	34.585
42	22.138	23.650	25.999	28.144	30.765	35.510
43	22.859	24.398	26.785	28.965	31.625	36.436
44	23.584	25.148	27.575	29.787	32.487	37.363
45	24.311	25.901	28.366	30.612	33.350	38.291

TABLE A.5.3 (Continued)

$P\{\text{chi square with } \nu \text{ degrees of freedom} \geq \text{tabled value}\} = \alpha$

ν \ α	0.25	0.10	0.05	0.025	0.01	0.005
1	1.323	2.706	3.841	5.024	6.635	7.879
2	2.773	4.605	5.991	7.378	9.210	10.597
3	4.108	6.251	7.815	9.348	11.345	12.838
4	5.385	7.779	9.488	11.143	13.277	14.860
5	6.626	9.236	11.071	12.833	15.086	16.750
6	7.841	10.645	12.592	14.449	16.812	18.548
7	9.037	12.017	14.067	16.013	18.475	20.278
8	10.219	13.362	15.507	17.535	20.090	21.955
9	11.389	14.684	16.919	19.023	21.666	23.589
10	12.549	15.987	18.307	20.483	23.209	25.188
11	13.701	17.275	19.675	21.920	24.725	26.757
12	14.845	18.549	21.026	23.337	26.217	28.299
13	15.984	19.812	22.362	24.736	27.688	29.819
14	17.117	21.064	23.685	26.119	29.141	31.319
15	18.245	22.307	24.996	27.488	30.578	32.801
16	19.369	23.542	26.296	28.845	32.000	34.267
17	20.489	24.769	27.587	30.191	33.409	35.718
18	21.605	25.989	28.869	31.526	34.805	37.156
19	22.718	27.204	30.144	32.852	36.191	38.582
20	23.828	28.412	31.410	34.170	37.566	39.997
21	24.935	29.615	32.671	35.479	38.932	41.401
22	26.039	30.813	33.924	36.781	40.289	42.796
23	27.141	32.007	35.172	38.076	41.638	44.181
24	28.241	33.196	36.415	39.364	42.980	45.559
25	29.339	34.382	37.652	40.646	44.314	46.928
26	30.435	35.563	38.885	41.923	45.642	48.290
27	31.528	36.741	40.113	43.194	46.963	49.645
28	32.620	37.916	41.337	44.461	48.278	50.993
29	33.711	39.087	42.557	45.722	49.588	52.336
30	34.800	40.256	43.773	46.979	50.892	53.672
31	35.887	41.422	44.985	48.232	52.191	55.003
32	36.973	42.585	46.194	49.480	53.486	56.328
33	38.058	43.745	47.400	50.725	54.776	57.648
34	39.141	44.903	48.602	51.966	56.061	58.964
35	40.223	46.059	49.802	53.203	57.342	60.275
36	41.304	47.212	50.998	54.437	58.619	61.581
37	42.383	48.363	52.192	55.668	59.892	62.883
38	43.462	49.513	53.384	56.896	61.162	64.181
39	44.539	50.660	54.572	58.120	62.428	65.476
40	45.616	51.805	55.758	59.342	63.691	66.766
41	46.692	52.949	56.942	60.561	64.950	68.053
42	47.766	54.090	58.124	61.777	66.206	69.336
43	48.840	55.230	59.304	62.990	67.459	70.616
44	49.913	56.369	60.481	64.201	68.710	71.893
45	50.985	57.505	61.656	65.410	69.957	73.166

* Reprinted by permission from D. B. Owen, *Handbook of Statistical Tables*, Addison-Wesley, Reading, Mass., 1962. (Courtesy of Atomic Energy Commission, Washington, D.C.).

TABLE A.5.4.* Summation of Terms of the Poisson Distribution

1000 $P\{\text{Poisson with parameter } \lambda \leq c\}$

λ \ c	0	1	2	3	4	5	6	7	8	9
0.02	980	1,000								
0.04	961	999	1,000							
0.06	942	998	1,000							
0.08	923	997	1,000							
0.10	905	995	1,000							
0.15	861	990	999	1,000						
0.20	819	982	999	1,000						
0.25	779	974	998	1,000						
0.30	741	963	996	1,000						
0.35	705	951	994	1,000						
0.40	670	938	992	999	1,000					
0.45	638	925	989	999	1,000					
0.50	607	910	986	998	1,000					
0.55	577	894	982	998	1,000					
0.60	549	878	977	997	1,000					
0.65	522	861	972	996	999	1,000				
0.70	497	844	966	994	999	1,000				
0.75	472	827	959	993	999	1,000				
0.80	449	809	953	991	999	1,000				
0.85	427	791	945	989	998	1,000				
0.90	407	772	937	987	998	1,000				
0.95	387	754	929	984	997	1,000				
1.00	368	736	920	981	996	999	1,000			
1.1	333	699	900	974	995	999	1,000			
1.2	301	663	879	966	992	998	1,000			
1.3	273	627	857	957	989	998	1,000			
1.4	247	592	833	946	986	997	999	1,000		
1.5	223	558	809	934	981	996	999	1,000		
1.6	202	525	783	921	976	994	999	1,000		
1.7	183	493	757	907	970	992	998	1,000		
1.8	165	463	731	891	964	990	997	999	1,000	
1.9	150	434	704	875	956	987	997	999	1,000	
2.0	135	406	677	857	947	983	995	999	1,000	
2.2	111	355	623	819	928	975	993	998	1,000	
2.4	091	308	570	779	904	964	988	997	999	1,000
2.6	074	267	518	736	877	951	983	995	999	1,000
2.8	061	231	469	692	848	935	976	992	998	999
3.0	050	199	423	647	815	916	966	988	996	999
3.2	041	171	380	603	781	895	955	983	994	998
3.4	033	147	340	558	744	871	942	977	992	997
3.6	027	126	303	515	706	844	927	969	988	996
3.8	022	107	269	473	668	816	909	960	984	994
4.0	018	092	238	433	629	785	889	949	979	992

* Reprinted by permission from E. L. Grant, *Statistical Quality Control*, McGraw-Hill, New York, 1964, 3rd ed.

TABLE A.5.4 (Continued)

1000 $P\{\text{Poisson with parameter } \lambda \leq c\}$

λ \ c	0	1	2	3	4	5	6	7	8	9
4.2	015	078	210	395	590	753	867	936	972	989
4.4	012	066	185	359	551	720	844	921	964	985
4.6	010	056	163	326	513	686	818	905	955	980
4.8	008	048	143	294	476	651	791	887	944	975
5.0	007	040	125	265	440	616	762	867	932	968
5.2	006	034	109	238	406	581	732	845	918	960
5.4	005	029	095	213	373	546	702	822	903	951
5.6	004	024	082	191	342	512	670	797	886	941
5.8	003	021	072	170	313	478	638	771	867	929
6.0	002	017	062	151	285	446	606	744	847	916
	10	11	12	13	14	15	16			
2.8	1,000									
3.0	1,000									
3.2	1,000									
3.4	999	1,000								
3.6	999	1,000								
3.8	998	999	1,000							
4.0	997	999	1,000							
4.2	996	999	1,000							
4.4	994	998	999	1,000						
4.6	992	997	999	1,000						
4.8	990	996	999	1,000						
5.0	986	995	998	999	1,000					
5.2	982	993	997	999	1,000					
5.4	977	990	996	999	1,000					
5.6	972	988	995	998	999	1,000				
5.8	965	984	993	997	999	1,000				
6.0	957	980	991	996	999	999	1,000			
6.2	002	015	054	134	259	414	574	716	826	902
6.4	002	012	046	119	235	384	542	687	803	886
6.6	001	010	040	105	213	355	511	658	780	869
6.8	001	009	034	093	192	327	480	628	755	850
7.0	001	007	030	082	173	301	450	599	729	830
7.2	001	006	025	072	156	276	420	569	703	810
7.4	001	005	022	063	140	253	392	539	676	788
7.6	001	004	019	055	125	231	365	510	648	765
7.8	000	004	016	048	112	210	338	481	620	741
8.0	000	003	014	042	100	191	313	453	593	717
8.5	000	002	009	030	074	150	256	386	523	653
9.0	000	001	006	021	055	116	207	324	456	587
9.5	000	001	004	015	040	089	165	269	392	522
10.0	000	000	003	010	029	067	130	220	333	458

(continued)

TABLE A.5.4 (Continued)

1000 $P\{\text{Poisson with parameter } \lambda \leq c\}$

λ \ c	0	1	2	3	4	5	6	7	8	9
	10	11	12	13	14	15	16	17	18	19
6.2	949	975	989	995	998	999	1,000			
6.4	939	969	986	994	997	999	1,000			
6.6	927	963	982	992	997	999	999	1,000		
6.8	915	955	978	990	996	998	999	1,000		
7.0	901	947	973	987	994	998	999	1,000		
7.2	887	937	967	984	993	997	999	999	1,000	
7.4	871	926	961	980	991	996	998	999	1,000	
7.6	854	915	954	976	989	995	998	999	1,000	
7.8	835	902	945	971	986	993	997	999	1,000	
8.0	816	888	936	966	983	992	996	998	999	1,000
8.5	763	849	909	949	973	986	993	997	999	999
9.0	706	803	876	926	959	978	989	995	998	999
9.5	645	752	836	898	940	967	982	991	996	998
10.0	583	697	792	864	917	951	973	986	993	997
	20	21	22							
8.5	1,000									
9.0	1,000									
9.5	999	1,000								
10.0	998	999	1,000							
10.5	000	000	002	007	021	050	102	179	279	397
11.0	000	000	001	005	015	038	079	143	232	341
11.5	000	000	001	003	011	028	060	114	191	289
12.0	000	000	001	002	008	020	046	090	155	242
12.5	000	000	000	002	005	015	035	070	125	201
13.0	000	000	000	001	004	011	026	054	100	166
13.5	000	000	000	001	003	008	019	041	079	135
14.0	000	000	000	000	002	006	014	032	062	109
14.5	000	000	000	000	001	004	010	024	048	088
15.0	000	000	000	000	001	003	008	018	037	070
	10	11	12	13	14	15	16	17	18	19
10.5	521	639	742	825	888	932	960	978	988	994
11.0	460	579	689	781	854	907	944	968	982	991
11.5	402	520	633	733	815	878	924	954	974	986
12.0	347	462	576	682	772	844	899	937	963	979
12.5	297	406	519	628	725	806	869	916	948	969
13.0	252	353	463	573	675	764	835	890	930	957
13.5	211	304	409	518	623	718	798	861	908	942
14.0	176	260	358	464	570	669	756	827	883	923
14.5	145	220	311	413	518	619	711	790	853	901
15.0	118	185	268	363	466	568	664	749	819	875

TABLE A.5.4 (Continued)

1000 $P\{\text{Poisson with parameter } \lambda \leq c\}$

λ \ c	4	5	6	7	8	9	10	11	12	13
	20	21	22	23	24	25	26	27	28	29
10.5	997	999	999	1,000						
11.0	995	998	999	1,000						
11.5	992	996	998	999	1,000					
12.0	988	994	997	999	999	1,000				
12.5	983	991	995	998	999	999	1,000			
13.0	975	986	992	996	998	999	1,000			
13.5	965	980	989	994	997	998	999	1,000		
14.0	952	971	983	991	995	997	999	999	1,000	
14.5	936	960	976	986	992	996	998	999	999	1,000
15.0	917	947	967	981	989	994	997	998	999	1,000
16	000	001	004	010	022	043	077	127	193	275
17	000	001	002	005	013	026	049	085	135	201
18	000	000	001	003	007	015	030	055	092	143
19	000	000	001	002	004	009	018	035	061	098
20	000	000	000	001	002	005	011	021	039	066
21	000	000	000	000	001	003	006	013	025	043
22	000	000	000	000	001	002	004	008	015	028
23	000	000	000	000	000	001	002	004	009	017
24	000	000	000	000	000	000	001	003	005	011
25	000	000	000	000	000	000	001	001	003	006
	14	15	16	17	18	19	20	21	22	23
16	368	467	566	659	742	812	868	911	942	963
17	281	371	468	564	655	736	805	861	905	937
18	208	287	375	469	562	651	731	799	855	899
19	150	215	292	378	469	561	647	725	793	849
20	105	157	221	297	381	470	559	644	721	787
21	072	111	163	227	302	384	471	558	640	716
22	048	077	117	169	232	306	387	472	556	637
23	031	052	082	123	175	238	310	389	472	555
24	020	034	056	087	128	180	243	314	392	473
25	012	022	038	060	092	134	185	247	318	394
	24	25	26	27	28	29	30	31	32	33
16	978	987	993	996	998	999	999	1,000		
17	959	975	985	991	995	997	999	999	1,000	
18	932	955	972	983	990	994	997	998	999	1,000
19	893	927	951	969	980	988	993	996	998	999
20	843	888	922	948	966	978	987	992	995	997
21	782	838	883	917	944	963	976	985	991	994
22	712	777	832	877	913	940	959	973	983	989
23	635	708	772	827	873	908	936	956	971	981
24	554	632	704	768	823	868	904	932	953	969
25	473	553	629	700	763	818	863	900	929	950

(continued)

TABLE A.5.4 (Continued)

1000 $P\{\text{Poisson with parameter } \lambda \leq c\}$

λ \ c	34	35	36	37	38	39	40	41	42	43
19	999	1,000								
20	999	999	1,000							
21	997	998	999	999	1,000					
22	994	996	998	999	999	1,000				
23	988	993	996	997	999	999	1,000			
24	979	987	992	995	997	998	999	999	1,000	
25	966	978	985	991	994	997	998	999	999	1,000

Index